PEARSON CUSTOM
MATHEMATICS

Probability & Statistics for Engineers, 9e

PEARSON

Senior Vice President, Editorial: Patrick F. Boles
Senior Acquisitions Editor: Debbie Coniglio
Development Editor: Christina Martin
Editorial Assistant: Jeanne Martin
Operations Manager: Eric M. Kenney
Production Manager: Jennifer Berry
Art Director: Renée Sartell
Cover Designer: Josh Read

Cover Art: "Perspective Angle of Business Skyscraper," courtesy of iStockphoto.

This special edition published in cooperation with Pearson Learning Solutions.

Printed in the United States of America.

Please visit our website at *www.pearsonlearningsolutions.com*.

Attention bookstores: For permission to return any unsold stock, contact us at *pe-uscustomreturns@pearson.com*.

Pearson Learning Solutions, 501 Boylston Street, Suite 900, Boston, MA 02116
A Pearson Education Company
www.pearsoned.com

ISBN 10: 1-256-19856-0
ISBN 13: 978-1-256-19856-7

Contents

Introduction to Statistics and Data Analysis

1 Overview: Statistical Inference, Samples, Populations, and the Role of Probability

Beginning in the 1980s and continuing into the 21st century, an inordinate amount of attention has been focused on *improvement of quality* in American industry. Much has been said and written about the Japanese "industrial miracle," which began in the middle of the 20th century. The Japanese were able to succeed where we and other countries had failed–namely, to create an atmosphere that allows the production of high-quality products. Much of the success of the Japanese has been attributed to the use of *statistical methods* and statistical thinking among management personnel.

Use of Scientific Data

The use of statistical methods in manufacturing, development of food products, computer software, energy sources, pharmaceuticals, and many other areas involves the gathering of information or **scientific data**. Of course, the gathering of data is nothing new. It has been done for well over a thousand years. Data have been collected, summarized, reported, and stored for perusal. However, there is a profound distinction between collection of scientific information and **inferential statistics**. It is the latter that has received rightful attention in recent decades.

The offspring of inferential statistics has been a large "toolbox" of statistical methods employed by statistical practitioners. These statistical methods are designed to contribute to the process of making scientific judgments in the face of **uncertainty** and **variation**. The product density of a particular material from a manufacturing process will not always be the same. Indeed, if the process involved is a batch process rather than continuous, there will be not only variation in material density among the batches that come off the line (batch-to-batch variation), but also within-batch variation. Statistical methods are used to analyze data from a process such as this one in order to gain more sense of where in the process changes may be made to improve the **quality** of the process. In this process, qual-

From Chapter 1 of *Probability & Statistics for Engineers & Scientists*, Ninth Edition, Ronald E. Walpole, Raymond H. Myers, Sharon L. Myers, Keying Ye. Copyright © 2012 by Pearson Education, Inc. Published by Pearson Prentice Hall. All rights reserved.

ity may well be defined in relation to closeness to a target density value in harmony with *what portion of the time* this closeness criterion is met. An engineer may be concerned with a specific instrument that is used to measure sulfur monoxide in the air during pollution studies. If the engineer has doubts about the effectiveness of the instrument, there are two **sources of variation** that must be dealt with. The first is the variation in sulfur monoxide values that are found at the same locale on the same day. The second is the variation between values observed and the **true** amount of sulfur monoxide that is in the air at the time. If either of these two sources of variation is exceedingly large (according to some standard set by the engineer), the instrument may need to be replaced. In a biomedical study of a new drug that reduces hypertension, 85% of patients experienced relief, while it is generally recognized that the current drug, or "old" drug, brings relief to 80% of patients that have chronic hypertension. However, the new drug is more expensive to make and may result in certain side effects. Should the new drug be adopted? This is a problem that is encountered (often with much more complexity) frequently by pharmaceutical firms in conjunction with the FDA (Federal Drug Administration). Again, the consideration of variation needs to be taken into account. The "85%" value is based on a certain number of patients chosen for the study. Perhaps if the study were repeated with new patients the observed number of "successes" would be 75%! It is the natural variation from study to study that must be taken into account in the decision process. Clearly this variation is important, since variation from patient to patient is endemic to the problem.

Variability in Scientific Data

In the problems discussed above the statistical methods used involve dealing with variability, and in each case the variability to be studied is that encountered in scientific data. If the observed product density in the process were always the same and were always on target, there would be no need for statistical methods. If the device for measuring sulfur monoxide always gives the same value and the value is accurate (i.e., it is correct), no statistical analysis is needed. If there were no patient-to-patient variability inherent in the response to the drug (i.e., it either always brings relief or not), life would be simple for scientists in the pharmaceutical firms and FDA and no statistician would be needed in the decision process. Statistics researchers have produced an enormous number of analytical methods that allow for analysis of data from systems like those described above. This reflects the true nature of the science that we call inferential statistics, namely, using techniques that allow us to go beyond merely reporting data to drawing conclusions (or inferences) about the scientific system. Statisticians make use of fundamental laws of probability and statistical inference to draw conclusions about scientific systems. Information is gathered in the form of **samples**, or collections of **observations**.

Samples are collected from **populations**, which are collections of all individuals or individual items of a particular type. At times a population signifies a scientific system. For example, a manufacturer of computer boards may wish to eliminate defects. A sampling process may involve collecting information on 50 computer boards sampled randomly from the process. Here, the population is all computer boards manufactured by the firm over a specific period of time. If an improvement is made in the computer board process and a second sample of boards is collected, any conclusions drawn regarding the effectiveness of the change in process should extend to the entire population of computer boards produced under the "improved process." In a drug experiment, a sample of patients is taken and each is given a specific drug to reduce blood pressure. The interest is focused on drawing conclusions about the population of those who suffer from hypertension.

Often, it is very important to collect scientific data in a systematic way, with planning being high on the agenda. At times the planning is, by necessity, quite limited. We often focus only on certain properties or characteristics of the items or objects in the population. Each characteristic has particular engineering or, say, biological importance to the "customer," the scientist or engineer who seeks to learn about the population. For example, in one of the illustrations above the quality of the process had to do with the product density of the output of a process. An engineer may need to study the effect of process conditions, temperature, humidity, amount of a particular ingredient, and so on. He or she can systematically move these **factors** to whatever levels are suggested according to whatever prescription or **experimental design** is desired. However, a forest scientist who is interested in a study of factors that influence wood density in a certain kind of tree cannot necessarily design an experiment. This case may require an **observational study** in which data are collected in the field but **factor levels** can not be preselected. Both of these types of studies lend themselves to methods of statistical inference. In the former, the quality of the inferences will depend on proper planning of the experiment. In the latter, the scientist is at the mercy of what can be gathered. For example, it is sad if an agronomist is interested in studying the effect of rainfall on plant yield and the data are gathered during a drought.

The importance of statistical thinking by managers and the use of statistical inference by scientific personnel is widely acknowledged. Research scientists gain much from scientific data. Data provide understanding of scientific phenomena. Product and process engineers learn a great deal in their off-line efforts to improve the process. They also gain valuable insight by gathering production data (on-line monitoring) on a regular basis. This allows them to determine necessary modifications in order to keep the process at a desired level of quality.

There are times when a scientific practitioner wishes only to gain some sort of summary of a set of data represented in the sample. In other words, inferential statistics is not required. Rather, a set of single-number statistics or **descriptive statistics** is helpful. These numbers give a sense of center of the location of the data, variability in the data, and the general nature of the distribution of observations in the sample. Though no specific statistical methods leading to **statistical inference** are incorporated, much can be learned. At times, descriptive statistics are accompanied by graphics. Modern statistical software packages allow for computation of **means**, **medians**, **standard deviations**, and other single-number statistics as well as production of graphs that show a "footprint" of the nature of the sample. Definitions and illustrations of the single-number statistics and graphs, including histograms, stem-and-leaf plots, scatter plots, dot plots, and box plots, will be given in sections that follow.

The Role of Probability

A thorough grounding in the fundamental notions of probability will allow the reader to have a better understanding of statistical inference. Without some formalism of probability theory, the student cannot appreciate the true interpretation from data analysis through modern statistical methods. It is quite natural to study probability prior to studying statistical inference. Elements of probability allow us to quantify the strength or "confidence" in our conclusions. In this sense, concepts in probability form a major component that supplements statistical methods and helps us gauge the strength of the statistical inference. The discipline of probability, then, provides the transition between descriptive statistics and inferential methods. Elements of probability allow the conclusion to be put into the language that the science or engineering practitioners require. An example follows that will enable the reader to understand the notion of a *P*-value, which often provides the "bottom line" in the interpretation of results from the use of statistical methods.

Example 1:

Suppose that an engineer encounters data from a manufacturing process in which 100 items are sampled and 10 are found to be defective. It is expected and anticipated that occasionally there will be defective items. Obviously these 100 items represent the sample. However, it has been determined that in the long run, the company can only tolerate 5% defective in the process. Now, the elements of probability allow the engineer to determine how conclusive the sample information is regarding the nature of the process. In this case, the **population** conceptually represents all possible items from the process. Suppose we learn that *if the process is acceptable*, that is, if it does produce items no more than 5% of which are defective, there is a probability of 0.0282 of obtaining 10 or more defective items in a random sample of 100 items from the process. This small probability suggests that the process does, indeed, have a long-run rate of defective items that exceeds 5%. In other words, under the condition of an acceptable process, the sample information obtained would rarely occur. However, it did occur! Clearly, though, it would occur with a much higher probability if the process defective rate exceeded 5% by a significant amount.

From this example it becomes clear that the elements of probability aid in the translation of sample information into something conclusive or inconclusive about the scientific system. In fact, what was learned likely is alarming information to the engineer or manager. Statistical methods produced a *P*-value of 0.0282. The result suggests that the process **very likely is not acceptable**. The concept of a ***P*-value** is dealt with at length in succeeding chapters. The example that follows provides a second illustration.

Example 2:

Often the nature of the scientific study will dictate the role that probability and deductive reasoning play in statistical inference. Exercise 9.40 on page 294 provides data associated with a study conducted at the Virginia Polytechnic Institute and State University on the development of a relationship between the roots of trees and the action of a fungus. Minerals are transferred from the fungus to the trees and sugars from the trees to the fungus. Two samples of 10 northern red oak seedlings were planted in a greenhouse, one containing seedlings treated with nitrogen and the other containing seedlings with no nitrogen. All other environmental conditions were held constant. All seedlings contained the fungus *Pisolithus tinctorus*. The stem weights in grams were recorded after the end of 140 days. The data are given in Table 1.

Table 1: Data Set for Example 2

No Nitrogen	Nitrogen
0.32	0.26
0.53	0.43
0.28	0.47
0.37	0.49
0.47	0.52
0.43	0.75
0.36	0.79
0.42	0.86
0.38	0.62
0.43	0.46

Figure 1: A dot plot of stem weight data.

In this example there are two samples from two **separate populations**. The purpose of the experiment is to determine if the use of nitrogen has an influence on the growth of the roots. The study is a comparative study (i.e., we seek to compare the two populations with regard to a certain important characteristic). It is instructive to plot the data as shown in the dot plot of Figure 1. The ○ values represent the "nitrogen" data and the × values represent the "no-nitrogen" data.

Notice that the general appearance of the data might suggest to the reader that, on average, the use of nitrogen increases the stem weight. Four nitrogen observations are considerably larger than any of the no-nitrogen observations. Most of the no-nitrogen observations appear to be below the center of the data. The appearance of the data set would seem to indicate that nitrogen is effective. But how can this be quantified? How can all of the apparent visual evidence be summarized in some sense? As in the preceding example, the fundamentals of probability can be used. The conclusions may be summarized in a probability statement or *P*-value. We will not show here the statistical inference that produces the summary probability. The issue revolves around the "probability that data like these could be observed" *given that nitrogen has no effect*, in other words, given that both samples were generated from the same population. Suppose that this probability is small, say 0.03. That would certainly be strong evidence that the use of nitrogen does indeed influence (apparently increases) average stem weight of the red oak seedlings.

How Do Probability and Statistical Inference Work Together?

It is important for the reader to understand the clear distinction between the discipline of probability, a science in its own right, and the discipline of inferential statistics. As we have already indicated, the use or application of concepts in probability allows real-life interpretation of the results of statistical inference. As a result, it can be said that statistical inference makes use of concepts in probability. One can glean from the two examples above that the sample information is made available to the analyst and, with the aid of statistical methods and elements of probability, conclusions are drawn about some feature of the population (the process does not appear to be acceptable in Example 1, and nitrogen does appear to influence average stem weights in Example 2). Thus for a statistical problem, **the sample along with inferential statistics allows us to draw conclusions about the population, with inferential statistics making clear use of elements of probability.** This reasoning is *inductive* in nature. The reader will note that, unlike what we do in our two examples here, we will not focus on solving statistical problems. Many examples will be given in which no sample is involved. There will be a population clearly described with all features of the population known. Then questions of importance will focus on the nature of data that might hypothetically be drawn from the population. Thus, one can say that **elements in probability allow us to draw conclusions about characteristics of hypothetical data taken from the population, based on known features of the population.** This type of reasoning is *deductive* in nature. Figure 2 shows the fundamental relationship between probability and inferential statistics.

Figure 2: Fundamental relationship between probability and inferential statistics.

Now, in the grand scheme of things, which is more important, the field of probability or the field of statistics? They are both very important and clearly are complementary. The only certainty concerning the pedagogy of the two disciplines lies in the fact that if statistics is to be taught at more than merely a "cookbook" level, then the discipline of probability must be taught first. This rule stems from the fact that nothing can be learned about a population from a sample until the analyst learns the rudiments of uncertainty in that sample. For example, consider Example 1. The question centers around whether or not the population, defined by the process, is no more than 5% defective. In other words, the conjecture is that **on the average** 5 out of 100 items are defective. Now, the sample contains 100 items and 10 are defective. Does this support the conjecture or refute it? On the surface it would appear to be a refutation of the conjecture because 10 out of 100 seem to be "a bit much." But without elements of probability, how do we know? Only through the study of the conditions under which the process is acceptable (5% defective) can we learn that. The probability of obtaining 10 or more defective items in a sample of 100 is 0.0282.

We have given two examples where the elements of probability provide a summary that the scientist or engineer can use as evidence on which to build a decision. The bridge between the data and the conclusion is, of course, based on foundations of statistical inference, distribution theory, and sampling distributions.

2   Sampling Procedures; Collection of Data

In Section 1 we discussed very briefly the notion of sampling and the sampling process. While sampling appears to be a simple concept, the complexity of the questions that must be answered about the population or populations necessitates that the sampling process be very complex at times. We shall endeavor here to give some common-sense notions of sampling. This is a natural transition to a discussion of the concept of variability.

Simple Random Sampling

The importance of proper sampling revolves around the degree of confidence with which the analyst is able to answer the questions being asked. Let us assume that only a single population exists in the problem. Recall that in Example 2 two populations were involved. **Simple random sampling** implies that any particular sample of a specified *sample size* has the same chance of being selected as any other sample of the same size. The term **sample size** simply means the number of elements in the sample. Obviously, a table of random numbers can be utilized in sample selection in many instances. The virtue of simple random sampling is that it aids in the elimination of the problem of having the sample reflect a different (possibly more confined) population than the one about which inferences need to be made. For example, a sample is to be chosen to answer certain questions regarding political preferences in a certain state in the United States. The sample involves the choice of, say, 1000 families, and a survey is to be conducted. Now, suppose it turns out that random sampling is not used. Rather, all or nearly all of the 1000 families chosen live in an urban setting. It is believed that political preferences in rural areas differ from those in urban areas. In other words, the sample drawn actually confined the population and thus the inferences need to be confined to the "limited population," and in this case confining may be undesirable. If, indeed, the inferences need to be made about the state as a whole, the sample of size 1000 described here is often referred to as a **biased sample**.

As we hinted earlier, simple random sampling is not always appropriate. Which alternative approach is used depends on the complexity of the problem. Often, for example, the sampling units are not homogeneous and naturally divide themselves into nonoverlapping groups that are homogeneous. These groups are called *strata,* and a procedure called *stratified random sampling* involves random selection of a sample *within* each stratum. The purpose is to be sure that each of the strata is neither over- nor underrepresented. For example, suppose a sample survey is conducted in order to gather preliminary opinions regarding a bond referendum that is being considered in a certain city. The city is subdivided into several ethnic groups which represent natural strata. In order not to disregard or overrepresent any group, separate random samples of families could be chosen from each group.

Experimental Design

The concept of randomness or random assignment plays a hugh role in the area of **experimental design,** which was introduced very briefly in Section 1 and is an important staple in almost any area of engineering or experimental science. However, it is instructive to give a brief presentation here in the context of random sampling. A set of so-called **treatments** or **treatment combinations** becomes the populations to be studied or compared in some sense. An example is the nitrogen versus no-nitrogen treatments in Example 2. Another simple example would be "placebo" versus "active drug," or in a corrosion fatigue study we might have treatment combinations that involve specimens that are coated or uncoated as well as conditions of low or high humidity to which the specimens are exposed. In fact, there are four treatment or factor combinations (i.e., 4 populations), and many scientific questions may be asked and answered through statistical and inferential methods. Consider first the situation in Example 2. There are 20 diseased seedlings involved in the experiment. It is easy to see from the data themselves that the seedlings are different from each other. Within the nitrogen group (or the no-nitrogen group) there is considerable **variability** in the stem weights. This variability is due to what is generally called the **experimental unit.** This is a very important concept in inferential statistics. The nature of the variability is very important. If it is too large, stemming from a condition of excessive nonhomogeneity in experimental units, the variability will "wash out" any detectable difference between the two populations. Recall that in this case that did not occur.

The dot plot in Figure 1 and *P*-value indicated a clear distinction between these two conditions. What role do those experimental units play in the data-taking process itself? The common-sense and, indeed, quite standard approach is to assign the 20 seedlings or experimental units **randomly to the two treatments or conditions**. In the drug study, we may decide to use a total of 200 available patients, patients that clearly will be different in some sense. They are the experimental units. However, they all may have the same chronic condition for which the drug is a potential treatment. Then in a so-called **completely randomized design**, 100 patients are assigned randomly to the placebo and 100 to the active drug. Again, it is these experimental units within a group or treatment that produce the variability in data results (i.e., variability in the measured result), say blood pressure, or whatever drug efficacy value is important. In the corrosion fatigue study, the experimental units are the specimens that are the subjects of the corrosion.

Why Assign Experimental Units Randomly?

What is the possible negative impact of not randomly assigning experimental units to the treatments or treatment combinations? This is seen most clearly in the case of the drug study. Among the characteristics of the patients that produce variability in the results are age, gender, and weight. Suppose merely by chance the placebo group contains a sample of people that are predominately heavier than those in the treatment group. Perhaps heavier individuals have a tendency to have a higher blood pressure. This clearly biases the result, and indeed, any result obtained through the application of statistical inference may have little to do with the drug and more to do with differences in weights among the two samples of patients.

We should emphasize the attachment of importance to the term **variability**. Excessive variability among experimental units "camouflages" scientific findings. In future sections, we attempt to characterize and quantify measures of variability. In sections that follow, we introduce and discuss specific quantities that can be computed in samples; the quantities give a sense of the nature of the sample with respect to center of location of the data and variability in the data. A discussion of several of these single-number measures serves to provide a preview of statistical information that are important components of the statistical methods. These measures that help characterize the nature of the data set fall into the category of **descriptive statistics**. This material is a prelude to a brief presentation of pictorial and graphical methods that go even further in characterizations of the data set. In order to offer the reader a clearer picture of what is involved in experimental design studies, we offer Example 3.

Example 3: A corrosion study was made in order to determine whether coating an aluminum metal with a corrosion retardation substance reduced the amount of corrosion. The coating is a protectant that is advertised to minimize fatigue damage in this type of material. Also of interest is the influence of humidity on the amount of corrosion. A corrosion measurement can be expressed in thousands of cycles to failure. Two levels of coating, no coating and chemical corrosion coating, were used. In addition, the two relative humidity levels are 20% relative humidity and 80% relative humidity.

The experiment involves four treatment combinations that are listed in the table that follows. There are eight experimental units used, and they are aluminum specimens prepared; two are assigned randomly to each of the four treatment combinations. The data are presented in Table 2.

The corrosion data are averages of two specimens. A plot of the averages is pictured in Figure 3. A relatively large value of cycles to failure represents a small amount of corrosion. As one might expect, an increase in humidity appears to make the corrosion worse. The use of the chemical corrosion coating procedure appears to reduce corrosion.

In this experimental design illustration, the engineer has systematically selected the four treatment combinations. In order to connect this situation to concepts with which the reader has been exposed to this point, it should be assumed that the

Table 2: Data for Example 3

Coating	Humidity	Average Corrosion in Thousands of Cycles to Failure
Uncoated	20%	975
	80%	350
Chemical Corrosion	20%	1750
	80%	1550

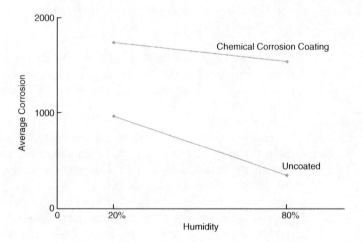

Figure 3: Corrosion results for Example 3.

conditions representing the four treatment combinations are four separate populations and that the two corrosion values observed for each population are important pieces of information. The importance of the average in capturing and summarizing certain features in the population will be highlighted in Section 3. While we might draw conclusions about the role of humidity and the impact of coating the specimens from the figure, we cannot truly evaluate the results from an analytical point of view without taking into account the *variability around* the average. Again, as we indicated earlier, if the two corrosion values for each treatment combination are close together, the picture in Figure 3 may be an accurate depiction. But if each corrosion value in the figure is an average of two values that are widely dispersed, then this variability may, indeed, truly "wash away" any information that appears to come through when one observes averages only. The foregoing example illustrates these concepts:

(1) random assignment of treatment combinations (coating, humidity) to experimental units (specimens)

(2) the use of sample averages (average corrosion values) in summarizing sample information

(3) the need for consideration of measures of variability in the analysis of any sample or sets of samples

This example suggests the need for what follows in Sections 3 and 4, namely, descriptive statistics that indicate measures of center of location in a set of data, and those that measure variability.

3   Measures of Location: The Sample Mean and Median

Measures of location are designed to provide the analyst with some quantitative values of where the center, or some other location, of data is located. In Example 2, it appears as if the center of the nitrogen sample clearly exceeds that of the no-nitrogen sample. One obvious and very useful measure is the **sample mean**. The mean is simply a numerical average.

Definition 1:

> Suppose that the observations in a sample are $x_1, x_2, \ldots, x_n$. The **sample mean**, denoted by $\bar{x}$, is
>
> $$\bar{x} = \sum_{i=1}^{n} \frac{x_i}{n} = \frac{x_1 + x_2 + \cdots + x_n}{n}.$$

One important measure is the **sample median**. The purpose of the sample median is to reflect the central tendency of the sample in such a way that it is uninfluenced by extreme values or outliers.

Definition 2:

> Given that the observations in a sample are $x_1, x_2, \ldots, x_n$, arranged in **increasing order** of magnitude, the sample median is
>
> $$\tilde{x} = \begin{cases} x_{(n+1)/2}, & \text{if } n \text{ is odd,} \\ \frac{1}{2}(x_{n/2} + x_{n/2+1}), & \text{if } n \text{ is even.} \end{cases}$$

As an example, suppose the data set is the following: 1.7, 2.2, 3.9, 3.11, and 14.7. The sample mean and median are, respectively,

$$\bar{x} = 5.12, \quad \tilde{x} = 3.9.$$

Clearly, the mean is influenced considerably by the presence of the extreme observation, 14.7, whereas the median places emphasis on the true "center" of the data set. In the case of the two-sample data set of Example 2, the two measures of central tendency for the individual samples are

$$\begin{aligned} \bar{x} \text{ (no nitrogen)} &= 0.399 \text{ gram,} \\ \tilde{x} \text{ (no nitrogen)} &= \frac{0.38 + 0.42}{2} = 0.400 \text{ gram,} \\ \bar{x} \text{ (nitrogen)} &= 0.565 \text{ gram,} \\ \tilde{x} \text{ (nitrogen)} &= \frac{0.49 + 0.52}{2} = 0.505 \text{ gram.} \end{aligned}$$

Clearly there is a difference in concept between the mean and median. It may be of interest to the reader with an engineering background that the sample mean is the **centroid of the data** in a sample. In a sense, it is the point at which a fulcrum can be placed to balance a system of "weights" which are the locations of the individual data. This is shown in Figure 4 with regard to the with-nitrogen sample.

Figure 4: Sample mean as a centroid of the with-nitrogen stem weight.

The basis for the computation of $\bar{x}$ is that of an **estimate** of the **population mean**. As we indicated earlier, the purpose of statistical inference is to draw conclusions about population characteristics or **parameters** and **estimation** is a very important feature of statistical inference.

The median and mean can be quite different from each other. Note, however, that in the case of the stem weight data the sample mean value for no-nitrogen is quite similar to the median value.

Other Measures of Locations

There are several other methods of quantifying the center of location of the data in the sample. We will not deal with them at this point. For the most part, alternatives to the sample mean are designed to produce values that represent compromises between the mean and the median. Rarely do we make use of these other measures. However, it is instructive to discuss one class of estimators, namely the class of **trimmed means**. A trimmed mean is computed by "trimming away" a certain percent of both the largest and the smallest set of values. For example, the 10% trimmed mean is found by eliminating the largest 10% and smallest 10% and computing the average of the remaining values. For example, in the case of the stem weight data, we would eliminate the largest and smallest since the sample size is 10 for each sample. So for the without-nitrogen group the 10% trimmed mean is given by

$$\bar{x}_{\text{tr}(10)} = \frac{0.32 + 0.37 + 0.47 + 0.43 + 0.36 + 0.42 + 0.38 + 0.43}{8} = 0.39750,$$

and for the 10% trimmed mean for the with-nitrogen group we have

$$\bar{x}_{\text{tr}(10)} = \frac{0.43 + 0.47 + 0.49 + 0.52 + 0.75 + 0.79 + 0.62 + 0.46}{8} = 0.56625.$$

Note that in this case, as expected, the trimmed means are close to both the mean and the median for the individual samples. The trimmed mean is, of course, more insensitive to outliers than the sample mean but not as insensitive as the median. On the other hand, the trimmed mean approach makes use of more information than the sample median. Note that the sample median is, indeed, a special case of the trimmed mean in which all of the sample data are eliminated apart from the middle one or two observations.

Exercises

1   The following measurements were recorded for the drying time, in hours, of a certain brand of latex paint.

3.4	2.5	4.8	2.9	3.6
2.8	3.3	5.6	3.7	2.8
4.4	4.0	5.2	3.0	4.8

Assume that the measurements are a simple random sample.

(a) What is the sample size for the above sample?

(b) Calculate the sample mean for these data.

(c) Calculate the sample median.

(d) Plot the data by way of a dot plot.

(e) Compute the 20% trimmed mean for the above data set.

(f) Is the sample mean for these data more or less descriptive as a center of location than the trimmed mean?

2   According to the journal *Chemical Engineering*, an important property of a fiber is its water absorbency. A random sample of 20 pieces of cotton fiber was taken and the absorbency on each piece was measured. The following are the absorbency values:

18.71	21.41	20.72	21.81	19.29	22.43	20.17
23.71	19.44	20.50	18.92	20.33	23.00	22.85
19.25	21.77	22.11	19.77	18.04	21.12	

(a) Calculate the sample mean and median for the above sample values.

(b) Compute the 10% trimmed mean.

(c) Do a dot plot of the absorbency data.

(d) Using only the values of the mean, median, and trimmed mean, do you have evidence of outliers in the data?

3   A certain polymer is used for evacuation systems for aircraft. It is important that the polymer be resistant to the aging process. Twenty specimens of the polymer were used in an experiment. Ten were assigned randomly to be exposed to an accelerated batch aging process that involved exposure to high temperatures for 10 days. Measurements of tensile strength of the specimens were made, and the following data were recorded on tensile strength in psi:

No aging:	227	222	218	217	225
	218	216	229	228	221
Aging:	219	214	215	211	209
	218	203	204	201	205

(a) Do a dot plot of the data.

(b) From your plot, does it appear as if the aging process has had an effect on the tensile strength of this polymer? Explain.

(c) Calculate the sample mean tensile strength of the two samples.

(d) Calculate the median for both. Discuss the similarity or lack of similarity between the mean and median of each group.

4   In a study conducted by the Department of Mechanical Engineering at Virginia Tech, the steel rods supplied by two different companies were compared. Ten sample springs were made out of the steel rods supplied by each company, and a measure of flexibility was recorded for each. The data are as follows:

Company A:	9.3	8.8	6.8	8.7	8.5
	6.7	8.0	6.5	9.2	7.0
Company B:	11.0	9.8	9.9	10.2	10.1
	9.7	11.0	11.1	10.2	9.6

(a) Calculate the sample mean and median for the data for the two companies.

(b) Plot the data for the two companies on the same line and give your impression regarding any apparent differences between the two companies.

5   Twenty adult males between the ages of 30 and 40 participated in a study to evaluate the effect of a specific health regimen involving diet and exercise on the blood cholesterol. Ten were randomly selected to be a control group, and ten others were assigned to take part in the regimen as the treatment group for a period of 6 months. The following data show the reduction in cholesterol experienced for the time period for the 20 subjects:

Control group:	7	3	−4	14	2
	5	22	−7	9	5
Treatment group:	−6	5	9	4	4
	12	37	5	3	3

(a) Do a dot plot of the data for both groups on the same graph.

(b) Compute the mean, median, and 10% trimmed mean for both groups.

(c) Explain why the difference in means suggests one conclusion about the effect of the regimen, while the difference in medians or trimmed means suggests a different conclusion.

6   The tensile strength of silicone rubber is thought to be a function of curing temperature. A study was carried out in which samples of 12 specimens of the rubber were prepared using curing temperatures of 20°C and 45°C. The data below show the tensile strength values in megapascals.

20°C:	2.07	2.14	2.22	2.03	2.21	2.03
	2.05	2.18	2.09	2.14	2.11	2.02
45°C:	2.52	2.15	2.49	2.03	2.37	2.05
	1.99	2.42	2.08	2.42	2.29	2.01

(a) Show a dot plot of the data with both low and high temperature tensile strength values.

(b) Compute sample mean tensile strength for both samples.

(c) Does it appear as if curing temperature has an influence on tensile strength, based on the plot? Comment further.

(d) Does anything else appear to be influenced by an increase in curing temperature? Explain.

4   Measures of Variability

Sample variability plays an important role in data analysis. Process and product variability is a fact of life in engineering and scientific systems: The control or reduction of process variability is often a source of major difficulty. More and more process engineers and managers are learning that product quality and, as a result, profits derived from manufactured products are very much a function of **process variability**. Even in small data analysis problems, the success of a particular statistical method may depend on the magnitude of the variability among the observations in the sample. Measures of location in a sample do not provide a proper summary of the nature of a data set. For instance, in Example 2 we cannot conclude that the use of nitrogen enhances growth without taking sample variability into account.

It should be clear from Figure 1 that variability among the no-nitrogen observations and variability among the nitrogen observations are certainly of some consequence. In fact, it appears that the variability within the nitrogen sample is larger than that of the no-nitrogen sample. Perhaps there is something about the inclusion of nitrogen that not only increases the stem height ($\bar{x}$ of 0.565 gram compared to an $\bar{x}$ of 0.399 gram for the no-nitrogen sample) but also increases the variability in stem height (i.e., renders the stem height more inconsistent).

As another example, contrast the two data sets below. Each contains two samples and the difference in the means is roughly the same for the two samples, but data set B seems to provide a much sharper contrast between the two populations from which the samples were taken. If the purpose of such an experiment is to detect differences between the two populations, the task is accomplished in the case of data set B. However, in data set A the large variability *within* the two samples creates diffculty. Infact, it is not clear that there is a distinction *between* the two populations.

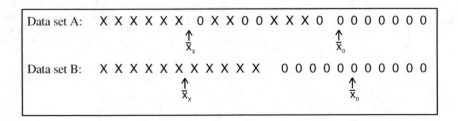

Sample Range and Sample Standard Deviation

Just as there are many measures of central tendency or location, there are many measures of spread or variability. Perhaps the simplest one is the **sample range** $X_{max} - X_{min}$. The range can be very useful. The sample measure of spread that is used most often is the **sample standard deviation**. We again let $x_1, x_2, \ldots, x_n$ denote sample values.

Definition 3:

> The **sample variance**, denoted by s^2, is given by
>
> $$s^2 = \sum_{i=1}^{n} \frac{(x_i - \bar{x})^2}{n-1}.$$
>
> The **sample standard deviation**, denoted by s, is the positive square root of s^2, that is,
>
> $$s = \sqrt{s^2}.$$

It should be clear to the reader that the sample standard deviation is, in fact, a measure of variability. Large variability in a data set produces relatively large values of $(x - \bar{x})^2$ and thus a large sample variance. The quantity $n - 1$ is often called the **degrees of freedom associated with the variance** estimate. In this simple example, the degrees of freedom depict the number of independent pieces of information available for computing variability. For example, suppose that we wish to compute the sample variance and standard deviation of the data set (5, 17, 6, 4). The sample average is $\bar{x} = 8$. The computation of the variance involves

$$(5 - 8)^2 + (17 - 8)^2 + (6 - 8)^2 + (4 - 8)^2 = (-3)^2 + 9^2 + (-2)^2 + (-4)^2.$$

The quantities inside parentheses sum to zero. In general, $\sum_{i=1}^{n} (x_i - \bar{x}) = 0$ (see Exercise 16). Then the computation of a sample variance does not involve n **independent squared deviations** from the mean $\bar{x}$. In fact, since the last value of $x - \bar{x}$ is determined by the initial $n - 1$ of them, we say that these are $n - 1$ "pieces of information" that produce s^2. Thus, there are $n - 1$ degrees of freedom rather than n degrees of freedom for computing a sample variance.

Example 4:

For example, an engineer is interested in testing the "bias" in a pH meter. Data are collected on the meter by measuring the pH of a neutral substance (pH = 7.0). A sample of size 10 is taken, with results given by

7.07 7.00 7.10 6.97 7.00 7.03 7.01 7.01 6.98 7.08.

The sample mean $\bar{x}$ is given by

$$\bar{x} = \frac{7.07 + 7.00 + 7.10 + \cdots + 7.08}{10} = 7.0250.$$

The sample variance s^2 is given by

$$s^2 = \frac{1}{9}[(7.07 - 7.025)^2 + (7.00 - 7.025)^2 + (7.10 - 7.025)^2$$
$$+ \cdots + (7.08 - 7.025)^2] = 0.001939.$$

As a result, the sample standard deviation is given by

$$s = \sqrt{0.001939} = 0.044.$$

So the sample standard deviation is 0.0440 with $n - 1 = 9$ degrees of freedom.

Units for Standard Deviation and Variance

It should be apparent from Definition 3 that the variance is a measure of the average squared deviation from the mean $\bar{x}$. We use the term *average squared deviation* even though the definition makes use of a division by degrees of freedom $n - 1$ rather than n. Of course, if n is large, the difference in the denominator is inconsequential. As a result, the sample variance possesses units that are the square of the units in the observed data whereas the sample standard deviation is found in linear units. As an example, consider the data of Example 2. The stem weights are measured in grams. As a result, the sample standard deviations are in grams and the variances are measured in grams^2. In fact, the individual standard deviations are 0.0728 gram for the no-nitrogen case and 0.1867 gram for the nitrogen group. Note that the standard deviation does indicate considerably larger variability in the nitrogen sample. This condition was displayed in Figure 1.

Which Variability Measure Is More Important?

As we indicated earlier, the sample range has applications in the area of statistical quality control. It may appear to the reader that the use of both the sample variance and the sample standard deviation is redundant. Both measures reflect the same concept in measuring variability, but the sample standard deviation measures variability in linear units whereas the sample variance is measured in squared units. Both play huge roles in the use of statistical methods. Much of what is accomplished in the context of statistical inference involves drawing conclusions about characteristics of populations. Among these characteristics are constants which are called **population parameters**. Two important parameters are the **population mean** and the **population variance**. The sample variance plays an explicit role in the statistical methods used to draw inferences about the population variance. The sample standard deviation has an important role along with the sample mean in inferences that are made about the population mean. In general, the variance is considered more in inferential theory, while the standard deviation is used more in applications.

Introduction to Statistics and Data Analysis

Exercises

7 Consider the drying time data for Exercise 1. Compute the sample variance and sample standard deviation.

8 Compute the sample variance and standard deviation for the water absorbency data of Exercise 2.

9 Exercise 3 showed tensile strength data for two samples, one in which specimens were exposed to an aging process and one in which there was no aging of the specimens.
(a) Calculate the sample variance as well as standard deviation in tensile strength for both samples.
(b) Does there appear to be any evidence that aging affects the variability in tensile strength? (See also the plot for Exercise 3.)

10 For the data of Exercise 4, compute both the mean and the variance in "flexibility" for both company A and company B. Does there appear to be a difference in flexibility between company A and company B?

11 Consider the data in Exercise 5. Compute the sample variance and the sample standard deviation for both control and treatment groups.

12 For Exercise 6, compute the sample standard deviation in tensile strength for the samples separately for the two temperatures. Does it appear as if an increase in temperature influences the variability in tensile strength? Explain.

5 Discrete and Continuous Data

Statistical inference through the analysis of observational studies or designed experiments is used in many scientific areas. The data gathered may be **discrete** or **continuous**, depending on the area of application. For example, a chemical engineer may be interested in conducting an experiment that will lead to conditions where yield is maximized. Here, of course, the yield may be in percent or grams/pound, measured on a continuum. On the other hand, a toxicologist conducting a combination drug experiment may encounter data that are binary in nature (i.e., the patient either responds or does not).
Great distinctions are made between discrete and continuous data in the prob- ability theory that allow us to draw statistical inferences. Often applications of statistical inference are found when the data are *count data*. For example, an en- gineer may be interested in studying the number of radioactive particles passing through a counter in, say, 1 millisecond. Personnel responsible for the efficiency of a port facility may be interested in the properties of the number of oil tankers arriving each day at a certain port city.

Special attention even at this early stage of the textbook should be paid to some details associated with binary data. Applications requiring statistical analysis of binary data are voluminous. Often the measure that is used in the analysis is the *sample proportion*. Obviously the binary situation involves two categories. If there are n units involved in the data and x is defined as the number that fall into category 1, then $n - x$ fall into category 2. Thus, x/n is the sample proportion in category 1, and $1 - x/n$ is the sample proportion in category 2. In the biomedical application, 50 patients may represent the sample units, and if 20 out of 50 experienced an improvement in a stomach ailment (common to all 50) after all were given the drug, then $\frac{20}{50} = 0.4$ is the sample proportion for which the drug was a success and $1 - 0.4 = 0.6$ is the sample proportion for which the drug was not successful. Actually the basic numerical measurement for binary data is generally denoted by either 0 or 1. For example, in our medical example, a successful result is denoted by a 1 and a nonsuccess a 0. As a result, the sample proportion is actually a sample mean of the ones and zeros. For the successful category,

$$\frac{x_1 + x_2 + \cdots + x_{50}}{50} = \frac{1 + 1 + 0 + \cdots + 0 + 1}{50} = \frac{20}{50} = 0.4.$$

What Kinds of Problems Are Solved in Binary Data Situations?

The kinds of problems facing scientists and engineers dealing in binary data are not a great deal unlike those seen where continuous measurements are of interest. However, different techniques are used since the statistical properties of sample proportions are quite different from those of the sample means that result from averages taken from continuous populations. Consider the example data in Exercise 6. The statistical problem underlying this illustration focuses on whether an intervention, say, an increase in curing temperature, will alter the population mean tensile strength associated with the silicone rubber process. On the other hand, in a quality control area, suppose an automobile tire manufacturer reports that a shipment of 5000 tires selected randomly from the process results in 100 of them showing blemishes. Here the sample proportion is $\frac{100}{5000} = 0.02$. Following a change in the process designed to reduce blemishes, a second sample of 5000 is taken and 90 tires are blemished. The sample proportion has been reduced to $\frac{90}{5000} = 0.018$. The question arises, "Is the decrease in the sample proportion from 0.02 to 0.018 substantial enough to suggest a real improvement in the population proportion?" Both of these illustrations require the use of the statistical properties of sample averages—one from samples from a continuous population, and the other from samples from a discrete (binary) population. In both cases, the sample mean is an **estimate** of a population parameter, a population mean in the first illustration (i.e., mean tensile strength), and a population proportion in the second case (i.e., proportion of blemished tires in the population). So here we have sample estimates used to draw scientific conclusions regarding population parameters. As we indicated in Section 3, this is the general theme in many practical problems using statistical inference.

6 Statistical Modeling, Scientific Inspection, and Graphical Diagnostics

Often the end result of a statistical analysis is the estimation of parameters of a **postulated model**. This is natural for scientists and engineers since they often deal in modeling. A statistical model is not deterministic but, rather, must entail some probabilistic aspects. A model form is often the foundation of **assumptions** that are made by the analyst. For example, in Example 2 the scientist may wish to draw some level of distinction between the nitrogen and no-nitrogen populations through the sample information. The analysis may require a certain model for the data, for example, that the two samples come from **normal** or **Gaussian distributions**.

Obviously, the user of statistical methods cannot generate sufficient information or experimental data to characterize the population totally. But sets of data are often used to learn about certain properties of the population. Scientists and engineers are accustomed to dealing with data sets. The importance of characterizing or *summarizing* the nature of collections of data should be obvious. Often a summary of a collection of data via a graphical display can provide insight regarding the system from which the data were taken. For instance, in Sections 1 and 3, we have shown dot plots.

In this section, the role of sampling and the display of data for enhancement of **statistical inference** is explored in detail. We merely introduce some simple but often effective displays that complement the study of statistical populations.

Scatter Plot

At times the model postulated may take on a somewhat complicated form. Consider, for example, a textile manufacturer who designs an experiment where cloth specimen that contain various percentages of cotton are produced. Consider the data in Table 3.

Table 3: Tensile Strength

Cotton Percentage	Tensile Strength
15	7, 7, 9, 8, 10
20	19, 20, 21, 20, 22
25	21, 21, 17, 19, 20
30	8, 7, 8, 9, 10

Five cloth specimens are manufactured for each of the four cotton percentages. In this case, both the model for the experiment and the type of analysis used should take into account the goal of the experiment and important input from the textile scientist. Some simple graphics can shed important light on the clear distinction between the samples. See Figure 5; the sample means and variability are depicted nicely in the scatter plot. One possible goal of this experiment is simply to determine which cotton percentages are truly distinct from the others. In other words, as in the case of the nitrogen/no-nitrogen data, for which cotton percentages are there clear distinctions between the populations or, more specifically, between the population means? In this case, perhaps a reasonable model is that each sample comes from a normal distribution. Here the goal is very much like that of the nitrogen/no-nitrogen data except that more samples are involved. The formalism of the analysis involves notions of hypothesis testing. Incidentally, this formality is perhaps not necessary in light of the diagnostic plot. But does this describe the real goal of the experiment and hence the proper approach to data analysis? It is likely that the scientist anticipates the existence of a *maximum population mean tensile strength* in the range of cotton concentration in the experiment. Here the analysis of the data should revolve around a different type of model, one that postulates a type of structure relating the population mean tensile strength to the cotton concentration. In other words, a model may be written

$$\mu_{t,c} = \beta_0 + \beta_1 C + \beta_2 C^2,$$

where $\mu_{t,c}$ is the population mean tensile strength, which varies with the amount of cotton in the product C. The implication of this model is that for a fixed cotton level, there is a population of tensile strength measurements and the population mean is $\mu_{t,c}$. This type of model is called a **regression model**. The functional form is chosen by the scientist. At times the data analysis may suggest that the model be changed. Then the data analyst "entertains" a model that may be altered after some analysis is done. The use of an empirical model is accompanied by **estimation theory**, where β_0, β_1, and β_2 are estimated by the data. Further, statistical inference can then be used to determine model adequacy.

Figure 5: Scatter plot of tensile strength and cotton percentages.

Two points become evident from the two data illustrations here: (1) The type of model used to describe the data often depends on the goal of the experiment; and (2) the structure of the model should take advantage of nonstatistical scientific input. A selection of a model represents a **fundamental assumption** upon which the resulting statistical inference is based. It will become apparent throughout the book how important graphics can be. Often, plots can illustrate information that allows the results of the formal statistical inference to be better communicated to the scientist or engineer. At times, plots or **exploratory data analysis** can teach the analyst something not retrieved from the formal analysis. Almost any formal analysis requires assumptions that evolve from the model of the data. Graphics can nicely highlight **violation of assumptions** that would otherwise go unnoticed. The following sections reveal some graphical tools that are useful in exploratory or descriptive data analysis.

Stem-and-Leaf Plot

Statistical data, generated in large masses, can be very useful for studying the behavior of the distribution if presented in a combined tabular and graphic display called a **stem-and-leaf plot**.

To illustrate the construction of a stem-and-leaf plot, consider the data of Table 4, which specifies the "life" of 40 similar car batteries recorded to the nearest tenth of a year. The batteries are guaranteed to last 3 years. First, split each observation into two parts consisting of a stem and a leaf such that the stem represents the digit preceding the decimal and the leaf corresponds to the decimal part of the number. In other words, for the number 3.7, the digit 3 is designated the stem and the digit 7 is the leaf. The four stems 1, 2, 3, and 4 for our data are listed vertically on the left side in Table 5; the leaves are recorded on the right side opposite the appropriate stem value. Thus, the leaf 6 of the number 1.6 is recorded opposite the stem 1; the leaf 5 of the number 2.5 is recorded opposite the stem 2; and so forth. The number of leaves recorded opposite each stem is summarized under the frequency column.

Table 4: Car Battery Life

2.2	4.1	3.5	4.5	3.2	3.7	3.0	2.6
3.4	1.6	3.1	3.3	3.8	3.1	4.7	3.7
2.5	4.3	3.4	3.6	2.9	3.3	3.9	3.1
3.3	3.1	3.7	4.4	3.2	4.1	1.9	3.4
4.7	3.8	3.2	2.6	3.9	3.0	4.2	3.5

Table 5: Stem-and-Leaf Plot of Battery Life

Stem	**Leaf**	**Frequency**
1	69	2
2	25669	5
3	0011112223334445567778899	25
4	11234577	8

The stem-and-leaf plot of Table 5 contains only four stems and consequently does not provide an adequate picture of the distribution. To remedy this problem, we need to increase the number of stems in our plot. One simple way to accomplish this is to write each stem value twice and then record the leaves 0, 1, 2, 3, and 4 opposite the appropriate stem value where it appears for the first time, and the leaves 5, 6, 7, 8, and 9 opposite this same stem value where it appears for the second time. This modified double-stem-and-leaf plot is illustrated in Table 6, where the stems corresponding to leaves 0 through 4 have been coded by the symbol ⋆ and the stems corresponding to leaves 5 through 9 by the symbol ·.

In any given problem, we must decide on the appropriate stem values. This decision is made somewhat arbitrarily, although we are guided by the size of our sample. Usually, we choose between 5 and 20 stems. The smaller the number of data available, the smaller is our choice for the number of stems. For example, if the data consist of numbers from 1 to 21 representing the number of people in a cafeteria line on 40 randomly selected workdays and we choose a double-stem-and-leaf plot, the stems will be 0⋆, 0·, 1⋆, 1·, and 2⋆ so that the smallest observation 1 has stem 0⋆ and leaf 1, the number 18 has stem 1· and leaf 8, and the largest observation 21 has stem 2⋆ and leaf 1. On the other hand, if the data consist of numbers from $18,800 to $19,600 representing the best possible deals on 100 new automobiles from a certain dealership and we choose a single-stem-and-leaf plot, the stems will be 188, 189, 190, ..., 196 and the leaves will now each contain two digits. A car that sold for $19,385 would have a stem value of 193 and the two-digit leaf 85. Multiple-digit leaves belonging to the same stem are usually separated by commas in the stem-and-leaf plot. Decimal points in the data are generally ignored when all the digits to the right of the decimal represent the leaf. Such was the case in Tables 5 and 6. However, if the data consist of numbers ranging from 21.8 to 74.9, we might choose the digits 2, 3, 4, 5, 6, and 7 as our stems so that a number such as 48.3 would have a stem value of 4 and a leaf of 8.3.

Table 6: Double-Stem-and-Leaf Plot of Battery Life

Stem	Leaf	Frequency
1·	69	2
2⋆	2	1
2·	5669	4
3⋆	001111222333444	15
3·	5567778899	10
4⋆	11234	5
4·	577	3

The stem-and-leaf plot represents an effective way to summarize data. Another way is through the use of the **frequency distribution**, where the data, grouped into different classes or intervals, can be constructed by counting the leaves belonging to each stem and noting that each stem defines a class interval. In Table 5, the stem 1 with 2 leaves defines the interval 1.0–1.9 containing 2 observations; the stem 2 with 5 leaves defines the interval 2.0–2.9 containing 5 observations; the stem 3 with 25 leaves defines the interval 3.0–3.9 with 25 observations; and the stem 4 with 8 leaves defines the interval 4.0–4.9 containing 8 observations. For the double-stem-and-leaf plot of Table 6, the stems define the seven class intervals 1.5–1.9, 2.0–2.4, 2.5–2.9, 3.0–3.4, 3.5–3.9, 4.0–4.4, and 4.5–4.9 with frequencies 2, 1, 4, 15, 10, 5, and 3, respectively.

Histogram

Dividing each class frequency by the total number of observations, we obtain the proportion of the set of observations in each of the classes. A table listing relative frequencies is called a **relative frequency distribution**. The relative frequency distribution for the data of Table 4, showing the midpoint of each class interval, is given in Table 7.

The information provided by a relative frequency distribution in tabular form is easier to grasp if presented graphically. Using the midpoint of each interval and the

Table 7: Relative Frequency Distribution of Battery Life

Class Interval	Class Midpoint	Frequency, f	Relative Frequency
1.5–1.9	1.7	2	0.050
2.0–2.4	2.2	1	0.025
2.5–2.9	2.7	4	0.100
3.0–3.4	3.2	15	0.375
3.5–3.9	3.7	10	0.250
4.0–4.4	4.2	5	0.125
4.5–4.9	4.7	3	0.075

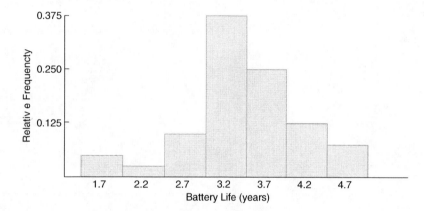

Figure 6: Relative frequency histogram.

corresponding relative frequency, we construct a **relative frequency histogram** (Figure 6).

Many continuous frequency distributions can be represented graphically by the characteristic bell-shaped curve of Figure 7. Graphical tools such as what we see in Figures 6 and 7 aid in the characterization of the nature of the population. While a more rigorous definition of a distribution or **probability distribution** will be given later in the text, at this point one can view it as what would be seen in Figure 7 in the limit as the size of the sample becomes larger.

A distribution is said to be **symmetric** if it can be folded along a vertical axis so that the two sides coincide. A distribution that lacks symmetry with respect to a vertical axis is said to be **skewed**. The distribution illustrated in Figure 8(a) is said to be skewed to the right since it has a long right tail and a much shorter left tail. In Figure 8(b) we see that the distribution is symmetric, while in Figure 8(c) it is skewed to the left.

If we rotate a stem-and-leaf plot counterclockwise through an angle of 90°, we observe that the resulting columns of leaves form a picture that is similar to a histogram. Consequently, if our primary purpose in looking at the data is to determine the general shape or form of the distribution, it will seldom be necessary

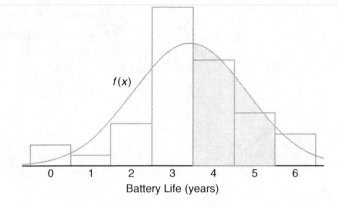

Figure 7: Estimating frequency distribution.

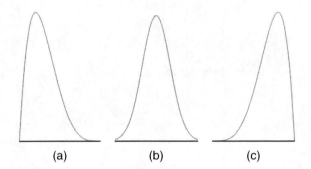

Figure 8: Skewness of data.

to construct a relative frequency histogram.

Box-and-Whisker Plot or Box Plot

Another display that is helpful for reflecting properties of a sample is the **box-and-whisker plot**. This plot encloses the *interquartile range* of the data in a box that has the median displayed within. The interquartile range has as its extremes the 75th percentile (upper quartile) and the 25th percentile (lower quartile). In addition to the box, "whiskers" extend, showing extreme observations in the sample. For reasonably large samples, the display shows center of location, variability, and the degree of asymmetry.

In addition, a variation called a **box plot** can provide the viewer with information regarding which observations may be **outliers**. Outliers are observations that are considered to be unusually far from the bulk of the data. There are many statistical tests that are designed to detect outliers. Technically, one may view an outlier as being an observation that represents a "rare event" (there is a small probability of obtaining a value that far from the bulk of the data).

Introduction to Statistics and Data Analysis

The visual information in the box-and-whisker plot or box plot is not intended to be a formal test for outliers. Rather, it is viewed as a diagnostic tool. While the determination of which observations are outliers varies with the type of software that is used, one common procedure is to use a **multiple of the interquartile range**. For example, if the distance from the box exceeds 1.5 times the interquartile range (in either direction), the observation may be labeled an outlier.

Example 5: Nicotine content was measured in a random sample of 40 cigarettes. The data are displayed in Table 8.

Table 8: Nicotine Data for Example 5

1.09	1.92	2.31	1.79	2.28	1.74	1.47	1.97
0.85	1.24	1.58	2.03	1.70	2.17	2.55	2.11
1.86	1.90	1.68	1.51	1.64	0.72	1.69	1.85
1.82	1.79	2.46	1.88	2.08	1.67	1.37	1.93
1.40	1.64	2.09	1.75	1.63	2.37	1.75	1.69

Figure 9: Box-and-whisker plot for Example 5.

Figure 9 shows the box-and-whisker plot of the data, depicting the observations 0.72 and 0.85 as mild outliers in the lower tail, whereas the observation 2.55 is a mild outlier in the upper tail. In this example, the interquartile range is 0.365, and 1.5 times the interquartile range is 0.5475. Figure 10, on the other hand, provides a stem-and-leaf plot.

Example 6: Consider the data in Table 9, consisting of 30 samples measuring the thickness of paint can "ears" (see the work by Hogg and Ledolter, 1992,)
Figure 11 depicts a box-and-whisker plot for this asymmetric set of data. Notice that the left block is considerably larger than the block on the right. The median is 35. The lower quartile is 31, while the upper quartile is 36. Notice also that the extreme observation on the right is farther away from the box than the extreme observation on the left. There are no outliers in this data set.

```
The decimal point is 1 digit(s) to the left of the |
  7 | 2
  8 | 5
  9 |
 10 | 9
 11 |
 12 | 4
 13 | 7
 14 | 07
 15 | 18
 16 | 3447899
 17 | 045599
 18 | 2568
 19 | 0237
 20 | 389
 21 | 17
 22 | 8
 23 | 17
 24 | 6
 25 | 5
```

Figure 10: Stem-and-leaf plot for the nicotine data.

Table 9: Data for Example 6

Sample	Measurements	Sample	Measurements
1	29 36 39 34 34	16	35 30 35 29 37
2	29 29 28 32 31	17	40 31 38 35 31
3	34 34 39 38 37	18	35 36 30 33 32
4	35 37 33 38 41	19	35 34 35 30 36
5	30 29 31 38 29	20	35 35 31 38 36
6	34 31 37 39 36	21	32 36 36 32 36
7	30 35 33 40 36	22	36 37 32 34 34
8	28 28 31 34 30	23	29 34 33 37 35
9	32 36 38 38 35	24	36 36 35 37 37
10	35 30 37 35 31	25	36 30 35 33 31
11	35 30 35 38 35	26	35 30 29 38 35
12	38 34 35 35 31	27	35 36 30 34 36
13	34 35 33 30 34	28	35 30 36 29 35
14	40 35 34 33 35	29	38 36 35 31 31
15	34 35 38 35 30	30	30 34 40 28 30

There are additional ways that box-and-whisker plots and other graphical displays can aid the analyst. Multiple samples can be compared graphically. Plots of data can suggest relationships between variables. Graphs can aid in the detection of anomalies or outlying observations in samples.

There are other types of graphical tools and plots that are used.

Figure 11: Box-and-whisker plot for thickness of paint can "ears."

Other Distinguishing Features of a Sample

There are features of the distribution or sample other than measures of center of location and variability that further define its nature. For example, while the median divides the data (or distribution) into two parts, there are other measures that divide parts or pieces of the distribution that can be very useful. Separation is made into four parts by *quartiles*, with the third quartile separating the upper quarter of the data from the rest, the second quartile being the median, and the first quartile separating the lower quarter of the data from the rest. The distribution can be even more finely divided by computing percentiles of the distribution. These quantities give the analyst a sense of the so-called *tails* of the distribution (i.e., values that are relatively extreme, either small or large). For example, the 95th percentile separates the highest 5% from the bottom 95%. Similar definitions prevail for extremes on the lower side or *lower tail* of the distribution. The 1st percentile separates the bottom 1% from the rest of the distribution.

7 General Types of Statistical Studies: Designed Experiment, Observational Study, and Retrospective Study

In the foregoing sections we have emphasized the notion of sampling from a population and the use of statistical methods to learn or perhaps affirm important information about the population. The information sought and learned through the use of these statistical methods can often be influential in decision making and problem solving in many important scientific and engineering areas. As an illustration, Example 3 describes a simple experiment in which the results may provide an aid in determining the kinds of conditions under which it is not advisable to use a particular aluminum alloy that may have a dangerous vulnerability to corrosion. The results may be of use not only to those who produce the alloy, but also to the customer who may consider using it. This illustration highlights the concept of designing or controlling experimental conditions (combinations of coating conditions and humidity) of interest to learn about some characteristic or measurement (level of corrosion) that results from these conditions. Statistical methods that make use of measures of central tendency in the corrosion measure, as well as measures of variability, are employed. As the reader will observe later in the text, these methods often lead to a statistical model like that discussed in Section 6. In this case, the model may be used to estimate (or predict) the corrosion measure as a function of humidity and the type of coating employed. Again, in developing this kind of model, descriptive statistics that highlight central tendency and variability become very useful.

The information supplied in Example 3 illustrates nicely the types of engineering questions asked and answered by the use of statistical methods that are employed through a designed experiment and presented in this text. They are

(i) What is the nature of the impact of relative humidity on the corrosion of the aluminum alloy within the range of relative humidity in this experiment?

(ii) Does the chemical corrosion coating reduce corrosion levels and can the effect be quantified in some fashion?

(iii) Is there **interaction** between coating type and relative humidity that impacts their influence on corrosion of the alloy? If so, what is its interpretation?

What Is Interaction?

The importance of questions (i) and (ii) should be clear to the reader, as they deal with issues important to both producers and users of the alloy. But what about question (iii)? Consider the plot in Figure 3. This is an illustration of the detection of interaction between two **factors** in a simple designed experiment. Note that the lines connecting the sample means are not parallel. **Parallelism** would have indicated that the effect (seen as a result of the slope of the lines) of relative humidity is the same, namely a negative effect, for both an uncoated condition and the chemical corrosion coating. Recall that the negative slope implies that corrosion becomes more pronounced as humidity rises. Lack of parallelism implies an interaction between coating type and relative humidity. The nearly "flat" line for the corrosion coating as opposed to a steeper slope for the uncoated condition suggests that *not only is the chemical corrosion coating beneficial (note the displacement between the lines), but the presence of the coating renders the effect of humidity negligible.* Clearly all these questions are very important to the effect of the two individual factors and to the interpretation of the interaction, if it is present.

Statistical models are extremely useful in answering questions such as those listed in (i), (ii), and (iii), where the data come from a designed experiment. But one does not always have the luxury or resources to employ a designed experiment. For example, there are many instances in which the conditions of interest to the scientist or engineer cannot be implemented simply because the *important factors cannot be controlled.* In Example 3, the relative humidity and coating type (or lack of coating) are quite easy to control. This of course is the defining feature of a designed experiment. In many fields, factors that need to be studied cannot be controlled for any one of various reasons. Tight control as in Example 1 allows the analyst to be confident that any differences found (for example, in corrosion levels) are due to the factors under control. As a second illustration, consider Exercise 6. Suppose in this case 24 specimens of silicone rubber are selected and 12 assigned to each of the curing temperature levels. The temperatures are controlled carefully, and thus this is an example of a designed experiment with a **single factor** being curing temperature. Differences found in the mean tensile strength would be assumed to be attributed to the different curing temperatures.

What If Factors Are Not Controlled?

Suppose there are no factors controlled and *no random assignment* of fixed treatments to experimental units and yet there is a need to glean information from a data set. As an illustration, consider a study in which interest centers around the relationship between blood cholesterol levels and the amount of sodium measured in the blood. A group of individuals were monitored over time for both blood cholesterol and sodium. Certainly some useful information can be gathered from such a data set. However, it should be clear that there certainly can be no strict control of blood sodium levels. Ideally, the subjects should be divided randomly into two groups, with one group assigned a specific high level of blood sodium and the other a specific low level of blood sodium. Obviously this cannot be done. Clearly changes in cholesterol can be experienced because of changes in one of a number of other factors that were not controlled. This kind of study, without factor control, is called an **observational study**. Much of the time it involves a situation in which subjects are observed across time.

Biological and biomedical studies are often by necessity observational studies. However, observational studies are not confined to those areas. For example, consider a study that is designed to determine the influence of ambient temperature on the electric power consumed by a chemical plant. Clearly, levels of ambient temperature cannot be controlled, and thus the data structure can only be a monitoring of the data from the plant over time.

It should be apparent that the striking difference between a well-designed experiment and observational studies is the difficulty in determination of true cause and effect with the latter. Also, differences found in the fundamental response (e.g., corrosion levels, blood cholesterol, plant electric power consumption) may be due to other underlying factors that were not controlled. Ideally, in a designed experiment the *nuisance factors* would be equalized via the randomization process. Certainly changes in blood cholesterol could be due to fat intake, exercise activity, and so on. Electric power consumption could be affected by the amount of product produced or even the purity of the product produced.

Another often ignored disadvantage of an observational study when compared to carefully designed experiments is that, unlike the latter, observational studies are at the mercy of nature, environmental or other uncontrolled circumstances that impact the ranges of factors of interest. For example, in the biomedical study regarding the influence of blood sodium levels on blood cholesterol, it is possible that there is indeed a strong influence but the particular data set used did not involve enough observed variation in sodium levels because of the nature of the subjects chosen. Of course, in a designed experiment, the analyst chooses and controls ranges of factors.

A third type of statistical study which can be very useful but has clear disadvantages when compared to a designed experiment is a **retrospective study**. This type of study uses strictly **historical data**, data taken over a specific period of time. One obvious advantage of retrospective data is that there is reduced cost in collecting the data. However, as one might expect, there are clear disadvantages.

(i) Validity and reliability of historical data are often in doubt.

(ii) If time is an important aspect of the structure of the data, there may be data missing.

(iii) There may be errors in collection of the data that are not known.

(iv) Again, as in the case of observational data, there is no control on the ranges of the measured variables (the factors in a study). Indeed, the ranges found in historical data may not be relevant for current studies.

In Section 6, some attention was given to modeling of relationships among variables. We introduced the notion of regression analysis. In Section 6, a model relating population mean tensile strength of cloth to percentages of cotton was used for illustration, where 20 specimens of cloth represented the experimental units. In that case, the data came from a simple designed experiment where the individual cotton percentages were selected by the scientist.

Often both observational data and retrospective data are used for the purpose of observing relationships among variables through model-building procedures. While the advantages of designed experiments certainly apply when the goal is statistical model building, there are many areas in which designing of experiments is not possible. Thus, *observational or historical data must be used*. The goal is to build a model that will result in an equation or relationship that relates monthly electric power consumed to average ambient temperature x_1, the number of days in the month x_2, the average product purity x_3, and the tons of product produced x_4. The data are the past year's historical data.

Exercises

13 A manufacturer of electronic components is interested in determining the lifetime of a certain type of battery. A sample, in hours of life, is as follows:

123, 116, 122, 110, 175, 126, 125, 111, 118, 117.

(a) Find the sample mean and median.
(b) What feature in this data set is responsible for the substantial difference between the two?

14 A tire manufacturer wants to determine the inner diameter of a certain grade of tire. Ideally, the diameter would be 570 mm. The data are as follows:

572, 572, 573, 568, 569, 575, 565, 570.

(a) Find the sample mean and median.
(b) Find the sample variance, standard deviation, and range.
(c) Using the calculated statistics in parts (a) and (b), can you comment on the quality of the tires?

15 Five independent coin tosses result in $HHHHH$. It turns out that if the coin is fair the probability of this outcome is $(1/2)^5 = 0.03125$. Does this produce strong evidence that the coin is not fair? Comment and use the concept of P-value discussed in Section 1.

16 Show that the n pieces of information in $\sum_{i=1}^{n}(x_i - \bar{x})^2$ are not independent; that is, show that

$$\sum_{i=1}^{n}(x_i - \bar{x}) = 0.$$

17 A study of the effects of smoking on sleep patterns is conducted. The measure observed is the time, in minutes, that it takes to fall asleep. These data are obtained:

Smokers:	69.3	56.0	22.1	47.6
	53.2	48.1	52.7	34.4
	60.2	43.8	23.2	13.8
Nonsmokers:	28.6	25.1	26.4	34.9
	29.8	28.4	38.5	30.2
	30.6	31.8	41.6	21.1
	36.0	37.9	13.9	

(a) Find the sample mean for each group.

(b) Find the sample standard deviation for each group.

(c) Make a dot plot of the data sets A and B on the same line.

(d) Comment on what kind of impact smoking appears to have on the time required to fall asleep.

18 The following scores represent the final examination grades for an elementary statistics course:

23	60	79	32	57	74	52	70	82
36	80	77	81	95	41	65	92	85
55	76	52	10	64	75	78	25	80
98	81	67	41	71	83	54	64	72
88	62	74	43	60	78	89	76	84
48	84	90	15	79	34	67	17	82
69	74	63	80	85	61			

(a) Construct a stem-and-leaf plot for the examination grades in which the stems are $1, 2, 3, \ldots, 9$.

(b) Construct a relative frequency histogram, draw an estimate of the graph of the distribution, and discuss the skewness of the distribution.

(c) Compute the sample mean, sample median, and sample standard deviation.

19 The following data represent the length of life in years, measured to the nearest tenth, of 30 similar fuel pumps:

2.0	3.0	0.3	3.3	1.3	0.4
0.2	6.0	5.5	6.5	0.2	2.3
1.5	4.0	5.9	1.8	4.7	0.7
4.5	0.3	1.5	0.5	2.5	5.0
1.0	6.0	5.6	6.0	1.2	0.2

(a) Construct a stem-and-leaf plot for the life in years of the fuel pumps, using the digit to the left of the decimal point as the stem for each observation.

(b) Set up a relative frequency distribution.

(c) Compute the sample mean, sample range, and sample standard deviation.

20 The following data represent the length of life, in seconds, of 50 fruit flies subject to a new spray in a controlled laboratory experiment:

17	20	10	9	23	13	12	19	18	24
12	14	6	9	13	6	7	10	13	7
16	18	8	13	3	32	9	7	10	11
13	7	18	7	10	4	27	19	16	8
7	10	5	14	15	10	9	6	7	15

(a) Construct a double-stem-and-leaf plot for the life span of the fruit flies using the stems $0\star$, $0\cdot$, $1\star$, $1\cdot$, $2\star$, $2\cdot$, and $3\star$ such that stems coded by the symbols $\star$ and $\cdot$ are associated, respectively, with leaves 0 through 4 and 5 through 9.

(b) Set up a relative frequency distribution.

(c) Construct a relative frequency histogram.

(d) Find the median.

21 The lengths of power failures, in minutes, are recorded in the following table.

22	18	135	15	90	78	69	98	102
83	55	28	121	120	13	22	124	112
70	66	74	89	103	24	21	112	21
40	98	87	132	115	21	28	43	37
50	96	118	158	74	78	83	93	95

(a) Find the sample mean and sample median of the power-failure times.

(b) Find the sample standard deviation of the power-failure times.

22 The following data are the measures of the diameters of 36 rivet heads in 1/100 of an inch.

6.72	6.77	6.82	6.70	6.78	6.70	6.62	6.75
6.66	6.66	6.64	6.76	6.73	6.80	6.72	6.76
6.76	6.68	6.66	6.62	6.72	6.76	6.70	6.78
6.76	6.67	6.70	6.72	6.74	6.81	6.79	6.78
6.66	6.76	6.76	6.72				

(a) Compute the sample mean and sample standard deviation.

(b) Construct a relative frequency histogram of the data.

(c) Comment on whether or not there is any clear indication that the sample came from a population that has a bell-shaped distribution.

23 The hydrocarbon emissions at idling speed in parts per million (ppm) for automobiles of 1980 and 1990 model years are given for 20 randomly selected cars.

1980 models:
   141 359 247 940 882 494 306 210 105 880
   200 223 188 940 241 190 300 435 241 380
1990 models:
   140 160   20   20 223   60   20   95 360 70
   220 400 217   58 235 380 200 175   85 65

(a) Construct a dot plot as in Figure 1.

(b) Compute the sample means for the two years and superimpose the two means on the plots.

(c) Comment on what the dot plot indicates regarding whether or not the population emissions changed from 1980 to 1990. Use the concept of variability in your comments.

24 The following are historical data on staff salaries (dollars per pupil) for 30 schools sampled in the eastern part of the United States in the early 1970s.

   3.79 2.99 2.77 2.91 3.10 1.84 2.52 3.22
   2.45 2.14 2.67 2.52 2.71 2.75 3.57 3.85
   3.36 2.05 2.89 2.83 3.13 2.44 2.10 3.71
   3.14 3.54 2.37 2.68 3.51 3.37

(a) Compute the sample mean and sample standard deviation.

(b) Construct a relative frequency histogram of the data.

(c) Construct a stem-and-leaf display of the data.

25 The following data set is related to that in Exercise 24. It gives the percentages of the families that are in the upper income level, for the same individual schools in the same order as in Exercise 24.

   72.2 31.9 26.5 29.1 27.3   8.6 22.3 26.5
   20.4 12.8 25.1 19.2 24.1 58.2 68.1 89.2
   55.1   9.4 14.5 13.9 20.7 17.9   8.5 55.4
   38.1 54.2 21.5 26.2 59.1 43.3

(a) Calculate the sample mean.

(b) Calculate the sample median.

(c) Construct a relative frequency histogram of the data.

(d) Compute the 10% trimmed mean. Compare with the results in (a) and (b) and comment.

26 Suppose it is of interest to use the data sets in Exercises 24 and 25 to derive a model that would predict staff salaries as a function of percentage of families in a high income level for current school systems. Comment on any disadvantage in carrying out this type of analysis.

27 A study is done to determine the influence of the wear, y, of a bearing as a function of the load, x, on the bearing. A designed experiment is used for this study. Three levels of load were used, 700 lb, 1000 lb, and 1300 lb. Four specimens were used at each level,

and the sample means were, respectively, 210, 325, and 375.

(a) Plot average wear against load.

(b) From the plot in (a), does it appear as if a relationship exists between wear and load?

(c) Suppose we look at the individual wear values for each of the four specimens at each load level (see the data that follow). Plot the wear results for all specimens against the three load values.

(d) From your plot in (c), does it appear as if a clear relationship exists? If your answer is different from that in (b), explain why.

	\multicolumn{3}{c}{x}		
	700	1000	1300
y_1	145	250	150
y_2	105	195	180
y_3	260	375	420
y_4	330	480	750
	$\bar{y}_1 = 210$	$\bar{y}_2 = 325$	$\bar{y}_3 = 375$

28 Many manufacturing companies in the United States and abroad use molded parts as components of a process. Shrinkage is often a major problem. Thus, a molded die for a part is built larger than nominal size to allow for part shrinkage. In an injection molding study it is known that the shrinkage is influenced by many factors, among which are the injection velocity in ft/sec and mold temperature in °C. The following two data sets show the results of a designed experiment in which injection velocity was held at two levels (low and high) and mold temperature was held constant at a low level. The shrinkage is measured in cm $\times$ 10^4.

Shrinkage values at low injection velocity:

   72.68 72.62 72.58 72.48 73.07
   72.55 72.42 72.84 72.58 72.92

Shrinkage values at high injection velocity:

   71.62 71.68 71.74 71.48 71.55
   71.52 71.71 71.56 71.70 71.50

(a) Construct a dot plot of both data sets on the same graph. Indicate on the plot both shrinkage means, that for low injection velocity and high injection velocity.

(b) Based on the graphical results in (a), using the location of the two means and your sense of variability, what do you conclude regarding the effect of injection velocity on shrinkage at low mold temperature?

29 Use the data in Exercise 24 to construct a box plot.

30 Below are the lifetimes, in hours, of fifty 40-watt, 110-volt internally frosted incandescent lamps, taken from forced life tests:

919	1196	785	1126	936	918
1156	920	948	1067	1092	1162
1170	929	950	905	972	1035
1045	855	1195	1195	1340	1122
938	970	1237	956	1102	1157
978	832	1009	1157	1151	1009
765	958	902	1022	1333	811
1217	1085	896	958	1311	1037
702	923				

Construct a box plot for these data.

31 Consider the situation of Exercise 28. But now use the following data set, in which shrinkage is measured once again at low injection velocity and high injection velocity. However, this time the mold temperature is raised to a high level and held constant.

Shrinkage values at low injection velocity:

$$76.20 \quad 76.09 \quad 75.98 \quad 76.15 \quad 76.17$$
$$75.94 \quad 76.12 \quad 76.18 \quad 76.25 \quad 75.82$$

Shrinkage values at high injection velocity:

$$93.25 \quad 93.19 \quad 92.87 \quad 93.29 \quad 93.37$$
$$92.98 \quad 93.47 \quad 93.75 \quad 93.89 \quad 91.62$$

(a) As in Exercise 28, construct a dot plot with both data sets on the same graph and identify both means (i.e., mean shrinkage for low injection velocity and for high injection velocity).

(b) As in Exercise 28, comment on the influence of injection velocity on shrinkage for high mold temperature. Take into account the position of the two means and the variability around each mean.

(c) Compare your conclusion in (b) with that in (b) of Exercise 28 in which mold temperature was held at a low level. Would you say that there is an interaction between injection velocity and mold temperature? Explain.

32 Use the results of Exercises 28 and 31 to create a plot that illustrates the interaction evident from the data. Use the plot in Figure 3 in Example 3 as a guide. Could the type of information found in Exercises 28 and 31 have been found in an observational study in which there was no control on injection velocity and mold temperature by the analyst? Explain why or why not.

33 **Group Project:** Collect the shoe size of everyone in the class. Use the sample means and variances and the types of plots presented in this chapter to summarize any features that draw a distinction between the distributions of shoe sizes for males and females. Do the same for the height of everyone in the class.

Answers to Odd-Numbered Non-Review Exercises

1   (a) Sample size $= 15$

     (b) Sample mean $= 3.787$

     (c) Sample median $= 3.6$

     (e) $\bar{x}_{tr(20)} = 3.678$

     (f) They are about the same.

3   (b) Yes, the aging process has reduced the tensile strength.

     (c) $\bar{x}_{Aging} = 209.90$, $\bar{x}_{No\ aging} = 222.10$

     (d) $\tilde{x}_{Aging} = 210.00$, $\tilde{x}_{No\ aging} = 221.50$. The means and medians are similar for each group.

5   (b) Control: $\bar{x} = 5.60$, $\tilde{x} = 5.00$, $\bar{x}_{tr(10)} = 5.13$. Treatment: $\bar{x} = 7.60$, $\tilde{x} = 4.50$, $\bar{x}_{tr(10)} = 5.63$.

     (c) The extreme value of 37 in the treatment group plays a strong leverage role for the mean calculation.

7   Sample variance $= 0.943$
     Sample standard deviation $= 0.971$

9   (a) No aging: sample variance $= 23.66$, sample standard deviation $= 4.86$. Aging: sample variance $= 42.10$, sample standard deviation $= 6.49$.

     (b) Based on the numbers in (a), the variation in "Aging" is smaller than the variation in "No aging," although the difference is not so apparent in the plot.

11   Control: sample variance $= 69.38$, sample standard deviation $= 8.33$. Treatment: sample variance $= 128.04$, sample standard deviation $= 11.32$.

13   (a) Mean $= 124.3$, median $= 120$

     (b) 175 is an extreme observation.

15   Yes, P-value $= 0.03125$, probability of obtaining $HHHHH$ with a fair coin.

17 (a) The sample means for nonsmokers and smokers are 30.32 and 43.70, respectively.

(b) The sample standard deviations for nonsmokers and smokers are 7.13 and 16.93, respectively.

(d) Smokers appear to take a longer time to fall asleep. For smokers the time to fall asleep is more variable.

19 (a)

Stem	Leaf	Frequency
0	22233457	8
1	023558	6
2	035	3
3	03	2
4	057	3
5	0569	4
6	0005	4

(b)

Class Interval	Class Midpoint	Freq.	Rel. Freq.
0.0−0.9	0.45	8	0.267
1.0−1.9	1.45	6	0.200
2.0−2.9	2.45	3	0.100
3.0−3.9	3.45	2	0.067
4.0−4.9	4.45	3	0.100
5.0−5.9	5.45	4	0.133
6.0−6.9	6.45	4	0.133

(c) Sample mean = 2.7967
Sample range = 6.3
Sample standard deviation = 2.2273

21 (a) $\bar{x} = 74.02$ and $\tilde{x} = 78$

(b) $s = 39.26$

23 (b) $\bar{x}_{1980} = 395.10$, $\bar{x}_{1990} = 160.15$

(c) The mean emissions dropped between 1980 and 1990; the variability also decreased because there were no longer extremely large emissions.

25 (a) Sample mean = 33.31

(b) Sample median = 26.35

(d) $\bar{x}_{\text{tr}(10)} = 30.97$

Probability

1 Sample Space

In the study of statistics, we are concerned basically with the presentation and interpretation of **chance outcomes** that occur in a planned study or scientific investigation. For example, we may record the number of accidents that occur monthly at the intersection of Driftwood Lane and Royal Oak Drive, hoping to justify the installation of a traffic light; we might classify items coming off an assembly line as "defective" or "nondefective"; or we may be interested in the volume of gas released in a chemical reaction when the concentration of an acid is varied. Hence, the statistician is often dealing with either numerical data, representing counts or measurements, or **categorical data**, which can be classified according to some criterion.

We shall refer to any recording of information, whether it be numerical or categorical, as an **observation**. Thus, the numbers 2, 0, 1, and 2, representing the number of accidents that occurred for each month from January through April during the past year at the intersection of Driftwood Lane and Royal Oak Drive, constitute a set of observations. Similarly, the categorical data *N, D, N, N*, and *D*, representing the items found to be defective or nondefective when five items are inspected, are recorded as observations.

Statisticians use the word **experiment** to describe any process that generates a set of data. A simple example of a statistical experiment is the tossing of a coin. In this experiment, there are only two possible outcomes, heads or tails. Another experiment might be the launching of a missile and observing of its velocity at specified times. The opinions of voters concerning a new sales tax can also be considered as observations of an experiment. We are particularly interested in the observations obtained by repeating the experiment several times. In most cases, the outcomes will depend on chance and, therefore, cannot be predicted with certainty. If a chemist runs an analysis several times under the same conditions, he or she will obtain different measurements, indicating an element of chance in the experimental procedure. Even when a coin is tossed repeatedly, we cannot be certain that a given toss will result in a head. However, we know the entire set of possibilities for each toss.

Let's deal with the breadth of the term *experiment*. There are three types of statistical studies, *designed experiments*, *observational studies*, and *retrospective studies* where the end result is a set of *data* that of course is subject to **uncertainty**. Though only one of these has the word *experiment* in its description, the process of generating the data or the process of observing the data is part of an experiment.

Definition 1:

> The set of all possible outcomes of a statistical experiment is called the **sample space** and is represented by the symbol S.

Each outcome in a sample space is called an **element** or a **member** of the sample space, or simply a **sample point**. If the sample space has a finite number of elements, we may *list* the members separated by commas and enclosed in braces. Thus, the sample space S, of possible outcomes when a coin is flipped, may be written

$$S = \{H, T\},$$

where H and T correspond to heads and tails, respectively.

Example 1:

Consider the experiment of tossing a die. If we are interested in the number that shows on the top face, the sample space is

$$S_1 = \{1, 2, 3, 4, 5, 6\}.$$

If we are interested only in whether the number is even or odd, the sample space is simply

$$S_2 = \{\text{even, odd}\}.$$

Example 1 illustrates the fact that more than one sample space can be used to describe the outcomes of an experiment. In this case, S_1 provides more information than S_2. If we know which element in S_1 occurs, we can tell which outcome in S_2 occurs; however, a knowledge of what happens in S_2 is of little help in determining which element in S_1 occurs. In general, it is desirable to use the sample space that gives the most information concerning the outcomes of the experiment. In some experiments, it is helpful to list the elements of the sample space systematically by means of a **tree diagram**.

Example 2:

An experiment consists of flipping a coin and then flipping it a second time if a head occurs. If a tail occurs on the first flip, then a die is tossed once. To list the elements of the sample space providing the most information, we construct the tree diagram of Figure 1. The various paths along the branches of the tree give the distinct sample points. Starting with the top left branch and moving to the right along the first path, we get the sample point HH, indicating the possibility that heads occurs on two successive flips of the coin. Likewise, the sample point $T3$ indicates the possibility that the coin will show a tail followed by a 3 on the toss of the die. By proceeding along all paths, we see that the sample space is

$$S = \{HH, \ HT, \ T1, \ T2, \ T3, \ T4, \ T5, \ T6\}.$$

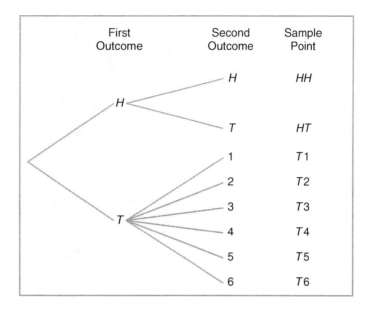

Figure 1: Tree diagram for Example 2.

Many of the concepts in this chapter are best illustrated with examples involving the use of dice and cards. These are particularly important applications to use early in the learning process, to facilitate the flow of these new concepts into scientific and engineering examples such as the following.

Example 3: Suppose that three items are selected at random from a manufacturing process. Each item is inspected and classified defective, *D*, or nondefective, *N*. To list the elements of the sample space providing the most information, we construct the tree diagram of Figure 2. Now, the various paths along the branches of the tree give the distinct sample points. Starting with the first path, we get the sample point *DDD*, indicating the possibility that all three items inspected are defective. As we proceed along the other paths, we see that the sample space is

$$S = \{DDD, DDN, DND, DNN, NDD, NDN, NND, NNN\}.$$

Sample spaces with a large or infinite number of sample points are best described by a **statement** or **rule method**. For example, if the possible outcomes of an experiment are the set of cities in the world with a population over 1 million, our sample space is written

$$S = \{x \mid x \text{ is a city with a population over 1 million}\},$$

which reads "*S* is the set of all *x* such that *x* is a city with a population over 1 million." The vertical bar is read "such that." Similarly, if *S* is the set of all points (x, y) on the boundary or the interior of a circle of radius 2 with center at the origin, we write the **rule**

$$S = \{(x, y) \mid x^2 + y^2 \le 4\}.$$

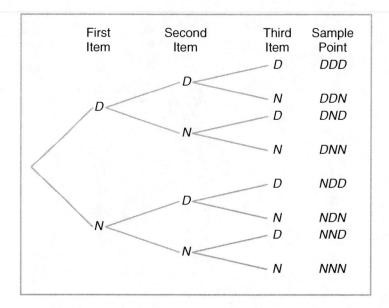

Figure 2: Tree diagram for Example 3.

Whether we describe the sample space by the rule method or by listing the elements will depend on the specific problem at hand. The rule method has practical advantages, particularly for many experiments where listing becomes a tedious chore.

Consider the situation of Example 3 in which items from a manufacturing process are either D, defective, or N, nondefective. There are many important statistical procedures called sampling plans that determine whether or not a "lot" of items is considered satisfactory. One such plan involves sampling until k defectives are observed. Suppose the experiment is to sample items randomly until one defective item is observed. The sample space for this case is

$$S = \{D, ND, NND, NNND, \dots\}.$$

2 Events

For any given experiment, we may be interested in the occurrence of certain **events** rather than in the occurrence of a specific element in the sample space. For instance, we may be interested in the event A that the outcome when a die is tossed is divisible by 3. This will occur if the outcome is an element of the subset $A = \{3, 6\}$ of the sample space S_1 in Example 1. As a further illustration, we may be interested in the event B that the number of defectives is greater than 1 in Example 3. This will occur if the outcome is an element of the subset

$$B = \{DDN, DND, NDD, DDD\}$$

of the sample space S.

To each event we assign a collection of sample points, which constitute a subset of the sample space. That subset represents all of the elements for which the event is true.

Definition 2: An **event** is a subset of a sample space.

Example 4: Given the sample space $S = \{t \mid t \geq 0\}$, where t is the life in years of a certain electronic component, then the event A that the component fails before the end of the fifth year is the subset $A = \{t \mid 0 \leq t < 5\}$.

It is conceivable that an event may be a subset that includes the entire sample space S or a subset of S called the **null set** and denoted by the symbol ϕ, which contains no elements at all. For instance, if we let A be the event of detecting a microscopic organism by the naked eye in a biological experiment, then $A = \phi$. Also, if

$$B = \{x \mid x \text{ is an even factor of } 7\},$$

then B must be the null set, since the only possible factors of 7 are the odd numbers 1 and 7.

Consider an experiment where the smoking habits of the employees of a manufacturing firm are recorded. A possible sample space might classify an individual as a nonsmoker, a light smoker, a moderate smoker, or a heavy smoker. Let the subset of smokers be some event. Then all the nonsmokers correspond to a different event, also a subset of S, which is called the **complement** of the set of smokers.

Definition 3: The **complement** of an event A with respect to S is the subset of all elements of S that are not in A. We denote the complement of A by the symbol A'.

Example 5: Let R be the event that a red card is selected from an ordinary deck of 52 playing cards, and let S be the entire deck. Then R' is the event that the card selected from the deck is not a red card but a black card.

Example 6: Consider the sample space

$$S = \{\text{book, cell phone, mp3, paper, stationery, laptop}\}.$$

Let $A = \{\text{book, stationery, laptop, paper}\}$. Then the complement of A is $A' = \{\text{cell phone, mp3}\}$.

We now consider certain operations with events that will result in the formation of new events. These new events will be subsets of the same sample space as the given events. Suppose that A and B are two events associated with an experiment. In other words, A and B are subsets of the same sample space S. For example, in the tossing of a die we might let A be the event that an even number occurs and B the event that a number greater than 3 shows. Then the subsets $A = \{2, 4, 6\}$ and $B = \{4, 5, 6\}$ are subsets of the same sample space

$$S = \{1, 2, 3, 4, 5, 6\}.$$

Note that *both* A and B will occur on a given toss if the outcome is an element of the subset $\{4, 6\}$, which is just the **intersection** of A and B.

Definition 4: The **intersection** of two events A and B, denoted by the symbol $A \cap B$, is the event containing all elements that are common to A and B.

Example 7: Let E be the event that a person selected at random in a classroom is majoring in engineering, and let F be the event that the person is female. Then $E \cap F$ is the event of all female engineering students in the classroom.

Example 8: Let $V = \{a, e, i, o, u\}$ and $C = \{l, r, s, t\}$; then it follows that $V \cap C = \phi$. That is, V and C have no elements in common and, therefore, cannot both simultaneously occur.

For certain statistical experiments it is by no means unusual to define two events, A and B, that cannot both occur simultaneously. The events A and B are then said to be **mutually exclusive**. Stated more formally, we have the following definition:

Definition 5: Two events A and B are **mutually exclusive**, or **disjoint**, if $A \cap B = \phi$, that is, if A and B have no elements in common.

Example 9: A cable television company offers programs on eight different channels, three of which are affiliated with ABC, two with NBC, and one with CBS. The other two are an educational channel and the ESPN sports channel. Suppose that a person subscribing to this service turns on a television set without first selecting the channel. Let A be the event that the program belongs to the NBC network and B the event that it belongs to the CBS network. Since a television program cannot belong to more than one network, the events A and B have no programs in common. Therefore, the intersection $A \cap B$ contains no programs, and consequently the events A and B are mutually exclusive.

Often one is interested in the occurrence of at least one of two events associated with an experiment. Thus, in the die-tossing experiment, if

$$A = \{2, 4, 6\} \text{ and } B = \{4, 5, 6\},$$

we might be interested in either A or B occurring or both A and B occurring. Such an event, called the **union** of A and B, will occur if the outcome is an element of the subset $\{2, 4, 5, 6\}$.

Definition 6: The **union** of the two events A and B, denoted by the symbol $A \cup B$, is the event containing all the elements that belong to A or B or both.

Example 10: Let $A = \{a, b, c\}$ and $B = \{b, c, d, e\}$; then $A \cup B = \{a, b, c, d, e\}$.

Example 11: Let P be the event that an employee selected at random from an oil drilling company smokes cigarettes. Let Q be the event that the employee selected drinks alcoholic beverages. Then the event $P \cup Q$ is the set of all employees who either drink or smoke or do both.

Example 12: If $M = \{x \mid 3 < x < 9\}$ and $N = \{y \mid 5 < y < 12\}$, then

$$M \cup N = \{z \mid 3 < z < 12\}.$$

The relationship between events and the corresponding sample space can be illustrated graphically by means of **Venn diagrams**. In a Venn diagram we let the sample space be a rectangle and represent events by circles drawn inside the rectangle. Thus, in Figure 3, we see that

$$A \cap B = \text{ regions 1 and 2,}$$
$$B \cap C = \text{ regions 1 and 3,}$$

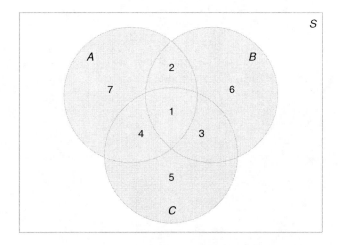

Figure 3: Events represented by various regions.

$$A \cup C = \text{ regions 1, 2, 3, 4, 5, and 7,}$$
$$B' \cap A = \text{ regions 4 and 7,}$$
$$A \cap B \cap C = \text{ region 1,}$$
$$(A \cup B) \cap C' = \text{ regions 2, 6, and 7,}$$

and so forth.

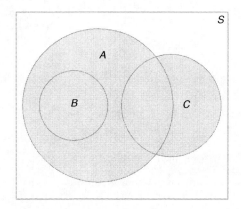

Figure 4: Events of the sample space S.

In Figure 4, we see that events A, B, and C are all subsets of the sample space S. It is also clear that event B is a subset of event A; event $B \cap C$ has no elements and hence B and C are mutually exclusive; event $A \cap C$ has at least one element; and event $A \cup B = A$. Figure 4 might, therefore, depict a situation where we select a card at random from an ordinary deck of 52 playing cards and observe whether the following events occur:

A: the card is red,

B: the card is the jack, queen, or king of diamonds,

C: the card is an ace.

Clearly, the event $A \cap C$ consists of only the two red aces.

Several results that follow from the foregoing definitions, which may easily be verified by means of Venn diagrams, are as follows:

1. $A \cap \phi = \phi$.
2. $A \cup \phi = A$.
3. $A \cap A' = \phi$.
4. $A \cup A' = S$.
5. $S' = \phi$.

6. $\phi' = S$.
7. $(A')' = A$.
8. $(A \cap B)' = A' \cup B'$.
9. $(A \cup B)' = A' \cap B'$.

Exercises

1 List the elements of each of the following sample spaces:
(a) the set of integers between 1 and 50 divisible by 8;
(b) the set $S = \{x \mid x^2 + 4x - 5 = 0\}$;
(c) the set of outcomes when a coin is tossed until a tail or three heads appear;
(d) the set $S = \{x \mid x \text{ is a continent}\}$;
(e) the set $S = \{x \mid 2x - 4 \geq 0 \text{ and } x < 1\}$.

2 Use the rule method to describe the sample space S consisting of all points in the first quadrant inside a circle of radius 3 with center at the origin.

3 Which of the following events are equal?
(a) $A = \{1, 3\}$;
(b) $B = \{x \mid x \text{ is a number on a die}\}$;
(c) $C = \{x \mid x^2 - 4x + 3 = 0\}$;
(d) $D = \{x \mid x \text{ is the number of heads when six coins are tossed}\}$.

4 An experiment involves tossing a pair of dice, one green and one red, and recording the numbers that come up. If x equals the outcome on the green die and y the outcome on the red die, describe the sample space S
(a) by listing the elements (x, y);
(b) by using the rule method.

5 An experiment consists of tossing a die and then flipping a coin once if the number on the die is even. If the number on the die is odd, the coin is flipped twice. Using the notation $4H$, for example, to denote the outcome that the die comes up 4 and then the coin comes up heads, and $3HT$ to denote the outcome that the die

comes up 3 followed by a head and then a tail on the coin, construct a tree diagram to show the 18 elements of the sample space S.

6 Two jurors are selected from 4 alternates to serve at a murder trial. Using the notation $A_1 A_3$, for example, to denote the simple event that alternates 1 and 3 are selected, list the 6 elements of the sample space S.

7 Four students are selected at random from a chemistry class and classified as male or female. List the elements of the sample space S_1, using the letter M for male and F for female. Define a second sample space S_2 where the elements represent the number of females selected.

8 For the sample space of Exercise 4,
(a) list the elements corresponding to the event A that the sum is greater than 8;
(b) list the elements corresponding to the event B that a 2 occurs on either die;
(c) list the elements corresponding to the event C that a number greater than 4 comes up on the green die;
(d) list the elements corresponding to the event $A \cap C$;
(e) list the elements corresponding to the event $A \cap B$;
(f) list the elements corresponding to the event $B \cap C$;
(g) construct a Venn diagram to illustrate the intersections and unions of the events A, B, and C.

9 For the sample space of Exercise 5,
(a) list the elements corresponding to the event A that a number less than 3 occurs on the die;
(b) list the elements corresponding to the event B that two tails occur;
(c) list the elements corresponding to the event A';

(d) list the elements corresponding to the event $A' \cap B$;

(e) list the elements corresponding to the event $A \cup B$.

10 An engineering firm is hired to determine if certain waterways in Virginia are safe for fishing. Samples are taken from three rivers.

(a) List the elements of a sample space S, using the letters F for safe to fish and N for not safe to fish.

(b) List the elements of S corresponding to event E that at least two of the rivers are safe for fishing.

(c) Define an event that has as its elements the points

$$\{FFF, NFF, FFN, NFN\}.$$

11 The resumés of two male applicants for a college teaching position in chemistry are placed in the same file as the resumés of two female applicants. Two positions become available, and the first, at the rank of assistant professor, is filled by selecting one of the four applicants at random. The second position, at the rank of instructor, is then filled by selecting at random one of the remaining three applicants. Using the notation $M_2 F_1$, for example, to denote the simple event that the first position is filled by the second male applicant and the second position is then filled by the first female applicant,

(a) list the elements of a sample space S;

(b) list the elements of S corresponding to event A that the position of assistant professor is filled by a male applicant;

(c) list the elements of S corresponding to event B that exactly one of the two positions is filled by a male applicant;

(d) list the elements of S corresponding to event C that neither position is filled by a male applicant;

(e) list the elements of S corresponding to the event $A \cap B$;

(f) list the elements of S corresponding to the event $A \cup C$;

(g) construct a Venn diagram to illustrate the intersections and unions of the events A, B, and C.

12 Exercise and diet are being studied as possible substitutes for medication to lower blood pressure. Three groups of subjects will be used to study the effect of exercise. Group 1 is sedentary, while group 2 walks and group 3 swims for 1 hour a day. Half of each of the three exercise groups will be on a salt-free diet. An additional group of subjects will not exercise or restrict their salt, but will take the standard medication. Use Z for sedentary, W for walker, S for swimmer, Y for salt, N for no salt, M for medication, and F for medication free.

(a) Show all of the elements of the sample space S.

(b) Given that A is the set of nonmedicated subjects and B is the set of walkers, list the elements of $A \cup B$.

(c) List the elements of $A \cap B$.

13 Construct a Venn diagram to illustrate the possible intersections and unions for the following events relative to the sample space consisting of all automobiles made in the United States.

F : Four door, S : Sun roof, P : Power steering.

14 If $S = \{0, 1, 2, 3, 4, 5, 6, 7, 8, 9\}$ and $A = \{0, 2, 4, 6, 8\}$, $B = \{1, 3, 5, 7, 9\}$, $C = \{2, 3, 4, 5\}$, and $D = \{1, 6, 7\}$, list the elements of the sets corresponding to the following events:

(a) $A \cup C$;

(b) $A \cap B$;

(c) C';

(d) $(C' \cap D) \cup B$;

(e) $(S \cap C)'$;

(f) $A \cap C \cap D'$.

15 Consider the sample space $S = \{$copper, sodium, nitrogen, potassium, uranium, oxygen, zinc$\}$ and the events

$$A = \{\text{copper, sodium, zinc}\},$$
$$B = \{\text{sodium, nitrogen, potassium}\},$$
$$C = \{\text{oxygen}\}.$$

List the elements of the sets corresponding to the following events:

(a) A';

(b) $A \cup C$;

(c) $(A \cap B') \cup C'$;

(d) $B' \cap C'$;

(e) $A \cap B \cap C$;

(f) $(A' \cup B') \cap (A' \cap C)$.

16 If $S = \{x \mid 0 < x < 12\}$, $M = \{x \mid 1 < x < 9\}$, and $N = \{x \mid 0 < x < 5\}$, find

(a) $M \cup N$;

(b) $M \cap N$;

(c) $M' \cap N'$.

17 Let A, B, and C be events relative to the sample space S. Using Venn diagrams, shade the areas representing the following events:

(a) $(A \cap B)'$;

(b) $(A \cup B)'$;

(c) $(A \cap C) \cup B$.

18   Which of the following pairs of events are mutually exclusive?

(a) A golfer scoring the lowest 18-hole round in a 72-hole tournament and losing the tournament.

(b) A poker player getting a flush (all cards in the same suit) and 3 of a kind on the same 5-card hand.

(c) A mother giving birth to a baby girl and a set of twin daughters on the same day.

(d) A chess player losing the last game and winning the match.

19   Suppose that a family is leaving on a summer vacation in their camper and that M is the event that they will experience mechanical problems, T is the event that they will receive a ticket for committing a traffic violation, and V is the event that they will arrive at a campsite with no vacancies. Referring to the Venn diagram of Figure 5, state in words the events represented by the following regions:

(a) region 5;

(b) region 3;

(c) regions 1 and 2 together;

(d) regions 4 and 7 together;

(e) regions 3, 6, 7, and 8 together.

20   Referring to Exercise 19 and the Venn diagram of Figure 5, list the numbers of the regions that represent the following events:

(a) The family will experience no mechanical problems and will not receive a ticket for a traffic violation but will arrive at a campsite with no vacancies.

(b) The family will experience both mechanical problems and trouble in locating a campsite with a vacancy but will not receive a ticket for a traffic violation.

(c) The family will either have mechanical trouble or arrive at a campsite with no vacancies but will not receive a ticket for a traffic violation.

(d) The family will not arrive at a campsite with no vacancies.

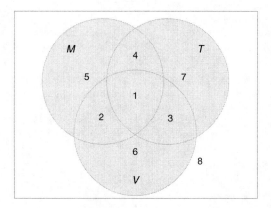

Figure 5: Venn diagram for Exercises 19 and 20.

3   Counting Sample Points

One of the problems that the statistician must consider and attempt to evaluate is the element of chance associated with the occurrence of certain events when an experiment is performed. These problems belong in the field of probability, a subject to be introduced in Section 4. In many cases, we shall be able to solve a probability problem by counting the number of points in the sample space without actually listing each element. The fundamental principle of counting, often referred to as the **multiplication rule**, is stated in Rule 1.

Rule 1: | If an operation can be performed in n_1 ways, and if for each of these ways a second operation can be performed in n_2 ways, then the two operations can be performed together in $n_1 n_2$ ways.

Example 13: How many sample points are there in the sample space when a pair of dice is thrown once?

Solution: The first die can land face-up in any one of $n_1 = 6$ ways. For each of these 6 ways, the second die can also land face-up in $n_2 = 6$ ways. Therefore, the pair of dice can land in $n_1 n_2 = (6)(6) = 36$ possible ways.

Example 14: A developer of a new subdivision offers prospective home buyers a choice of Tudor, rustic, colonial, and traditional exterior styling in ranch, two-story, and split-level floor plans. In how many different ways can a buyer order one of these homes?

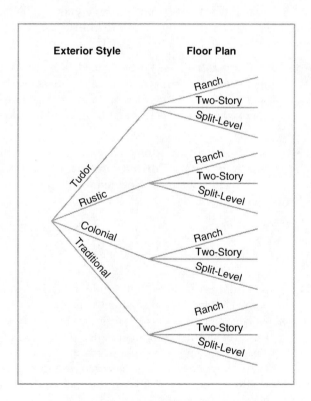

Figure 6: Tree diagram for Example 14.

Solution: Since $n_1 = 4$ and $n_2 = 3$, a buyer must choose from

$$n_1 n_2 = (4)(3) = 12 \text{ possible homes.}$$

The answers to the two preceding examples can be verified by constructing tree diagrams and counting the various paths along the branches. For instance, in Example 14 there will be $n_1 = 4$ branches corresponding to the different exterior styles, and then there will be $n_2 = 3$ branches extending from each of these 4 branches to represent the different floor plans. This tree diagram yields the $n_1 n_2 = 12$ choices of homes given by the paths along the branches, as illustrated in Figure 6.

Example 15: If a 22-member club needs to elect a chair and a treasurer, how many different ways can these two to be elected?

Solution: For the chair position, there are 22 total possibilities. For each of those 22 possibilities, there are 21 possibilities to elect the treasurer. Using the multiplication rule, we obtain $n_1 \times n_2 = 22 \times 21 = 462$ different ways.

The multiplication rule, Rule 1 may be extended to cover any number of operations. Suppose, for instance, that a customer wishes to buy a new cell phone and can choose from $n_1 = 5$ brands, $n_2 = 5$ sets of capability, and $n_3 = 4$ colors. These three classifications result in $n_1 n_2 n_3 = (5)(5)(4) = 100$ different ways for a customer to order one of these phones. The **generalized multiplication rule** covering k operations is stated in the following.

Rule 2: If an operation can be performed in n_1 ways, and if for each of these a second operation can be performed in n_2 ways, and for each of the first two a third operation can be performed in n_3 ways, and so forth, then the sequence of k operations can be performed in $n_1 n_2 \cdots n_k$ ways.

Example 16: Sam is going to assemble a computer by himself. He has the choice of chips from two brands, a hard drive from four, memory from three, and an accessory bundle from five local stores. How many different ways can Sam order the parts?

Solution: Since $n_1 = 2$, $n_2 = 4$, $n_3 = 3$, and $n_4 = 5$, there are

$$n_l \times n_2 \times n_3 \times n_4 = 2 \times 4 \times 3 \times 5 = 120$$

different ways to order the parts.

Example 17: How many even four-digit numbers can be formed from the digits 0, 1, 2, 5, 6, and 9 if each digit can be used only once?

Solution: Since the number must be even, we have only $n_1 = 3$ choices for the units position. However, for a four-digit number the thousands position cannot be 0. Hence, we consider the units position in two parts, 0 or not 0. If the units position is 0 (i.e., $n_1 = 1$), we have $n_2 = 5$ choices for the thousands position, $n_3 = 4$ for the hundreds position, and $n_4 = 3$ for the tens position. Therefore, in this case we have a total of

$$n_1 n_2 n_3 n_4 = (1)(5)(4)(3) = 60$$

even four-digit numbers. On the other hand, if the units position is not 0 (i.e., $n_1 = 2$), we have $n_2 = 4$ choices for the thousands position, $n_3 = 4$ for the hundreds position, and $n_4 = 3$ for the tens position. In this situation, there are a total of

$$n_1 n_2 n_3 n_4 = (2)(4)(4)(3) = 96$$

even four-digit numbers.

Since the above two cases are mutually exclusive, the total number of even four-digit numbers can be calculated as $60 + 96 = 156$.

Frequently, we are interested in a sample space that contains as elements all possible orders or arrangements of a group of objects. For example, we may want to know how many different arrangements are possible for sitting 6 people around a table, or we may ask how many different orders are possible for drawing 2 lottery tickets from a total of 20. The different arrangements are called **permutations**.

Definition 7: | A **permutation** is an arrangement of all or part of a set of objects.

Consider the three letters a, b, and c. The possible permutations are abc, acb, bac, bca, cab, and cba. Thus, we see that there are 6 distinct arrangements. Using Rule 2, we could arrive at the answer 6 without actually listing the different orders by the following arguments: There are $n_1 = 3$ choices for the first position. No matter which letter is chosen, there are always $n_2 = 2$ choices for the second position. No matter which two letters are chosen for the first two positions, there is only $n_3 = 1$ choice for the last position, giving a total of

$$n_1 n_2 n_3 = (3)(2)(1) = 6 \text{ permutations}$$

by Rule 2. In general, n distinct objects can be arranged in

$$n(n-1)(n-2)\cdots(3)(2)(1) \text{ ways.}$$

There is a notation for such a number.

Definition 8: | For any non-negative integer n, $n!$, called "n factorial," is defined as
$$n! = n(n-1)\cdots(2)(1),$$
with special case $0! = 1$.

Using the argument above, we arrive at the following theorem.

Theorem 1: | The number of permutations of n objects is $n!$.

The number of permutations of the four letters a, b, c, and d will be $4! = 24$. Now consider the number of permutations that are possible by taking two letters at a time from four. These would be ab, ac, ad, ba, bc, bd, ca, cb, cd, da, db, and dc. Using Rule 1 again, we have two positions to fill, with $n_1 = 4$ choices for the first and then $n_2 = 3$ choices for the second, for a total of

$$n_1 n_2 = (4)(3) = 12$$

permutations. In general, n distinct objects taken r at a time can be arranged in

$$n(n-1)(n-2)\cdots(n-r+1)$$

ways. We represent this product by the symbol

$$_nP_r = \frac{n!}{(n-r)!}.$$

Probability

As a result, we have the theorem that follows.

Theorem 2: The number of permutations of n distinct objects taken r at a time is

$$_nP_r = \frac{n!}{(n-r)!}.$$

Example 18: In one year, three awards (research, teaching, and service) will be given to a class of 25 graduate students in a statistics department. If each student can receive at most one award, how many possible selections are there?

Solution: Since the awards are distinguishable, it is a permutation problem. The total number of sample points is

$$_{25}P_3 = \frac{25!}{(25-3)!} = \frac{25!}{22!} = (25)(24)(23) = 13,800.$$

Example 19: A president and a treasurer are to be chosen from a student club consisting of 50 people. How many different choices of officers are possible if

(a) there are no restrictions;

(b) A will serve only if he is president;

(c) B and C will serve together or not at all;

(d) D and E will not serve together?

Solution: (a) The total number of choices of officers, without any restrictions, is

$$_{50}P_2 = \frac{50!}{48!} = (50)(49) = 2450.$$

(b) Since A will serve only if he is president, we have two situations here: (i) A is selected as the president, which yields 49 possible outcomes for the treasurer's position, or (ii) officers are selected from the remaining 49 people without A, which has the number of choices $_{49}P_2 = (49)(48) = 2352$. Therefore, the total number of choices is $49 + 2352 = 2401$.

(c) The number of selections when B and C serve together is 2. The number of selections when both B and C are not chosen is $_{48}P_2 = 2256$. Therefore, the total number of choices in this situation is $2 + 2256 = 2258$.

(d) The number of selections when D serves as an officer but not E is $(2)(48) = 96$, where 2 is the number of positions D can take and 48 is the number of selections of the other officer from the remaining people in the club except E. The number of selections when E serves as an officer but not D is also $(2)(48) = 96$. The number of selections when both D and E are not chosen is $_{48}P_2 = 2256$. Therefore, the total number of choices is $(2)(96) + 2256 = 2448$. This problem also has another short solution: Since D and E can only serve together in 2 ways, the answer is $2450 - 2 = 2448$.

Permutations that occur by arranging objects in a circle are called **circular permutations**. Two circular permutations are not considered different unless corresponding objects in the two arrangements are preceded or followed by a different object as we proceed in a clockwise direction. For example, if 4 people are playing bridge, we do not have a new permutation if they all move one position in a clockwise direction. By considering one person in a fixed position and arranging the other three in 3! ways, we find that there are 6 distinct arrangements for the bridge game.

Theorem 3: | The number of permutations of n objects arranged in a circle is $(n-1)!$.

So far we have considered permutations of distinct objects. That is, all the objects were completely different or distinguishable. Obviously, if the letters b and c are both equal to x, then the 6 permutations of the letters a, b, and c become axx, axx, xax, xax, xxa, and xxa, of which only 3 are distinct. Therefore, with 3 letters, 2 being the same, we have $3!/2! = 3$ distinct permutations. With 4 different letters a, b, c, and d, we have 24 distinct permutations. If we let $a = b = x$ and $c = d = y$, we can list only the following distinct permutations: $xxyy$, $xyxy$, $yxxy$, $yyxx$, $xyyx$, and $yxyx$. Thus, we have $4!/(2!\,2!) = 6$ distinct permutations.

Theorem 4: | The number of distinct permutations of n things of which n_1 are of one kind, n_2 of a second kind, ..., n_k of a kth kind is

$$\frac{n!}{n_1!n_2!\cdots n_k!}.$$

Example 20: In a college football training session, the defensive coordinator needs to have 10 players standing in a row. Among these 10 players, there are 1 freshman, 2 sophomores, 4 juniors, and 3 seniors. How many different ways can they be arranged in a row if only their class level will be distinguished?

Solution: Directly using Theorem 4, we find that the total number of arrangements is

$$\frac{10!}{1!\,2!\,4!\,3!} = 12,600.$$

Often we are concerned with the number of ways of partitioning a set of n objects into r subsets called **cells**. A partition has been achieved if the intersection of every possible pair of the r subsets is the empty set ϕ and if the union of all subsets gives the original set. The order of the elements within a cell is of no importance. Consider the set $\{a, e, i, o, u\}$. The possible partitions into two cells in which the first cell contains 4 elements and the second cell 1 element are

$$\{(a,e,i,o),(u)\}, \{(a,i,o,u),(e)\}, \{(e,i,o,u),(a)\}, \{(a,e,o,u),(i)\}, \{(a,e,i,u),(o)\}.$$

We see that there are 5 ways to partition a set of 4 elements into two subsets, or cells, containing 4 elements in the first cell and 1 element in the second.

The number of partitions for this illustration is denoted by the symbol

$$\binom{5}{4,1} = \frac{5!}{4!\,1!} = 5,$$

where the top number represents the total number of elements and the bottom numbers represent the number of elements going into each cell. We state this more generally in Theorem 5.

Theorem 5: The number of ways of partitioning a set of n objects into r cells with n_1 elements in the first cell, n_2 elements in the second, and so forth, is

$$\binom{n}{n_1, n_2, \ldots, n_r} = \frac{n!}{n_1!n_2!\cdots n_r!},$$

where $n_1 + n_2 + \cdots + n_r = n$.

Example 21: In how many ways can 7 graduate students be assigned to 1 triple and 2 double hotel rooms during a conference?

Solution: The total number of possible partitions would be

$$\binom{7}{3,2,2} = \frac{7!}{3!\,2!\,2!} = 210.$$

In many problems, we are interested in the number of ways of selecting r objects from n without regard to order. These selections are called **combinations**. A combination is actually a partition with two cells, the one cell containing the r objects selected and the other cell containing the $(n-r)$ objects that are left. The number of such combinations, denoted by

$$\binom{n}{r, n-r}, \text{ is usually shortened to } \binom{n}{r},$$

since the number of elements in the second cell must be $n - r$.

Theorem 6: The number of combinations of n distinct objects taken r at a time is

$$\binom{n}{r} = \frac{n!}{r!(n-r)!}.$$

Example 22: A young boy asks his mother to get 5 Game-Boy™ cartridges from his collection of 10 arcade and 5 sports games. How many ways are there that his mother can get 3 arcade and 2 sports games?

Solution: The number of ways of selecting 3 cartridges from 10 is

$$\binom{10}{3} = \frac{10!}{3!\,(10-3)!} = 120.$$

The number of ways of selecting 2 cartridges from 5 is

$$\binom{5}{2} = \frac{5!}{2!\,3!} = 10.$$

Using the multiplication rule (Rule 2.1) with $n_1 = 120$ and $n_2 = 10$, we have $(120)(10) = 1200$ ways.

Example 23: How many different letter arrangements can be made from the letters in the word *STATISTICS*?

Solution: Using the same argument as in the discussion for Theorem 6, in this example we can actually apply Theorem 5 to obtain

$$\binom{10}{3, 3, 2, 1, 1} = \frac{10!}{3!\ 3!\ 2!\ 1!\ 1!} = 50,400.$$

Here we have 10 total letters, with 2 letters (S, T) appearing 3 times each, letter I appearing twice, and letters A and C appearing once each. On the other hand, this result can be directly obtained by using Theorem 4.

Exercises

21   Registrants at a large convention are offered 6 sightseeing tours on each of 3 days. In how many ways can a person arrange to go on a sightseeing tour planned by this convention?

22   In a medical study, patients are classified in 8 ways according to whether they have blood type AB^+, AB^-, A^+, A^-, B^+, B^-, O^+, or O^-, and also according to whether their blood pressure is low, normal, or high. Find the number of ways in which a patient can be classified.

23   If an experiment consists of throwing a die and then drawing a letter at random from the English alphabet, how many points are there in the sample space?

24   Students at a private liberal arts college are classified as being freshmen, sophomores, juniors, or seniors, and also according to whether they are male or female. Find the total number of possible classifications for the students of that college.

25   A certain brand of shoes comes in 5 different styles, with each style available in 4 distinct colors. If the store wishes to display pairs of these shoes showing all of its various styles and colors, how many different pairs will the store have on display?

26   A California study concluded that following 7 simple health rules can extend a man's life by 11 years on the average and a woman's life by 7 years. These 7 rules are as follows: no smoking, get regular exercise, use alcohol only in moderation, get 7 to 8 hours of sleep, maintain proper weight, eat breakfast, and do not eat between meals. In how many ways can a person adopt 5 of these rules to follow

(a) if the person presently violates all 7 rules?

(b) if the person never drinks and always eats breakfast?

27   A developer of a new subdivision offers a prospective home buyer a choice of 4 designs, 3 different heating systems, a garage or carport, and a patio or screened porch. How many different plans are available to this buyer?

28   A drug for the relief of asthma can be purchased from 5 different manufacturers in liquid, tablet, or capsule form, all of which come in regular and extra strength. How many different ways can a doctor prescribe the drug for a patient suffering from asthma?

29   In a fuel economy study, each of 3 race cars is tested using 5 different brands of gasoline at 7 test sites located in different regions of the country. If 2 drivers are used in the study, and test runs are made once under each distinct set of conditions, how many test runs are needed?

30   In how many different ways can a true-false test consisting of 9 questions be answered?

31   A witness to a hit-and-run accident told the police that the license number contained the letters RLH followed by 3 digits, the first of which was a 5. If the witness cannot recall the last 2 digits, but is certain that all 3 digits are different, find the maximum number of automobile registrations that the police may have to check.

32   (a) In how many ways can 6 people be lined up to get on a bus?

(b) If 3 specific persons, among 6, insist on following each other, how many ways are possible?

(c) If 2 specific persons, among 6, refuse to follow each other, how many ways are possible?

33   If a multiple-choice test consists of 5 questions, each with 4 possible answers of which only 1 is correct,

(a) in how many different ways can a student check off one answer to each question?

(b) in how many ways can a student check off one answer to each question and get all the answers wrong?

34   (a) How many distinct permutations can be made from the letters of the word *COLUMNS*?

(b) How many of these permutations start with the letter *M*?

35   A contractor wishes to build 9 houses, each different in design. In how many ways can he place these houses on a street if 6 lots are on one side of the street and 3 lots are on the opposite side?

36   (a) How many three-digit numbers can be formed from the digits 0, 1, 2, 3, 4, 5, and 6 if each digit can be used only once?

(b) How many of these are odd numbers?

(c) How many are greater than 330?

37   In how many ways can 4 boys and 5 girls sit in a row if the boys and girls must alternate?

38   Four married couples have bought 8 seats in the same row for a concert. In how many different ways can they be seated

(a) with no restrictions?

(b) if each couple is to sit together?

(c) if all the men sit together to the right of all the women?

39   In a regional spelling bee, the 8 finalists consist of 3 boys and 5 girls. Find the number of sample points in the sample space S for the number of possible orders at the conclusion of the contest for

(a) all 8 finalists;

(b) the first 3 positions.

40   In how many ways can 5 starting positions on a basketball team be filled with 8 men who can play any of the positions?

41   Find the number of ways that 6 teachers can be assigned to 4 sections of an introductory psychology course if no teacher is assigned to more than one section.

42   Three lottery tickets for first, second, and third prizes are drawn from a group of 40 tickets. Find the number of sample points in S for awarding the 3 prizes if each contestant holds only 1 ticket.

43   In how many ways can 5 different trees be planted in a circle?

44   In how many ways can a caravan of 8 covered wagons from Arizona be arranged in a circle?

45   How many distinct permutations can be made from the letters of the word *INFINITY*?

46   In how many ways can 3 oaks, 4 pines, and 2 maples be arranged along a property line if one does not distinguish among trees of the same kind?

47   How many ways are there to select 3 candidates from 8 equally qualified recent graduates for openings in an accounting firm?

48   How many ways are there that no two students will have the same birth date in a class of size 60?

4   Probability of an Event

Perhaps it was humankind's unquenchable thirst for gambling that led to the early development of probability theory. In an effort to increase their winnings, gamblers called upon mathematicians to provide optimum strategies for various games of chance. Some of the mathematicians providing these strategies were Pascal, Leibniz, Fermat, and James Bernoulli. As a result of this development of probability theory, statistical inference, with all its predictions and generalizations, has branched out far beyond games of chance to encompass many other fields associated with chance occurrences, such as politics, business, weather forecasting, and scientific research. For these predictions and generalizations to be reasonably accurate, an understanding of basic probability theory is essential.

What do we mean when we make the statement "John will probably win the tennis match," or "I have a fifty-fifty chance of getting an even number when a die is tossed," or "The university is not likely to win the football game tonight," or "Most of our graduating class will likely be married within 3 years"? In each case, we are expressing an outcome of which we are not certain, but owing to past information or from an understanding of the structure of the experiment, we have some degree of confidence in the validity of the statement.

Throughout the remainder of this chapter, we consider only those experiments for which the sample space contains a finite number of elements. The likelihood of the occurrence of an event resulting from such a statistical experiment is evaluated by means of a set of real numbers, called **weights** or **probabilities**, ranging from 0 to 1. To every point in the sample space we assign a probability such that the sum of all probabilities is 1. If we have reason to believe that a certain sample point is quite likely to occur when the experiment is conducted, the probability assigned should be close to 1. On the other hand, a probability closer to 0 is assigned to a sample point that is not likely to occur. In many experiments, such as tossing a coin or a die, all the sample points have the same chance of occurring and are assigned equal probabilities. For points outside the sample space, that is, for simple events that cannot possibly occur, we assign a probability of 0.

To find the probability of an event A, we sum all the probabilities assigned to the sample points in A. This sum is called the **probability** of A and is denoted by $P(A)$.

Definition 9:

> The **probability** of an event A is the sum of the weights of all sample points in A. Therefore,
>
> $$0 \leq P(A) \leq 1, \quad P(\phi) = 0, \quad \text{and} \quad P(S) = 1.$$
>
> Furthermore, if $A_1, A_2, A_3, \ldots$ is a sequence of mutually exclusive events, then
>
> $$P(A_1 \cup A_2 \cup A_3 \cup \cdots) = P(A_1) + P(A_2) + P(A_3) + \cdots.$$

Example 24: A coin is tossed twice. What is the probability that at least 1 head occurs?

Solution: The sample space for this experiment is

$$S = \{HH, HT, TH, TT\}.$$

If the coin is balanced, each of these outcomes is equally likely to occur. Therefore, we assign a probability of ω to each sample point. Then $4\omega = 1$, or $\omega = 1/4$. If A represents the event of at least 1 head occurring, then

$$A = \{HH, HT, TH\} \text{ and } P(A) = \frac{1}{4} + \frac{1}{4} + \frac{1}{4} = \frac{3}{4}.$$

Example 25: A die is loaded in such a way that an even number is twice as likely to occur as an odd number. If E is the event that a number less than 4 occurs on a single toss of the die, find $P(E)$.

Solution: The sample space is $S = \{1, 2, 3, 4, 5, 6\}$. We assign a probability of w to each odd number and a probability of $2w$ to each even number. Since the sum of the probabilities must be 1, we have $9w = 1$ or $w = 1/9$. Hence, probabilities of $1/9$ and $2/9$ are assigned to each odd and even number, respectively. Therefore,

$$E = \{1, 2, 3\} \text{ and } P(E) = \frac{1}{9} + \frac{2}{9} + \frac{1}{9} = \frac{4}{9}.$$

Example 26: In Example 25, let A be the event that an even number turns up and let B be the event that a number divisible by 3 occurs. Find $P(A \cup B)$ and $P(A \cap B)$.

Solution: For the events $A = \{2, 4, 6\}$ and $B = \{3, 6\}$, we have

$$A \cup B = \{2, 3, 4, 6\} \text{ and } A \cap B = \{6\}.$$

By assigning a probability of $1/9$ to each odd number and $2/9$ to each even number, we have

$$P(A \cup B) = \frac{2}{9} + \frac{1}{9} + \frac{2}{9} + \frac{2}{9} = \frac{7}{9} \quad \text{and} \quad P(A \cap B) = \frac{2}{9}.$$

If the sample space for an experiment contains N elements, all of which are equally likely to occur, we assign a probability equal to $1/N$ to each of the N points. The probability of any event A containing n of these N sample points is then the ratio of the number of elements in A to the number of elements in S.

Rule 3: If an experiment can result in any one of N different equally likely outcomes, and if exactly n of these outcomes correspond to event A, then the probability of event A is

$$P(A) = \frac{n}{N}.$$

Example 27: A statistics class for engineers consists of 25 industrial, 10 mechanical, 10 electrical, and 8 civil engineering students. If a person is randomly selected by the instructor to answer a question, find the probability that the student chosen is (a) an industrial engineering major and (b) a civil engineering or an electrical engineering major.

Solution: Denote by I, M, E, and C the students majoring in industrial, mechanical, electrical, and civil engineering, respectively. The total number of students in the class is 53, all of whom are equally likely to be selected.

(a) Since 25 of the 53 students are majoring in industrial engineering, the probability of event I, selecting an industrial engineering major at random, is

$$P(I) = \frac{25}{53}.$$

(b) Since 18 of the 53 students are civil or electrical engineering majors, it follows that

$$P(C \cup E) = \frac{18}{53}.$$

Example 28: In a poker hand consisting of 5 cards, find the probability of holding 2 aces and 3 jacks.

Solution: The number of ways of being dealt 2 aces from 4 cards is

$$\binom{4}{2} = \frac{4!}{2!\,2!} = 6,$$

and the number of ways of being dealt 3 jacks from 4 cards is

$$\binom{4}{3} = \frac{4!}{3!\,1!} = 4.$$

By the multiplication rule (Rule 1), there are $n = (6)(4) = 24$ hands with 2 aces and 3 jacks. The total number of 5-card poker hands, all of which are equally likely, is

$$N = \binom{52}{5} = \frac{52!}{5!\,47!} = 2{,}598{,}960.$$

Therefore, the probability of getting 2 aces and 3 jacks in a 5-card poker hand is

$$P(C) = \frac{24}{2,598,960} = 0.9 \times 10^{-5}.$$

If the outcomes of an experiment are not equally likely to occur, the probabilities must be assigned on the basis of prior knowledge or experimental evidence. For example, if a coin is not balanced, we could estimate the probabilities of heads and tails by tossing the coin a large number of times and recording the outcomes. According to the **relative frequency** definition of probability, the true probabilities would be the fractions of heads and tails that occur in the long run. Another intuitive way of understanding probability is the **indifference** approach. For instance, if you have a die that you believe is balanced, then using this indifference approach, you determine that the probability that each of the six sides will show up after a throw is 1/6.

To find a numerical value that represents adequately the probability of winning at tennis, we must depend on our past performance at the game as well as that of the opponent and, to some extent, our belief in our ability to win. Similarly, to find the probability that a horse will win a race, we must arrive at a probability based on the previous records of all the horses entered in the race as well as the records of the jockeys riding the horses. Intuition would undoubtedly also play a part in determining the size of the bet that we might be willing to wager. The use of intuition, personal beliefs, and other indirect information in arriving at probabilities is referred to as the **subjective** definition of probability.

In most of the applications of probability in this book, the relative frequency interpretation of probability is the operative one. Its foundation is the statistical experiment rather than subjectivity, and it is best viewed as the **limiting relative frequency**. As a result, many applications of probability in science and engineering must be based on experiments that can be repeated. Less objective notions of probability are encountered when we assign probabilities based on prior information and opinions, as in "There is a good chance that the Giants will lose the Super

Bowl." When opinions and prior information differ from individual to individual, subjective probability becomes the relevant resource. In Bayesian statistics, a more subjective interpretation of probability will be used, based on an elicitation of prior probability information.

5 Additive Rules

Often it is easiest to calculate the probability of some event from known probabilities of other events. This may well be true if the event in question can be represented as the union of two other events or as the complement of some event. Several important laws that frequently simplify the computation of probabilities follow. The first, called the **additive rule**, applies to unions of events.

Theorem 7: | If A and B are two events, then

$$P(A \cup B) = P(A) + P(B) - P(A \cap B).$$

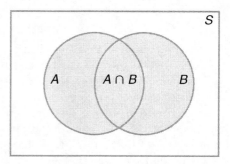

Figure 7: Additive rule of probability.

Proof: Consider the Venn diagram in Figure 7. The $P(A \cup B)$ is the sum of the probabilities of the sample points in $A \cup B$. Now $P(A) + P(B)$ is the sum of all the probabilities in A plus the sum of all the probabilities in B. Therefore, we have added the probabilities in $(A \cap B)$ twice. Since these probabilities add up to $P(A \cap B)$, we must subtract this probability once to obtain the sum of the probabilities in $A \cup B$.

Corollary 1: | If A and B are mutually exclusive, then

$$P(A \cup B) = P(A) + P(B).$$

Corollary 1 is an immediate result of Theorem 7, since if A and B are mutually exclusive, $A \cap B = 0$ and then $P(A \cap B) = P(\phi) = 0$. In general, we can write Corollary 2.

Corollary 2:

If $A_1,\ A_2,\ldots,A_n$ are mutually exclusive, then

$$P(A_1 \cup A_2 \cup \cdots \cup A_n) = P(A_1) + P(A_2) + \cdots + P(A_n).$$

A collection of events $\{A_1, A_2,\ldots,A_n\}$ of a sample space S is called a **partition** of S if $A_1, A_2,\ldots,A_n$ are mutually exclusive and $A_1 \cup A_2 \cup \cdots \cup A_n = S$. Thus, we have

Corollary 3:

If $A_1,\ A_2,\ldots,A_n$ is a partition of sample space S, then

$$P(A_1 \cup A_2 \cup \cdots \cup A_n) = P(A_1) + P(A_2) + \cdots + P(A_n) = P(S) = 1.$$

As one might expect, Theorem 7 extends in an analogous fashion.

Theorem 8:

For three events A, B, and C,

$$P(A \cup B \cup C) = P(A) + P(B) + P(C)$$
$$- P(A \cap B) - P(A \cap C) - P(B \cap C) + P(A \cap B \cap C).$$

Example 29: John is going to graduate from an industrial engineering department in a university by the end of the semester. After being interviewed at two companies he likes, he assesses that his probability of getting an offer from company A is 0.8, and his probability of getting an offer from company B is 0.6. If he believes that the probability that he will get offers from both companies is 0.5, what is the probability that he will get at least one offer from these two companies?

Solution: Using the additive rule, we have

$$P(A \cup B) = P(A) + P(B) - P(A \cap B) = 0.8 + 0.6 - 0.5 = 0.9.$$

Example 30: What is the probability of getting a total of 7 or 11 when a pair of fair dice is tossed?

Solution: Let A be the event that 7 occurs and B the event that 11 comes up. Now, a total of 7 occurs for 6 of the 36 sample points, and a total of 11 occurs for only 2 of the sample points. Since all sample points are equally likely, we have $P(A) = 1/6$ and $P(B) = 1/18$. The events A and B are mutually exclusive, since a total of 7 and 11 cannot both occur on the same toss. Therefore,

$$P(A \cup B) = P(A) + P(B) = \frac{1}{6} + \frac{1}{18} = \frac{2}{9}.$$

This result could also have been obtained by counting the total number of points for the event $A \cup B$, namely 8, and writing

$$P(A \cup B) = \frac{n}{N} = \frac{8}{36} = \frac{2}{9}.$$

Theorem 7 and its three corollaries should help the reader gain more insight into probability and its interpretation. Corollaries 1 and 2 suggest the very intuitive result dealing with the probability of occurrence of at least one of a number of events, no two of which can occur simultaneously. The probability that at least one occurs is the sum of the probabilities of occurrence of the individual events. The third corollary simply states that the highest value of a probability (unity) is assigned to the entire sample space S.

Example 31: If the probabilities are, respectively, 0.09, 0.15, 0.21, and 0.23 that a person purchasing a new automobile will choose the color green, white, red, or blue, what is the probability that a given buyer will purchase a new automobile that comes in one of those colors?

Solution: Let G, W, R, and B be the events that a buyer selects, respectively, a green, white, red, or blue automobile. Since these four events are mutually exclusive, the probability is

$$P(G \cup W \cup R \cup B) = P(G) + P(W) + P(R) + P(B)$$
$$= 0.09 + 0.15 + 0.21 + 0.23 = 0.68.$$

Often it is more difficult to calculate the probability that an event occurs than it is to calculate the probability that the event does not occur. Should this be the case for some event A, we simply find $P(A')$ first and then, using Theorem 7, find $P(A)$ by subtraction.

Theorem 9: If A and A' are complementary events, then

$$P(A) + P(A') = 1.$$

Proof: Since $A \cup A' = S$ and the sets A and A' are disjoint,

$$1 = P(S) = P(A \cup A') = P(A) + P(A').$$

Example 32: If the probabilities that an automobile mechanic will service 3, 4, 5, 6, 7, or 8 or more cars on any given workday are, respectively, 0.12, 0.19, 0.28, 0.24, 0.10, and 0.07, what is the probability that he will service at least 5 cars on his next day at work?

Solution: Let E be the event that at least 5 cars are serviced. Now, $P(E) = 1 - P(E')$, where E' is the event that fewer than 5 cars are serviced. Since

$$P(E') = 0.12 + 0.19 = 0.31,$$

it follows from Theorem 9 that

$$P(E) = 1 - 0.31 = 0.69.$$

Example 33: Suppose the manufacturer's specifications for the length of a certain type of computer cable are 2000 ± 10 millimeters. In this industry, it is known that small cable is just as likely to be defective (not meeting specifications) as large cable. That is, the probability of randomly producing a cable with length exceeding 2010 millimeters is equal to the probability of producing a cable with length smaller than 1990 millimeters. The probability that the production procedure meets specifications is known to be 0.99.

(a) What is the probability that a cable selected randomly is too large?

(b) What is the probability that a randomly selected cable is larger than 1990 millimeters?

Solution: Let M be the event that a cable meets specifications. Let S and L be the events that the cable is too small and too large, respectively. Then

(a) $P(M) = 0.99$ and $P(S) = P(L) = (1 - 0.99)/2 = 0.005$.

(b) Denoting by X the length of a randomly selected cable, we have

$$P(1990 \leq X \leq 2010) = P(M) = 0.99.$$

Since $P(X \geq 2010) = P(L) = 0.005$,

$$P(X \geq 1990) = P(M) + P(L) = 0.995.$$

This also can be solved by using Theorem 2.9:

$$P(X \geq 1990) + P(X < 1990) = 1.$$

Thus, $P(X \geq 1990) = 1 - P(S) = 1 - 0.005 = 0.995.$

Exercises

49 Find the errors in each of the following statements:

(a) The probabilities that an automobile salesperson will sell 0, 1, 2, or 3 cars on any given day in February are, respectively, 0.19, 0.38, 0.29, and 0.15.

(b) The probability that it will rain tomorrow is 0.40, and the probability that it will not rain tomorrow is 0.52.

(c) The probabilities that a printer will make 0, 1, 2, 3, or 4 or more mistakes in setting a document are, respectively, $0.19, 0.34, -0.25, 0.43$, and 0.29.

(d) On a single draw from a deck of playing cards, the probability of selecting a heart is 1/4, the probability of selecting a black card is 1/2, and the probability of selecting both a heart and a black card is 1/8.

50 Assuming that all elements of S in Exercise 8 are equally likely to occur, find

(a) the probability of event A;

(b) the probability of event C;

(c) the probability of event $A \cap C$.

51 A box contains 500 envelopes, of which 75 contain \$100 in cash, 150 contain \$25, and 275 contain \$10. An envelope may be purchased for \$25. What is the sample space for the different amounts of money? Assign probabilities to the sample points and then find the probability that the first envelope purchased contains less than \$100.

52 Suppose that in a senior college class of 500 students it is found that 210 smoke, 258 drink alcoholic beverages, 216 eat between meals, 122 smoke and drink alcoholic beverages, 83 eat between meals and drink alcoholic beverages, 97 smoke and eat between meals, and 52 engage in all three of these bad health practices. If a member of this senior class is selected at random, find the probability that the student

(a) smokes but does not drink alcoholic beverages;

(b) eats between meals and drinks alcoholic beverages but does not smoke;

(c) neither smokes nor eats between meals.

53 The probability that an American industry will locate in Shanghai, China, is 0.7, the probability that it will locate in Beijing, China, is 0.4, and the probability that it will locate in either Shanghai or Beijing or both is 0.8. What is the probability that the industry will locate

(a) in both cities?

(b) in neither city?

54 From past experience, a stockbroker believes that under present economic conditions a customer will invest in tax-free bonds with a probability of 0.6, will invest in mutual funds with a probability of 0.3, and will invest in both tax-free bonds and mutual funds with a probability of 0.15. At this time, find the probability that a customer will invest

(a) in either tax-free bonds or mutual funds;

(b) in neither tax-free bonds nor mutual funds.

55 If each coded item in a catalog begins with 3 distinct letters followed by 4 distinct nonzero digits, find the probability of randomly selecting one of these coded items with the first letter a vowel and the last digit even.

56 An automobile manufacturer is concerned about a possible recall of its best-selling four-door sedan. If there were a recall, there is a probability of 0.25 of a defect in the brake system, 0.18 of a defect in the transmission, 0.17 of a defect in the fuel system, and 0.40 of a defect in some other area.

(a) What is the probability that the defect is the brakes or the fueling system if the probability of defects in both systems simultaneously is 0.15?

(b) What is the probability that there are no defects in either the brakes or the fueling system?

57 If a letter is chosen at random from the English alphabet, find the probability that the letter

(a) is a vowel exclusive of y;

(b) is listed somewhere ahead of the letter j;

(c) is listed somewhere after the letter g.

58 A pair of fair dice is tossed. Find the probability of getting

(a) a total of 8;

(b) at most a total of 5.

59 In a poker hand consisting of 5 cards, find the probability of holding

(a) 3 aces;

(b) 4 hearts and 1 club.

60 If 3 books are picked at random from a shelf containing 5 novels, 3 books of poems, and a dictionary, what is the probability that

(a) the dictionary is selected?

(b) 2 novels and 1 book of poems are selected?

61 In a high school graduating class of 100 students, 54 studied mathematics, 69 studied history, and 35 studied both mathematics and history. If one of these students is selected at random, find the probability that

(a) the student took mathematics or history;

(b) the student did not take either of these subjects;

(c) the student took history but not mathematics.

62 Dom's Pizza Company uses taste testing and statistical analysis of the data prior to marketing any new product. Consider a study involving three types of crusts (thin, thin with garlic and oregano, and thin with bits of cheese). Dom's is also studying three sauces (standard, a new sauce with more garlic, and a new sauce with fresh basil).

(a) How many combinations of crust and sauce are involved?

(b) What is the probability that a judge will get a plain thin crust with a standard sauce for his first taste test?

63 According to *Consumer Digest* (July/August 1996), the probable location of personal computers (PC) in the home is as follows:

Adult bedroom:	0.03
Child bedroom:	0.15
Other bedroom:	0.14
Office or den:	0.40
Other rooms:	0.28

(a) What is the probability that a PC is in a bedroom?

(b) What is the probability that it is not in a bedroom?

(c) Suppose a household is selected at random from households with a PC; in what room would you expect to find a PC?

64 Interest centers around the life of an electronic component. Suppose it is known that the probability that the component survives for more than 6000 hours is 0.42. Suppose also that the probability that the component survives *no longer than* 4000 hours is 0.04.

(a) What is the probability that the life of the component is less than or equal to 6000 hours?

(b) What is the probability that the life is greater than 4000 hours?

65   Consider the situation of Exercise 64. Let A be the event that the component fails a particular test and B be the event that the component displays strain but does not actually fail. Event A occurs with probability 0.20, and event B occurs with probability 0.35.

(a) What is the probability that the component does not fail the test?

(b) What is the probability that the component works perfectly well (i.e., neither displays strain nor fails the test)?

(c) What is the probability that the component either fails or shows strain in the test?

66   Factory workers are constantly encouraged to practice zero tolerance when it comes to accidents in factories. Accidents can occur because the working environment or conditions themselves are unsafe. On the other hand, accidents can occur due to carelessness or so-called human error. In addition, the worker's shift, 7:00 A.M.–3:00 P.M. (day shift), 3:00 P.M.–11:00 P.M. (evening shift), or 11:00 P.M.–7:00 A.M. (graveyard shift), may be a factor. During the last year, 300 accidents have occurred. The percentages of the accidents for the condition combinations are as follows:

Shift	Unsafe Conditions	Human Error
Day	5%	32%
Evening	6%	25%
Graveyard	2%	30%

If an accident report is selected randomly from the 300 reports,

(a) what is the probability that the accident occurred on the graveyard shift?

(b) what is the probability that the accident occurred due to human error?

(c) what is the probability that the accident occurred due to unsafe conditions?

(d) what is the probability that the accident occurred on either the evening or the graveyard shift?

67   Consider the situation of Example 32.

(a) What is the probability that no more than 4 cars will be serviced by the mechanic?

(b) What is the probability that he will service fewer than 8 cars?

(c) What is the probability that he will service either 3 or 4 cars?

68   Interest centers around the nature of an oven purchased at a particular department store. It can be either a gas or an electric oven. Consider the decisions made by six distinct customers.

(a) Suppose that the probability is 0.40 that at most two of these individuals purchase an electric oven. What is the probability that at least three purchase the electric oven?

(b) Suppose it is known that the probability that all six purchase the electric oven is 0.007 while 0.104 is the probability that all six purchase the gas oven. What is the probability that at least one of each type is purchased?

69   It is common in many industrial areas to use a filling machine to fill boxes full of product. This occurs in the food industry as well as other areas in which the product is used in the home, for example, detergent. These machines are not perfect, and indeed they may A, fill to specification, B, underfill, and C, overfill. Generally, the practice of underfilling is that which one hopes to avoid. Let $P(B) = 0.001$ while $P(A) = 0.990$.

(a) Give $P(C)$.

(b) What is the probability that the machine does not underfill?

(c) What is the probability that the machine either overfills or underfills?

70   Consider the situation of Exercise 69. Suppose 50,000 boxes of detergent are produced per week and suppose also that those underfilled are "sent back," with customers requesting reimbursement of the purchase price. Suppose also that the cost of production is known to be $4.00 per box while the purchase price is $4.50 per box.

(a) What is the weekly profit under the condition of no defective boxes?

(b) What is the loss in profit expected due to underfilling?

71   As the situation of Exercise 69 might suggest, statistical procedures are often used for control of quality (i.e., industrial quality control). At times, the *weight* of a product is an important variable to control. Specifications are given for the weight of a certain packaged product, and a package is rejected if it is either too light or too heavy. Historical data suggest that 0.95 is the probability that the product meets weight specifications whereas 0.002 is the probability that the product is too light. For each single packaged product, the manufacturer invests $20.00 in production and the purchase price for the consumer is $25.00.

(a) What is the probability that a package chosen randomly from the production line is too heavy?

(b) For each 10,000 packages sold, what profit is received by the manufacturer if all packages meet weight specification?

(c) Assuming that all defective packages are rejected

and rendered worthless, how much is the profit reduced on 10,000 packages due to failure to meet weight specification?

72 Prove that

$$P(A' \cap B') = 1 + P(A \cap B) - P(A) - P(B).$$

6 Conditional Probability, Independence, and the Product Rule

One very important concept in probability theory is conditional probability. In some applications, the practitioner is interested in the probability structure under certain restrictions. For instance, in epidemiology, rather than studying the chance that a person from the general population has diabetes, it might be of more interest to know this probability for a distinct group such as Asian women in the age range of 35 to 50 or Hispanic men in the age range of 40 to 60. This type of probability is called a conditional probability.

Conditional Probability

The probability of an event B occurring when it is known that some event A has occurred is called a **conditional probability** and is denoted by $P(B|A)$. The symbol $P(B|A)$ is usually read "the probability that B occurs given that A occurs" or simply "the probability of B, given A."

Consider the event B of getting a perfect square when a die is tossed. The die is constructed so that the even numbers are twice as likely to occur as the odd numbers. Based on the sample space $S = \{1, 2, 3, 4, 5, 6\}$, with probabilities of $1/9$ and $2/9$ assigned, respectively, to the odd and even numbers, the probability of B occurring is $1/3$. Now suppose that it is known that the toss of the die resulted in a number greater than 3. We are now dealing with a reduced sample space $A = \{4, 5, 6\}$, which is a subset of S. To find the probability that B occurs, relative to the space A, we must first assign new probabilities to the elements of A proportional to their original probabilities such that their sum is 1. Assigning a probability of w to the odd number in A and a probability of $2w$ to the two even numbers, we have $5w = 1$, or $w = 1/5$. Relative to the space A, we find that B contains the single element 4. Denoting this event by the symbol $B|A$, we write $B|A = \{4\}$, and hence

$$P(B|A) = \frac{2}{5}.$$

This example illustrates that events may have different probabilities when considered relative to different sample spaces.

We can also write

$$P(B|A) = \frac{2}{5} = \frac{2/9}{5/9} = \frac{P(A \cap B)}{P(A)},$$

where $P(A \cap B)$ and $P(A)$ are found from the original sample space S. In other words, a conditional probability relative to a subspace A of S may be calculated directly from the probabilities assigned to the elements of the original sample space S.

Definition 10:

> The conditional probability of B, given A, denoted by $P(B|A)$, is defined by
>
> $$P(B|A) = \frac{P(A \cap B)}{P(A)}, \quad \text{provided} \quad P(A) > 0.$$

As an additional illustration, suppose that our sample space S is the population of adults in a small town who have completed the requirements for a college degree. We shall categorize them according to gender and employment status. The data are given in Table 1.

Table 1: Categorization of the Adults in a Small Town

	Employed	Unemployed	Total
Male	460	40	500
Female	140	260	400
Total	600	300	900

One of these individuals is to be selected at random for a tour throughout the country to publicize the advantages of establishing new industries in the town. We shall be concerned with the following events:

M: a man is chosen,

E: the one chosen is employed.

Using the reduced sample space E, we find that

$$P(M|E) = \frac{460}{600} = \frac{23}{30}.$$

Let $n(A)$ denote the number of elements in any set A. Using this notation, since each adult has an equal chance of being selected, we can write

$$P(M|E) = \frac{n(E \cap M)}{n(E)} = \frac{n(E \cap M)/n(S)}{n(E)/n(S)} = \frac{P(E \cap M)}{P(E)},$$

where $P(E \cap M)$ and $P(E)$ are found from the original sample space S. To verify this result, note that

$$P(E) = \frac{600}{900} = \frac{2}{3} \quad \text{and} \quad P(E \cap M) = \frac{460}{900} = \frac{23}{45}.$$

Hence,

$$P(M|E) = \frac{23/45}{2/3} = \frac{23}{30},$$

as before.

Example 34:

The probability that a regularly scheduled flight departs on time is $P(D) = 0.83$; the probability that it arrives on time is $P(A) = 0.82$; and the probability that it departs and arrives on time is $P(D \cap A) = 0.78$. Find the probability that a plane

(a) arrives on time, given that it departed on time, and (b) departed on time, given that it has arrived on time.

Solution: Using Definition 10, we have the following.

(a) The probability that a plane arrives on time, given that it departed on time, is

$$P(A|D) = \frac{P(D \cap A)}{P(D)} = \frac{0.78}{0.83} = 0.94.$$

(b) The probability that a plane departed on time, given that it has arrived on time, is

$$P(D|A) = \frac{P(D \cap A)}{P(A)} = \frac{0.78}{0.82} = 0.95.$$

The notion of conditional probability provides the capability of reevaluating the idea of probability of an event in light of additional information, that is, when it is known that another event has occurred. The probability $P(A|B)$ is an updating of $P(A)$ based on the knowledge that event B has occurred. In Example 34, it is important to know the probability that the flight arrives on time. One is given the information that the flight did not depart on time. Armed with this additional information, one can calculate the more pertinent probability $P(A|D')$, that is, the probability that it arrives on time, given that it did not depart on time. In many situations, the conclusions drawn from observing the more important conditional probability change the picture entirely. In this example, the computation of $P(A|D')$ is

$$P(A|D') = \frac{P(A \cap D')}{P(D')} = \frac{0.82 - 0.78}{0.17} = 0.24.$$

As a result, the probability of an on-time arrival is diminished severely in the presence of the additional information.

Example 35: The concept of conditional probability has countless uses in both industrial and biomedical applications. Consider an industrial process in the textile industry in which strips of a particular type of cloth are being produced. These strips can be defective in two ways, length and nature of texture. For the case of the latter, the process of identification is very complicated. It is known from historical information on the process that 10% of strips fail the length test, 5% fail the texture test, and only 0.8% fail both tests. If a strip is selected randomly from the process and a quick measurement identifies it as failing the length test, what is the probability that it is texture defective?

Solution: Consider the events

$$L: \text{length defective,} \qquad T: \text{texture defective.}$$

Given that the strip is length defective, the probability that this strip is texture defective is given by

$$P(T|L) = \frac{P(T \cap L)}{P(L)} = \frac{0.008}{0.1} = 0.08.$$

Independent Events

In the die-tossing experiment, we note that $P(B|A) = 2/5$ whereas $P(B) = 1/3$. That is, $P(B|A) \neq P(B)$, indicating that B depends on A. Now consider an experiment in which 2 cards are drawn in succession from an ordinary deck, with replacement. The events are defined as

A: the first card is an ace,

B: the second card is a spade.

Since the first card is replaced, our sample space for both the first and the second draw consists of 52 cards, containing 4 aces and 13 spades. Hence,

$$P(B|A) = \frac{13}{52} = \frac{1}{4} \quad \text{and} \quad P(B) = \frac{13}{52} = \frac{1}{4}.$$

That is, $P(B|A) = P(B)$. When this is true, the events A and B are said to be **independent**.

Although conditional probability allows for an alteration of the probability of an event in the light of additional material, it also enables us to understand better the very important concept of **independence** or, in the present context, independent events. In the airport illustration in Example 34, $P(A|D)$ differs from $P(A)$. This suggests that the occurrence of D influenced A, and this is certainly expected in this illustration. However, consider the situation where we have events A and B and

$$P(A|B) = P(A).$$

In other words, the occurrence of B had no impact on the odds of occurrence of A. Here the occurrence of A is independent of the occurrence of B. The importance of the concept of independence cannot be overemphasized. It plays a vital role in material in virtually all chapters in this book and in all areas of applied statistics.

Definition 11:

> Two events A and B are **independent** if and only if
>
> $$P(B|A) = P(B) \quad \text{or} \quad P(A|B) = P(A),$$
>
> assuming the existences of the conditional probabilities. Otherwise, A and B are **dependent**.

The condition $P(B|A) = P(B)$ implies that $P(A|B) = P(A)$, and conversely. For the card-drawing experiments, where we showed that $P(B|A) = P(B) = 1/4$, we also can see that $P(A|B) = P(A) = 1/13$.

The Product Rule, or the Multiplicative Rule

Multiplying the formula in Definition 10 by $P(A)$, we obtain the following important **multiplicative rule** (or **product rule**), which enables us to calculate the probability that two events will both occur.

Theorem 10:

> If in an experiment the events A and B can both occur, then
> $$P(A \cap B) = P(A)P(B|A), \text{ provided } P(A) > 0.$$

Thus, the probability that both A and B occur is equal to the probability that A occurs multiplied by the conditional probability that B occurs, given that A occurs. Since the events $A \cap B$ and $B \cap A$ are equivalent, it follows from Theorem 10 that we can also write

$$P(A \cap B) = P(B \cap A) = P(B)P(A|B).$$

In other words, it does not matter which event is referred to as A and which event is referred to as B.

Example 36: Suppose that we have a fuse box containing 20 fuses, of which 5 are defective. If 2 fuses are selected at random and removed from the box in succession without replacing the first, what is the probability that both fuses are defective?

Solution: We shall let A be the event that the first fuse is defective and B the event that the second fuse is defective; then we interpret $A \cap B$ as the event that A occurs and then B occurs after A has occurred. The probability of first removing a defective fuse is 1/4; then the probability of removing a second defective fuse from the remaining 4 is 4/19. Hence,

$$P(A \cap B) = \left(\frac{1}{4}\right)\left(\frac{4}{19}\right) = \frac{1}{19}.$$

Example 37: One bag contains 4 white balls and 3 black balls, and a second bag contains 3 white balls and 5 black balls. One ball is drawn from the first bag and placed unseen in the second bag. What is the probability that a ball now drawn from the second bag is black?

Solution: Let B_1, B_2, and W_1 represent, respectively, the drawing of a black ball from bag 1, a black ball from bag 2, and a white ball from bag 1. We are interested in the union of the mutually exclusive events $B_1 \cap B_2$ and $W_1 \cap B_2$. The various possibilities and their probabilities are illustrated in Figure 8. Now

$$
\begin{aligned}
P[(B_1 \cap B_2) \text{ or } (W_1 \cap B_2)] &= P(B_1 \cap B_2) + P(W_1 \cap B_2) \\
&= P(B_1)P(B_2|B_1) + P(W_1)P(B_2|W_1) \\
&= \left(\frac{3}{7}\right)\left(\frac{6}{9}\right) + \left(\frac{4}{7}\right)\left(\frac{5}{9}\right) = \frac{38}{63}.
\end{aligned}
$$

If, in Example 36, the first fuse is replaced and the fuses thoroughly rearranged before the second is removed, then the probability of a defective fuse on the second selection is still 1/4; that is, $P(B|A) = P(B)$ and the events A and B are independent. When this is true, we can substitute $P(B)$ for $P(B|A)$ in Theorem 10 to obtain the following special multiplicative rule.

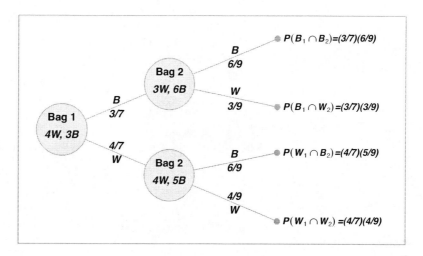

Figure 8: Tree diagram for Example 37.

Theorem 11:

> Two events A and B are independent if and only if
>
> $$P(A \cap B) = P(A)P(B).$$
>
> Therefore, to obtain the probability that two independent events will both occur, we simply find the product of their individual probabilities.

Example 38: A small town has one fire engine and one ambulance available for emergencies. The probability that the fire engine is available when needed is 0.98, and the probability that the ambulance is available when called is 0.92. In the event of an injury resulting from a burning building, find the probability that both the ambulance and the fire engine will be available, assuming they operate independently.

Solution: Let A and B represent the respective events that the fire engine and the ambulance are available. Then

$$P(A \cap B) = P(A)P(B) = (0.98)(0.92) = 0.9016.$$

Example 39: An electrical system consists of four components as illustrated in Figure 9. The system works if components A and B work and either of the components C or D works. The reliability (probability of working) of each component is also shown in Figure 9. Find the probability that (a) the entire system works and (b) the component C does not work, given that the entire system works. Assume that the four components work independently.

Solution: In this configuration of the system, A, B, and the subsystem C and D constitute a serial circuit system, whereas the subsystem C and D itself is a parallel circuit system.

(a) Clearly the probability that the entire system works can be calculated as follows:

$$P[A \cap B \cap (C \cup D)] = P(A)P(B)P(C \cup D) = P(A)P(B)[1 - P(C' \cap D')]$$
$$= P(A)P(B)[1 - P(C')P(D')]$$
$$= (0.9)(0.9)[1 - (1 - 0.8)(1 - 0.8)] = 0.7776.$$

The equalities above hold because of the independence among the four components.

(b) To calculate the conditional probability in this case, notice that

$$P = \frac{P(\text{the system works but } C \text{ does not work})}{P(\text{the system works})}$$
$$= \frac{P(A \cap B \cap C' \cap D)}{P(\text{the system works})} = \frac{(0.9)(0.9)(1 - 0.8)(0.8)}{0.7776} = 0.1667.$$

Figure 9: An electrical system for Example 39.

The multiplicative rule can be extended to more than two-event situations.

Theorem 12:

If, in an experiment, the events $A_1, A_2, \ldots, A_k$ can occur, then

$$P(A_1 \cap A_2 \cap \cdots \cap A_k)$$
$$= P(A_1)P(A_2|A_1)P(A_3|A_1 \cap A_2) \cdots P(A_k|A_1 \cap A_2 \cap \cdots \cap A_{k-1}).$$

If the events $A_1, A_2, \ldots, A_k$ are independent, then

$$P(A_1 \cap A_2 \cap \cdots \cap A_k) = P(A_1)P(A_2) \cdots P(A_k).$$

Example 40:

Three cards are drawn in succession, without replacement, from an ordinary deck of playing cards. Find the probability that the event $A_1 \cap A_2 \cap A_3$ occurs, where A_1 is the event that the first card is a red ace, A_2 is the event that the second card is a 10 or a jack, and A_3 is the event that the third card is greater than 3 but less than 7.

Solution: First we define the events

A_1: the first card is a red ace,

A_2: the second card is a 10 or a jack,

A_3: the third card is greater than 3 but less than 7.

Now

$$P(A_1) = \frac{2}{52}, \quad P(A_2|A_1) = \frac{8}{51}, \quad P(A_3|A_1 \cap A_2) = \frac{12}{50},$$

and hence, by Theorem 12,

$$P(A_1 \cap A_2 \cap A_3) = P(A_1)P(A_2|A_1)P(A_3|A_1 \cap A_2)$$
$$= \left(\frac{2}{52}\right)\left(\frac{8}{51}\right)\left(\frac{12}{50}\right) = \frac{8}{5525}.$$

The property of independence stated in Theorem 11 can be extended to deal with more than two events. Consider, for example, the case of three events A, B, and C. It is not sufficient to only have that $P(A \cap B \cap C) = P(A)P(B)P(C)$ as a definition of independence among the three. Suppose $A = B$ and $C = \phi$, the null set. Although $A \cap B \cap C = \phi$, which results in $P(A \cap B \cap C) = 0 = P(A)P(B)P(C)$, events A and B are not independent. Hence, we have the following definition.

Definition 12:

> A collection of events $\mathcal{A} = \{A_1, \ldots, A_n\}$ are mutually independent if for any subset of $\mathcal{A}$, $A_{i_1}, \ldots, A_{i_k}$, for $k \leq n$, we have
> $$P(A_{i_1} \cap \cdots \cap A_{i_k}) = P(A_{i_1}) \cdots P(A_{i_k}).$$

Exercises

73   If R is the event that a convict committed armed robbery and D is the event that the convict pushed dope, state in words what probabilities are expressed by
(a) $P(R|D)$;
(b) $P(D'|R)$;
(c) $P(R'|D')$.

74   A class in advanced physics is composed of 10 juniors, 30 seniors, and 10 graduate students. The final grades show that 3 of the juniors, 10 of the seniors, and 5 of the graduate students received an A for the course. If a student is chosen at random from this class and is found to have earned an A, what is the probability that he or she is a senior?

75   A random sample of 200 adults are classified below by sex and their level of education attained.

Education	Male	Female
Elementary	38	45
Secondary	28	50
College	22	17

If a person is picked at random from this group, find the probability that
(a) the person is a male, given that the person has a secondary education;

(b) the person does not have a college degree, given that the person is a female.

76   In an experiment to study the relationship of hypertension and smoking habits, the following data are collected for 180 individuals:

	Nonsmokers	Moderate Smokers	Heavy Smokers
H	21	36	30
NH	48	26	19

where H and NH in the table stand for *Hypertension* and *Nonhypertension*, respectively. If one of these individuals is selected at random, find the probability that the person is

(a) experiencing hypertension, given that the person is a heavy smoker;

(b) a nonsmoker, given that the person is experiencing no hypertension.

77   In the senior year of a high school graduating class of 100 students, 42 studied mathematics, 68 studied psychology, 54 studied history, 22 studied both mathematics and history, 25 studied both mathematics and psychology, 7 studied history but neither mathematics nor psychology, 10 studied all three subjects, and 8 did not take any of the three. Randomly select a student from the class and find the probabilities of the following events.

(a) A person enrolled in psychology takes all three subjects.

(b) A person not taking psychology is taking both history and mathematics.

78 A manufacturer of a flu vaccine is concerned about the quality of its flu serum. Batches of serum are processed by three different departments having rejection rates of 0.10, 0.08, and 0.12, respectively. The inspections by the three departments are sequential and independent.

(a) What is the probability that a batch of serum survives the first departmental inspection but is rejected by the second department?

(b) What is the probability that a batch of serum is rejected by the third department?

79 In *USA Today* (Sept. 5, 1996), the results of a survey involving the use of sleepwear while traveling were listed as follows:

	Male	Female	Total
Underwear	0.220	0.024	0.244
Nightgown	0.002	0.180	0.182
Nothing	0.160	0.018	0.178
Pajamas	0.102	0.073	0.175
T-shirt	0.046	0.088	0.134
Other	0.084	0.003	0.087

(a) What is the probability that a traveler is a female who sleeps in the nude?

(b) What is the probability that a traveler is male?

(c) Assuming the traveler is male, what is the probability that he sleeps in pajamas?

(d) What is the probability that a traveler is male if the traveler sleeps in pajamas or a T-shirt?

80 The probability that an automobile being filled with gasoline also needs an oil change is 0.25; the probability that it needs a new oil filter is 0.40; and the probability that both the oil and the filter need changing is 0.14.

(a) If the oil has to be changed, what is the probability that a new oil filter is needed?

(b) If a new oil filter is needed, what is the probability that the oil has to be changed?

81 The probability that a married man watches a certain television show is 0.4, and the probability that a married woman watches the show is 0.5. The probability that a man watches the show, given that his wife does, is 0.7. Find the probability that

(a) a married couple watches the show;

(b) a wife watches the show, given that her husband does;

(c) at least one member of a married couple will watch the show.

82 For married couples living in a certain suburb, the probability that the husband will vote on a bond referendum is 0.21, the probability that the wife will vote on the referendum is 0.28, and the probability that both the husband and the wife will vote is 0.15. What is the probability that

(a) at least one member of a married couple will vote?

(b) a wife will vote, given that her husband will vote?

(c) a husband will vote, given that his wife will not vote?

83 The probability that a vehicle entering the Luray Caverns has Canadian license plates is 0.12; the probability that it is a camper is 0.28; and the probability that it is a camper with Canadian license plates is 0.09. What is the probability that

(a) a camper entering the Luray Caverns has Canadian license plates?

(b) a vehicle with Canadian license plates entering the Luray Caverns is a camper?

(c) a vehicle entering the Luray Caverns does not have Canadian plates or is not a camper?

84 The probability that the head of a household is home when a telemarketing representative calls is 0.4. Given that the head of the house is home, the probability that goods will be bought from the company is 0.3. Find the probability that the head of the house is home and goods are bought from the company.

85 The probability that a doctor correctly diagnoses a particular illness is 0.7. Given that the doctor makes an incorrect diagnosis, the probability that the patient files a lawsuit is 0.9. What is the probability that the doctor makes an incorrect diagnosis and the patient sues?

86 In 1970, 11% of Americans completed four years of college; 43% of them were women. In 1990, 22% of Americans completed four years of college; 53% of them were women (*Time*, Jan. 19, 1996).

(a) Given that a person completed four years of college in 1970, what is the probability that the person was a woman?

(b) What is the probability that a woman finished four years of college in 1990?

(c) What is the probability that a man had not finished college in 1990?

87 A real estate agent has 8 master keys to open several new homes. Only 1 master key will open any given house. If 40% of these homes are usually left unlocked, what is the probability that the real estate agent can get into a specific home if the agent selects 3 master keys at random before leaving the office?

88 Before the distribution of certain statistical software, every fourth compact disk (CD) is tested for accuracy. The testing process consists of running four independent programs and checking the results. The failure rates for the four testing programs are, respectively, 0.01, 0.03, 0.02, and 0.01.

(a) What is the probability that a CD was tested and failed any test?

(b) Given that a CD was tested, what is the probability that it failed program 2 or 3?

(c) In a sample of 100, how many CDs would you expect to be rejected?

(d) Given that a CD was defective, what is the probability that it was tested?

89 A town has two fire engines operating independently. The probability that a specific engine is available when needed is 0.96.

(a) What is the probability that neither is available when needed?

(b) What is the probability that a fire engine is available when needed?

90 Pollution of the rivers in the United States has been a problem for many years. Consider the following events:

  A: the river is polluted,

  B: a sample of water tested detects pollution,

  C: fishing is permitted.

Assume $P(A) = 0.3$, $P(B|A) = 0.75$, $P(B|A') = 0.20$, $P(C|A \cap B) = 0.20$, $P(C|A' \cap B) = 0.15$, $P(C|A \cap B') = 0.80$, and $P(C|A' \cap B') = 0.90$.

(a) Find $P(A \cap B \cap C)$.

(b) Find $P(B' \cap C)$.

(c) Find $P(C)$.

(d) Find the probability that the river is polluted, given that fishing is permitted and the sample tested did not detect pollution.

91 Find the probability of randomly selecting 4 good quarts of milk in succession from a cooler containing 20 quarts of which 5 have spoiled, by using

(a) the first formula of Theorem 12;

(b) the formulas of Theorem 6 and Rule 3.

92 Suppose the diagram of an electrical system is as given in Figure 10. What is the probability that the system works? Assume the components fail independently.

93 A circuit system is given in Figure 11. Assume the components fail independently.

(a) What is the probability that the entire system works?

(b) Given that the system works, what is the probability that the component A is not working?

94 In the situation of Exercise 93, it is known that the system does not work. What is the probability that the component A also does not work?

Figure 10: Diagram for Exercise 92.

Figure 11: Diagram for Exercise 93.

7   Bayes' Rule

Bayesian statistics is a collection of tools that is used in a special form of statistical inference which applies in the analysis of experimental data in many practical situations in science and engineering. Bayes' rule is one of the most important rules in probability theory. It is the foundation of Bayesian inference.

Total Probability

Let us now return to the illustration of Section 6, where an individual is being selected at random from the adults of a small town to tour the country and publicize the advantages of establishing new industries in the town. Suppose that we are now given the additional information that 36 of those employed and 12 of those unemployed are members of the Rotary Club. We wish to find the probability of the event A that the individual selected is a member of the Rotary Club. Referring to Figure 2, we can write A as the union of the two mutually exclusive events $E \cap A$ and $E' \cap A$. Hence, $A = (E \cap A) \cup (E' \cap A)$, and by Corollary 1 of Theorem 7, and then Theorem 10, we can write

$$P(A) = P[(E \cap A) \cup (E' \cap A)] = P(E \cap A) + P(E' \cap A)$$
$$= P(E)P(A|E) + P(E')P(A|E').$$

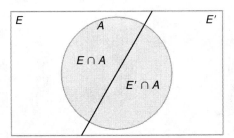

Figure 12: Venn diagram for the events A, E, and E'.

The data of Section 6, together with the additional data given above for the set A, enable us to compute

$$P(E) = \frac{600}{900} = \frac{2}{3}, \quad P(A|E) = \frac{36}{600} = \frac{3}{50},$$

and

$$P(E') = \frac{1}{3}, \quad P(A|E') = \frac{12}{300} = \frac{1}{25}.$$

If we display these probabilities by means of the tree diagram of Figure 13, where the first branch yields the probability $P(E)P(A|E)$ and the second branch yields

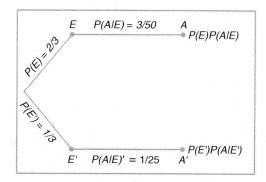

Figure 13: Tree diagram for the data from Section 6, using additional information from Section 7.

the probability $P(E')P(A|E')$, it follows that

$$P(A) = \left(\frac{2}{3}\right)\left(\frac{3}{50}\right) + \left(\frac{1}{3}\right)\left(\frac{1}{25}\right) = \frac{4}{75}.$$

A generalization of the foregoing illustration to the case where the sample space is partitioned into k subsets is covered by the following theorem, sometimes called the **theorem of total probability** or the **rule of elimination**.

Theorem 13: | If the events $B_1, B_2, \ldots, B_k$ constitute a partition of the sample space S such that $P(B_i) \neq 0$ for $i = 1, 2, \ldots, k$, then for any event A of S,

$$P(A) = \sum_{i=1}^{k} P(B_i \cap A) = \sum_{i=1}^{k} P(B_i)P(A|B_i).$$

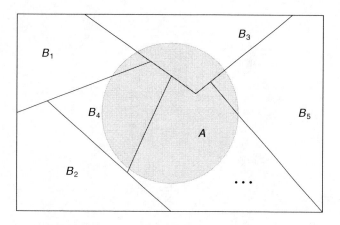

Figure 14: Partitioning the sample space S.

73

Proof: Consider the Venn diagram of Figure 14. The event A is seen to be the union of the mutually exclusive events

$$B_1 \cap A, \ B_2 \cap A, \ \ldots, \ B_k \cap A;$$

that is,

$$A = (B_1 \cap A) \cup (B_2 \cap A) \cup \cdots \cup (B_k \cap A).$$

Using Corollary 2 of Theorem 7 and Theorem 10, we have

$$\begin{aligned}
P(A) &= P[(B_1 \cap A) \cup (B_2 \cap A) \cup \cdots \cup (B_k \cap A)] \\
&= P(B_1 \cap A) + P(B_2 \cap A) + \cdots + P(B_k \cap A) \\
&= \sum_{i=1}^{k} P(B_i \cap A) \\
&= \sum_{i=1}^{k} P(B_i) P(A|B_i).
\end{aligned}$$

Example 41: In a certain assembly plant, three machines, B_1, B_2, and B_3, make 30%, 45%, and 25%, respectively, of the products. It is known from past experience that 2%, 3%, and 2% of the products made by each machine, respectively, are defective. Now, suppose that a finished product is randomly selected. What is the probability that it is defective?

Solution: Consider the following events:

A: the product is defective,

B_1: the product is made by machine B_1,

B_2: the product is made by machine B_2,

B_3: the product is made by machine B_3.

Applying the rule of elimination, we can write

$$P(A) = P(B_1)P(A|B_1) + P(B_2)P(A|B_2) + P(B_3)P(A|B_3).$$

Referring to the tree diagram of Figure 15, we find that the three branches give the probabilities

$$\begin{aligned}
P(B_1)P(A|B_1) &= (0.3)(0.02) = 0.006, \\
P(B_2)P(A|B_2) &= (0.45)(0.03) = 0.0135, \\
P(B_3)P(A|B_3) &= (0.25)(0.02) = 0.005,
\end{aligned}$$

and hence

$$P(A) = 0.006 + 0.0135 + 0.005 = 0.0245.$$

Probability

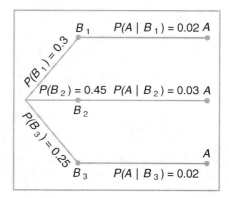

Figure 15: Tree diagram for Example 41.

Bayes' Rule

Instead of asking for $P(A)$ in Example 41, by the rule of elimination, suppose that we now consider the problem of finding the conditional probability $P(B_i|A)$. In other words, suppose that a product was randomly selected and it is defective. What is the probability that this product was made by machine B_i? Questions of this type can be answered by using the following theorem, called **Bayes' rule**:

Theorem 14:

(**Bayes' Rule**) If the events $B_1, B_2, \ldots, B_k$ constitute a partition of the sample space S such that $P(B_i) \neq 0$ for $i = 1, 2, \ldots, k$, then for any event A in S such that $P(A) \neq 0$,

$$P(B_r|A) = \frac{P(B_r \cap A)}{\sum_{i=1}^{k} P(B_i \cap A)} = \frac{P(B_r)P(A|B_r)}{\sum_{i=1}^{k} P(B_i)P(A|B_i)} \quad \text{for } r = 1, 2, \ldots, k.$$

Proof: By the definition of conditional probability,

$$P(B_r|A) = \frac{P(B_r \cap A)}{P(A)},$$

and then using Theorem 13 in the denominator, we have

$$P(B_r|A) = \frac{P(B_r \cap A)}{\sum_{i=1}^{k} P(B_i \cap A)} = \frac{P(B_r)P(A|B_r)}{\sum_{i=1}^{k} P(B_i)P(A|B_i)},$$

which completes the proof.

Example 42: With reference to Example 41, if a product was chosen randomly and found to be defective, what is the probability that it was made by machine B_3?

Solution: Using Bayes' rule to write

$$P(B_3|A) = \frac{P(B_3)P(A|B_3)}{P(B_1)P(A|B_1) + P(B_2)P(A|B_2) + P(B_3)P(A|B_3)},$$

and then substituting the probabilities calculated in Example 41, we have

$$P(B_3|A) = \frac{0.005}{0.006 + 0.0135 + 0.005} = \frac{0.005}{0.0245} = \frac{10}{49}.$$

In view of the fact that a defective product was selected, this result suggests that it probably was not made by machine B_3.

Example 43: A manufacturing firm employs three analytical plans for the design and development of a particular product. For cost reasons, all three are used at varying times. In fact, plans 1, 2, and 3 are used for 30%, 20%, and 50% of the products, respectively. The defect rate is different for the three procedures as follows:

$$P(D|P_1) = 0.01, \qquad P(D|P_2) = 0.03, \qquad P(D|P_3) = 0.02,$$

where $P(D|P_j)$ is the probability of a defective product, given plan j. If a random product was observed and found to be defective, which plan was most likely used and thus responsible?

Solution: From the statement of the problem

$$P(P_1) = 0.30, \quad P(P_2) = 0.20, \quad \text{and} \quad P(P_3) = 0.50,$$

we must find $P(P_j|D)$ for $j = 1, 2, 3$. Bayes' rule (Theorem 14) shows

$$P(P_1|D) = \frac{P(P_1)P(D|P_1)}{P(P_1)P(D|P_1) + P(P_2)P(D|P_2) + P(P_3)P(D|P_3)}$$

$$= \frac{(0.30)(0.01)}{(0.3)(0.01) + (0.20)(0.03) + (0.50)(0.02)} = \frac{0.003}{0.019} = 0.158.$$

Similarly,

$$P(P_2|D) = \frac{(0.03)(0.20)}{0.019} = 0.316 \text{ and } P(P_3|D) = \frac{(0.02)(0.50)}{0.019} = 0.526.$$

The conditional probability of a defect given plan 3 is the largest of the three; thus a defective for a random product is most likely the result of the use of plan 3.

Using Bayes' rule, a statistical methodology called the Bayesian approach has attracted a lot of attention in applications.

Exercises

95 In a certain region of the country it is known from past experience that the probability of selecting an adult over 40 years of age with cancer is 0.05. If the probability of a doctor correctly diagnosing a person with cancer as having the disease is 0.78 and the probability of incorrectly diagnosing a person without cancer as having the disease is 0.06, what is the probability that an adult over 40 years of age is diagnosed as having cancer?

96 Police plan to enforce speed limits by using radar traps at four different locations within the city limits. The radar traps at each of the locations L_1, L_2, L_3, and L_4 will be operated 40%, 30%, 20%, and 30% of the time. If a person who is speeding on her way to work has probabilities of 0.2, 0.1, 0.5, and 0.2, respectively, of passing through these locations, what is the probability that she will receive a speeding ticket?

97 Referring to Exercise 95, what is the probability that a person diagnosed as having cancer actually has the disease?

98 If the person in Exercise 96 received a speeding ticket on her way to work, what is the probability that she passed through the radar trap located at L_2?

99 Suppose that the four inspectors at a film factory are supposed to stamp the expiration date on each package of film at the end of the assembly line. John, who stamps 20% of the packages, fails to stamp the expiration date once in every 200 packages; Tom, who stamps 60% of the packages, fails to stamp the expiration date once in every 100 packages; Jeff, who stamps 15% of the packages, fails to stamp the expiration date once in every 90 packages; and Pat, who stamps 5% of the packages, fails to stamp the expiration date once in every 200 packages. If a customer complains that her package of film does not show the expiration date, what is the probability that it was inspected by John?

100 A regional telephone company operates three identical relay stations at different locations. During a one-year period, the number of malfunctions reported by each station and the causes are shown below.

Station	A	B	C
Problems with electricity supplied	2	1	1
Computer malfunction	4	3	2
Malfunctioning electrical equipment	5	4	2
Caused by other human errors	7	7	5

Suppose that a malfunction was reported and it was found to be caused by other human errors. What is the probability that it came from station C?

101 A paint-store chain produces and sells latex and semigloss paint. Based on long-range sales, the probability that a customer will purchase latex paint is 0.75. Of those that purchase latex paint, 60% also purchase rollers. But only 30% of semigloss paint buyers purchase rollers. A randomly selected buyer purchases a roller and a can of paint. What is the probability that the paint is latex?

102 Denote by A, B, and C the events that a grand prize is behind doors A, B, and C, respectively. Suppose you randomly picked a door, say A. The game host opened a door, say B, and showed there was no prize behind it. Now the host offers you the option of either staying at the door that you picked (A) or switching to the remaining unopened door (C). Use probability to explain whether you should switch or not.

Review Exercises

103 A truth serum has the property that 90% of the guilty suspects are properly judged while, of course, 10% of the guilty suspects are improperly found innocent. On the other hand, innocent suspects are misjudged 1% of the time. If the suspect was selected from a group of suspects of which only 5% have ever committed a crime, and the serum indicates that he is guilty, what is the probability that he is innocent?

104 An allergist claims that 50% of the patients she tests are allergic to some type of weed. What is the probability that

(a) exactly 3 of her next 4 patients are allergic to weeds?

(b) none of her next 4 patients is allergic to weeds?

105 By comparing appropriate regions of Venn diagrams, verify that

(a) $(A \cap B) \cup (A \cap B') = A$;

(b) $A' \cap (B' \cup C) = (A' \cap B') \cup (A' \cap C)$.

106 The probabilities that a service station will pump gas into 0, 1, 2, 3, 4, or 5 or more cars during a certain 30-minute period are 0.03, 0.18, 0.24, 0.28, 0.10, and 0.17, respectively. Find the probability that in this 30-minute period

(a) more than 2 cars receive gas;

(b) at most 4 cars receive gas;

(c) 4 or more cars receive gas.

107 How many bridge hands are possible containing 4 spades, 6 diamonds, 1 club, and 2 hearts?

108 If the probability is 0.1 that a person will make a mistake on his or her state income tax return, find the probability that

(a) four totally unrelated persons each make a mistake;

(b) Mr. Jones and Ms. Clark both make mistakes, and Mr. Roberts and Ms. Williams do not make a mistake.

109 A large industrial firm uses three local motels to provide overnight accommodations for its clients. From past experience it is known that 20% of the clients are assigned rooms at the Ramada Inn, 50% at the Sheraton, and 30% at the Lakeview Motor Lodge. If the plumbing is faulty in 5% of the rooms at the Ramada Inn, in 4% of the rooms at the Sheraton, and in 8% of the rooms at the Lakeview Motor Lodge, what is the probability that

(a) a client will be assigned a room with faulty plumbing?

(b) a person with a room having faulty plumbing was assigned accommodations at the Lakeview Motor Lodge?

110 The probability that a patient recovers from a delicate heart operation is 0.8. What is the probability that

(a) exactly 2 of the next 3 patients who have this operation survive?

(b) all of the next 3 patients who have this operation survive?

111 In a certain federal prison, it is known that 2/3 of the inmates are under 25 years of age. It is also known that 3/5 of the inmates are male and that 5/8 of the inmates are female or 25 years of age or older. What is the probability that a prisoner selected at random from this prison is female and at least 25 years old?

112 From 4 red, 5 green, and 6 yellow apples, how many selections of 9 apples are possible if 3 of each color are to be selected?

113 From a box containing 6 black balls and 4 green balls, 3 balls are drawn in succession, each ball being replaced in the box before the next draw is made. What is the probability that

(a) all 3 are the same color?

(b) each color is represented?

114 A shipment of 12 television sets contains 3 defective sets. In how many ways can a hotel purchase 5 of these sets and receive at least 2 of the defective sets?

115 A certain federal agency employs three consulting firms (A, B, and C) with probabilities 0.40, 0.35, and 0.25, respectively. From past experience it is known that the probability of cost overruns for the firms are 0.05, 0.03, and 0.15, respectively. Suppose a cost overrun is experienced by the agency.

(a) What is the probability that the consulting firm involved is company C?

(b) What is the probability that it is company A?

116 A manufacturer is studying the effects of cooking temperature, cooking time, and type of cooking oil for making potato chips. Three different temperatures, 4 different cooking times, and 3 different oils are to be used.

(a) What is the total number of combinations to be studied?

(b) How many combinations will be used for each type of oil?

(c) Discuss why permutations are not an issue in this exercise.

117 Consider the situation in Exercise 116, and suppose that the manufacturer can try only two combinations in a day.

(a) What is the probability that any given set of two runs is chosen?

(b) What is the probability that the highest temperature is used in either of these two combinations?

118 A certain form of cancer is known to be found in women over 60 with probability 0.07. A blood test exists for the detection of the disease, but the test is not infallible. In fact, it is known that 10% of the time the test gives a false negative (i.e., the test incorrectly gives a negative result) and 5% of the time the test gives a false positive (i.e., incorrectly gives a positive result). If a woman over 60 is known to have taken the test and received a favorable (i.e., negative) result, what is the probability that she has the disease?

119 A producer of a certain type of electronic component ships to suppliers in lots of twenty. Suppose that 60% of all such lots contain no defective components, 30% contain one defective component, and 10% contain two defective components. A lot is picked, two components from the lot are randomly selected and tested, and neither is defective.

(a) What is the probability that zero defective components exist in the lot?

(b) What is the probability that one defective exists in the lot?

(c) What is the probability that two defectives exist in the lot?

120 A rare disease exists with which only 1 in 500 is affected. A test for the disease exists, but of course it is not infallible. A correct positive result (patient actually has the disease) occurs 95% of the time, while a false positive result (patient does not have the disease) occurs 1% of the time. If a randomly selected individual is tested and the result is positive, what is the probability that the individual has the disease?

121 A construction company employs two sales engineers. Engineer 1 does the work of estimating cost for 70% of jobs bid by the company. Engineer 2 does the work for 30% of jobs bid by the company. It is known that the error rate for engineer 1 is such that 0.02 is the probability of an error when he does the work, whereas the probability of an error in the work of engineer 2 is 0.04. Suppose a bid arrives and a serious error occurs in estimating cost. Which engineer would you guess did the work? Explain and show all work.

122 In the field of quality control, the science of statistics is often used to determine if a process is "out of control." Suppose the process is, indeed, out of control and 20% of items produced are defective.

(a) If three items arrive off the process line in succession, what is the probability that all three are defective?

(b) If four items arrive in succession, what is the probability that three are defective?

123 An industrial plant is conducting a study to determine how quickly injured workers are back on the job following injury. Records show that 10% of all injured workers are admitted to the hospital for treatment and 15% are back on the job the next day. In addition, studies show that 2% are both admitted for hospital treatment and back on the job the next day. If a worker is injured, what is the probability that the worker will either be admitted to a hospital or be back on the job the next day or both?

124 A firm is accustomed to training operators who do certain tasks on a production line. Those operators who attend the training course are known to be able to meet their production quotas 90% of the time. New operators who do not take the training course only meet their quotas 65% of the time. Fifty percent of new operators attend the course. Given that a new operator meets her production quota, what is the probability that she attended the program?

125 A survey of those using a particular statistical software system indicated that 10% were dissatisfied.

Half of those dissatisfied purchased the system from vendor A. It is also known that 20% of those surveyed purchased from vendor A. Given that the software was purchased from vendor A, what is the probability that that particular user is dissatisfied?

126 During bad economic times, industrial workers are dismissed and are often replaced by machines. The history of 100 workers whose loss of employment is attributable to technological advances is reviewed. For each of these individuals, it is determined if he or she was given an alternative job within the same company, found a job with another company in the same field, found a job in a new field, or has been unemployed for 1 year. In addition, the union status of each worker is recorded. The following table summarizes the results.

	Union	Nonunion
Same Company	40	15
New Company (same field)	13	10
New Field	4	11
Unemployed	2	5

(a) If the selected worker found a job with a new company in the same field, what is the probability that the worker is a union member?

(b) If the worker is a union member, what is the probability that the worker has been unemployed for a year?

127 There is a 50-50 chance that the queen carries the gene of hemophilia. If she is a carrier, then each prince has a 50-50 chance of having hemophilia independently. If the queen is not a carrier, the prince will not have the disease. Suppose the queen has had three princes without the disease. What is the probability the queen is a carrier?

128 **Group Project**: Give each student a bag of chocolate M&Ms. Divide the students into groups of 5 or 6. Calculate the relative frequency distribution for color of M&Ms for each group.

(a) What is your estimated probability of randomly picking a yellow? a red?

(b) Redo the calculations for the whole classroom. Did the estimates change?

(c) Do you believe there is an equal number of each color in a process batch? Discuss.

8   Potential Misconceptions and Hazards

This chapter contains the fundamental definitions, rules, and theorems that provide a foundation that renders probability an important tool for evaluating

Probability

scientific and engineering systems. The evaluations are often in the form of probability computations, as is illustrated in examples and exercises. Concepts such as independence, conditional probability, Bayes' rule, and others tend to mesh nicely to solve practical problems in which the bottom line is to produce a probability value. Illustrations in exercises are abundant. See, for example, Exercises 100 and 101. In these and many other exercises, an evaluation of a scientific system is being made judiciously from a probability calculation, using rules and definitions discussed in the chapter.

Answers to Odd-Numbered Non-Review Exercises

1. (a) $S = \{8, 16, 24, 32, 40, 48\}$
   (b) $S = \{-5, 1\}$
   (c) $S = \{T, HT, HHT, HHH\}$
   (d) $S =$ {Africa, Antarctica, Asia, Australia, Europe, North America, South America}
   (e) $S = \phi$

3. $A = C$

5. Using the tree diagram, we obtain
   $S = \{1HH, 1HT, 1TH, 1TT, 2H, 2T, 3HH,$
   $3HT, 3TH, 3TT, 4H, 4T, 5HH, 5HT, 5TH,$
   $5TT, 6H, 6T\}$

7. $S_1 = \{MMMM, MMMF, MMFM, MFMM,$
   $FMMM, MMFF, MFMF, MFFM, FMFM,$
   $FFMM, FMMF, MFFF, FMFF, FFMF,$
   $FFFM, FFFF\};$
   $S_2 = \{0, 1, 2, 3, 4\}$

9. (a) $A = \{1HH, 1HT, 1TH, 1TT, 2H, 2T\}$
   (b) $B = \{1TT, 3TT, 5TT\}$
   (c) $A' = \{3HH, 3HT, 3TH, 3TT, 4H, 4T, 5HH,$
   $5HT, 5TH, 5TT, 6H, 6T\}$
   (d) $A' \cap B = \{3TT, 5TT\}$
   (e) $A \cup B = \{1HH, 1HT, 1TH, 1TT, 2H, 2T,$
   $3TT, 5TT\}$

11. (a) $S = \{M_1M_2, M_1F_1, M_1F_2, M_2M_1, M_2F_1,$
   $M_2F_2, F_1M_1, F_1M_2, F_1F_2, F_2M_1, F_2M_2,$
   $F_2F_1\}$
   (b) $A = \{M_1M_2, M_1F_1, M_1F_2, M_2M_1, M_2F_1,$
   $M_2F_2\}$
   (c) $B = \{M_1F_1, M_1F_2, M_2F_1, M_2F_2, F_1M_1,$
   $F_1M_2, F_2M_1, F_2M_2\}$
   (d) $C = \{F_1F_2, F_2F_1\}$
   (e) $A \cap B = \{M_1F_1, M_1F_2, M_2F_1, M_2F_2\}$
   (f) $A \cup C = \{M_1M_2, M_1F_1, M_1F_2, M_2M_1,$
   $M_2F_1, M_2F_2, F_1F_2, F_2F_1\}$

15. (a) {nitrogen, potassium, uranium, oxygen}
   (b) {copper, sodium, zinc, oxygen}
   (c) {copper, sodium, nitrogen, potassium, uranium, zinc}
   (d) {copper, uranium, zinc}
   (e) ϕ
   (f) {oxygen}

19. (a) The family will experience mechanical problems but will receive no ticket for a traffic violation and will not arrive at a campsite that has no vacancies.
   (b) The family will receive a traffic ticket and arrive at a campsite that has no vacancies but will not experience mechanical problems.
   (c) The family will experience mechanical problems and will arrive at a campsite that has no vacancies.
   (d) The family will receive a traffic ticket but will not arrive at a campsite that has no vacancies.
   (e) The family will not experience mechanical problems.

21. 18

23. 156

25. 20

27. 48

29. 210

31. 72

33. (a) 1024; (b) 243

35. 362,880

37. 2880

39 (a) 40,320; (b) 336

41 360

43 24

45 3360

47 56

49 (a) Sum of the probabilities exceeds 1.

(b) Sum of the probabilities is less than 1.

(c) A negative probability

(d) Probability of both a heart and a black card is zero.

51 $S = \{\$10, \$25, \$100\}$; $P(10) = \frac{11}{20}$, $P(25) = \frac{3}{10}$, $P(100) = \frac{15}{100}$; $\frac{17}{20}$

53 (a) 0.3; (b) 0.2

55 10/117

57 (a) 5/26; (b) 9/26; (c) 19/26

59 (a) 94/54,145; (b) 143/39,984

61 (a) 22/25; (b) 3/25; (c) 17/50

63 (a) 0.32; (b) 0.68; (c) office or den

65 (a) 0.8; (b) 0.45; (c) 0.55

67 (a) 0.31; (b) 0.93; (c) 0.31

69 (a) 0.009; (b) 0.999; (c) 0.01

71 (a) 0.048; (b) \$50,000; (c) \$12,500

73 (a) The probability that a convict who pushed dope also committed armed robbery.

(b) The probability that a convict who committed armed robbery did not push dope.

(c) The probability that a convict who did not push dope also did not commit armed robbery.

75 (a) 14/39; (b) 95/112

77 (a) 5/34; (b) 3/8

79 (a) 0.018; (b) 0.614; (c) 0.166; (d) 0.479

81 (a) 0.35; (b) 0.875; (c) 0.55

83 (a) 9/28; (b) 3/4; (c) 0.91

85 0.27

87 5/8

89 (a) 0.0016; (b) 0.9984

91 (a) 91/323; (b) 91/323

93 (a) 0.75112; (b) 0.2045

95 0.0960

97 0.40625

99 0.1124

101 0.857

Random Variables and Probability Distributions

1 Concept of a Random Variable

Statistics is concerned with making inferences about populations and population characteristics. Experiments are conducted with results that are subject to chance. The testing of a number of electronic components is an example of a **statistical experiment**, a term that is used to describe any process by which several chance observations are generated. It is often important to allocate a numerical description to the outcome. For example, the sample space giving a detailed description of each possible outcome when three electronic components are tested may be written

$$S = \{NNN, NND, NDN, DNN, NDD, DND, DDN, DDD\},$$

where N denotes nondefective and D denotes defective. One is naturally concerned with the number of defectives that occur. Thus, each point in the sample space will be *assigned a numerical value* of 0, 1, 2, or 3. These values are, of course, random quantities *determined by the outcome of the experiment*. They may be viewed as values assumed by the *random variable* X, the number of defective items when three electronic components are tested.

Definition 1:

> A **random variable** is a function that associates a real number with each element in the sample space.

We shall use a capital letter, say X, to denote a random variable and its corresponding small letter, x in this case, for one of its values. In the electronic component testing illustration above, we notice that the random variable X assumes the value 2 for all elements in the subset

$$E = \{DDN, DND, NDD\}$$

of the sample space S. That is, each possible value of X represents an event that is a subset of the sample space for the given experiment.

From Chapter 3 of *Probability & Statistics for Engineers & Scientists*, Ninth Edition, Ronald E. Walpole, Raymond H. Myers, Sharon L. Myers, Keying Ye. Copyright © 2012 by Pearson Education, Inc. Published by Pearson Prentice Hall. All rights reserved.

Example 1: Two balls are drawn in succession without replacement from an urn containing 4 red balls and 3 black balls. The possible outcomes and the values y of the random variable Y, where Y is the number of red balls, are

Sample Space	y
RR	2
RB	1
BR	1
BB	0

Example 2: A stockroom clerk returns three safety helmets at random to three steel mill employees who had previously checked them. If Smith, Jones, and Brown, in that order, receive one of the three hats, list the sample points for the possible orders of returning the helmets, and find the value m of the random variable M that represents the number of correct matches.

Solution: If S, J, and B stand for Smith's, Jones's, and Brown's helmets, respectively, then the possible arrangements in which the helmets may be returned and the number of correct matches are

Sample Space	m
SJB	3
SBJ	1
BJS	1
JSB	1
JBS	0
BSJ	0

In each of the two preceding examples, the sample space contains a finite number of elements. On the other hand, when a die is thrown until a 5 occurs, we obtain a sample space with an unending sequence of elements,

$$S = \{F, NF, NNF, NNNF, \dots\},$$

where F and N represent, respectively, the occurrence and nonoccurrence of a 5. But even in this experiment, the number of elements can be equated to the number of whole numbers so that there is a first element, a second element, a third element, and so on, and in this sense can be counted.

There are cases where the random variable is categorical in nature. Variables, often called *dummy* variables, are used. A good illustration is the case in which the random variable is binary in nature, as shown in the following example.

Example 3: Consider the simple condition in which components are arriving from the production line and they are stipulated to be defective or not defective. Define the random variable X by

$$X = \begin{cases} 1, & \text{if the component is defective,} \\ 0, & \text{if the component is not defective.} \end{cases}$$

Clearly the assignment of 1 or 0 is arbitrary though quite convenient. This will become clear in later chapters. The random variable for which 0 and 1 are chosen to describe the two possible values is called a **Bernoulli random variable**.

Further illustrations of random variables are revealed in the following examples.

Example 4: Statisticians use **sampling plans** to either accept or reject batches or lots of material. Suppose one of these sampling plans involves sampling independently 10 items from a lot of 100 items in which 12 are defective.

Let X be the random variable defined as the number of items found defective in the sample of 10. In this case, the random variable takes on the values $0, 1, 2, \ldots, 9, 10$.

Example 5: Suppose a sampling plan involves sampling items from a process until a defective is observed. The evaluation of the process will depend on how many consecutive items are observed. In that regard, let X be a random variable defined by the number of items observed before a defective is found. With N a nondefective and D a defective, sample spaces are $S = \{D\}$ given $X = 1$, $S = \{ND\}$ given $X = 2$, $S = \{NND\}$ given $X = 3$, and so on.

Example 6: Interest centers around the proportion of people who respond to a certain mail order solicitation. Let X be that proportion. X is a random variable that takes on all values x for which $0 \leq x \leq 1$.

Example 7: Let X be the random variable defined by the waiting time, in hours, between successive speeders spotted by a radar unit. The random variable X takes on all values x for which $x \geq 0$.

Definition 2:

> If a sample space contains a finite number of possibilities or an unending sequence with as many elements as there are whole numbers, it is called a **discrete sample space**.

The outcomes of some statistical experiments may be neither finite nor countable. Such is the case, for example, when one conducts an investigation measuring the distances that a certain make of automobile will travel over a prescribed test course on 5 liters of gasoline. Assuming distance to be a variable measured to any degree of accuracy, then clearly we have an infinite number of possible distances in the sample space that cannot be equated to the number of whole numbers. Or, if one were to record the length of time for a chemical reaction to take place, once again the possible time intervals making up our sample space would be infinite in number and uncountable. We see now that all sample spaces need not be discrete.

Definition 3:

> If a sample space contains an infinite number of possibilities equal to the number of points on a line segment, it is called a **continuous sample space**.

A random variable is called a **discrete random variable** if its set of possible outcomes is countable. The random variables in Examples 1 to 5 are discrete random variables. But a random variable whose set of possible values is an entire interval of numbers is not discrete. When a random variable can take on values on a continuous scale, it is called a **continuous random variable**. Often the possible values of a continuous random variable are precisely the same values that are contained in the continuous sample space. Obviously, the random variables described in Examples 6 and 7 are continuous random variables.

In most practical problems, continuous random variables represent *measured* data, such as all possible heights, weights, temperatures, distance, or life periods, whereas discrete random variables represent *count* data, such as the number of defectives in a sample of k items or the number of highway fatalities per year in a given state. Note that the random variables Y and M of Examples 1 and 2 both represent count data, Y the number of red balls and M the number of correct hat matches.

2   Discrete Probability Distributions

A discrete random variable assumes each of its values with a certain probability. In the case of tossing a coin three times, the variable X, representing the number of heads, assumes the value 2 with probability 3/8, since 3 of the 8 equally likely sample points result in two heads and one tail. If one assumes equal weights for the simple events in Example 2, the probability that no employee gets back the right helmet, that is, the probability that M assumes the value 0, is 1/3. The possible values m of M and their probabilities are

m	0	1	3
$P(M = m)$	$\frac{1}{3}$	$\frac{1}{2}$	$\frac{1}{6}$

Note that the values of m exhaust all possible cases and hence the probabilities add to 1.

Frequently, it is convenient to represent all the probabilities of a random variable X by a formula. Such a formula would necessarily be a function of the numerical values x that we shall denote by $f(x)$, $g(x)$, $r(x)$, and so forth. Therefore, we write $f(x) = P(X = x)$; that is, $f(3) = P(X = 3)$. The set of ordered pairs $(x, f(x))$ is called the **probability function**, **probability mass function**, or **probability distribution** of the discrete random variable X.

Definition 4:

> The set of ordered pairs $(x, f(x))$ is a **probability function, probability mass function**, or **probability distribution** of the discrete random variable X if, for each possible outcome x,
>
> 1. $f(x) \geq 0$,
>
> 2. $\sum_x f(x) = 1$,
>
> 3. $P(X = x) = f(x)$.

Example 8: A shipment of 20 similar laptop computers to a retail outlet contains 3 that are defective. If a school makes a random purchase of 2 of these computers, find the probability distribution for the number of defectives.

Solution: Let X be a random variable whose values x are the possible numbers of defective computers purchased by the school. Then x can only take the numbers 0, 1, and

2. Now

$$f(0) = P(X = 0) = \frac{\binom{3}{0}\binom{17}{2}}{\binom{20}{2}} = \frac{68}{95}, \quad f(1) = P(X = 1) = \frac{\binom{3}{1}\binom{17}{1}}{\binom{20}{2}} = \frac{51}{190},$$

$$f(2) = P(X = 2) = \frac{\binom{3}{2}\binom{17}{0}}{\binom{20}{2}} = \frac{3}{190}.$$

Thus, the probability distribution of X is

x	0	1	2
$f(x)$	$\frac{68}{95}$	$\frac{51}{190}$	$\frac{3}{190}$

Example 9: If a car agency sells 50% of its inventory of a certain foreign car equipped with side airbags, find a formula for the probability distribution of the number of cars with side airbags among the next 4 cars sold by the agency.

Solution: Since the probability of selling an automobile with side airbags is 0.5, the $2^4 = 16$ points in the sample space are equally likely to occur. Therefore, the denominator for all probabilities, and also for our function, is 16. To obtain the number of ways of selling 3 cars with side airbags, we need to consider the number of ways of partitioning 4 outcomes into two cells, with 3 cars with side airbags assigned to one cell and the model without side airbags assigned to the other. This can be done in $\binom{4}{3} = 4$ ways. In general, the event of selling x models with side airbags and $4 - x$ models without side airbags can occur in $\binom{4}{x}$ ways, where x can be 0, 1, 2, 3, or 4. Thus, the probability distribution $f(x) = P(X = x)$ is

$$f(x) = \frac{1}{16}\binom{4}{x}, \quad \text{for } x = 0, 1, 2, 3, 4.$$

There are many problems where we may wish to compute the probability that the observed value of a random variable X will be less than or equal to some real number x. Writing $F(x) = P(X \leq x)$ for every real number x, we define $F(x)$ to be the **cumulative distribution function** of the random variable X.

Definition 5: | The **cumulative distribution function** $F(x)$ of a discrete random variable X with probability distribution $f(x)$ is

$$F(x) = P(X \leq x) = \sum_{t \leq x} f(t), \quad \text{for } -\infty < x < \infty.$$

For the random variable M, the number of correct matches in Example 2, we have

$$F(2) = P(M \leq 2) = f(0) + f(1) = \frac{1}{3} + \frac{1}{2} = \frac{5}{6}.$$

The cumulative distribution function of M is

$$F(m) = \begin{cases} 0, & \text{for } m < 0, \\ \frac{1}{3}, & \text{for } 0 \leq m < 1, \\ \frac{5}{6}, & \text{for } 1 \leq m < 3, \\ 1, & \text{for } m \geq 3. \end{cases}$$

One should pay particular notice to the fact that the cumulative distribution function is a monotone nondecreasing function defined not only for the values assumed by the given random variable but for all real numbers.

| Example 10: | Find the cumulative distribution function of the random variable X in Example 9. Using $F(x)$, verify that $f(2) = 3/8$. |

Solution: Direct calculations of the probability distribution of Example 9 give $f(0) = 1/16$, $f(1) = 1/4$, $f(2) = 3/8$, $f(3) = 1/4$, and $f(4) = 1/16$. Therefore,

$$F(0) = f(0) = \frac{1}{16},$$

$$F(1) = f(0) + f(1) = \frac{5}{16},$$

$$F(2) = f(0) + f(1) + f(2) = \frac{11}{16},$$

$$F(3) = f(0) + f(1) + f(2) + f(3) = \frac{15}{16},$$

$$F(4) = f(0) + f(1) + f(2) + f(3) + f(4) = 1.$$

Hence,

$$F(x) = \begin{cases} 0, & \text{for } x < 0, \\ \frac{1}{16}, & \text{for } 0 \leq x < 1, \\ \frac{5}{16}, & \text{for } 1 \leq x < 2, \\ \frac{11}{16}, & \text{for } 2 \leq x < 3, \\ \frac{15}{16}, & \text{for } 3 \leq x < 4, \\ 1 & \text{for } x \geq 4. \end{cases}$$

Now

$$f(2) = F(2) - F(1) = \frac{11}{16} - \frac{5}{16} = \frac{3}{8}.$$

It is often helpful to look at a probability distribution in graphic form. One might plot the points $(x, f(x))$ of Example 9 to obtain Figure 1. By joining the points to the x axis either with a dashed or with a solid line, we obtain a probability mass function plot. Figure 1 makes it easy to see what values of X are most likely to occur, and it also indicates a perfectly symmetric situation in this case.

Instead of plotting the points $(x, f(x))$, we more frequently construct rectangles, as in Figure 2. Here the rectangles are constructed so that their bases of equal width are centered at each value x and their heights are equal to the corresponding probabilities given by $f(x)$. The bases are constructed so as to leave no space between the rectangles. Figure 2 is called a **probability histogram**.

Since each base in Figure 2 has unit width, $P(X = x)$ is equal to the area of the rectangle centered at x. Even if the bases were not of unit width, we could adjust the heights of the rectangles to give areas that would still equal the probabilities of X assuming any of its values x. This concept of using areas to represent

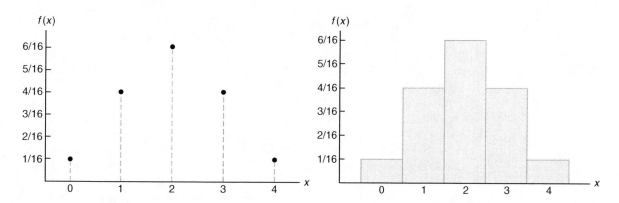

Figure 1: Probability mass function plot.   Figure 2: Probability histogram.

probabilities is necessary for our consideration of the probability distribution of a continuous random variable.

The graph of the cumulative distribution function of Example 9, which appears as a step function in Figure 3, is obtained by plotting the points $(x, F(x))$.

Certain probability distributions are applicable to more than one physical situation. The probability distribution of Example 9, for example, also applies to the random variable Y, where Y is the number of heads when a coin is tossed 4 times, or to the random variable W, where W is the number of red cards that occur when 4 cards are drawn at random from a deck in succession with each card replaced and the deck shuffled before the next drawing.

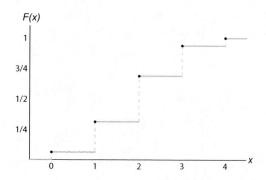

Figure 3: Discrete cumulative distribution function.

3   Continuous Probability Distributions

A continuous random variable has a probability of 0 of assuming *exactly* any of its values. Consequently, its probability distribution cannot be given in tabular form.

At first this may seem startling, but it becomes more plausible when we consider a particular example. Let us discuss a random variable whose values are the heights of all people over 21 years of age. Between any two values, say 163.5 and 164.5 centimeters, or even 163.99 and 164.01 centimeters, there are an infinite number of heights, one of which is 164 centimeters. The probability of selecting a person at random who is exactly 164 centimeters tall and not one of the infinitely large set of heights so close to 164 centimeters that you cannot humanly measure the difference is remote, and thus we assign a probability of 0 to the event. This is not the case, however, if we talk about the probability of selecting a person who is at least 163 centimeters but not more than 165 centimeters tall. Now we are dealing with an interval rather than a point value of our random variable.

We shall concern ourselves with computing probabilities for various intervals of continuous random variables such as $P(a < X < b)$, $P(W \geq c)$, and so forth. Note that when X is continuous,

$$P(a < X \leq b) = P(a < X < b) + P(X = b) = P(a < X < b).$$

That is, it does not matter whether we include an endpoint of the interval or not. This is not true, though, when X is discrete.

Although the probability distribution of a continuous random variable cannot be presented in tabular form, it can be stated as a formula. Such a formula would necessarily be a function of the numerical values of the continuous random variable X and as such will be represented by the functional notation $f(x)$. In dealing with continuous variables, $f(x)$ is usually called the **probability density function**, or simply the **density function**, of X. Since X is defined over a continuous sample space, it is possible for $f(x)$ to have a finite number of discontinuities. However, most density functions that have practical applications in the analysis of statistical data are continuous and their graphs may take any of several forms, some of which are shown in Figure 4. Because areas will be used to represent probabilities and probabilities are positive numerical values, the density function must lie entirely above the x axis.

(a) (b) (c) (d)

Figure 4: Typical density functions.

A probability density function is constructed so that the area under its curve bounded by the x axis is equal to 1 when computed over the range of X for which $f(x)$ is defined. Should this range of X be a finite interval, it is always possible to extend the interval to include the entire set of real numbers by defining $f(x)$ to be zero at all points in the extended portions of the interval. In Figure 5, the probability that X assumes a value between a and b is equal to the shaded area under the density function between the ordinates at $x = a$ and $x = b$, and from integral calculus is given by

$$P(a < X < b) = \int_a^b f(x)\, dx.$$

Figure 5: $P(a < X < b)$.

Definition 6:	The function $f(x)$ is a **probability density function** (pdf) for the continuous random variable X, defined over the set of real numbers, if 1. $f(x) \geq 0$, for all $x \in R$. 2. $\int_{-\infty}^{\infty} f(x)\, dx = 1$. 3. $P(a < X < b) = \int_a^b f(x)\, dx$.

Example 11: Suppose that the error in the reaction temperature, in °C, for a controlled laboratory experiment is a continuous random variable X having the probability density function

$$f(x) = \begin{cases} \frac{x^2}{3}, & -1 < x < 2, \\ 0, & \text{elsewhere.} \end{cases}$$

(a) Verify that $f(x)$ is a density function.

(b) Find $P(0 < X \leq 1)$.

Solution: We use Definition 6.

(a) Obviously, $f(x) \geq 0$. To verify condition 2 in Definition 6, we have

$$\int_{-\infty}^{\infty} f(x)\, dx = \int_{-1}^{2} \frac{x^2}{3}\, dx = \frac{x^3}{9}\Big|_{-1}^{2} = \frac{8}{9} + \frac{1}{9} = 1.$$

(b) Using formula 3 in Definition 6, we obtain

$$P(0 < X \le 1) = \int_0^1 \frac{x^2}{3}\,dx = \frac{x^3}{9}\Big|_0^1 = \frac{1}{9}.$$

Definition 7:

> The **cumulative distribution function** $F(x)$ of a continuous random variable X with density function $f(x)$ is
>
> $$F(x) = P(X \le x) = \int_{-\infty}^x f(t)\,dt, \quad \text{for } -\infty < x < \infty.$$

As an immediate consequence of Definition 7, one can write the two results

$$P(a < X < b) = F(b) - F(a) \text{ and } f(x) = \frac{dF(x)}{dx},$$

if the derivative exists.

Example 12: For the density function of Example 11, find $F(x)$, and use it to evaluate $P(0 < X \le 1)$.

Solution: For $-1 < x < 2$,

$$F(x) = \int_{-\infty}^x f(t)\,dt = \int_{-1}^x \frac{t^2}{3}\,dt = \frac{t^3}{9}\Big|_{-1}^x = \frac{x^3 + 1}{9}.$$

Therefore,

$$F(x) = \begin{cases} 0, & x < -1, \\ \frac{x^3+1}{9}, & -1 \le x < 2, \\ 1, & x \ge 2. \end{cases}$$

The cumulative distribution function $F(x)$ is expressed in Figure 6. Now

$$P(0 < X \le 1) = F(1) - F(0) = \frac{2}{9} - \frac{1}{9} = \frac{1}{9},$$

which agrees with the result obtained by using the density function in Example 11.

Example 13: The Department of Energy (DOE) puts projects out on bid and generally estimates what a reasonable bid should be. Call the estimate b. The DOE has determined that the density function of the winning (low) bid is

$$f(y) = \begin{cases} \frac{5}{8b}, & \frac{2}{5}b \le y \le 2b, \\ 0, & \text{elsewhere.} \end{cases}$$

Find $F(y)$ and use it to determine the probability that the winning bid is less than the DOE's preliminary estimate b.

Solution: For $2b/5 \le y \le 2b$,

$$F(y) = \int_{2b/5}^y \frac{5}{8b}\,dy = \frac{5t}{8b}\Big|_{2b/5}^y = \frac{5y}{8b} - \frac{1}{4}.$$

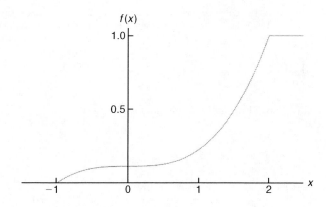

Figure 6: Continuous cumulative distribution function.

Thus,

$$F(y) = \begin{cases} 0, & y < \frac{2}{5}b, \\ \frac{5y}{8b} - \frac{1}{4}, & \frac{2}{5}b \le y < 2b, \\ 1, & y \ge 2b. \end{cases}$$

To determine the probability that the winning bid is less than the preliminary bid estimate b, we have

$$P(Y \le b) = F(b) = \frac{5}{8} - \frac{1}{4} = \frac{3}{8}.$$

Exercises

1   Classify the following random variables as discrete or continuous:

X: the number of automobile accidents per year in Virginia.

Y: the length of time to play 18 holes of golf.

M: the amount of milk produced yearly by a particular cow.

N: the number of eggs laid each month by a hen.

P: the number of building permits issued each month in a certain city.

Q: the weight of grain produced per acre.

2   An overseas shipment of 5 foreign automobiles contains 2 that have slight paint blemishes. If an agency receives 3 of these automobiles at random, list the elements of the sample space S, using the letters B and N for blemished and nonblemished, respectively; then to each sample point assign a value x of the random variable X representing the number of automobiles with paint blemishes purchased by the agency.

3   Let W be a random variable giving the number of heads minus the number of tails in three tosses of a coin. List the elements of the sample space S for the three tosses of the coin and to each sample point assign a value w of W.

4   A coin is flipped until 3 heads in succession occur. List only those elements of the sample space that require 6 or less tosses. Is this a discrete sample space? Explain.

5   Determine the value c so that each of the following functions can serve as a probability distribution of the discrete random variable X:

(a) $f(x) = c(x^2 + 4)$, for $x = 0, 1, 2, 3$;

(b) $f(x) = c\binom{2}{x}\binom{3}{3-x}$, for $x = 0, 1, 2$.

6 The shelf life, in days, for bottles of a certain prescribed medicine is a random variable having the density function

$$f(x) = \begin{cases} \frac{20,000}{(x+100)^3}, & x > 0, \\ 0, & \text{elsewhere.} \end{cases}$$

Find the probability that a bottle of this medicine will have a shell life of

(a) at least 200 days;

(b) anywhere from 80 to 120 days.

7 The total number of hours, measured in units of 100 hours, that a family runs a vacuum cleaner over a period of one year is a continuous random variable X that has the density function

$$f(x) = \begin{cases} x, & 0 < x < 1, \\ 2 - x, & 1 \le x < 2, \\ 0, & \text{elsewhere.} \end{cases}$$

Find the probability that over a period of one year, a family runs their vacuum cleaner

(a) less than 120 hours;

(b) between 50 and 100 hours.

8 Find the probability distribution of the random variable W in Exercise 3, assuming that the coin is biased so that a head is twice as likely to occur as a tail.

9 The proportion of people who respond to a certain mail-order solicitation is a continuous random variable X that has the density function

$$f(x) = \begin{cases} \frac{2(x+2)}{5}, & 0 < x < 1, \\ 0, & \text{elsewhere.} \end{cases}$$

(a) Show that $P(0 < X < 1) = 1$.

(b) Find the probability that more than 1/4 but fewer than 1/2 of the people contacted will respond to this type of solicitation.

10 Find a formula for the probability distribution of the random variable X representing the outcome when a single die is rolled once.

11 A shipment of 7 television sets contains 2 defective sets. A hotel makes a random purchase of 3 of the sets. If x is the number of defective sets purchased by the hotel, find the probability distribution of X. Express the results graphically as a probability histogram.

12 An investment firm offers its customers municipal bonds that mature after varying numbers of years. Given that the cumulative distribution function of T, the number of years to maturity for a randomly selected bond, is

$$F(t) = \begin{cases} 0, & t < 1, \\ \frac{1}{4}, & 1 \le t < 3, \\ \frac{1}{2}, & 3 \le t < 5, \\ \frac{3}{4}, & 5 \le t < 7, \\ 1, & t \ge 7, \end{cases}$$

find

(a) $P(T = 5)$;

(b) $P(T > 3)$;

(c) $P(1.4 < T < 6)$;

(d) $P(T \le 5 \mid T \ge 2)$.

13 The probability distribution of X, the number of imperfections per 10 meters of a synthetic fabric in continuous rolls of uniform width, is given by

x	0	1	2	3	4
$f(x)$	0.41	0.37	0.16	0.05	0.01

Construct the cumulative distribution function of X.

14 The waiting time, in hours, between successive speeders spotted by a radar unit is a continuous random variable with cumulative distribution function

$$F(x) = \begin{cases} 0, & x < 0, \\ 1 - e^{-8x}, & x \ge 0. \end{cases}$$

Find the probability of waiting less than 12 minutes between successive speeders

(a) using the cumulative distribution function of X;

(b) using the probability density function of X.

15 Find the cumulative distribution function of the random variable X representing the number of defectives in Exercise 11. Then using $F(x)$, find

(a) $P(X = 1)$;

(b) $P(0 < X \le 2)$.

16 Construct a graph of the cumulative distribution function of Exercise 15.

17 A continuous random variable X that can assume values between $x = 1$ and $x = 3$ has a density function given by $f(x) = 1/2$.

(a) Show that the area under the curve is equal to 1.

(b) Find $P(2 < X < 2.5)$.

(c) Find $P(X \le 1.6)$.

18 A continuous random variable X that can assume values between $x = 2$ and $x = 5$ has a density function given by $f(x) = 2(1 + x)/27$. Find
(a) $P(X < 4)$;
(b) $P(3 \leq X < 4)$.

19 For the density function of Exercise 17, find $F(x)$. Use it to evaluate $P(2 < X < 2.5)$.

20 For the density function of Exercise 18, find $F(x)$, and use it to evaluate $P(3 \leq X < 4)$.

21 Consider the density function

$$f(x) = \begin{cases} k\sqrt{x}, & 0 < x < 1, \\ 0, & \text{elsewhere.} \end{cases}$$

(a) Evaluate k.
(b) Find $F(x)$ and use it to evaluate

$$P(0.3 < X < 0.6).$$

22 Three cards are drawn in succession from a deck without replacement. Find the probability distribution for the number of spades.

23 Find the cumulative distribution function of the random variable W in Exercise 8. Using $F(w)$, find
(a) $P(W > 0)$;
(b) $P(-1 \leq W < 3)$.

24 Find the probability distribution for the number of jazz CDs when 4 CDs are selected at random from a collection consisting of 5 jazz CDs, 2 classical CDs, and 3 rock CDs. Express your results by means of a formula.

25 From a box containing 4 dimes and 2 nickels, 3 coins are selected at random without replacement. Find the probability distribution for the total T of the 3 coins. Express the probability distribution graphically as a probability histogram.

26 From a box containing 4 black balls and 2 green balls, 3 balls are drawn in succession, each ball being replaced in the box before the next draw is made. Find the probability distribution for the number of green balls.

27 The time to failure in hours of an important piece of electronic equipment used in a manufactured DVD player has the density function

$$f(x) = \begin{cases} \frac{1}{2000} \exp(-x/2000), & x \geq 0, \\ 0, & x < 0. \end{cases}$$

(a) Find $F(x)$.
(b) Determine the probability that the component (and thus the DVD player) lasts more than 1000 hours before the component needs to be replaced.
(c) Determine the probability that the component fails before 2000 hours.

28 A cereal manufacturer is aware that the weight of the product in the box varies slightly from box to box. In fact, considerable historical data have allowed the determination of the density function that describes the probability structure for the weight (in ounces). Letting X be the random variable weight, in ounces, the density function can be described as

$$f(x) = \begin{cases} \frac{2}{5}, & 23.75 \leq x \leq 26.25, \\ 0, & \text{elsewhere.} \end{cases}$$

(a) Verify that this is a valid density function.
(b) Determine the probability that the weight is smaller than 24 ounces.
(c) The company desires that the weight exceeding 26 ounces be an extremely rare occurrence. What is the probability that this rare occurrence does actually occur?

29 An important factor in solid missile fuel is the particle size distribution. Significant problems occur if the particle sizes are too large. From production data in the past, it has been determined that the particle size (in micrometers) distribution is characterized by

$$f(x) = \begin{cases} 3x^{-4}, & x > 1, \\ 0, & \text{elsewhere.} \end{cases}$$

(a) Verify that this is a valid density function.
(b) Evaluate $F(x)$.
(c) What is the probability that a random particle from the manufactured fuel exceeds 4 micrometers?

30 Measurements of scientific systems are always subject to variation, some more than others. There are many structures for measurement error, and statisticians spend a great deal of time modeling these errors. Suppose the measurement error X of a certain physical quantity is decided by the density function

$$f(x) = \begin{cases} k(3 - x^2), & -1 \leq x \leq 1, \\ 0, & \text{elsewhere.} \end{cases}$$

(a) Determine k that renders $f(x)$ a valid density function.
(b) Find the probability that a random error in measurement is less than $1/2$.
(c) For this particular measurement, it is undesirable if the *magnitude* of the error (i.e., $|x|$) exceeds 0.8. What is the probability that this occurs?

31 Based on extensive testing, it is determined by the manufacturer of a washing machine that the time Y (in years) before a major repair is required is characterized by the probability density function

$$f(y) = \begin{cases} \frac{1}{4}e^{-y/4}, & y \geq 0, \\ 0, & \text{elsewhere.} \end{cases}$$

(a) Critics would certainly consider the product a bargain if it is unlikely to require a major repair before the sixth year. Comment on this by determining $P(Y > 6)$.

(b) What is the probability that a major repair occurs in the first year?

32 The proportion of the budget for a certain type of industrial company that is allotted to environmental and pollution control is coming under scrutiny. A data collection project determines that the distribution of these proportions is given by

$$f(y) = \begin{cases} 5(1-y)^4, & 0 \leq y \leq 1, \\ 0, & \text{elsewhere.} \end{cases}$$

(a) Verify that the above is a valid density function.

(b) What is the probability that a company chosen at random expends less than 10% of its budget on environmental and pollution controls?

(c) What is the probability that a company selected at random spends more than 50% of its budget on environmental and pollution controls?

33 Suppose a certain type of small data processing firm is so specialized that some have difficulty making a profit in their first year of operation. The probability density function that characterizes the proportion Y that make a profit is given by

$$f(y) = \begin{cases} ky^4(1-y)^3, & 0 \leq y \leq 1, \\ 0, & \text{elsewhere.} \end{cases}$$

(a) What is the value of k that renders the above a valid density function?

(b) Find the probability that at most 50% of the firms make a profit in the first year.

(c) Find the probability that at least 80% of the firms make a profit in the first year.

34 Magnetron tubes are produced on an automated assembly line. A sampling plan is used periodically to assess quality of the lengths of the tubes. This measurement is subject to uncertainty. It is thought that the probability that a random tube meets length specification is 0.99. A sampling plan is used in which the lengths of 5 random tubes are measured.

(a) Show that the probability function of Y, the number out of 5 that meet length specification, is given by the following discrete probability function:

$$f(y) = \frac{5!}{y!(5-y)!}(0.99)^y(0.01)^{5-y},$$

for $y = 0, 1, 2, 3, 4, 5$.

(b) Suppose random selections are made off the line and 3 are outside specifications. Use $f(y)$ above either to support or to refute the conjecture that the probability is 0.99 that a single tube meets specifications.

35 Suppose it is known from large amounts of historical data that X, the number of cars that arrive at a specific intersection during a 20-second time period, is characterized by the following discrete probability function:

$$f(x) = e^{-6}\frac{6^x}{x!}, \text{ for } x = 0, 1, 2, \ldots.$$

(a) Find the probability that in a specific 20-second time period, more than 8 cars arrive at the intersection.

(b) Find the probability that only 2 cars arrive.

36 On a laboratory assignment, if the equipment is working, the density function of the observed outcome, X, is

$$f(x) = \begin{cases} 2(1-x), & 0 < x < 1, \\ 0, & \text{otherwise.} \end{cases}$$

(a) Calculate $P(X \leq 1/3)$.

(b) What is the probability that X will exceed 0.5?

(c) Given that $X \geq 0.5$, what is the probability that X will be less than 0.75?

4 Joint Probability Distributions

Our study of random variables and their probability distributions in the preceding sections is restricted to one-dimensional sample spaces, in that we recorded outcomes of an experiment as values assumed by a single random variable. There will be situations, however, where we may find it desirable to record the simultaneous outcomes of several random variables. For example, we might measure the amount of precipitate P and volume V of gas released from a controlled chemical experiment, giving rise to a two-dimensional sample space consisting of the outcomes (p, v), or we might be interested in the hardness H and tensile strength T of cold-drawn copper, resulting in the outcomes (h, t). In a study to determine the likelihood of success in college based on high school data, we might use a three-dimensional sample space and record for each individual his or her aptitude test score, high school class rank, and grade-point average at the end of freshman year in college.

If X and Y are two discrete random variables, the probability distribution for their simultaneous occurrence can be represented by a function with values $f(x, y)$ for any pair of values (x, y) within the range of the random variables X and Y. It is customary to refer to this function as the **joint probability distribution** of X and Y.

Hence, in the discrete case,

$$f(x, y) = P(X = x, Y = y);$$

that is, the values $f(x, y)$ give the probability that outcomes x and y occur at the same time. For example, if an 18-wheeler is to have its tires serviced and X represents the number of miles these tires have been driven and Y represents the number of tires that need to be replaced, then $f(30000, 5)$ is the probability that the tires are used over 30,000 miles and the truck needs 5 new tires.

Definition 8:

> The function $f(x, y)$ is a **joint probability distribution** or **probability mass function** of the discrete random variables X and Y if
>
> 1. $f(x, y) \geq 0$ for all (x, y),
>
> 2. $\sum_x \sum_y f(x, y) = 1$,
>
> 3. $P(X = x, Y = y) = f(x, y)$.
>
> For any region A in the xy plane, $P[(X, Y) \in A] = \sum\sum_A f(x, y)$.

Example 14:

Two ballpoint pens are selected at random from a box that contains 3 blue pens, 2 red pens, and 3 green pens. If X is the number of blue pens selected and Y is the number of red pens selected, find

(a) the joint probability function $f(x, y)$,

(b) $P[(X, Y) \in A]$, where A is the region $\{(x, y) | x + y \leq 1\}$.

Solution: The possible pairs of values (x, y) are $(0, 0)$, $(0, 1)$, $(1, 0)$, $(1, 1)$, $(0, 2)$, and $(2, 0)$.

(a) Now, $f(0, 1)$, for example, represents the probability that a red and a green pens are selected. The total number of equally likely ways of selecting any 2 pens from the 8 is $\binom{8}{2} = 28$. The number of ways of selecting 1 red from 2 red pens and 1 green from 3 green pens is $\binom{2}{1}\binom{3}{1} = 6$. Hence, $f(0, 1) = 6/28 = 3/14$. Similar calculations yield the probabilities for the other cases, which are presented in Table 1. Note that the probabilities sum to 1.

It will become clear that the joint probability distribution of Table 1 can be represented by the formula

$$f(x,y) = \frac{\binom{3}{x}\binom{2}{y}\binom{3}{2-x-y}}{\binom{8}{2}},$$

for $x = 0$, 1, 2; $y = 0$, 1, 2; and $0 \leq x + y \leq 2$.

(b) The probability that (X, Y) fall in the region A is

$$P[(X,Y) \in A] = P(X + Y \leq 1) = f(0,0) + f(0,1) + f(1,0)$$

$$= \frac{3}{28} + \frac{3}{14} + \frac{9}{28} = \frac{9}{14}.$$

Table 1: Joint Probability Distribution for Example 14

	$f(x,y)$	x 0	1	2	Row Totals
	0	$\frac{3}{28}$	$\frac{9}{28}$	$\frac{3}{28}$	$\frac{15}{28}$
y	1	$\frac{3}{14}$	$\frac{3}{14}$	0	$\frac{3}{7}$
	2	$\frac{1}{28}$	0	0	$\frac{1}{28}$
	Column Totals	$\frac{5}{14}$	$\frac{15}{28}$	$\frac{3}{28}$	1

When X and Y are continuous random variables, the **joint density function** $f(x,y)$ is a surface lying above the xy plane, and $P[(X,Y) \in A]$, where A is any region in the xy plane, is equal to the volume of the right cylinder bounded by the base A and the surface.

Definition 9:

> The function $f(x,y)$ is a **joint density function** of the continuous random variables X and Y if
>
> 1. $f(x,y) \geq 0$, for all (x,y),
>
> 2. $\int_{-\infty}^{\infty} \int_{-\infty}^{\infty} f(x,y)\, dx\, dy = 1$,
>
> 3. $P[(X,Y) \in A] = \int \int_A f(x,y)\, dx\, dy$, for any region A in the xy plane.

Example 15:

A privately owned business operates both a drive-in facility and a walk-in facility. On a randomly selected day, let X and Y, respectively, be the proportions of the time that the drive-in and the walk-in facilities are in use, and suppose that the joint density function of these random variables is

$$f(x,y) = \begin{cases} \frac{2}{5}(2x + 3y), & 0 \leq x \leq 1, 0 \leq y \leq 1, \\ 0, & \text{elsewhere.} \end{cases}$$

(a) Verify condition 2 of Definition 9.

(b) Find $P[(X,Y) \in A]$, where $A = \{(x,y) \mid 0 < x < \frac{1}{2}, \frac{1}{4} < y < \frac{1}{2}\}$.

Solution: (a) The integration of $f(x,y)$ over the whole region is

$$\int_{-\infty}^{\infty}\int_{-\infty}^{\infty} f(x,y)\,dx\,dy = \int_0^1\int_0^1 \frac{2}{5}(2x+3y)\,dx\,dy$$

$$= \int_0^1 \left(\frac{2x^2}{5}+\frac{6xy}{5}\right)\Bigg|_{x=0}^{x=1} dy$$

$$= \int_0^1 \left(\frac{2}{5}+\frac{6y}{5}\right)dy = \left(\frac{2y}{5}+\frac{3y^2}{5}\right)\Bigg|_0^1 = \frac{2}{5}+\frac{3}{5}=1.$$

(b) To calculate the probability, we use

$$P[(X,Y)\in A] = P\left(0<X<\frac{1}{2},\frac{1}{4}<Y<\frac{1}{2}\right)$$

$$= \int_{1/4}^{1/2}\int_0^{1/2}\frac{2}{5}(2x+3y)\,dx\,dy$$

$$= \int_{1/4}^{1/2}\left(\frac{2x^2}{5}+\frac{6xy}{5}\right)\Bigg|_{x=0}^{x=1/2} dy = \int_{1/4}^{1/2}\left(\frac{1}{10}+\frac{3y}{5}\right)dy$$

$$= \left(\frac{y}{10}+\frac{3y^2}{10}\right)\Bigg|_{1/4}^{1/2}$$

$$= \frac{1}{10}\left[\left(\frac{1}{2}+\frac{3}{4}\right)-\left(\frac{1}{4}+\frac{3}{16}\right)\right] = \frac{13}{160}.$$

Given the joint probability distribution $f(x,y)$ of the discrete random variables X and Y, the probability distribution $g(x)$ of X alone is obtained by summing $f(x,y)$ over the values of Y. Similarly, the probability distribution $h(y)$ of Y alone is obtained by summing $f(x,y)$ over the values of X. We define $g(x)$ and $h(y)$ to be the **marginal distributions** of X and Y, respectively. When X and Y are continuous random variables, summations are replaced by integrals. We can now make the following general definition.

Definition 10:

The **marginal distributions** of X alone and of Y alone are

$$g(x)=\sum_y f(x,y) \quad\text{and}\quad h(y)=\sum_x f(x,y)$$

for the discrete case, and

$$g(x)=\int_{-\infty}^{\infty} f(x,y)\,dy \quad\text{and}\quad h(y)=\int_{-\infty}^{\infty} f(x,y)\,dx$$

for the continuous case.

The term *marginal* is used here because, in the discrete case, the values of $g(x)$ and $h(y)$ are just the marginal totals of the respective columns and rows when the values of $f(x,y)$ are displayed in a rectangular table.

Example 16: Show that the column and row totals of Table 1 give the marginal distribution of X alone and of Y alone.

Solution: For the random variable X, we see that

$$g(0) = f(0,0) + f(0,1) + f(0,2) = \frac{3}{28} + \frac{3}{14} + \frac{1}{28} = \frac{5}{14},$$
$$g(1) = f(1,0) + f(1,1) + f(1,2) = \frac{9}{28} + \frac{3}{14} + 0 = \frac{15}{28},$$

and

$$g(2) = f(2,0) + f(2,1) + f(2,2) = \frac{3}{28} + 0 + 0 = \frac{3}{28},$$

which are just the column totals of Table 1. In a similar manner we could show that the values of $h(y)$ are given by the row totals. In tabular form, these marginal distributions may be written as follows:

x	0	1	2
$g(x)$	$\frac{5}{14}$	$\frac{15}{28}$	$\frac{3}{28}$

y	0	1	2
$h(y)$	$\frac{15}{28}$	$\frac{3}{7}$	$\frac{1}{28}$

Example 17: Find $g(x)$ and $h(y)$ for the joint density function of Example 15.

Solution: By definition,

$$g(x) = \int_{-\infty}^{\infty} f(x,y)\,dy = \int_0^1 \frac{2}{5}(2x+3y)\,dy = \left(\frac{4xy}{5} + \frac{6y^2}{10}\right)\Big|_{y=0}^{y=1} = \frac{4x+3}{5},$$

for $0 \le x \le 1$, and $g(x) = 0$ elsewhere. Similarly,

$$h(y) = \int_{-\infty}^{\infty} f(x,y)\,dx = \int_0^1 \frac{2}{5}(2x+3y)\,dx = \frac{2(1+3y)}{5},$$

for $0 \le y \le 1$, and $h(y) = 0$ elsewhere.

The fact that the marginal distributions $g(x)$ and $h(y)$ are indeed the probability distributions of the individual variables X and Y alone can be verified by showing that the conditions of Definition 4 or Definition 6 are satisfied. For example, in the continuous case

$$\int_{-\infty}^{\infty} g(x)\,dx = \int_{-\infty}^{\infty}\int_{-\infty}^{\infty} f(x,y)\,dy\,dx = 1,$$

and

$$P(a < X < b) = P(a < X < b, -\infty < Y < \infty)$$
$$= \int_a^b \int_{-\infty}^{\infty} f(x,y)\,dy\,dx = \int_a^b g(x)\,dx.$$

In Section 1, we stated that the value x of the random variable X represents an event that is a subset of the sample space. If we use the definition of conditional probability,

$$P(B|A) = \frac{P(A \cap B)}{P(A)}, \text{ provided } P(A) > 0,$$

where A and B are now the events defined by $X = x$ and $Y = y$, respectively, then

$$P(Y = y \mid X = x) = \frac{P(X = x, Y = y)}{P(X = x)} = \frac{f(x,y)}{g(x)}, \text{ provided } g(x) > 0,$$

where X and Y are discrete random variables.

It is not difficult to show that the function $f(x,y)/g(x)$, which is strictly a function of y with x fixed, satisfies all the conditions of a probability distribution. This is also true when $f(x,y)$ and $g(x)$ are the joint density and marginal distribution, respectively, of continuous random variables. As a result, it is extremely important that we make use of the special type of distribution of the form $f(x,y)/g(x)$ in order to be able to effectively compute conditional probabilities. This type of distribution is called a **conditional probability distribution**; the formal definition follows.

Definition 11:

Let X and Y be two random variables, discrete or continuous. The **conditional distribution** of the random variable Y given that $X = x$ is

$$f(y|x) = \frac{f(x,y)}{g(x)}, \text{ provided } g(x) > 0.$$

Similarly, the conditional distribution of X given that $Y = y$ is

$$f(x|y) = \frac{f(x,y)}{h(y)}, \text{ provided } h(y) > 0.$$

If we wish to find the probability that the discrete random variable X falls between a and b when it is known that the discrete variable $Y = y$, we evaluate

$$P(a < X < b \mid Y = y) = \sum_{a<x<b} f(x|y),$$

where the summation extends over all values of X between a and b. When X and Y are continuous, we evaluate

$$P(a < X < b \mid Y = y) = \int_a^b f(x|y) \, dx.$$

Example 18: Referring to Example 14, find the conditional distribution of X, given that $Y = 1$, and use it to determine $P(X = 0 \mid Y = 1)$.

Solution: We need to find $f(x|y)$, where $y = 1$. First, we find that

$$h(1) = \sum_{x=0}^2 f(x,1) = \frac{3}{14} + \frac{3}{14} + 0 = \frac{3}{7}.$$

Now

$$f(x|1) = \frac{f(x,1)}{h(1)} = \left(\frac{7}{3}\right) f(x,1), \quad x = 0, 1, 2.$$

Therefore,

$$f(0|1) = \left(\frac{7}{3}\right) f(0,1) = \left(\frac{7}{3}\right)\left(\frac{3}{14}\right) = \frac{1}{2}, \ f(1|1) = \left(\frac{7}{3}\right) f(1,1) = \left(\frac{7}{3}\right)\left(\frac{3}{14}\right) = \frac{1}{2},$$

$$f(2|1) = \left(\frac{7}{3}\right) f(2,1) = \left(\frac{7}{3}\right)(0) = 0,$$

and the conditional distribution of X, given that $Y = 1$, is

x	0	1	2
$f(x|1)$	$\frac{1}{2}$	$\frac{1}{2}$	0

Finally,

$$P(X = 0 \mid Y = 1) = f(0|1) = \frac{1}{2}.$$

Therefore, if it is known that 1 of the 2 pen refills selected is red, we have a probability equal to 1/2 that the other refill is not blue.

Example 19: The joint density for the random variables (X, Y), where X is the unit temperature change and Y is the proportion of spectrum shift that a certain atomic particle produces, is

$$f(x,y) = \begin{cases} 10xy^2, & 0 < x < y < 1, \\ 0, & \text{elsewhere.} \end{cases}$$

(a) Find the marginal densities $g(x)$, $h(y)$, and the conditional density $f(y|x)$.

(b) Find the probability that the spectrum shifts more than half of the total observations, given that the temperature is increased by 0.25 unit.

Solution: (a) By definition,

$$g(x) = \int_{-\infty}^{\infty} f(x,y) \, dy = \int_{x}^{1} 10xy^2 \, dy$$

$$= \frac{10}{3}xy^3 \Big|_{y=x}^{y=1} = \frac{10}{3}x(1-x^3), \ 0 < x < 1,$$

$$h(y) = \int_{-\infty}^{\infty} f(x,y) \, dx = \int_{0}^{y} 10xy^2 \, dx = 5x^2y^2 \big|_{x=0}^{x=y} = 5y^4, \ 0 < y < 1.$$

Now

$$f(y|x) = \frac{f(x,y)}{g(x)} = \frac{10xy^2}{\frac{10}{3}x(1-x^3)} = \frac{3y^2}{1-x^3}, \ 0 < x < y < 1.$$

(b) Therefore,

$$P\left(Y > \frac{1}{2} \ \Big| \ X = 0.25\right) = \int_{1/2}^{1} f(y \mid x = 0.25) \, dy = \int_{1/2}^{1} \frac{3y^2}{1-0.25^3} \, dy = \frac{8}{9}.$$

Example 20: Given the joint density function

$$f(x,y) = \begin{cases} \frac{x(1+3y^2)}{4}, & 0 < x < 2, \ 0 < y < 1, \\ 0, & \text{elsewhere,} \end{cases}$$

find $g(x)$, $h(y)$, $f(x|y)$, and evaluate $P(\frac{1}{4} < X < \frac{1}{2} \mid Y = \frac{1}{3})$.

Solution: By definition of the marginal density, for $0 < x < 2$,

$$g(x) = \int_{-\infty}^{\infty} f(x,y) \, dy = \int_{0}^{1} \frac{x(1+3y^2)}{4} \, dy$$

$$= \left(\frac{xy}{4} + \frac{xy^3}{4} \right) \Big|_{y=0}^{y=1} = \frac{x}{2},$$

and for $0 < y < 1$,

$$h(y) = \int_{-\infty}^{\infty} f(x,y) \, dx = \int_{0}^{2} \frac{x(1+3y^2)}{4} \, dx$$

$$= \left(\frac{x^2}{8} + \frac{3x^2 y^2}{8} \right) \Big|_{x=0}^{x=2} = \frac{1+3y^2}{2}.$$

Therefore, using the conditional density definition, for $0 < x < 2$,

$$f(x|y) = \frac{f(x,y)}{h(y)} = \frac{x(1+3y^2)/4}{(1+3y^2)/2} = \frac{x}{2},$$

and

$$P\left(\frac{1}{4} < X < \frac{1}{2} \;\middle|\; Y = \frac{1}{3} \right) = \int_{1/4}^{1/2} \frac{x}{2} \, dx = \frac{3}{64}.$$

Statistical Independence

If $f(x|y)$ does not depend on y, as is the case for Example 20, then $f(x|y) = g(x)$ and $f(x,y) = g(x)h(y)$. The proof follows by substituting

$$f(x,y) = f(x|y)h(y)$$

into the marginal distribution of X. That is,

$$g(x) = \int_{-\infty}^{\infty} f(x,y) \, dy = \int_{-\infty}^{\infty} f(x|y)h(y) \, dy.$$

If $f(x|y)$ does not depend on y, we may write

$$g(x) = f(x|y) \int_{-\infty}^{\infty} h(y) \, dy.$$

Now

$$\int_{-\infty}^{\infty} h(y) \, dy = 1,$$

since $h(y)$ is the probability density function of Y. Therefore,

$$g(x) = f(x|y) \quad \text{and then} \quad f(x,y) = g(x)h(y).$$

It should make sense to the reader that if $f(x|y)$ does not depend on y, then of course the outcome of the random variable Y has no impact on the outcome of the random variable X. In other words, we say that X and Y are independent random variables. We now offer the following formal definition of statistical independence.

Definition 12:

Let X and Y be two random variables, discrete or continuous, with joint probability distribution $f(x, y)$ and marginal distributions $g(x)$ and $h(y)$, respectively. The random variables X and Y are said to be **statistically independent** if and only if

$$f(x, y) = g(x)h(y)$$

for all (x, y) within their range.

The continuous random variables of Example 20 are statistically independent, since the product of the two marginal distributions gives the joint density function. This is obviously not the case, however, for the continuous variables of Example 19. Checking for statistical independence of discrete random variables requires a more thorough investigation, since it is possible to have the product of the marginal distributions equal to the joint probability distribution for some but not all combinations of (x, y). If you can find any point (x, y) for which $f(x, y)$ is defined such that $f(x, y) \neq g(x)h(y)$, the discrete variables X and Y are not statistically independent.

Example 21: Show that the random variables of Example 14 are not statistically independent.

Proof: Let us consider the point $(0, 1)$. From Table 1 we find the three probabilities $f(0, 1)$, $g(0)$, and $h(1)$ to be

$$f(0, 1) = \frac{3}{14},$$

$$g(0) = \sum_{y=0}^{2} f(0, y) = \frac{3}{28} + \frac{3}{14} + \frac{1}{28} = \frac{5}{14},$$

$$h(1) = \sum_{x=0}^{2} f(x, 1) = \frac{3}{14} + \frac{3}{14} + 0 = \frac{3}{7}.$$

Clearly,

$$f(0, 1) \neq g(0)h(1),$$

and therefore X and Y are not statistically independent.

All the preceding definitions concerning two random variables can be generalized to the case of n random variables. Let $f(x_1, x_2, \ldots, x_n)$ be the joint probability function of the random variables $X_1, X_2, \ldots, X_n$. The marginal distribution of X_1, for example, is

$$g(x_1) = \sum_{x_2} \cdots \sum_{x_n} f(x_1, x_2, \ldots, x_n)$$

for the discrete case, and

$$g(x_1) = \int_{-\infty}^{\infty} \cdots \int_{-\infty}^{\infty} f(x_1, x_2, \ldots, x_n)\, dx_2\, dx_3 \cdots dx_n$$

for the continuous case. We can now obtain **joint marginal distributions** such as $g(x_1, x_2)$, where

$$g(x_1, x_2) = \begin{cases} \sum_{x_3} \cdots \sum_{x_n} f(x_1, x_2, \ldots, x_n) & \text{(discrete case)}, \\ \int_{-\infty}^{\infty} \cdots \int_{-\infty}^{\infty} f(x_1, x_2, \ldots, x_n)\, dx_3\, dx_4 \cdots dx_n & \text{(continuous case)}. \end{cases}$$

We could consider numerous conditional distributions. For example, the **joint conditional distribution** of X_1, X_2, and X_3, given that $X_4 = x_4, X_5 = x_5, \ldots, X_n = x_n$, is written

$$f(x_1, x_2, x_3 \mid x_4, x_5, \ldots, x_n) = \frac{f(x_1, x_2, \ldots, x_n)}{g(x_4, x_5, \ldots, x_n)},$$

where $g(x_4, x_5, \ldots, x_n)$ is the joint marginal distribution of the random variables $X_4, X_5, \ldots, X_n$.

A generalization of Definition 12 leads to the following definition for the mutual statistical independence of the variables $X_1, X_2, \ldots, X_n$.

Definition 13:

Let $X_1, X_2, \ldots, X_n$ be n random variables, discrete or continuous, with joint probability distribution $f(x_1, x_2, \ldots, x_n)$ and marginal distribution $f_1(x_1), f_2(x_2), \ldots, f_n(x_n)$, respectively. The random variables $X_1, X_2, \ldots, X_n$ are said to be mutually **statistically independent** if and only if

$$f(x_1, x_2, \ldots, x_n) = f_1(x_1)f_2(x_2) \cdots f_n(x_n)$$

for all $(x_1, x_2, \ldots, x_n)$ within their range.

Example 22: Suppose that the shelf life, in years, of a certain perishable food product packaged in cardboard containers is a random variable whose probability density function is given by

$$f(x) = \begin{cases} e^{-x}, & x > 0, \\ 0, & \text{elsewhere.} \end{cases}$$

Let X_1, X_2, and X_3 represent the shelf lives for three of these containers selected independently and find $P(X_1 < 2, 1 < X_2 < 3, X_3 > 2)$.

Solution: Since the containers were selected independently, we can assume that the random variables X_1, X_2, and X_3 are statistically independent, having the joint probability density

$$f(x_1, x_2, x_3) = f(x_1)f(x_2)f(x_3) = e^{-x_1}e^{-x_2}e^{-x_3} = e^{-x_1-x_2-x_3},$$

for $x_1 > 0$, $x_2 > 0$, $x_3 > 0$, and $f(x_1, x_2, x_3) = 0$ elsewhere. Hence

$$P(X_1 < 2, 1 < X_2 < 3, X_3 > 2) = \int_2^{\infty} \int_1^3 \int_0^2 e^{-x_1-x_2-x_3}\, dx_1\, dx_2\, dx_3$$
$$= (1 - e^{-2})(e^{-1} - e^{-3})e^{-2} = 0.0372.$$

What Are Important Characteristics of Probability Distributions and Where Do They Come From?

We have given illustrations in both examples and exercises of practical scientific and engineering situations in which probability distributions and their properties are used to solve important problems. These probability distributions, either discrete or continuous, were introduced through phrases like "it is known that" or "suppose that" or even in some cases "historical evidence suggests that." These are situations in which the nature of the distribution and even a good estimate of the probability structure can be determined through historical data, data from long-term studies, or even large amounts of planned data. Recall how frequency distributions are estimated from the histograms. However, not all probability functions and probability density functions are derived from large amounts of historical data. There are a substantial number of situations in which the nature of the scientific scenario suggests a distribution type. Indeed, many of these are reflected in exercises in this chapter. When independent repeated observations are binary in nature (e.g., defective or not, survive or not, allergic or not) with value 0 or 1, the distribution covering this situation is called the **binomial distribution** and the probability function is known. Exercise 34 in Section 3 and Review Exercise 80 are examples, and there are others that the reader should recognize. The scenario of a continuous distribution in time to failure, as in Review Exercise 69 or Exercise 27, often suggests a distribution type called the **exponential distribution**. These types of illustrations are merely two of any so-called standard distributions that are used extensively in real-world problems because the scientific scenario that gives rise to each of them is recognizable and occurs often in practice.

Exercises

37 Determine the values of c so that the following functions represent joint probability distributions of the random variables X and Y:

(a) $f(x, y) = cxy$, for $x = 1, 2, 3$; $y = 1, 2, 3$;

(b) $f(x, y) = c|x - y|$, for $x = -2, 0, 2$; $y = -2, 3$.

38 If the joint probability distribution of X and Y is given by

$$f(x, y) = \frac{x + y}{30}, \quad \text{for } x = 0, 1, 2, 3; \ y = 0, 1, 2,$$

find

(a) $P(X \leq 2, Y = 1)$;

(b) $P(X > 2, Y \leq 1)$;

(c) $P(X > Y)$;

(d) $P(X + Y = 4)$.

39 From a sack of fruit containing 3 oranges, 2 apples, and 3 bananas, a random sample of 4 pieces of fruit is selected. If X is the number of oranges and Y is the number of apples in the sample, find

(a) the joint probability distribution of X and Y;

(b) $P[(X, Y) \in A]$, where A is the region that is given by $\{(x, y) \mid x + y \leq 2\}$.

40 A fast-food restaurant operates both a drive-through facility and a walk-in facility. On a randomly selected day, let X and Y, respectively, be the proportions of the time that the drive-through and walk-in facilities are in use, and suppose that the joint density function of these random variables is

$$f(x, y) = \begin{cases} \frac{2}{3}(x + 2y), & 0 \leq x \leq 1, \ 0 \leq y \leq 1, \\ 0, & \text{elsewhere.} \end{cases}$$

(a) Find the marginal density of X.

(b) Find the marginal density of Y.

(c) Find the probability that the drive-through facility is busy less than one-half of the time.

41 A candy company distributes boxes of chocolates with a mixture of creams, toffees, and cordials. Suppose that the weight of each box is 1 kilogram, but the individual weights of the creams, toffees, and cordials vary from box to box. For a randomly selected box, let X and Y represent the weights of the creams and the toffees, respectively, and suppose that the joint density function of these variables is

$$f(x, y) = \begin{cases} 24xy, & 0 \leq x \leq 1, \ 0 \leq y \leq 1, \ x + y \leq 1, \\ 0, & \text{elsewhere.} \end{cases}$$

(a) Find the probability that in a given box the cordials account for more than 1/2 of the weight.

(b) Find the marginal density for the weight of the creams.

(c) Find the probability that the weight of the toffees in a box is less than 1/8 of a kilogram if it is known that creams constitute 3/4 of the weight.

42 Let X and Y denote the lengths of life, in years, of two components in an electronic system. If the joint density function of these variables is

$$f(x, y) = \begin{cases} e^{-(x+y)}, & x > 0, \ y > 0, \\ 0, & \text{elsewhere,} \end{cases}$$

find $P(0 < X < 1 \mid Y = 2)$.

43 Let X denote the reaction time, in seconds, to a certain stimulus and Y denote the temperature (°F) at which a certain reaction starts to take place. Suppose that two random variables X and Y have the joint density

$$f(x, y) = \begin{cases} 4xy, & 0 < x < 1, \ 0 < y < 1, \\ 0, & \text{elsewhere.} \end{cases}$$

Find

(a) $P(0 \leq X \leq \frac{1}{2} \text{ and } \frac{1}{4} \leq Y \leq \frac{1}{2})$;

(b) $P(X < Y)$.

44 Each rear tire on an experimental airplane is supposed to be filled to a pressure of 40 pounds per square inch (psi). Let X denote the actual air pressure for the right tire and Y denote the actual air pressure for the left tire. Suppose that X and Y are random variables with the joint density function

$$f(x, y) = \begin{cases} k(x^2 + y^2), & 30 \leq x < 50, \ 30 \leq y < 50, \\ 0, & \text{elsewhere.} \end{cases}$$

(a) Find k.

(b) Find $P(30 \leq X \leq 40 \text{ and } 40 \leq Y < 50)$.

(c) Find the probability that both tires are underfilled.

45 Let X denote the diameter of an armored electric cable and Y denote the diameter of the ceramic mold that makes the cable. Both X and Y are scaled so that they range between 0 and 1. Suppose that X and Y have the joint density

$$f(x, y) = \begin{cases} \frac{1}{y}, & 0 < x < y < 1, \\ 0, & \text{elsewhere.} \end{cases}$$

Find $P(X + Y > 1/2)$.

46 Referring to Exercise 38, find

(a) the marginal distribution of X;

(b) the marginal distribution of Y.

47 The amount of kerosene, in thousands of liters, in a tank at the beginning of any day is a random amount Y from which a random amount X is sold during that day. Suppose that the tank is not resupplied during the day so that $x \leq y$, and assume that the joint density function of these variables is

$$f(x, y) = \begin{cases} 2, & 0 < x \leq y < 1, \\ 0, & \text{elsewhere.} \end{cases}$$

(a) Determine if X and Y are independent.

(b) Find $P(1/4 < X < 1/2 \mid Y = 3/4)$.

48   Referring to Exercise 39, find
(a) $f(y|2)$ for all values of y;
(b) $P(Y = 0 \mid X = 2)$.

49   Let X denote the number of times a certain numerical control machine will malfunction: 1, 2, or 3 times on any given day. Let Y denote the number of times a technician is called on an emergency call. Their joint probability distribution is given as

$f(x,y)$		x	
	1	2	3
1	0.05	0.05	0.10
y 3	0.05	0.10	0.35
5	0.00	0.20	0.10

(a) Evaluate the marginal distribution of X.
(b) Evaluate the marginal distribution of Y.
(c) Find $P(Y = 3 \mid X = 2)$.

50   Suppose that X and Y have the following joint probability distribution:

$f(x,y)$	x	
	2	4
1	0.10	0.15
y 3	0.20	0.30
5	0.10	0.15

(a) Find the marginal distribution of X.
(b) Find the marginal distribution of Y.

51   Three cards are drawn without replacement from the 12 face cards (jacks, queens, and kings) of an ordinary deck of 52 playing cards. Let X be the number of kings selected and Y the number of jacks. Find
(a) the joint probability distribution of X and Y;
(b) $P[(X, Y) \in A]$, where A is the region given by $\{(x,y) \mid x + y \geq 2\}$.

52   A coin is tossed twice. Let Z denote the number of heads on the first toss and W the total number of heads on the 2 tosses. If the coin is unbalanced and a head has a 40% chance of occurring, find
(a) the joint probability distribution of W and Z;
(b) the marginal distribution of W;
(c) the marginal distribution of Z;
(d) the probability that at least 1 head occurs.

53   Given the joint density function

$$f(x,y) = \begin{cases} \frac{6-x-y}{8}, & 0 < x < 2,\ 2 < y < 4, \\ 0, & \text{elsewhere,} \end{cases}$$

find $P(1 < Y < 3 \mid X = 1)$.

54   Determine whether the two random variables of Exercise 49 are dependent or independent.

55   Determine whether the two random variables of Exercise 50 are dependent or independent.

56   The joint density function of the random variables X and Y is

$$f(x,y) = \begin{cases} 6x, & 0 < x < 1,\ 0 < y < 1 - x, \\ 0, & \text{elsewhere.} \end{cases}$$

(a) Show that X and Y are not independent.
(b) Find $P(X > 0.3 \mid Y = 0.5)$.

57   Let X, Y, and Z have the joint probability density function

$$f(x,y,z) = \begin{cases} kxy^2 z, & 0 < x, y < 1,\ 0 < z < 2, \\ 0, & \text{elsewhere.} \end{cases}$$

(a) Find k.
(b) Find $P(X < \frac{1}{4}, Y > \frac{1}{2}, 1 < Z < 2)$.

58   Determine whether the two random variables of Exercise 43 are dependent or independent.

59   Determine whether the two random variables of Exercise 44 are dependent or independent.

60   The joint probability density function of the random variables X, Y, and Z is

$$f(x,y,z) = \begin{cases} \frac{4xyz^2}{9}, & 0 < x, y < 1,\ 0 < z < 3, \\ 0, & \text{elsewhere.} \end{cases}$$

Find
(a) the joint marginal density function of Y and Z;
(b) the marginal density of Y;
(c) $P(\frac{1}{4} < X < \frac{1}{2}, Y > \frac{1}{3}, 1 < Z < 2)$;
(d) $P(0 < X < \frac{1}{2} \mid Y = \frac{1}{4}, Z = 2)$.

Review Exercises

61 A tobacco company produces blends of tobacco, with each blend containing various proportions of Turkish, domestic, and other tobaccos. The proportions of Turkish and domestic in a blend are random variables with joint density function (X = Turkish and Y = domestic)

$$f(x, y) = \begin{cases} 24xy, & 0 \le x, y \le 1, \; x + y \le 1, \\ 0, & \text{elsewhere.} \end{cases}$$

(a) Find the probability that in a given box the Turkish tobacco accounts for over half the blend.

(b) Find the marginal density function for the proportion of the domestic tobacco.

(c) Find the probability that the proportion of Turkish tobacco is less than 1/8 if it is known that the blend contains 3/4 domestic tobacco.

62 An insurance company offers its policyholders a number of different premium payment options. For a randomly selected policyholder, let X be the number of months between successive payments. The cumulative distribution function of X is

$$F(x) = \begin{cases} 0, & \text{if } x < 1, \\ 0.4, & \text{if } 1 \le x < 3, \\ 0.6, & \text{if } 3 \le x < 5, \\ 0.8, & \text{if } 5 \le x < 7, \\ 1.0, & \text{if } x \ge 7. \end{cases}$$

(a) What is the probability mass function of X?

(b) Compute $P(4 < X \le 7)$.

63 Two electronic components of a missile system work in harmony for the success of the total system. Let X and Y denote the life in hours of the two components. The joint density of X and Y is

$$f(x, y) = \begin{cases} ye^{-y(1+x)}, & x, y \ge 0, \\ 0, & \text{elsewhere.} \end{cases}$$

(a) Give the marginal density functions for both random variables.

(b) What is the probability that the lives of both components will exceed 2 hours?

64 A service facility operates with two service lines. On a randomly selected day, let X be the proportion of time that the first line is in use whereas Y is the proportion of time that the second line is in use. Suppose that the joint probability density function for (X, Y) is

$$f(x, y) = \begin{cases} \frac{3}{2}(x^2 + y^2), & 0 \le x, y \le 1, \\ 0, & \text{elsewhere.} \end{cases}$$

(a) Compute the probability that neither line is busy more than half the time.

(b) Find the probability that the first line is busy more than 75% of the time.

65 Let the number of phone calls received by a switchboard during a 5-minute interval be a random variable X with probability function

$$f(x) = \frac{e^{-2}2^x}{x!}, \quad \text{for } x = 0, 1, 2, \ldots.$$

(a) Determine the probability that X equals 0, 1, 2, 3, 4, 5, and 6.

(b) Graph the probability mass function for these values of x.

(c) Determine the cumulative distribution function for these values of X.

66 Consider the random variables X and Y with joint density function

$$f(x, y) = \begin{cases} x + y, & 0 \le x, y \le 1, \\ 0, & \text{elsewhere.} \end{cases}$$

(a) Find the marginal distributions of X and Y.

(b) Find $P(X > 0.5, Y > 0.5)$.

67 An industrial process manufactures items that can be classified as either defective or not defective. The probability that an item is defective is 0.1. An experiment is conducted in which 5 items are drawn randomly from the process. Let the random variable X be the number of defectives in this sample of 5. What is the probability mass function of X?

68 Consider the following joint probability density function of the random variables X and Y:

$$f(x, y) = \begin{cases} \frac{3x - y}{9}, & 1 < x < 3, \; 1 < y < 2, \\ 0, & \text{elsewhere.} \end{cases}$$

(a) Find the marginal density functions of X and Y.

(b) Are X and Y independent?

(c) Find $P(X > 2)$.

69 The life span in hours of an electrical component is a random variable with cumulative distribution function

$$F(x) = \begin{cases} 1 - e^{-\frac{x}{50}}, & x > 0, \\ 0, & \text{elewhere.} \end{cases}$$

(a) Determine its probability density function.

(b) Determine the probability that the life span of such a component will exceed 70 hours.

70 Pairs of pants are being produced by a particular outlet facility. The pants are checked by a group of 10 workers. The workers inspect pairs of pants taken randomly from the production line. Each inspector is assigned a number from 1 through 10. A buyer selects a pair of pants for purchase. Let the random variable X be the inspector number.

(a) Give a reasonable probability mass function for X.

(b) Plot the cumulative distribution function for X.

71 The shelf life of a product is a random variable that is related to consumer acceptance. It turns out that the shelf life Y in days of a certain type of bakery product has a density function

$$f(y) = \begin{cases} \frac{1}{2}e^{-y/2}, & 0 \le y < \infty, \\ 0, & \text{elsewhere.} \end{cases}$$

What fraction of the loaves of this product stocked today would you expect to be sellable 3 days from now?

72 Passenger congestion is a service problem in airports. Trains are installed within the airport to reduce the congestion. With the use of the train, the time X in minutes that it takes to travel from the main terminal to a particular concourse has density function

$$f(x) = \begin{cases} \frac{1}{10}, & 0 \le x \le 10, \\ 0, & \text{elsewhere.} \end{cases}$$

(a) Show that the above is a valid probability density function.

(b) Find the probability that the time it takes a passenger to travel from the main terminal to the concourse will not exceed 7 minutes.

73 Impurities in a batch of final product of a chemical process often reflect a serious problem. From considerable plant data gathered, it is known that the proportion Y of impurities in a batch has a density function given by

$$f(y) = \begin{cases} 10(1-y)^9, & 0 \le y \le 1, \\ 0, & \text{elsewhere.} \end{cases}$$

(a) Verify that the above is a valid density function.

(b) A batch is considered not sellable and then not acceptable if the percentage of impurities exceeds 60%. With the current quality of the process, what is the percentage of batches that are not acceptable?

74 The time Z in minutes between calls to an electrical supply system has the probability density function

$$f(z) = \begin{cases} \frac{1}{10}e^{-z/10}, & 0 < z < \infty, \\ 0, & \text{elsewhere.} \end{cases}$$

(a) What is the probability that there are no calls within a 20-minute time interval?

(b) What is the probability that the first call comes within 10 minutes of opening?

75 A chemical system that results from a chemical reaction has two important components among others in a blend. The joint distribution describing the proportions X_1 and X_2 of these two components is given by

$$f(x_1, x_2) = \begin{cases} 2, & 0 < x_1 < x_2 < 1, \\ 0, & \text{elsewhere.} \end{cases}$$

(a) Give the marginal distribution of X_1.

(b) Give the marginal distribution of X_2.

(c) What is the probability that component proportions produce the results $X_1 < 0.2$ and $X_2 > 0.5$?

(d) Give the conditional distribution $f_{X_1|X_2}(x_1|x_2)$.

76 Consider the situation of Review Exercise 75. But suppose the joint distribution of the two proportions is given by

$$f(x_1, x_2) = \begin{cases} 6x_2, & 0 < x_2 < x_1 < 1, \\ 0, & \text{elsewhere.} \end{cases}$$

(a) Give the marginal distribution $f_{X_1}(x_1)$ of the proportion X_1 and verify that it is a valid density function.

(b) What is the probability that proportion X_2 is less than 0.5, given that X_1 is 0.7?

77 Consider the random variables X and Y that represent the number of vehicles that arrive at two separate street corners during a certain 2-minute period. These street corners are fairly close together so it is important that traffic engineers deal with them jointly if necessary. The joint distribution of X and Y is known to be

$$f(x, y) = \frac{9}{16} \cdot \frac{1}{4^{(x+y)}},$$

for $x = 0, 1, 2, \ldots$ and $y = 0, 1, 2, \ldots$.

(a) Are the two random variables X and Y independent? Explain why or why not.

(b) What is the probability that during the time period in question less than 4 vehicles arrive at the two street corners?

78 The behavior of series of components plays a huge role in scientific and engineering reliability problems. The reliability of the entire system is certainly no better than that of the weakest component in the series. In a series system, the components operate independently of each other. In a particular system containing three components, the probabilities of meeting specifications for components 1, 2, and 3, respectively, are 0.95, 0.99, and 0.92. What is the probability that the entire system works?

79 Another type of system that is employed in engineering work is a group of parallel components or a parallel system. In this more conservative approach, the probability that the system operates is larger than the probability that any component operates. The system fails only when all components fail. Consider a situation in which there are 4 independent components in a parallel system with probability of operation given by

Component 1: 0.95;   Component 2: 0.94;

Component 3: 0.90;   Component 4: 0.97.

What is the probability that the system does not fail?

80 Consider a system of components in which there are 5 independent components, each of which possesses an operational probability of 0.92. The system does have a redundancy built in such that it does not fail if 3 out of the 5 components are operational. What is the probability that the total system is operational?

81 **Project**: Take 5 class periods to observe the shoe color of individuals in class. Assume the shoe color categories are red, white, black, brown, and other. Complete a frequency table for each color category.

(a) Estimate and interpret the meaning of the probability distribution.

(b) What is the estimated probability that in the next class period a randomly selected student will be wearing a red or a white pair of shoes?

5   Potential Misconceptions and Hazards

Probability distributions represent the structure through which probabilities that are computed aid in the evaluation and understanding of a process. For example, in Review Exercise 65, the probability distribution that quantifies the probability of a heavy load during certain time periods can be very useful in planning for any changes in the system. Review Exercise 69 describes a scenario in which the life span of an electronic component is studied. Knowledge of the probability structure for the component will contribute significantly to an understanding of the reliability of a large system of which the component is a part. In addition, an understanding of the general nature of probability distributions will enhance understanding of the concept of a ***P*-value**.

As far as potential hazards with the use of material in this chapter, the warning to the reader is not to read more into the material than is evident. The general nature of the probability distribution for a specific scientific phenomenon is not obvious from what is learned in this chapter. The purpose of this chapter is for readers to learn how to manipulate a probability distribution, not to learn how to identify a specific type.

Answers to Odd-Numbered Non-Review Exercises

1 Discrete; continuous; continuous; discrete; discrete; continuous

3

Sample Space	w
HHH	3
HHT	1
HTH	1
THH	1
HTT	-1
THT	-1
TTH	-1
TTT	-3

5 (a) 1/30; (b) 1/10

7 (a) 0.68; (b) 0.375

9 (b) 19/80

11

x	0	1	2
$f(x)$	$\frac{2}{7}$	$\frac{4}{7}$	$\frac{1}{7}$

13
$$F(x) = \begin{cases} 0, & \text{for } x < 0, \\ 0.41, & \text{for } 0 \le x < 1, \\ 0.78, & \text{for } 1 \le x < 2, \\ 0.94, & \text{for } 2 \le x < 3, \\ 0.99, & \text{for } 3 \le x < 4, \\ 1, & \text{for } x \ge 4 \end{cases}$$

15
$$F(x) = \begin{cases} 0, & \text{for } x < 0, \\ \frac{2}{7}, & \text{for } 0 \le x < 1, \\ \frac{6}{7}, & \text{for } 1 \le x < 2, \\ 1, & \text{for } x \ge 2 \end{cases}$$

(a) 4/7; (b) 5/7

17 (b) 1/4; (c) 0.3

19 $F(x) = \begin{cases} 0, & x < 1 \\ \frac{x-1}{2}, & 1 \le x < 3 \, ; \, 1/4 \\ 1, & x \ge 3 \end{cases}$

21 (a) 3/2; (b) $F(x) = \begin{cases} 0, & x < 0 \\ x^{3/2}, & 0 \le x < 1 \, ; \, 0.3004 \\ 1, & x \ge 1 \end{cases}$

23
$$F(w) = \begin{cases} 0, & \text{for } w < -3, \\ \frac{1}{27}, & \text{for } -3 \le w < -1, \\ \frac{7}{27}, & \text{for } -1 \le w < 1, \\ \frac{19}{27}, & \text{for } 1 \le w < 3, \\ 1, & \text{for } w \ge 3 \end{cases}$$

(a) 20/27; (b) 2/3

25

t	20	25	30
$P(T = t)$	$\frac{1}{5}$	$\frac{3}{5}$	$\frac{1}{5}$

27 (a)
$$F(x) = \begin{cases} 0, & x < 0, \\ 1 - \exp(-x/2000), & x \ge 0 \end{cases}$$
(b) 0.6065; (c) 0.6321

29 (b)
$$F(x) = \begin{cases} 0, & x < 1, \\ 1 - x^{-3}, & x \ge 1 \end{cases}$$
(c) 0.0156

31 (a) 0.2231; (b) 0.2212

33 (a) $k = 280$; (b) 0.3633; (c) 0.0563

35 (a) 0.1528; (b) 0.0446

37 (a) 1/36; (b) 1/15

39 (a)

				x	
$f(x,y)$		0	1	2	3
	0	0	$\frac{3}{70}$	$\frac{9}{70}$	$\frac{3}{70}$
y	1	$\frac{2}{70}$	$\frac{18}{70}$	$\frac{18}{70}$	$\frac{2}{70}$
	2	$\frac{3}{70}$	$\frac{9}{70}$	$\frac{3}{70}$	0

(b) 1/2

41 (a) 1/16; (b) $g(x) = 12x(1-x)^2$, for $0 \le x \le 1$; (c) 1/4

43 (a) 3/64; (b) 1/2

45 0.6534

47 (a) Dependent; (b) 1/3

49 (a)

x	1	2	3
$g(x)$	0.10	0.35	0.55

(b)

y	1	2	3
$h(y)$	0.20	0.50	0.30

(c) 0.2857

51 (a)

			x		
$f(x,y)$		0	1	2	3
	0	$\frac{1}{55}$	$\frac{6}{55}$	$\frac{6}{55}$	$\frac{1}{55}$
y	1	$\frac{6}{55}$	$\frac{16}{55}$	$\frac{6}{55}$	0
	2	$\frac{6}{55}$	$\frac{6}{55}$	0	0
	3	$\frac{1}{55}$	0	0	0

(b) 42/55

53 5/8

55 Independent

57 (a) 3; (b) 21/512

59 Dependent

Mathematical Expectation

1 Mean of a Random Variable

The sample mean is the arithmetic mean of the data. Now consider the following. If two coins are tossed 16 times and X is the number of heads that occur per toss, then the value of X are 0, 1, and 2. Suppose that the experiment yields no heads, one head, and two heads a total of 4, 7, and 5 times, respectively. The average number of heads per toss of the two coins is then

$$\frac{(0)(4) + (1)(7) + (2)(5)}{16} = 1.06.$$

This is an average value of the data and yet it is not a possible outcome of $\{0, 1, 2\}$. Hence, an average is not necessarily a possible outcome for the experiment. For instance, a salesman's average monthly income is not likely to be equal to any of his monthly paychecks.

Let us now restructure our computation for the average number of heads so as to have the following equivalent form:

$$(0)\left(\frac{4}{16}\right) + (1)\left(\frac{7}{16}\right) + (2)\left(\frac{5}{16}\right) = 1.06.$$

The numbers 4/16, 7/16, and 5/16 are the fractions of the total tosses resulting in 0, 1, and 2 heads, respectively. These fractions are also the relative frequencies for the different values of X in our experiment. In fact, then, we can calculate the mean, or average, of a set of data by knowing the distinct values that occur and their relative frequencies, without any knowledge of the total number of observations in our set of data. Therefore, if 4/16, or 1/4, of the tosses result in no heads, 7/16 of the tosses result in one head, and 5/16 of the tosses result in two heads, the mean number of heads per toss would be 1.06 no matter whether the total number of tosses were 16, 1000, or even 10,000.

This method of relative frequencies is used to calculate the average number of heads per toss of two coins that we might expect in the long run. We shall refer to this average value as the **mean of the random variable** X or the **mean of the probability distribution of** X and write it as μ_x or simply as μ when it is

From Chapter 4 of *Probability & Statistics for Engineers & Scientists*, Ninth Edition, Ronald E. Walpole, Raymond H. Myers, Sharon L. Myers, Keying Ye. Copyright © 2012 by Pearson Education, Inc. Published by Pearson Prentice Hall. All rights reserved.

clear to which random variable we refer. It is also common among statisticians to refer to this mean as the mathematical expectation, or the expected value of the random variable X, and denote it as $E(X)$.

Assuming that 1 fair coin was tossed twice, we find that the sample space for our experiment is

$$S = \{HH, HT, TH, TT\}.$$

Since the 4 sample points are all equally likely, it follows that

$$P(X=0) = P(TT) = \frac{1}{4}, \quad P(X=1) = P(TH) + P(HT) = \frac{1}{2},$$

and

$$P(X=2) = P(HH) = \frac{1}{4},$$

where a typical element, say TH, indicates that the first toss resulted in a tail followed by a head on the second toss. Now, these probabilities are just the relative frequencies for the given events in the long run. Therefore,

$$\mu = E(X) = (0)\left(\frac{1}{4}\right) + (1)\left(\frac{1}{2}\right) + (2)\left(\frac{1}{4}\right) = 1.$$

This result means that a person who tosses 2 coins over and over again will, on the average, get 1 head per toss.

The method described above for calculating the expected number of heads per toss of 2 coins suggests that the mean, or expected value, of any discrete random variable may be obtained by multiplying each of the values $x_1, x_2, \ldots, x_n$ of the random variable X by its corresponding probability $f(x_1), f(x_2), \ldots, f(x_n)$ and summing the products. This is true, however, only if the random variable is discrete. In the case of continuous random variables, the definition of an expected value is essentially the same with summations replaced by integrations.

Definition 1:

Let X be a random variable with probability distribution $f(x)$. The **mean**, or **expected value**, of X is

$$\mu = E(X) = \sum_x x f(x)$$

if X is discrete, and

$$\mu = E(X) = \int_{-\infty}^{\infty} x f(x) \, dx$$

if X is continuous.

The reader should note that the way to calculate the expected value, or mean, shown here is different from the way to calculate the sample mean described elsewhere, where the sample mean is obtained by using data. In mathematical expectation, the expected value is calculated by using the probability distribution.

However, the mean is usually understood as a "center" value of the underlying distribution if we use the expected value, as in Definition 1.

Example 1: A lot containing 7 components is sampled by a quality inspector; the lot contains 4 good components and 3 defective components. A sample of 3 is taken by the inspector. Find the expected value of the number of good components in this sample.

Solution: Let X represent the number of good components in the sample. The probability distribution of X is

$$f(x) = \frac{\binom{4}{x}\binom{3}{3-x}}{\binom{7}{3}}, \qquad x = 0, 1, 2, 3.$$

Simple calculations yield $f(0) = 1/35$, $f(1) = 12/35$, $f(2) = 18/35$, and $f(3) = 4/35$. Therefore,

$$\mu = E(X) = (0)\left(\frac{1}{35}\right) + (1)\left(\frac{12}{35}\right) + (2)\left(\frac{18}{35}\right) + (3)\left(\frac{4}{35}\right) = \frac{12}{7} = 1.7.$$

Thus, if a sample of size 3 is selected at random over and over again from a lot of 4 good components and 3 defective components, it will contain, on average, 1.7 good components.

Example 2: A salesperson for a medical device company has two appointments on a given day. At the first appointment, he believes that he has a 70% chance to make the deal, from which he can earn $1000 commission if successful. On the other hand, he thinks he only has a 40% chance to make the deal at the second appointment, from which, if successful, he can make $1500. What is his expected commission based on his own probability belief? Assume that the appointment results are independent of each other.

Solution: First, we know that the salesperson, for the two appointments, can have 4 possible commission totals: $0, $1000, $1500, and $2500. We then need to calculate their associated probabilities. By independence, we obtain

$$f(\$0) = (1 - 0.7)(1 - 0.4) = 0.18, \quad f(\$2500) = (0.7)(0.4) = 0.28,$$
$$f(\$1000) = (0.7)(1 - 0.4) = 0.42, \text{ and } f(\$1500) = (1 - 0.7)(0.4) = 0.12.$$

Therefore, the expected commission for the salesperson is

$$E(X) = (\$0)(0.18) + (\$1000)(0.42) + (\$1500)(0.12) + (\$2500)(0.28)$$
$$= \$1300.$$

Examples 1 and 2 are designed to allow the reader to gain some insight into what we mean by the expected value of a random variable. In both cases the random variables are discrete. We follow with an example involving a continuous random variable, where an engineer is interested in the *mean life* of a certain type of electronic device. This is an illustration of a *time to failure* problem that occurs often in practice. The expected value of the life of a device is an important parameter for its evaluation.

Example 3: Let X be the random variable that denotes the life in hours of a certain electronic device. The probability density function is

$$f(x) = \begin{cases} \frac{20,000}{x^3}, & x > 100, \\ 0, & \text{elsewhere.} \end{cases}$$

Find the expected life of this type of device.

Solution: Using Definition 1, we have

$$\mu = E(X) = \int_{100}^{\infty} x \frac{20,000}{x^3}\, dx = \int_{100}^{\infty} \frac{20,000}{x^2}\, dx = 200.$$

Therefore, we can expect this type of device to last, *on average*, 200 hours.

Now let us consider a new random variable $g(X)$, which depends on X; that is, each value of $g(X)$ is determined by the value of X. For instance, $g(X)$ might be X^2 or $3X - 1$, and whenever X assumes the value 2, $g(X)$ assumes the value $g(2)$. In particular, if X is a discrete random variable with probability distribution $f(x)$, for $x = -1, 0, 1, 2$, and $g(X) = X^2$, then

$$P[g(X) = 0] = P(X = 0) = f(0),$$
$$P[g(X) = 1] = P(X = -1) + P(X = 1) = f(-1) + f(1),$$
$$P[g(X) = 4] = P(X = 2) = f(2),$$

and so the probability distribution of $g(X)$ may be written

$g(x)$	0	1	4
$P[g(X) = g(x)]$	$f(0)$	$f(-1) + f(1)$	$f(2)$

By the definition of the expected value of a random variable, we obtain

$$\mu_{g(X)} = E[g(x)] = 0f(0) + 1[f(-1) + f(1)] + 4f(2)$$
$$= (-1)^2 f(-1) + (0)^2 f(0) + (1)^2 f(1) + (2)^2 f(2) = \sum_x g(x)f(x).$$

This result is generalized in Theorem 1 for both discrete and continuous random variables.

Theorem 1: Let X be a random variable with probability distribution $f(x)$. The expected value of the random variable $g(X)$ is

$$\mu_{g(X)} = E[g(X)] = \sum_x g(x)f(x)$$

if X is discrete, and

$$\mu_{g(X)} = E[g(X)] = \int_{-\infty}^{\infty} g(x)f(x)\, dx$$

if X is continuous.

Example 4: Suppose that the number of cars X that pass through a car wash between 4:00 P.M. and 5:00 P.M. on any sunny Friday has the following probability distribution:

x	4	5	6	7	8	9
$P(X = x)$	$\frac{1}{12}$	$\frac{1}{12}$	$\frac{1}{4}$	$\frac{1}{4}$	$\frac{1}{6}$	$\frac{1}{6}$

Let $g(X) = 2X - 1$ represent the amount of money, in dollars, paid to the attendant by the manager. Find the attendant's expected earnings for this particular time period.

Solution: By Theorem 1, the attendant can expect to receive

$$E[g(X)] = E(2X - 1) = \sum_{x=4}^{9}(2x - 1)f(x)$$

$$= (7)\left(\frac{1}{12}\right) + (9)\left(\frac{1}{12}\right) + (11)\left(\frac{1}{4}\right) + (13)\left(\frac{1}{4}\right)$$

$$+ (15)\left(\frac{1}{6}\right) + (17)\left(\frac{1}{6}\right) = \$12.67.$$

Example 5: Let X be a random variable with density function

$$f(x) = \begin{cases} \frac{x^2}{3}, & -1 < x < 2, \\ 0, & \text{elsewhere.} \end{cases}$$

Find the expected value of $g(X) = 4X + 3$.

Solution: By Theorem 1, we have

$$E(4X + 3) = \int_{-1}^{2} \frac{(4x + 3)x^2}{3}\, dx = \frac{1}{3}\int_{-1}^{2}(4x^3 + 3x^2)\, dx = 8.$$

We shall now extend our concept of mathematical expectation to the case of two random variables X and Y with joint probability distribution $f(x, y)$.

Definition 2:

> Let X and Y be random variables with joint probability distribution $f(x, y)$. The mean, or expected value, of the random variable $g(X, Y)$ is
>
> $$\mu_{g(X,Y)} = E[g(X, Y)] = \sum_x \sum_y g(x, y)f(x, y)$$
>
> if X and Y are discrete, and
>
> $$\mu_{g(X,Y)} = E[g(X, Y)] = \int_{-\infty}^{\infty}\int_{-\infty}^{\infty} g(x, y)f(x, y)\, dx\, dy$$
>
> if X and Y are continuous.

Generalization of Definition 2 for the calculation of mathematical expectations of functions of several random variables is straightforward.

Example 6: Let X and Y be the random variables with joint probability distribution indicated in the table below. Find the expected value of $g(X,Y) = XY$.

$f(x,y)$		x 0	x 1	x 2	Row Totals
	0	$\frac{3}{28}$	$\frac{9}{28}$	$\frac{3}{28}$	$\frac{15}{28}$
y	1	$\frac{3}{14}$	$\frac{3}{14}$	0	$\frac{3}{7}$
	2	$\frac{1}{28}$	0	0	$\frac{1}{28}$
Column Totals		$\frac{5}{14}$	$\frac{15}{28}$	$\frac{3}{28}$	1

Solution: By Definition 2, we write

$$E(XY) = \sum_{x=0}^{2}\sum_{y=0}^{2} xyf(x,y)$$

$$= (0)(0)f(0,0) + (0)(1)f(0,1)$$
$$+ (1)(0)f(1,0) + (1)(1)f(1,1) + (2)(0)f(2,0)$$
$$= f(1,1) = \frac{3}{14}.$$

Example 7: Find $E(Y/X)$ for the density function

$$f(x,y) = \begin{cases} \frac{x(1+3y^2)}{4}, & 0 < x < 2,\ 0 < y < 1, \\ 0, & \text{elsewhere.} \end{cases}$$

Solution: We have

$$E\left(\frac{Y}{X}\right) = \int_0^1 \int_0^2 \frac{y(1+3y^2)}{4}\, dxdy = \int_0^1 \frac{y+3y^3}{2}\, dy = \frac{5}{8}.$$

Note that if $g(X,Y) = X$ in Definition 2, we have

$$E(X) = \begin{cases} \sum_x \sum_y xf(x,y) = \sum_x xg(x) & \text{(discrete case)}, \\ \int_{-\infty}^{\infty}\int_{-\infty}^{\infty} xf(x,y)\, dy\, dx = \int_{-\infty}^{\infty} xg(x)\, dx & \text{(continuous case)}, \end{cases}$$

where $g(x)$ is the marginal distribution of X. Therefore, in calculating $E(X)$ over a two-dimensional space, one may use either the joint probability distribution of X and Y or the marginal distribution of X. Similarly, we define

$$E(Y) = \begin{cases} \sum_y \sum_x yf(x,y) = \sum_y yh(y) & \text{(discrete case)}, \\ \int_{-\infty}^{\infty}\int_{-\infty}^{\infty} yf(x,y)\, dxdy = \int_{-\infty}^{\infty} yh(y)\, dy & \text{(continuous case)}, \end{cases}$$

where $h(y)$ is the marginal distribution of the random variable Y.

Exercises

1 The probability distribution of X, the number of imperfections per 10 meters of a synthetic fabric in continuous rolls of uniform width, is given in Exercise 13 from chapter **Random Variables and Probability Distributions** as

x	0	1	2	3	4
$f(x)$	0.41	0.37	0.16	0.05	0.01

Find the average number of imperfections per 10 meters of this fabric.

2 The probability distribution of the discrete random variable X is

$$f(x) = \binom{3}{x} \left(\frac{1}{4}\right)^x \left(\frac{3}{4}\right)^{3-x}, \quad x = 0, 1, 2, 3.$$

Find the mean of X.

3 Find the mean of the random variable T representing the total of the three coins in Exercise 25.

4 A coin is biased such that a head is three times as likely to occur as a tail. Find the expected number of tails when this coin is tossed twice.

5 In a gambling game, a woman is paid \$3 if she draws a jack or a queen and \$5 if she draws a king or an ace from an ordinary deck of 52 playing cards. If she draws any other card, she loses. How much should she pay to play if the game is fair?

6 An attendant at a car wash is paid according to the number of cars that pass through. Suppose the probabilities are 1/12, 1/12, 1/4, 1/4, 1/6, and 1/6, respectively, that the attendant receives \$7, \$9, \$11, \$13, \$15, or \$17 between 4:00 P.M. and 5:00 P.M. on any sunny Friday. Find the attendant's expected earnings for this particular period.

7 By investing in a particular stock, a person can make a profit in one year of \$4000 with probability 0.3 or take a loss of \$1000 with probability 0.7. What is this person's expected gain?

8 Suppose that an antique jewelry dealer is interested in purchasing a gold necklace for which the probabilities are 0.22, 0.36, 0.28, and 0.14, respectively, that she will be able to sell it for a profit of \$250, sell it for a profit of \$150, break even, or sell it for a loss of \$150. What is her expected profit?

9 A private pilot wishes to insure his airplane for \$200,000. The insurance company estimates that a total loss will occur with probability 0.002, a 50% loss with probability 0.01, and a 25% loss with probability

0.1. Ignoring all other partial losses, what premium should the insurance company charge each year to realize an average profit of \$500?

10 Two tire-quality experts examine stacks of tires and assign a quality rating to each tire on a 3-point scale. Let X denote the rating given by expert A and Y denote the rating given by B. The following table gives the joint distribution for X and Y.

$f(x,y)$		y	
	1	2	3
x 1	0.10	0.05	0.02
2	0.10	0.35	0.05
3	0.03	0.10	0.20

Find μ_X and μ_Y.

11 The density function of coded measurements of the pitch diameter of threads of a fitting is

$$f(x) = \begin{cases} \frac{4}{\pi(1+x^2)}, & 0 < x < 1, \\ 0, & \text{elsewhere.} \end{cases}$$

Find the expected value of X.

12 If a dealer's profit, in units of \$5000, on a new automobile can be looked upon as a random variable X having the density function

$$f(x) = \begin{cases} 2(1-x), & 0 < x < 1, \\ 0, & \text{elsewhere,} \end{cases}$$

find the average profit per automobile.

13 The density function of the continuous random variable X, the total number of hours, in units of 100 hours, that a family runs a vacuum cleaner over a period of one year, is given in Exercise 7 from chapter **Random Variables and Probability Distributions** as

$$f(x) = \begin{cases} x, & 0 < x < 1, \\ 2 - x, & 1 \le x < 2, \\ 0, & \text{elsewhere.} \end{cases}$$

Find the average number of hours per year that families run their vacuum cleaners.

14 Find the proportion X of individuals who can be expected to respond to a certain mail-order solicitation if X has the density function

$$f(x) = \begin{cases} \frac{2(x+2)}{5}, & 0 < x < 1, \\ 0, & \text{elsewhere.} \end{cases}$$

15 Assume that two random variables (X, Y) are uniformly distributed on a circle with radius a. Then the joint probability density function is

$$f(x, y) = \begin{cases} \frac{1}{\pi a^2}, & x^2 + y^2 \leq a^2, \\ 0, & \text{otherwise.} \end{cases}$$

Find μ_X, the expected value of X.

16 Suppose that you are inspecting a lot of 1000 light bulbs, among which 20 are defectives. You choose two light bulbs randomly from the lot without replacement. Let

$$X_1 = \begin{cases} 1, & \text{if the 1st light bulb is defective,} \\ 0, & \text{otherwise,} \end{cases}$$

$$X_2 = \begin{cases} 1, & \text{if the 2nd light bulb is defective,} \\ 0, & \text{otherwise.} \end{cases}$$

Find the probability that at least one light bulb chosen is defective. [*Hint*: Compute $P(X_1 + X_2 = 1)$.]

17 Let X be a random variable with the following probability distribution:

x	-3	6	9
$f(x)$	$1/6$	$1/2$	$1/3$

Find $\mu_{g(X)}$, where $g(X) = (2X + 1)^2$.

18 Find the expected value of the random variable $g(X) = X^2$, where X has the probability distribution of Exercise 2.

19 A large industrial firm purchases several new word processors at the end of each year, the exact number depending on the frequency of repairs in the previous year. Suppose that the number of word processors, X, purchased each year has the following probability distribution:

x	0	1	2	3
$f(x)$	$1/10$	$3/10$	$2/5$	$1/5$

If the cost of the desired model is \$1200 per unit and at the end of the year a refund of $50X^2$ dollars will be issued, how much can this firm expect to spend on new word processors during this year?

20 A continuous random variable X has the density function

$$f(x) = \begin{cases} e^{-x}, & x > 0, \\ 0, & \text{elsewhere.} \end{cases}$$

Find the expected value of $g(X) = e^{2X/3}$.

21 What is the dealer's average profit per automobile if the profit on each automobile is given by $g(X) = X^2$, where X is a random variable having the density function of Exercise 12?

22 The hospitalization period, in days, for patients following treatment for a certain type of kidney disorder is a random variable $Y = X + 4$, where X has the density function

$$f(x) = \begin{cases} \frac{32}{(x+4)^3}, & x > 0, \\ 0, & \text{elsewhere.} \end{cases}$$

Find the average number of days that a person is hospitalized following treatment for this disorder.

23 Suppose that X and Y have the following joint probability function:

$f(x, y)$		x	
		2	4
	1	0.10	0.15
y 3		0.20	0.30
	5	0.10	0.15

(a) Find the expected value of $g(X, Y) = XY^2$.

(b) Find μ_X and μ_Y.

24 Referring to the random variables whose joint probability distribution is given in Exercise 39 from chapter **Random Variables and Probability Distributions,**

(a) find $E(X^2Y - 2XY)$;

(b) find $\mu_X - \mu_Y$.

25 Referring to the random variables whose joint probability distribution is given in Exercise 51, find the mean for the total number of jacks and kings when 3 cards are drawn without replacement from the 12 face cards of an ordinary deck of 52 playing cards.

26 Let X and Y be random variables with joint density function

$$f(x, y) = \begin{cases} 4xy, & 0 < x, \ y < 1, \\ 0, & \text{elsewhere.} \end{cases}$$

Find the expected value of $Z = \sqrt{X^2 + Y^2}$.

27 In Exercise 27, from chapter **Random Variables and Probability Distributions**, a density function is given for the time to failure of an important component of a DVD player. Find the mean number of hours to failure of the component and thus the DVD player.

28 Consider the information in Exercise 28 from chapter **Random Variables and Probability Distributions**. The problem deals with the weight in ounces of the product in a cereal box, with

$$f(x) = \begin{cases} \frac{2}{5}, & 23.75 \leq x \leq 26.25, \\ 0, & \text{elsewhere.} \end{cases}$$

(a) Plot the density function.

(b) Compute the expected value, or mean weight, in ounces.

(c) Are you surprised at your answer in (b)? Explain why or why not.

29 Exercise 29 from chapter **Random Variables and Probability Distributions** dealt with an important particle size distribution characterized by

$$f(x) = \begin{cases} 3x^{-4}, & x > 1, \\ 0, & \text{elsewhere}. \end{cases}$$

(a) Plot the density function.

(b) Give the mean particle size.

30 In Exercise 31 from chapter **Random Variables and Probability Distributions**, the distribution of-times before a major repair of a washing machine was given as

$$f(y) = \begin{cases} \frac{1}{4}e^{-y/4}, & y \geq 0, \\ 0, & \text{elsewhere}. \end{cases}$$

What is the population mean of the times to repair?

31 Consider Exercise 32 from chapter **Random Variables and Probability Distributions**.

(a) What is the mean proportion of the budget allocated to environmental and pollution control?

(b) What is the probability that a company selected at random will have allocated to environmental and pollution control a proportion that exceeds the population mean given in (a)?

32 In Exercise 13 from chapter **Random Variables and Probability Distributions**, the distribution of the number of imperfections per 10 meters of synthetic fabric is given by

x	0	1	2	3	4
$f(x)$	0.41	0.37	0.16	0.05	0.01

(a) Plot the probability function.

(b) Find the expected number of imperfections, $E(X) = \mu$.

(c) Find $E(X^2)$.

2   Variance and Covariance of Random Variables

The mean, or expected value, of a random variable X is of special importance in statistics because it describes where the probability distribution is centered. By itself, however, the mean does not give an adequate description of the shape of the distribution. We also need to characterize the variability in the distribution. In Figure 1, we have the histograms of two discrete probability distributions that have the same mean, $\mu = 2$, but differ considerably in variability, or the dispersion of their observations about the mean.

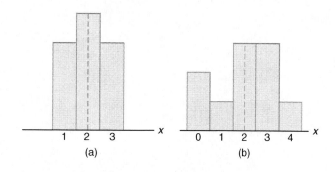

Figure 1: Distributions with equal means and unequal dispersions.

The most important measure of variability of a random variable X is obtained by applying Theorem 1 with $g(X) = (X - \mu)^2$.[2] The quantity is referred to as the **variance of the random variable** X or the **variance of the probability**

distribution of X and is denoted by $\text{Var}(X)$ or the symbol σ_X^2, or simply by σ^2 when it is clear to which random variable we refer.

Definition 3: | Let X be a random variable with probability distribution $f(x)$ and mean μ. The variance of X is
$$\sigma^2 = E[(X - \mu)^2] = \sum_x (x - \mu)^2 f(x), \qquad \text{if } X \text{ is discrete, and}$$
$$\sigma^2 = E[(X - \mu)^2] = \int_{-\infty}^{\infty} (x - \mu)^2 f(x) \, dx, \qquad \text{if } X \text{ is continuous.}$$
The positive square root of the variance, σ, is called the **standard deviation** of X.

The quantity $x - \mu$ in Definition 3 is called the **deviation of an observation** from its mean. Since the deviations are squared and then averaged, σ^2 will be much smaller for a set of x values that are close to μ than it will be for a set of values that vary considerably from μ.

Example 8: | Let the random variable X represent the number of automobiles that are used for official business purposes on any given workday. The probability distribution for company A [Figure 1(a)] is

x	1	2	3
$f(x)$	0.3	0.4	0.3

and that for company B [Figure 4.1(b)] is

x	0	1	2	3	4
$f(x)$	0.2	0.1	0.3	0.3	0.1

Show that the variance of the probability distribution for company B is greater than that for company A.

Solution: For company A, we find that

$$\mu_A = E(X) = (1)(0.3) + (2)(0.4) + (3)(0.3) = 2.0,$$

and then

$$\sigma_A^2 = \sum_{x=1}^{3} (x - 2)^2 = (1 - 2)^2(0.3) + (2 - 2)^2(0.4) + (3 - 2)^2(0.3) = 0.6.$$

For company B, we have

$$\mu_B = E(X) = (0)(0.2) + (1)(0.1) + (2)(0.3) + (3)(0.3) + (4)(0.1) = 2.0,$$

and then

$$\sigma_B^2 = \sum_{x=0}^{4} (x - 2)^2 f(x)$$
$$= (0 - 2)^2(0.2) + (1 - 2)^2(0.1) + (2 - 2)^2(0.3)$$
$$+ (3 - 2)^2(0.3) + (4 - 2)^2(0.1) = 1.6.$$

Clearly, the variance of the number of automobiles that are used for official business purposes is greater for company B than for company A.

An alternative and preferred formula for finding σ^2, which often simplifies the calculations, is stated in the following theorem.

Theorem 2:

> The variance of a random variable X is
> $$\sigma^2 = E(X^2) - \mu^2.$$

Proof: For the discrete case, we can write

$$\sigma^2 = \sum_x (x - \mu)^2 f(x) = \sum_x (x^2 - 2\mu x + \mu^2) f(x)$$

$$= \sum_x x^2 f(x) - 2\mu \sum_x x f(x) + \mu^2 \sum_x f(x).$$

Since $\mu = \sum_x x f(x)$ by definition, and $\sum_x f(x) = 1$ for any discrete probability distribution, it follows that

$$\sigma^2 = \sum_x x^2 f(x) - \mu^2 = E(X^2) - \mu^2.$$

For the continuous case the proof is step by step the same, with summations replaced by integrations.

Example 9:

Let the random variable X represent the number of defective parts for a machine when 3 parts are sampled from a production line and tested. The following is the probability distribution of X.

x	0	1	2	3
$f(x)$	0.51	0.38	0.10	0.01

Using Theorem 2, calculate σ^2.

Solution: First, we compute

$$\mu = (0)(0.51) + (1)(0.38) + (2)(0.10) + (3)(0.01) = 0.61.$$

Now,

$$E(X^2) = (0)(0.51) + (1)(0.38) + (4)(0.10) + (9)(0.01) = 0.87.$$

Therefore,

$$\sigma^2 = 0.87 - (0.61)^2 = 0.4979.$$

Example 10:

The weekly demand for a drinking-water product, in thousands of liters, from a local chain of efficiency stores is a continuous random variable X having the probability density

$$f(x) = \begin{cases} 2(x-1), & 1 < x < 2, \\ 0, & \text{elsewhere.} \end{cases}$$

Find the mean and variance of X.

Solution: Calculating $E(X)$ and $E(X^2)$, we have

$$\mu = E(X) = 2 \int_1^2 x(x-1) \, dx = \frac{5}{3}$$

and

$$E(X^2) = 2 \int_1^2 x^2(x-1) \, dx = \frac{17}{6}.$$

Therefore,

$$\sigma^2 = \frac{17}{6} - \left(\frac{5}{3}\right)^2 = \frac{1}{18}.$$

At this point, the variance or standard deviation has meaning only when we compare two or more distributions that have the same units of measurement. Therefore, we could compare the variances of the distributions of contents, measured in liters, of bottles of orange juice from two companies, and the larger value would indicate the company whose product was more variable or less uniform. It would not be meaningful to compare the variance of a distribution of heights to the variance of a distribution of aptitude scores. In Section 4, we show how the standard deviation can be used to describe a single distribution of observations.

We shall now extend our concept of the variance of a random variable X to include random variables related to X. For the random variable $g(X)$, the variance is denoted by $\sigma^2_{g(X)}$ and is calculated by means of the following theorem.

Theorem 3: Let X be a random variable with probability distribution $f(x)$. The variance of the random variable $g(X)$ is

$$\sigma^2_{g(X)} = E\{[g(X) - \mu_{g(X)}]^2\} = \sum_x [g(x) - \mu_{g(X)}]^2 f(x)$$

if X is discrete, and

$$\sigma^2_{g(X)} = E\{[g(X) - \mu_{g(X)}]^2\} = \int_{-\infty}^{\infty} [g(x) - \mu_{g(X)}]^2 f(x) \, dx$$

if X is continuous.

Proof: Since $g(X)$ is itself a random variable with mean $\mu_{g(X)}$ as defined in Theorem 1, it follows from Definition 3 that

$$\sigma^2_{g(X)} = E\{[g(X) - \mu_{g(X)}]\}.$$

Now, applying Theorem 1 again to the random variable $[g(X) - \mu_{g(X)}]^2$ completes the proof.

Example 11: Calculate the variance of $g(X) = 2X + 3$, where X is a random variable with probability distribution

x	0	1	2	3
$f(x)$	$\frac{1}{4}$	$\frac{1}{8}$	$\frac{1}{2}$	$\frac{1}{8}$

Solution: First, we find the mean of the random variable $2X + 3$. According to Theorem 1,

$$\mu_{2X+3} = E(2X + 3) = \sum_{x=0}^{3}(2x + 3)f(x) = 6.$$

Now, using Theorem 3, we have

$$\sigma_{2X+3}^2 = E\{[(2X + 3) - \mu_{2x+3}]^2\} = E[(2X + 3 - 6)^2]$$

$$= E(4X^2 - 12X + 9) = \sum_{x=0}^{3}(4x^2 - 12x + 9)f(x) = 4.$$

Example 12: Let X be a random variable having the density function given in Example 5 Find the variance of the random variable $g(X) = 4X + 3$.

Solution: In Example 5, we found that $\mu_{4X+3} = 8$. Now, using Theorem 3,

$$\sigma_{4X+3}^2 = E\{[(4X + 3) - 8]^2\} = E[(4X - 5)^2]$$

$$= \int_{-1}^{2}(4x - 5)^2 \frac{x^2}{3}\, dx = \frac{1}{3}\int_{-1}^{2}(16x^4 - 40x^3 + 25x^2)\, dx = \frac{51}{5}.$$

If $g(X, Y) = (X - \mu_X)(Y - \mu_Y)$, where $\mu_X = E(X)$ and $\mu_Y = E(Y)$, Definition 4.2 yields an expected value called the **covariance** of X and Y, which we denote by σ_{XY} or $\text{Cov}(X, Y)$.

Definition 4:

Let X and Y be random variables with joint probability distribution $f(x, y)$. The covariance of X and Y is

$$\sigma_{XY} = E[(X - \mu_X)(Y - \mu_Y)] = \sum_x \sum_y (x - \mu_X)(y - \mu_y)f(x, y)$$

if X and Y are discrete, and

$$\sigma_{XY} = E[(X - \mu_X)(Y - \mu_Y)] = \int_{-\infty}^{\infty}\int_{-\infty}^{\infty}(x - \mu_X)(y - \mu_y)f(x, y)\, dx\, dy$$

if X and Y are continuous.

The covariance between two random variables is a measure of the nature of the association between the two. If large values of X often result in large values of Y or small values of X result in small values of Y, positive $X - \mu_X$ will often result in positive $Y - \mu_Y$ and negative $X - \mu_X$ will often result in negative $Y - \mu_Y$. Thus, the product $(X - \mu_X)(Y - \mu_Y)$ will tend to be positive. On the other hand, if large X values often result in small Y values, the product $(X - \mu_X)(Y - \mu_Y)$ will tend to be negative. The *sign* of the covariance indicates whether the relationship between two dependent random variables is positive or negative. When X and Y are statistically independent, it can be shown that the covariance is zero (see Corollary 5). The converse, however, is not generally true. Two variables may have zero covariance and still not be statistically independent. Note that the covariance only describes the *linear* relationship between two random variables. Therefore, if a covariance between X and Y is zero, X and Y may have a nonlinear relationship, which means that they are not necessarily independent.

Mathematical Expectation

The alternative and preferred formula for σ_{XY} is stated by Theorem 4.

Theorem 4:

The covariance of two random variables X and Y with means μ_X and μ_Y, respectively, is given by

$$\sigma_{XY} = E(XY) - \mu_X \mu_Y.$$

Proof: For the discrete case, we can write

$$\sigma_{XY} = \sum_x \sum_y (x - \mu_X)(y - \mu_Y) f(x, y)$$

$$= \sum_x \sum_y xy f(x, y) - \mu_X \sum_x \sum_y y f(x, y)$$

$$- \mu_Y \sum_x \sum_y x f(x, y) + \mu_X \mu_Y \sum_x \sum_y f(x, y).$$

Since

$$\mu_X = \sum_x x f(x, y), \quad \mu_Y = \sum_y y f(x, y), \quad \text{and} \quad \sum_x \sum_y f(x, y) = 1$$

for any joint discrete distribution, it follows that

$$\sigma_{XY} = E(XY) - \mu_X \mu_Y - \mu_Y \mu_X + \mu_X \mu_Y = E(XY) - \mu_X \mu_Y.$$

For the continuous case, the proof is identical with summations replaced by integrals.

Example 13:

Example 14 from chapter **Random Variables and Probability Distributions** describes a situation involving the number of blue refills X and the number of red refills Y. Two refills for a ballpoint pen are selected at random from a certain box, and the following is the joint probability distribution:

	$f(x, y)$	x = 0	1	2	$h(y)$
	0	$\frac{3}{28}$	$\frac{9}{28}$	$\frac{3}{28}$	$\frac{15}{28}$
y	1	$\frac{3}{14}$	$\frac{3}{14}$	0	$\frac{3}{7}$
	2	$\frac{1}{28}$	0	0	$\frac{1}{28}$
	$g(x)$	$\frac{5}{14}$	$\frac{15}{28}$	$\frac{3}{28}$	1

Find the covariance of X and Y.

Solution: From Example 6, we see that $E(XY) = 3/14$. Now

$$\mu_X = \sum_{x=0}^{2} x g(x) = (0)\left(\frac{5}{14}\right) + (1)\left(\frac{15}{28}\right) + (2)\left(\frac{3}{28}\right) = \frac{3}{4},$$

and

$$\mu_Y = \sum_{y=0}^{2} y h(y) = (0)\left(\frac{15}{28}\right) + (1)\left(\frac{3}{7}\right) + (2)\left(\frac{1}{28}\right) = \frac{1}{2}.$$

Therefore,

$$\sigma_{XY} = E(XY) - \mu_X \mu_Y = \frac{3}{14} - \left(\frac{3}{4}\right)\left(\frac{1}{2}\right) = -\frac{9}{56}.$$

Example 14: The fraction X of male runners and the fraction Y of female runners who compete in marathon races are described by the joint density function

$$f(x, y) = \begin{cases} 8xy, & 0 \leq y \leq x \leq 1, \\ 0, & \text{elsewhere.} \end{cases}$$

Find the covariance of X and Y.

Solution: We first compute the marginal density functions. They are

$$g(x) = \begin{cases} 4x^3, & 0 \leq x \leq 1, \\ 0, & \text{elsewhere,} \end{cases}$$

and

$$h(y) = \begin{cases} 4y(1 - y^2), & 0 \leq y \leq 1, \\ 0, & \text{elsewhere.} \end{cases}$$

From these marginal density functions, we compute

$$\mu_X = E(X) = \int_0^1 4x^4 \, dx = \frac{4}{5} \text{ and } \mu_Y = \int_0^1 4y^2(1 - y^2) \, dy = \frac{8}{15}.$$

From the joint density function given above, we have

$$E(XY) = \int_0^1 \int_y^1 8x^2 y^2 \, dx \, dy = \frac{4}{9}.$$

Then

$$\sigma_{XY} = E(XY) - \mu_X \mu_Y = \frac{4}{9} - \left(\frac{4}{5}\right)\left(\frac{8}{15}\right) = \frac{4}{225}.$$

Although the covariance between two random variables does provide information regarding the nature of the relationship, the magnitude of σ_{XY} *does not indicate anything regarding the strength of the relationship*, since σ_{XY} is not scale-free. Its magnitude will depend on the units used to measure both X and Y. There is a scale-free version of the covariance called the **correlation coefficient** that is used widely in statistics.

Definition 5:

Let X and Y be random variables with covariance σ_{XY} and standard deviations σ_X and σ_Y, respectively. The correlation coefficient of X and Y is

$$\rho_{XY} = \frac{\sigma_{XY}}{\sigma_X \sigma_Y}.$$

It should be clear to the reader that ρ_{XY} is free of the units of X and Y. The correlation coefficient satisfies the inequality $-1 \leq \rho_{XY} \leq 1$. It assumes a value of zero when $\sigma_{XY} = 0$. Where there is an exact linear dependency, say $Y \equiv a + bX$,

$$\rho_{XY} = 1 \text{ if } b > 0 \text{ and } \rho_{XY} = -1 \text{ if } b < 0. \text{ (See Exercise 48.)}$$

Example 15: Find the correlation coefficient between X and Y in Example 13.

Solution: Since

$$E(X^2) = (0^2)\left(\frac{5}{14}\right) + (1^2)\left(\frac{15}{28}\right) + (2^2)\left(\frac{3}{28}\right) = \frac{27}{28}$$

and

$$E(Y^2) = (0^2)\left(\frac{15}{28}\right) + (1^2)\left(\frac{3}{7}\right) + (2^2)\left(\frac{1}{28}\right) = \frac{4}{7},$$

we obtain

$$\sigma_X^2 = \frac{27}{28} - \left(\frac{3}{4}\right)^2 = \frac{45}{112} \text{ and } \sigma_Y^2 = \frac{4}{7} - \left(\frac{1}{2}\right)^2 = \frac{9}{28}.$$

Therefore, the correlation coefficient between X and Y is

$$\rho_{XY} = \frac{\sigma_{XY}}{\sigma_X \sigma_Y} = \frac{-9/56}{\sqrt{(45/112)(9/28)}} = -\frac{1}{\sqrt{5}}.$$

Example 16: Find the correlation coefficient of X and Y in Example 14.

Solution: Because

$$E(X^2) = \int_0^1 4x^5 \, dx = \frac{2}{3} \text{ and } E(Y^2) = \int_0^1 4y^3(1-y^2) \, dy = 1 - \frac{2}{3} = \frac{1}{3},$$

we conclude that

$$\sigma_X^2 = \frac{2}{3} - \left(\frac{4}{5}\right)^2 = \frac{2}{75} \text{ and } \sigma_Y^2 = \frac{1}{3} - \left(\frac{8}{15}\right)^2 = \frac{11}{225}.$$

Hence,

$$\rho_{XY} = \frac{4/225}{\sqrt{(2/75)(11/225)}} = \frac{4}{\sqrt{66}}.$$

Note that although the covariance in Example 15 is larger in magnitude (disregarding the sign) than that in Example 16, the relationship of the magnitudes of the correlation coefficients in these two examples is just the reverse. This is evidence that we cannot look at the magnitude of the covariance to decide on how strong the relationship is.

Exercises

33   Use Definition 3 to find the variance of the random variable X of Exercise 7.

34   Let X be a random variable with the following probability distribution:

x	-2	3	5
$f(x)$	0.3	0.2	0.5

Find the standard deviation of X.

35   The random variable X, representing the number of errors per 100 lines of software code, has the following probability distribution:

x	2	3	4	5	6
$f(x)$	0.01	0.25	0.4	0.3	0.04

Using Theorem 2, find the variance of X.

36   Suppose that the probabilities are 0.4, 0.3, 0.2, and 0.1, respectively, that 0, 1, 2, or 3 power failures will strike a certain subdivision in any given year. Find the mean and variance of the random variable X representing the number of power failures striking this subdivision.

37   A dealer's profit, in units of $5000, on a new automobile is a random variable X having the density function given in Exercise 12. Find the variance of X.

38   The proportion of people who respond to a certain mail-order solicitation is a random variable X having the density function given in Exercise 13. Find the variance of X.

39   The total number of hours, in units of 100 hours, that a family runs a vacuum cleaner over a period of one year is a random variable X having the density function given in Exercise 13. Find the variance of X.

40   Referring to Exercise 14, find $\sigma^2_{g(X)}$ for the function $g(X) = 3X^2 + 4$.

41   Find the standard deviation of the random variable $g(X) = (2X + 1)^2$ in Exercise 16.

42   Using the results of Exercise 2, find the variance of $g(X) = X^2$, where X is a random variable having the density function given in Exercise 12.

43   The length of time, in minutes, for an airplane to obtain clearance for takeoff at a certain airport is a random variable $Y = 3X - 2$, where X has the density function

$$f(x) = \begin{cases} \frac{1}{4}e^{-x/4}, & x > 0 \\ 0, & \text{elsewhere.} \end{cases}$$

Find the mean and variance of the random variable Y.

44   Find the covariance of the random variables X and Y of Exercise 39 from chapter **Random Variables and Probability Distributions**.

45   Find the covariance of the random variables X and Y of Exercise 49 from chapter **Random Variables and Probability Distributions**.

46   Find the covariance of the random variables X and Y of Exercise 44 from chapter **Random Variables and Probability Distributions**.

47   For the random variables X and Y whose joint density function is given in Exercise 40 from chapter **Random Variables and Probability Distributions**, find the covariance.

48   Given a random variable X, with standard deviation σ_X, and a random variable $Y = a + bX$, show that if $b < 0$, the correlation coefficient $\rho_{XY} = -1$, and if $b > 0$, $\rho_{XY} = 1$.

49   Consider the situation in Exercise 32. The distribution of the number of imperfections per 10 meters of synthetic failure is given by

x	0	1	2	3	4
$f(x)$	0.41	0.37	0.16	0.05	0.01

Find the variance and standard deviation of the number of imperfections.

50   For a laboratory assignment, if the equipment is working, the density function of the observed outcome X is

$$f(x) = \begin{cases} 2(1-x), & 0 < x < 1, \\ 0, & \text{otherwise.} \end{cases}$$

Find the variance and standard deviation of X.

51   For the random variables X and Y in Exercise 39 from chapter **Random Variables and Probability Distributions**, determine the correlation coefficient between X and Y.

52   Random variables X and Y follow a joint distribution

$$f(x,y) = \begin{cases} 2, & 0 < x \le y < 1, \\ 0, & \text{otherwise.} \end{cases}$$

Determine the correlation coefficient between X and Y.

3 Means and Variances of Linear Combinations of Random Variables

We now develop some useful properties that will simplify the calculations of means and variances of random variables that appear in later chapters. These properties will permit us to deal with expectations in terms of other parameters that are either known or easily computed. All the results that we present here are valid for both discrete and continuous random variables. Proofs are given only for the continuous case. We begin with a theorem and two corollaries that should be, intuitively, reasonable to the reader.

Theorem 5: If a and b are constants, then

$$E(aX + b) = aE(X) + b.$$

Proof: By the definition of expected value,

$$E(aX + b) = \int_{-\infty}^{\infty} (ax + b)f(x) \, dx = a \int_{-\infty}^{\infty} xf(x) \, dx + b \int_{-\infty}^{\infty} f(x) \, dx.$$

The first integral on the right is $E(X)$ and the second integral equals 1. Therefore, we have

$$E(aX + b) = aE(X) + b.$$

Corollary 1: Setting $a = 0$, we see that $E(b) = b$.

Corollary 2: Setting $b = 0$, we see that $E(aX) = aE(X)$.

Example 17: Applying Theorem 5 to the discrete random variable $f(X) = 2X - 1$, rework Example 4.

Solution: According to Theorem 5, we can write

$$E(2X - 1) = 2E(X) - 1.$$

Now

$$\mu = E(X) = \sum_{x=4}^{9} xf(x)$$

$$= (4)\left(\frac{1}{12}\right) + (5)\left(\frac{1}{12}\right) + (6)\left(\frac{1}{4}\right) + (7)\left(\frac{1}{4}\right) + (8)\left(\frac{1}{6}\right) + (9)\left(\frac{1}{6}\right) = \frac{41}{6}.$$

Therefore,

$$\mu_{2X-1} = (2)\left(\frac{41}{6}\right) - 1 = \$12.67,$$

as before.

Example 18: Applying Theorem 5 to the continuous random variable $g(X) = 4X + 3$, rework Example 5.

Solution: For Example 5, we may use Theorem 5 to write

$$E(4X + 3) = 4E(X) + 3.$$

Now

$$E(X) = \int_{-1}^{2} x\left(\frac{x^2}{3}\right) dx = \int_{-1}^{2} \frac{x^3}{3}\, dx = \frac{5}{4}.$$

Therefore,

$$E(4X + 3) = (4)\left(\frac{5}{4}\right) + 3 = 8,$$

as before.

Theorem 6: The expected value of the sum or difference of two or more functions of a random variable X is the sum or difference of the expected values of the functions. That is,

$$E[g(X) \pm h(X)] = E[g(X)] \pm E[h(X)].$$

Proof: By definition,

$$E[g(X) \pm h(X)] = \int_{-\infty}^{\infty} [g(x) \pm h(x)]f(x)\, dx$$
$$= \int_{-\infty}^{\infty} g(x)f(x)\, dx \pm \int_{-\infty}^{\infty} h(x)f(x)\, dx$$
$$= E[g(X)] \pm E[h(X)].$$

Example 19: Let X be a random variable with probability distribution as follows:

x	0	1	2	3
$f(x)$	$\frac{1}{3}$	$\frac{1}{2}$	0	$\frac{1}{6}$

Find the expected value of $Y = (X - 1)^2$.

Solution: Applying Theorem 6 to the function $Y = (X - 1)^2$, we can write

$$E[(X - 1)^2] = E(X^2 - 2X + 1) = E(X^2) - 2E(X) + E(1).$$

From Corollary 1, $E(1) = 1$, and by direct computation,

$$E(X) = (0)\left(\frac{1}{3}\right) + (1)\left(\frac{1}{2}\right) + (2)(0) + (3)\left(\frac{1}{6}\right) = 1 \text{ and}$$
$$E(X^2) = (0)\left(\frac{1}{3}\right) + (1)\left(\frac{1}{2}\right) + (4)(0) + (9)\left(\frac{1}{6}\right) = 2.$$

Hence,

$$E[(X - 1)^2] = 2 - (2)(1) + 1 = 1.$$

Example 20: The weekly demand for a certain drink, in thousands of liters, at a chain of convenience stores is a continuous random variable $g(X) = X^2 + X - 2$, where X has the density function

$$f(x) = \begin{cases} 2(x-1), & 1 < x < 2, \\ 0, & \text{elsewhere.} \end{cases}$$

Find the expected value of the weekly demand for the drink.

Solution: By Theorem 6, we write

$$E(X^2 + X - 2) = E(X^2) + E(X) - E(2).$$

From Corollary 1, $E(2) = 2$, and by direct integration,

$$E(X) = \int_1^2 2x(x-1)\,dx = \frac{5}{3} \text{ and } E(X^2) = \int_1^2 2x^2(x-1)\,dx = \frac{17}{6}.$$

Now

$$E(X^2 + X - 2) = \frac{17}{6} + \frac{5}{3} - 2 = \frac{5}{2},$$

so the average weekly demand for the drink from this chain of efficiency stores is 2500 liters.

Suppose that we have two random variables X and Y with joint probability distribution $f(x, y)$. Two additional properties that will be very useful in succeeding chapters involve the expected values of the sum, difference, and product of these two random variables. First, however, let us prove a theorem on the expected value of the sum or difference of functions of the given variables. This, of course, is merely an extension of Theorem 6.

Theorem 7: The expected value of the sum or difference of two or more functions of the random variables X and Y is the sum or difference of the expected values of the functions. That is,

$$E[g(X, Y) \pm h(X, Y)] = E[g(X, Y)] \pm E[h(X, Y)].$$

Proof: By Definition 2,

$$E[g(X, Y) \pm h(X, Y)] = \int_{-\infty}^{\infty} \int_{-\infty}^{\infty} [g(x, y) \pm h(x, y)]f(x, y)\,dx\,dy$$

$$= \int_{-\infty}^{\infty} \int_{-\infty}^{\infty} g(x, y)f(x, y)\,dx\,dy \pm \int_{-\infty}^{\infty} \int_{-\infty}^{\infty} h(x, y)f(x, y)\,dx\,dy$$

$$= E[g(X, Y)] \pm E[h(X, Y)].$$

Corollary 3: Setting $g(X, Y) = g(X)$ and $h(X, Y) = h(Y)$, we see that

$$E[g(X) \pm h(Y)] = E[g(X)] \pm E[h(Y)].$$

Corollary 4:

Setting $g(X, Y) = X$ and $h(X, Y) = Y$, we see that

$$E[X \pm Y] = E[X] \pm E[Y].$$

If X represents the daily production of some item from machine A and Y the daily production of the same kind of item from machine B, then $X + Y$ represents the total number of items produced daily by both machines. Corollary 4 states that the average daily production for both machines is equal to the sum of the average daily production of each machine.

Theorem 8:

Let X and Y be two independent random variables. Then

$$E(XY) = E(X)E(Y).$$

Proof: By Definition 2,

$$E(XY) = \int_{-\infty}^{\infty} \int_{-\infty}^{\infty} xy f(x, y) \, dx \, dy.$$

Since X and Y are independent, we may write

$$f(x, y) = g(x)h(y),$$

where $g(x)$ and $h(y)$ are the marginal distributions of X and Y, respectively. Hence,

$$E(XY) = \int_{-\infty}^{\infty} \int_{-\infty}^{\infty} xy g(x)h(y) \, dx \, dy = \int_{-\infty}^{\infty} xg(x) \, dx \int_{-\infty}^{\infty} yh(y) \, dy$$
$$= E(X)E(Y).$$

Theorem 8 can be illustrated for discrete variables by considering the experiment of tossing a green die and a red die. Let the random variable X represent the outcome on the green die and the random variable Y represent the outcome on the red die. Then XY represents the product of the numbers that occur on the pair of dice. In the long run, the average of the products of the numbers is equal to the product of the average number that occurs on the green die and the average number that occurs on the red die.

Corollary 5:

Let X and Y be two independent random variables. Then $\sigma_{XY} = 0$.

Proof: The proof can be carried out by using Theorems 4 and 8.

Example 21:

It is known that the ratio of gallium to arsenide does not affect the functioning of gallium-arsenide wafers, which are the main components of microchips. Let X denote the ratio of gallium to arsenide and Y denote the functional wafers retrieved during a 1-hour period. X and Y are independent random variables with the joint density function

$$f(x, y) = \begin{cases} \frac{x(1+3y^2)}{4}, & 0 < x < 2, \ 0 < y < 1, \\ 0, & \text{elsewhere.} \end{cases}$$

Show that $E(XY) = E(X)E(Y)$, as Theorem 8 suggests.

Solution: By definition,

$$E(XY) = \int_0^1 \int_0^2 \frac{x^2 y(1 + 3y^2)}{4} \, dx\, dy = \frac{5}{6}, \; E(X) = \frac{4}{3}, \text{ and } E(Y) = \frac{5}{8}.$$

Hence,

$$E(X)E(Y) = \left(\frac{4}{3}\right)\left(\frac{5}{8}\right) = \frac{5}{6} = E(XY).$$

We conclude this section by proving one theorem and presenting several corollaries that are useful for calculating variances or standard deviations.

Theorem 9:

If X and Y are random variables with joint probability distribution $f(x, y)$ and a, b, and c are constants, then

$$\sigma^2_{aX+bY+c} = a^2\sigma^2_X + b^2\sigma^2_Y + 2ab\sigma_{XY}.$$

Proof: By definition, $\sigma^2_{aX+bY+c} = E\{[(aX + bY + c) - \mu_{aX+bY+c}]^2\}$. Now

$$\mu_{aX+bY+c} = E(aX + bY + c) = aE(X) + bE(Y) + c = a\mu_X + b\mu_Y + c,$$

by using Corollary 4 followed by Corollary 2. Therefore,

$$\begin{aligned}
\sigma^2_{aX+bY+c} &= E\{[a(X - \mu_X) + b(Y - \mu_Y)]^2\} \\
&= a^2 E[(X - \mu_X)^2] + b^2 E[(Y - \mu_Y)^2] + 2ab E[(X - \mu_X)(Y - \mu_Y)] \\
&= a^2\sigma^2_X + b^2\sigma^2_Y + 2ab\sigma_{XY}.
\end{aligned}$$

Using Theorem 9, we have the following corollaries.

Corollary 6:

Setting $b = 0$, we see that

$$\sigma^2_{aX+c} = a^2\sigma^2_X = a^2\sigma^2.$$

Corollary 7:

Setting $a = 1$ and $b = 0$, we see that

$$\sigma^2_{X+c} = \sigma^2_X = \sigma^2.$$

Corollary 8:

Setting $b = 0$ and $c = 0$, we see that

$$\sigma^2_{aX} = a^2\sigma^2_X = a^2\sigma^2.$$

Corollaries 6 and 7 state that the variance is unchanged if a constant is added to or subtracted from a random variable. The addition or subtraction of a constant simply shifts the values of X to the right or to the left but does not change their variability. However, if a random variable is multiplied or divided by a constant, then Corollaries 6 and 8 state that the variance is multiplied or divided by the square of the constant.

Corollary 9: If X and Y are independent random variables, then

$$\sigma^2_{aX+bY} = a^2\sigma^2_X + b^2\sigma^2_Y.$$

The result stated in Corollary 9 is obtained from Theorem 9 by invoking Corollary 5.

Corollary 10: If X and Y are independent random variables, then

$$\sigma^2_{aX-bY} = a^2\sigma^2_X + b^2\sigma^2_Y.$$

Corollary 10 follows when b in Corollary 9 is replaced by $-b$. Generalizing to a linear combination of n independent random variables, we have Corollary 11.

Corollary 11: If $X_1, X_2, \ldots, X_n$ are independent random variables, then

$$\sigma^2_{a_1X_1+a_2X_2+\cdots+a_nX_n} = a_1^2\sigma^2_{X_1} + a_2^2\sigma^2_{X_2} + \cdots + a_n^2\sigma^2_{X_n}.$$

Example 22: If X and Y are random variables with variances $\sigma^2_X = 2$ and $\sigma^2_Y = 4$ and covariance $\sigma_{XY} = -2$, find the variance of the random variable $Z = 3X - 4Y + 8$.

Solution:
$$\begin{aligned}
\sigma^2_Z = \sigma^2_{3X-4Y+8} &= \sigma^2_{3X-4Y} \quad &&\text{(by Corollary 6)} \\
&= 9\sigma^2_X + 16\sigma^2_Y - 24\sigma_{XY} \quad &&\text{(by Theorem 9)} \\
&= (9)(2) + (16)(4) - (24)(-2) = 130.
\end{aligned}$$

Example 23: Let X and Y denote the amounts of two different types of impurities in a batch of a certain chemical product. Suppose that X and Y are independent random variables with variances $\sigma^2_X = 2$ and $\sigma^2_Y = 3$. Find the variance of the random variable $Z = 3X - 2Y + 5$.

Solution:
$$\begin{aligned}
\sigma^2_Z = \sigma^2_{3X-2Y+5} &= \sigma^2_{3X-2Y} \quad &&\text{(by Corollary 6)} \\
&= 9\sigma^2_x + 4\sigma^2_y \quad &&\text{(by Corollary 10)} \\
&= (9)(2) + (4)(3) = 30.
\end{aligned}$$

What If the Function Is Nonlinear?

In that which has preceded this section, we have dealt with properties of linear functions of random variables for very important reasons. In practical real-world problems in which the analyst is constructing a **linear model** to describe a data set and thus to describe or explain the behavior of a certain scientific phenomenon. Thus, it is natural that expected values and variances of linear combinations of random variables are encountered. However, there are situations in which properties of **nonlinear** functions of random variables become important. Certainly there are many scientific phenomena that are nonlinear, and certainly statistical modeling using nonlinear functions is very important. Indeed, even a simple function of random variables, such as $Z = X/Y$, occurs quite frequently in practice, and yet unlike in the case of the expected value of linear combinations of random variables, there is no simple general rule. For example,

$$E(Z) = E(X/Y) \neq E(X)/E(Y),$$

except in very special circumstances.

The material provided by Theorems 5 through 9 and the various corollaries is extremely useful in that there are no restrictions on the form of the density or probability functions, apart from the property of independence when it is required as in the corollaries following Theorems 9. To illustrate, consider Example 23; the variance of $Z = 3X - 2Y + 5$ does not require restrictions on the distributions of the amounts X and Y of the two types of impurities. Only independence between X and Y is required. Now, we do have at our disposal the capacity to find $\mu_{g(X)}$ and $\sigma^2_{g(X)}$ for any function $g(\cdot)$ from first principles established in Theorems 1 and 3, where it is assumed that the corresponding distribution $f(x)$ is **known**. Exercises 40, 41, and 42, among others, illustrate the use of these theorems. Thus, if the function $g(x)$ is nonlinear and the density function (or probability function in the discrete case) is known, $\mu_{g(X)}$ and $\sigma^2_{g(X)}$ can be evaluated exactly. But, similar to the rules given for linear combinations, are there rules for nonlinear functions that can be used when the form of the distribution of the pertinent random variables is not known?

In general, suppose X is a random variable and $Y = g(x)$. The general solution for $E(Y)$ or Var(Y) can be difficult to find and depends on the complexity of the function $g(\cdot)$. However, there are approximations available that depend on a linear approximation of the function $g(x)$. For example, suppose we denote $E(X)$ as μ and Var$(X) = \sigma^2_X$. Then a Taylor series approximation of $g(x)$ around $X = \mu_X$ gives

$$g(x) = g(\mu_X) + \left.\frac{\partial g(x)}{\partial x}\right|_{x=\mu_X}(x-\mu_X) + \left.\frac{\partial^2 g(x)}{\partial x^2}\right|_{x=\mu_X}\frac{(x-\mu_X)^2}{2} + \cdots.$$

As a result, if we truncate after the linear term and take the expected value of both sides, we obtain $E[g(X)] \approx g(\mu_X)$, which is certainly intuitive and in some cases gives a reasonable approximation. However, if we include the second-order term of the Taylor series, then we have a second-order adjustment for this *first-order approximation* as follows:

Approximation of $E[g(X)]$	$E[g(X)] \approx g(\mu_X) + \left.\dfrac{\partial^2 g(x)}{\partial x^2}\right|_{x=\mu_X}\dfrac{\sigma^2_X}{2}.$

Example 24: Given the random variable X with mean μ_X and variance σ^2_X, give the second-order approximation to $E(e^X)$.

Solution: Since $\frac{\partial e^x}{\partial x} = e^x$ and $\frac{\partial^2 e^x}{\partial x^2} = e^x$, we obtain $E(e^X) \approx e^{\mu_X}(1 + \sigma^2_X/2)$.

Similarly, we can develop an approximation for Var$[g(x)]$ by taking the variance of both sides of the first-order Taylor series expansion of $g(x)$.

Approximation of Var$[g(X)]$	$\text{Var}[g(X)] \approx \left[\left.\dfrac{\partial g(x)}{\partial x}\right|_{x=\mu_X}\right]^2 \sigma^2_X.$

Example 25: Given the random variable X as in Example 24, give an approximate formula for Var$[g(x)]$.

Solution: Again $\frac{\partial e^x}{\partial x} = e^x$; thus, $\text{Var}(X) \approx e^{2\mu_X}\sigma_X^2$.

These approximations can be extended to nonlinear functions of more than one random variable.

Given a set of independent random variables $X_1, X_2, \ldots, X_k$ with means $\mu_1, \mu_2, \ldots, \mu_k$ and variances $\sigma_1^2, \sigma_2^2, \ldots, \sigma_k^2$, respectively, let

$$Y = h(X_1, X_2, \ldots, X_k)$$

be a nonlinear function; then the following are approximations for $E(Y)$ and $\text{Var}(Y)$:

$$E(Y) \approx h(\mu_1, \mu_2, \ldots, \mu_k) + \sum_{i=1}^{k} \frac{\sigma_i^2}{2} \left[\frac{\partial^2 h(x_1, x_2, \ldots, x_k)}{\partial x_i^2}\right]\Bigg|_{x_i = \mu_i, \ 1 \leq i \leq k},$$

$$\text{Var}(Y) \approx \sum_{i=1}^{k} \left[\frac{\partial h(x_1, x_2, \ldots, x_k)}{\partial x_i}\right]^2\Bigg|_{x_i = \mu_i, \ 1 \leq i \leq k} \sigma_i^2.$$

Example 26: Consider two independent random variables X and Z with means μ_X and μ_Z and variances σ_X^2 and σ_Z^2, respectively. Consider a random variable

$$Y = X/Z.$$

Give approximations for $E(Y)$ and $\text{Var}(Y)$.

Solution: For $E(Y)$, we must use $\frac{\partial y}{\partial x} = \frac{1}{z}$ and $\frac{\partial y}{\partial z} = -\frac{x}{z^2}$. Thus,

$$\frac{\partial^2 y}{\partial x^2} = 0 \text{ and } \frac{\partial^2 y}{\partial z^2} = \frac{2x}{z^3}.$$

As a result,

$$E(Y) \approx \frac{\mu_X}{\mu_Z} + \frac{\mu_X}{\mu_Z^3}\sigma_Z^2 = \frac{\mu_X}{\mu_Z}\left(1 + \frac{\sigma_Z^2}{\mu_Z^2}\right),$$

and the approximation for the variance of Y is given by

$$\text{Var}(Y) \approx \frac{1}{\mu_Z^2}\sigma_X^2 + \frac{\mu_X^2}{\mu_Z^4}\sigma_Z^2 = \frac{1}{\mu_Z^2}\left(\sigma_X^2 + \frac{\mu_X^2}{\mu_Z^2}\sigma_Z^2\right).$$

4   Chebyshev's Theorem

In Section 2 we stated that the variance of a random variable tells us something about the variability of the observations about the mean. If a random variable has a small variance or standard deviation, we would expect most of the values to be grouped around the mean. Therefore, the probability that the random variable assumes a value within a certain interval about the mean is greater than for a similar random variable with a larger standard deviation. If we think of probability in terms of area, we would expect a continuous distribution with a large value of σ to indicate a greater variability, and therefore we should expect the area to be more spread out, as in Figure 2(a). A distribution with a small standard deviation should have most of its area close to μ, as in Figure 2(b).

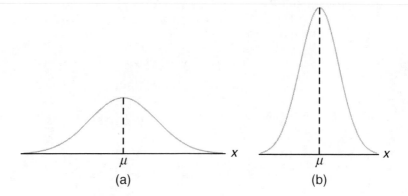

Figure 2: Variability of continuous observations about the mean.

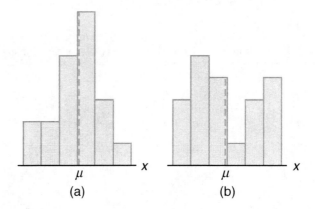

Figure 3: Variability of discrete observations about the mean.

We can argue the same way for a discrete distribution. The area in the probability histogram in Figure 3(b) is spread out much more than that in Figure 3(a) indicating a more variable distribution of measurements or outcomes.

The Russian mathematician P. L. Chebyshev (1821–1894) discovered that the fraction of the area between any two values symmetric about the mean is related to the standard deviation. Since the area under a probability distribution curve or in a probability histogram adds to 1, the area between any two numbers is the probability of the random variable assuming a value between these numbers.

The following theorem, due to Chebyshev, gives a conservative estimate of the probability that a random variable assumes a value within k standard deviations of its mean for any real number k.

Theorem 10: (**Chebyshev's Theorem**) The probability that any random variable X will assume a value within k standard deviations of the mean is at least $1 - 1/k^2$. That is,

$$P(\mu - k\sigma < X < \mu + k\sigma) \geq 1 - \frac{1}{k^2}.$$

For $k = 2$, the theorem states that the random variable X has a probability of at least $1 - 1/2^2 = 3/4$ of falling within two standard deviations of the mean. That is, three-fourths or more of the observations of any distribution lie in the interval $\mu \pm 2\sigma$. Similarly, the theorem says that at least eight-ninths of the observations of any distribution fall in the interval $\mu \pm 3\sigma$.

Example 27: A random variable X has a mean $\mu = 8$, a variance $\sigma^2 = 9$, and an unknown probability distribution. Find

(a) $P(-4 < X < 20)$,

(b) $P(|X - 8| \geq 6)$.

Solution: (a) $P(-4 < X < 20) = P[8 - (4)(3) < X < 8 + (4)(3)] \geq \frac{15}{16}$.

(b) $P(|X - 8| \geq 6) = 1 - P(|X - 8| < 6) = 1 - P(-6 < X - 8 < 6)$

$$= 1 - P[8 - (2)(3) < X < 8 + (2)(3)] \leq \frac{1}{4}.$$

Chebyshev's theorem holds for any distribution of observations, and for this reason the results are usually weak. The value given by the theorem is a lower bound only. That is, we know that the probability of a random variable falling within two standard deviations of the mean can be *no less* than 3/4, but we never know how much more it might actually be. Only when the probability distribution is known can we determine exact probabilities. For this reason we call the theorem a *distribution-free* result. When specific distributions are assumed, the results will be less conservative. The use of Chebyshev's theorem is relegated to situations where the form of the distribution is unknown.

Exercises

53 Referring to Exercise 35, find the mean and variance of the discrete random variable $Z = 3X - 2$, when X represents the number of errors per 100 lines of code.

54 Using Theorem 5 and Corollary 6, find the mean and variance of the random variable $Z = 5X + 3$, where X has the probability distribution of Exercise 36.

55 Suppose that a grocery store purchases 5 cartons of skim milk at the wholesale price of \$1.20 per carton and retails the milk at \$1.65 per carton. After the expiration date, the unsold milk is removed from the shelf and the grocer receives a credit from the dis-

tributor equal to three-fourths of the wholesale price. If the probability distribution of the random variable X, the number of cartons that are sold from this lot, is

x	0	1	2	3	4	5
$f(x)$	$\frac{1}{15}$	$\frac{2}{15}$	$\frac{2}{15}$	$\frac{3}{15}$	$\frac{4}{15}$	$\frac{3}{15}$

find the expected profit.

56 Repeat Exercise 43 by applying Theorem 5 and Corollary 6.

57 Let X be a random variable with the following probability distribution:

x	-3	6	9
$f(x)$	$\frac{1}{6}$	$\frac{1}{2}$	$\frac{1}{3}$

Find $E(X)$ and $E(X^2)$ and then, using these values, evaluate $E[(2X+1)^2]$.

58 The total time, measured in units of 100 hours, that a teenager runs her hair dryer over a period of one year is a continuous random variable X that has the density function

$$f(x) = \begin{cases} x, & 0 < x < 1, \\ 2-x, & 1 \le x < 2, \\ 0, & \text{elsewhere.} \end{cases}$$

Use Theorem 6 to evaluate the mean of the random variable $Y = 60X^2 + 39X$, where Y is equal to the number of kilowatt hours expended annually.

59 If a random variable X is defined such that

$$E[(X-1)^2] = 10 \text{ and } E[(X-2)^2] = 6,$$

find μ and σ^2.

60 Suppose that X and Y are independent random variables having the joint probability distribution

$f(x,y)$	x	
	2	4
y 1	0.10	0.15
3	0.20	0.30
5	0.10	0.15

Find
(a) $E(2X - 3Y)$;
(b) $E(XY)$.

61 Use Theorem 7 to evaluate $E(2XY^2 - X^2Y)$ for the joint probability distribution shown in Table 1.

62 If X and Y are independent random variables with variances $\sigma_X^2 = 5$ and $\sigma_Y^2 = 3$, find the variance of the random variable $Z = -2X + 4Y - 3$.

63 Repeat Exercise 62 if X and Y are not independent and $\sigma_{XY} = 1$.

64 Suppose that X and Y are independent random variables with probability densities and

$$g(x) = \begin{cases} \frac{8}{x^3}, & x > 2, \\ 0, & \text{elsewhere,} \end{cases}$$

and

$$h(y) = \begin{cases} 2y, & 0 < y < 1, \\ 0, & \text{elsewhere.} \end{cases}$$

Find the expected value of $Z = XY$.

65 Let X represent the number that occurs when a red die is tossed and Y the number that occurs when a green die is tossed. Find
(a) $E(X+Y)$;
(b) $E(X-Y)$;
(c) $E(XY)$.

66 Let X represent the number that occurs when a green die is tossed and Y the number that occurs when a red die is tossed. Find the variance of the random variable
(a) $2X - Y$;
(b) $X + 3Y - 5$.

67 If the joint density function of X and Y is given by

$$f(x,y) = \begin{cases} \frac{2}{7}(x+2y), & 0 < x < 1,\ 1 < y < 2, \\ 0, & \text{elsewhere,} \end{cases}$$

find the expected value of $g(X,Y) = \frac{X}{Y^3} + X^2Y$.

68 The power P in watts which is dissipated in an electric circuit with resistance R is known to be given by $P = I^2R$, where I is current in amperes and R is a constant fixed at 50 ohms. However, I is a random variable with $\mu_I = 15$ amperes and $\sigma_I^2 = 0.03$ amperes^2. Give numerical approximations to the mean and variance of the power P.

69 Consider Review Exercise 77 from Chapter **Random Variables and Probability Distributions**. The random variables X and Y represent the number of vehicles that arrive at two separate street corners during a certain 2-minute period in the day. The joint distribution is

$$f(x,y) = \left(\frac{1}{4^{(x+y)}} \right) \left(\frac{9}{16} \right),$$

for $x = 0, 1, 2, \ldots$ and $y = 0, 1, 2, \ldots$.
(a) Give $E(X)$, $E(Y)$, $\text{Var}(X)$, and $\text{Var}(Y)$.
(b) Consider $Z = X + Y$, the sum of the two. Find $E(Z)$ and $\text{Var}(Z)$.

70 Consider Review Exercise 64 from Chapter **Random Variables and Probability Distributions**. There are two service lines. The random variables X and Y are the proportions of time that line 1 and line 2 are in use, respectively. The joint probability density function for (X, Y) is given by

$$f(x,y) = \begin{cases} \frac{3}{2}(x^2 + y^2), & 0 \le x,\ y \le 1, \\ 0, & \text{elsewhere.} \end{cases}$$

(a) Determine whether or not X and Y are independent.

(b) It is of interest to know something about the proportion of $Z = X + Y$, the sum of the two proportions. Find $E(X + Y)$. Also find $E(XY)$.

(c) Find $\text{Var}(X)$, $\text{Var}(Y)$, and $\text{Cov}(X, Y)$.

(d) Find $\text{Var}(X + Y)$.

71 The length of time Y, in minutes, required to generate a human reflex to tear gas has the density function

$$f(y) = \begin{cases} \frac{1}{4}e^{-y/4}, & 0 \le y < \infty, \\ 0, & \text{elsewhere.} \end{cases}$$

(a) What is the mean time to reflex?

(b) Find $E(Y^2)$ and $\text{Var}(Y)$.

72 A manufacturing company has developed a machine for cleaning carpet that is fuel-efficient because it delivers carpet cleaner so rapidly. Of interest is a random variable Y, the amount in gallons per minute delivered. It is known that the density function is given by

$$f(y) = \begin{cases} 1, & 7 \le y \le 8, \\ 0, & \text{elsewhere.} \end{cases}$$

(a) Sketch the density function.

(b) Give $E(Y)$, $E(Y^2)$, and $\text{Var}(Y)$.

73 For the situation in Exercise 72, compute $E(e^Y)$ using Theorem 4.1, that is, by using

$$E(e^Y) = \int_7^8 e^y f(y)\, dy.$$

Then compute $E(e^Y)$ not by using $f(y)$, but rather by using the second-order adjustment to the first-order approximation of $E(e^Y)$. Comment.

74 Consider again the situation of Exercise 72. It is required to find $\text{Var}(e^Y)$. Use Theorems 2 and 3 and define $Z = e^Y$. Thus, use the conditions of Exercise 73 to find

$$\text{Var}(Z) = E(Z^2) - [E(Z)]^2.$$

Review Exercises

79 Prove Chebyshev's theorem.

80 Find the covariance of random variables X and Y having the joint probability density function

$$f(x, y) = \begin{cases} x + y, & 0 < x < 1,\ 0 < y < 1, \\ 0, & \text{elsewhere.} \end{cases}$$

Then do it not by using $f(y)$, but rather by using the first-order Taylor series approximation to $\text{Var}(e^Y)$. Comment!

75 An electrical firm manufactures a 100-watt light bulb, which, according to specifications written on the package, has a mean life of 900 hours with a standard deviation of 50 hours. At most, what percentage of the bulbs fail to last even 700 hours? Assume that the distribution is symmetric about the mean.

76 Seventy new jobs are opening up at an automobile manufacturing plant, and 1000 applicants show up for the 70 positions. To select the best 70 from among the applicants, the company gives a test that covers mechanical skill, manual dexterity, and mathematical ability. The mean grade on this test turns out to be 60, and the scores have a standard deviation of 6. Can a person who scores 84 count on getting one of the jobs? [*Hint*: Use Chebyshev's theorem.] Assume that the distribution is symmetric about the mean.

77 A random variable X has a mean $\mu = 10$ and a variance $\sigma^2 = 4$. Using Chebyshev's theorem, find

(a) $P(|X - 10| \ge 3)$;

(b) $P(|X - 10| < 3)$;

(c) $P(5 < X < 15)$;

(d) the value of the constant c such that

$$P(|X - 10| \ge c) \le 0.04.$$

78 Compute $P(\mu - 2\sigma < X < \mu + 2\sigma)$, where X has the density function

$$f(x) = \begin{cases} 6x(1 - x), & 0 < x < 1, \\ 0, & \text{elsewhere,} \end{cases}$$

and compare with the result given in Chebyshev's theorem.

81 Referring to the random variables whose joint probability density function is given in Exercise 47 from Chapter **Random Variables and Probability Distributions**, find the average amount of kerosene left in the tank at the end of the day.

82 Assume the length X, in minutes, of a particular type of telephone conversation is a random variable

Mathematical Expectation

with probability density function

$$f(x) = \begin{cases} \frac{1}{5}e^{-x/5}, & x > 0, \\ 0, & \text{elsewhere.} \end{cases}$$

(a) Determine the mean length $E(X)$ of this type of telephone conversation.

(b) Find the variance and standard deviation of X.

(c) Find $E[(X+5)^2]$.

83 Referring to the random variables whose joint density function is given in Exercise 41 from Chapter **Random Variables and Probability Distributions**, find the covariance between the weight of the creams and the weight of the toffees in those boxes of chocolates.

84 Referring to the random variables whose joint probability density function is given in Exercise 41, find the expected weight for the sum of the creams and toffees if one purchased a box of these chocolates.

85 Suppose it is known that the life X of a particular compressor, in hours, has the density function

$$f(x) = \begin{cases} \frac{1}{900}e^{-x/900}, & x > 0, \\ 0, & \text{elsewhere.} \end{cases}$$

(a) Find the mean life of the compressor.

(b) Find $E(X^2)$.

(c) Find the variance and standard deviation of the random variable X.

86 Referring to the random variables whose joint density function is given in Exercise 40 from Chapter **Random Variables and Probability Distributions,**
(a) find μ_X and μ_Y;

(b) find $E[(X+Y)/2]$.

87 Show that $\text{Cov}(aX, bY) = ab\,\text{Cov}(X, Y)$.

88 Consider the density function of Review Exercise 85. Demonstrate that Chebyshev's theorem holds for $k = 2$ and $k = 3$.

89 Consider the joint density function

$$f(x, y) = \begin{cases} \frac{16y}{x^3}, & x > 2,\ 0 < y < 1, \\ 0, & \text{elsewhere.} \end{cases}$$

Compute the correlation coefficient ρ_{XY}.

90 Consider random variables X and Y of Exercise 63. Compute ρ_{XY}.

91 A dealer's profit, in units of \$5000, on a new automobile is a random variable X having density function

$$f(x) = \begin{cases} 2(1-x), & 0 \le x \le 1, \\ 0, & \text{elsewhere.} \end{cases}$$

(a) Find the variance of the dealer's profit.

(b) Demonstrate that Chebyshev's theorem holds for $k = 2$ with the density function above.

(c) What is the probability that the profit exceeds \$500?

92 Consider Exercise 10. Can it be said that the ratings given by the two experts are independent? Explain why or why not.

93 A company's marketing and accounting departments have determined that if the company markets its newly developed product, the contribution of the product to the firm's profit during the next 6 months will be described by the following:

Profit Contribution	Probability
$-\$5,000$	0.2
$\$10,000$	0.5
$\$30,000$	0.3

What is the company's expected profit?

94 In a support system in the U.S. space program, a single crucial component works only 85% of the time. In order to enhance the reliability of the system, it is decided that 3 components will be installed in parallel such that the system fails only if they all fail. Assume the components act independently and that they are equivalent in the sense that all 3 of them have an 85% success rate. Consider the random variable X as the number of components out of 3 that fail.

(a) Write out a probability function for the random variable X.

(b) What is $E(X)$ (i.e., the mean number of components out of 3 that fail)?

(c) What is $\text{Var}(X)$?

(d) What is the probability that the entire system is successful?

(e) What is the probability that the system fails?

(f) If the desire is to have the system be successful with probability 0.99, are three components sufficient? If not, how many are required?

95 In business, it is important to plan and carry out research in order to anticipate what will occur at the end of the year. Research suggests that the profit (loss) spectrum for a certain company, with corresponding probabilities, is as follows:

Profit	Probability
−$15,000	0.05
$0	0.15
$15,000	0.15
$25,000	0.30
$40,000	0.15
$50,000	0.10
$100,000	0.05
$150,000	0.03
$200,000	0.02

(a) What is the expected profit?

(b) Give the standard deviation of the profit.

96   It is known through data collection and considerable research that the amount of time in seconds that a certain employee of a company is late for work is a random variable X with density function

$$f(x) = \begin{cases} \frac{3}{(4)(50^3)}(50^2 - x^2), & -50 \le x \le 50, \\ 0, & \text{elsewhere.} \end{cases}$$

In other words, he not only is slightly late at times, but also can be early to work.

(a) Find the expected value of the time in seconds that he is late.

(b) Find $E(X^2)$.

(c) What is the standard deviation of the amount of time he is late?

97   A delivery truck travels from point A to point B and back using the same route each day. There are four traffic lights on the route. Let X_1 denote the number of red lights the truck encounters going from A to B and X_2 denote the number encountered on the return trip. Data collected over a long period suggest that the joint probability distribution for (X_1, X_2) is given by

			x_2		
x_1	0	1	2	3	4
0	0.01	0.01	0.03	0.07	0.01
1	0.03	0.05	0.08	0.03	0.02
2	0.03	0.11	0.15	0.01	0.01
3	0.02	0.07	0.10	0.03	0.01
4	0.01	0.06	0.03	0.01	0.01

(a) Give the marginal density of X_1.

(b) Give the marginal density of X_2.

(c) Give the conditional density distribution of X_1 given $X_2 = 3$.

(d) Give $E(X_1)$.

(e) Give $E(X_2)$.

(f) Give $E(X_1 \mid X_2 = 3)$.

(g) Give the standard deviation of X_1.

98   A convenience store has two separate locations where customers can be checked out as they leave. These locations each have two cash registers and two employees who check out customers. Let X be the number of cash registers being used at a particular time for location 1 and Y the number being used at the same time for location 2. The joint probability function is given by

		y	
x	0	1	2
0	0.12	0.04	0.04
1	0.08	0.19	0.05
2	0.06	0.12	0.30

(a) Give the marginal density of both X and Y as well as the probability distribution of X given $Y = 2$.

(b) Give $E(X)$ and $\mathrm{Var}(X)$.

(c) Give $E(X \mid Y = 2)$ and $\mathrm{Var}(X \mid Y = 2)$.

99   Consider a ferry that can carry both buses and cars across a waterway. Each trip costs the owner approximately $10. The fee for cars is $3 and the fee for buses is $8. Let X and Y denote the number of buses and cars, respectively, carried on a given trip. The joint distribution of X and Y is given by

		x	
y	0	1	2
0	0.01	0.01	0.03
1	0.03	0.08	0.07
2	0.03	0.06	0.06
3	0.07	0.07	0.13
4	0.12	0.04	0.03
5	0.08	0.06	0.02

Compute the expected profit for the ferry trip.

100   Statistical methods associated with linear and nonlinear models are very important. In fact, exponential functions are often used in a wide variety of scientific and engineering problems. Consider a model that is fit to a set of data involving measured values k_1 and k_2 and a certain response Y to the measurements. The model postulated is

$$\hat{Y} = e^{b_0 + b_1 k_1 + b_2 k_2},$$

where $\hat{Y}$ denotes the **estimated value of Y**, k_1 and k_2 are fixed values, and b_0, b_1, and b_2 are **estimates** of constants and hence are random variables. Assume that these random variables are independent and use the approximate formula for the variance of a nonlinear function of more than one variable. Give an expression for $\mathrm{Var}(\hat{Y})$. Assume that the means of b_0, b_1, and b_2 are known and are β_0, β_1, and β_2, and assume that the variances of b_0, b_1, and b_2 are known and are σ_0^2, σ_1^2, and σ_2^2.

101 Consider Review Exercise 73 from Chapter **Random Variables and Probability Distributions**. It involved Y, the proportion of impurities in a batch, and the density function is given by

$$f(y) = \begin{cases} 10(1-y)^9, & 0 \leq y \leq 1, \\ 0, & \text{elsewhere.} \end{cases}$$

(a) Find the expected percentage of impurities.

(b) Find the expected value of the proportion of quality material (i.e., find $E(1-Y)$).

(c) Find the variance of the random variable $Z = 1-Y$.

102 **Project**: Let $X =$ number of hours each student in the class slept the night before. Create a discrete variable by using the following arbitrary intervals: $X < 3$, $3 \leq X < 6$, $6 \leq X < 9$, and $X \geq 9$.

(a) Estimate the probability distribution for X.

(b) Calculate the estimated mean and variance for X.

5 Potential Misconceptions and Hazards; Relationship to Material in Other Chapters

The material in this chapter is extremely fundamental in nature. In this chapter we defined important quantities or *parameters* that characterize the general nature of the system. The **mean** of a distribution reflects *central tendency*, and the **variance** or **standard deviation** reflects *variability* in the system. In addition, covariance reflects the tendency for two random variables to "move together" in a system. These important parameters will remain fundamental to all.

The reader should understand that the distribution type is often dictated by the scientific scenario. However, the parameter values need to be estimated from scientific data. For example, in the case of Review Exercise 85, the manufacturer of the compressor may know from experience and knowledge of the type of compressor that the nature of the distribution is as indicated in the exercise. But the mean $\mu = 900$ would be **estimated** from experimentation on the machine. Though the parameter value of 900 is given as known here, it will not be known in real-life situations without the use of experimental data.

Answers to Odd-Numbered Non-Review Exercises

1   0.88

3   25¢

5   $1.23

7   $500

9   $6900

11   $(\ln 4)/\pi$

13   100 hours

15   0

17   209

19   $1855

21   $833.33

23   (a) 35.2; (b) $\mu_X = 3.20$, $\mu_Y = 3.00$

25   2

27   2000 hours

29   (b) 3/2

31   (a) 1/6; (b) $(5/6)^5$

33   $5,250,000

35   0.74

37   1/18; in terms of actual profit, the variance is $\frac{1}{18}(5000)^2$

39   1/6

41   118.9

43   $\mu_Y = 10$; $\sigma_Y^2 = 144$

45   0.01

47   −0.0062

49   $\sigma_X^2 = 0.8456$, $\sigma_X = 0.9196$

51   $-1/\sqrt{5}$

53   $\mu_{g(X)} = 10.33$, $\sigma_{g(X)} = 6.66$

55   $0.80

57   209

59   $\mu = 7/2$, $\sigma^2 = 15/4$

61   3/14

63   52

65   (a) 7; (b) 0; (c) 12.25

67   46/63

69   (a) $E(X) = E(Y) = 1/3$ and $\text{Var}(X) = \text{Var}(Y) = 4/9$; (b) $E(Z) = 2/3$ and $\text{Var}(Z) = 8/9$

71   (a) 4; (b) 32; 16

73   By direct calculation, $E(e^Y) = 1884.32$. Using the second-order approximation, $E(e^Y) \approx 1883.38$, which is very close to the true value.

75   0.03125

77   (a) At most 4/9; (b) at least 5/9; (c) at least 21/25; (d) 10

Some Discrete Probability Distributions

1   Introduction and Motivation

No matter whether a discrete probability distribution is represented graphically by a histogram, in tabular form, or by means of a formula, the behavior of a random variable is described. Often, the observations generated by different statistical experiments have the same general type of behavior. Consequently, discrete random variables associated with these experiments can be described by essentially the same probability distribution and therefore can be represented by a single formula. In fact, one needs only a handful of important probability distributions to describe many of the discrete random variables encountered in practice.

Such a handful of distributions describe several real-life random phenomena. For instance, in a study involving testing the effectiveness of a new drug, the number of cured patients among all the patients who use the drug approximately follows a binomial distribution (Section 2). In an industrial example, when a sample of items selected from a batch of production is tested, the number of defective items in the sample usually can be modeled as a hypergeometric random variable (Section 3). In a statistical quality control problem, the experimenter will signal a shift of the process mean when observational data exceed certain limits. The number of samples required to produce a false alarm follows a geometric distribution which is a special case of the negative binomial distribution (Section 4). On the other hand, the number of white cells from a fixed amount of an individual's blood sample is usually random and may be described by a Poisson distribution (Section 5). In this chapter, we present these commonly used distributions with various examples.

2   Binomial and Multinomial Distributions

An experiment often consists of repeated trials, each with two possible outcomes that may be labeled **success** or **failure**. The most obvious application deals with

From Chapter 5 of *Probability & Statistics for Engineers & Scientists*, Ninth Edition, Ronald E. Walpole, Raymond H. Myers, Sharon L. Myers, Keying Ye. Copyright © 2012 by Pearson Education, Inc. Published by Pearson Prentice Hall. All rights reserved.

the testing of items as they come off an assembly line, where each trial may indicate a defective or a nondefective item. We may choose to define either outcome as a success. The process is referred to as a **Bernoulli process**. Each trial is called a **Bernoulli trial**. Observe, for example, if one were drawing cards from a deck, the probabilities for repeated trials change if the cards are not replaced. That is, the probability of selecting a heart on the first draw is 1/4, but on the second draw it is a conditional probability having a value of 13/51 or 12/51, depending on whether a heart appeared on the first draw: this, then, would no longer be considered a set of Bernoulli trials.

The Bernoulli Process

Strictly speaking, the Bernoulli process must possess the following properties:

1. The experiment consists of repeated trials.

2. Each trial results in an outcome that may be classified as a success or a failure.

3. The probability of success, denoted by p, remains constant from trial to trial.

4. The repeated trials are independent.

Consider the set of Bernoulli trials where three items are selected at random from a manufacturing process, inspected, and classified as defective or nondefective. A defective item is designated a success. The number of successes is a random variable X assuming integral values from 0 through 3. The eight possible outcomes and the corresponding values of X are

Outcome	NNN	NDN	NND	DNN	NDD	DND	DDN	DDD
x	0	1	1	1	2	2	2	3

Since the items are selected independently and we assume that the process produces 25% defectives, we have

$$P(NDN) = P(N)P(D)P(N) = \left(\frac{3}{4}\right)\left(\frac{1}{4}\right)\left(\frac{3}{4}\right) = \frac{9}{64}.$$

Similar calculations yield the probabilities for the other possible outcomes. The probability distribution of X is therefore

x	0	1	2	3
$f(x)$	$\frac{27}{64}$	$\frac{27}{64}$	$\frac{9}{64}$	$\frac{1}{64}$

Binomial Distribution

The number X of successes in n Bernoulli trials is called a **binomial random variable**. The probability distribution of this discrete random variable is called the **binomial distribution**, and its values will be denoted by $b(x; n, p)$ since they depend on the number of trials and the probability of a success on a given trial. Thus, for the probability distribution of X, the number of defectives is

$$P(X = 2) = f(2) = b\left(2; 3, \frac{1}{4}\right) = \frac{9}{64}.$$

Let us now generalize the above illustration to yield a formula for $b(x; n, p)$. That is, we wish to find a formula that gives the probability of x successes in n trials for a binomial experiment. First, consider the probability of x successes and $n - x$ failures in a specified order. Since the trials are independent, we can multiply all the probabilities corresponding to the different outcomes. Each success occurs with probability p and each failure with probability $q = 1 - p$. Therefore, the probability for the specified order is $p^x q^{n-x}$. We must now determine the total number of sample points in the experiment that have x successes and $n - x$ failures. This number is equal to the number of partitions of n outcomes into two groups with x in one group and $n - x$ in the other and is written $\binom{n}{x}$. Because these partitions are mutually exclusive, we add the probabilities of all the different partitions to obtain the general formula, or simply multiply $p^x q^{n-x}$ by $\binom{n}{x}$.

Binomial Distribution	A Bernoulli trial can result in a success with probability p and a failure with probability $q = 1 - p$. Then the probability distribution of the binomial random variable X, the number of successes in n independent trials, is

$$b(x; n, p) = \binom{n}{x} p^x q^{n-x}, \quad x = 0, 1, 2, \ldots, n.$$

Note that when $n = 3$ and $p = 1/4$, the probability distribution of X, the number of defectives, may be written as

$$b\left(x; 3, \frac{1}{4}\right) = \binom{3}{x} \left(\frac{1}{4}\right)^x \left(\frac{3}{4}\right)^{3-x}, \quad x = 0, 1, 2, 3,$$

rather than in the tabular form.

Example 1: The probability that a certain kind of component will survive a shock test is $3/4$. Find the probability that exactly 2 of the next 4 components tested survive.

Solution: Assuming that the tests are independent and $p = 3/4$ for each of the 4 tests, we obtain

$$b\left(2; 4, \frac{3}{4}\right) = \binom{4}{2} \left(\frac{3}{4}\right)^2 \left(\frac{1}{4}\right)^2 = \left(\frac{4!}{2! \, 2!}\right) \left(\frac{3^2}{4^4}\right) = \frac{27}{128}.$$

Where Does the Name *Binomial* Come From?

The binomial distribution derives its name from the fact that the $n + 1$ terms in the binomial expansion of $(q + p)^n$ correspond to the various values of $b(x; n, p)$ for $x = 0, 1, 2, \ldots, n$. That is,

$$(q + p)^n = \binom{n}{0} q^n + \binom{n}{1} pq^{n-1} + \binom{n}{2} p^2 q^{n-2} + \cdots + \binom{n}{n} p^n$$

$$= b(0; n, p) + b(1; n, p) + b(2; n, p) + \cdots + b(n; n, p).$$

Since $p + q = 1$, we see that

$$\sum_{x=0}^{n} b(x; n, p) = 1,$$

a condition that must hold for any probability distribution.

Frequently, we are interested in problems where it is necessary to find $P(X < r)$ or $P(a \leq X \leq b)$. Binomial sums

$$B(r; n, p) = \sum_{x=0}^{r} b(x; n, p)$$

are given in Table Binomial Probability Sums at the end of this chapter for $n = 1$, $2, \ldots, 20$ for selected values of p from 0.1 to 0.9. We illustrate the use of this table with the following example.

Example 2: The probability that a patient recovers from a rare blood disease is 0.4. If 15 people are known to have contracted this disease, what is the probability that (a) at least 10 survive, (b) from 3 to 8 survive, and (c) exactly 5 survive?

Solution: Let X be the number of people who survive.

(a) $\quad P(X \geq 10) = 1 - P(X < 10) = 1 - \sum_{x=0}^{9} b(x; 15, 0.4) = 1 - 0.9662$

$\quad\quad\quad = 0.0338$

(b) $\quad P(3 \leq X \leq 8) = \sum_{x=3}^{8} b(x; 15, 0.4) = \sum_{x=0}^{8} b(x; 15, 0.4) - \sum_{x=0}^{2} b(x; 15, 0.4)$

$\quad\quad\quad = 0.9050 - 0.0271 = 0.8779$

(c) $\quad P(X = 5) = b(5; 15, 0.4) = \sum_{x=0}^{5} b(x; 15, 0.4) - \sum_{x=0}^{4} b(x; 15, 0.4)$

$\quad\quad\quad = 0.4032 - 0.2173 = 0.1859$

Example 3: A large chain retailer purchases a certain kind of electronic device from a manufacturer. The manufacturer indicates that the defective rate of the device is 3%.

(a) The inspector randomly picks 20 items from a shipment. What is the probability that there will be at least one defective item among these 20?

(b) Suppose that the retailer receives 10 shipments in a month and the inspector randomly tests 20 devices per shipment. What is the probability that there will be exactly 3 shipments each containing at least one defective device among the 20 that are selected and tested from the shipment?

Solution: (a) Denote by X the number of defective devices among the 20. Then X follows a $b(x; 20, 0.03)$ distribution. Hence,

$$P(X \geq 1) = 1 - P(X = 0) = 1 - b(0; 20, 0.03)$$
$$= 1 - (0.03)^0 (1 - 0.03)^{20-0} = 0.4562.$$

(b) In this case, each shipment can either contain at least one defective item or not. Hence, testing of each shipment can be viewed as a Bernoulli trial with $p = 0.4562$ from part (a). Assuming independence from shipment to shipment and denoting by Y the number of shipments containing at least one defective item, Y follows another binomial distribution $b(y; 10, 0.4562)$. Therefore,

$$P(Y = 3) = \binom{10}{3} 0.4562^3 (1 - 0.4562)^7 = 0.1602.$$

Areas of Application

From Examples 1 through 3, it should be clear that the binomial distribution finds applications in many scientific fields. An industrial engineer is keenly interested in the "proportion defective" in an industrial process. Often, quality control measures and sampling schemes for processes are based on the binomial distribution. This distribution applies to any industrial situation where an outcome of a process is dichotomous and the results of the process are independent, with the probability of success being constant from trial to trial. The binomial distribution is also used extensively for medical and military applications. In both fields, a success or failure result is important. For example, "cure" or "no cure" is important in pharmaceutical work, and "hit" or "miss" is often the interpretation of the result of firing a guided missile.

Since the probability distribution of any binomial random variable depends only on the values assumed by the parameters n, p, and q, it would seem reasonable to assume that the mean and variance of a binomial random variable also depend on the values assumed by these parameters. Indeed, this is true, and in the proof of Theorem 1 we derive general formulas that can be used to compute the mean and variance of any binomial random variable as functions of n, p, and q.

Theorem 1:

> The mean and variance of the binomial distribution $b(x; n, p)$ are
> $$\mu = np \text{ and } \sigma^2 = npq.$$

***Proof*:** Let the outcome on the jth trial be represented by a Bernoulli random variable I_j, which assumes the values 0 and 1 with probabilities q and p, respectively. Therefore, in a binomial experiment the number of successes can be written as the sum of the n independent indicator variables. Hence,

$$X = I_1 + I_2 + \cdots + I_n.$$

The mean of any I_j is $E(I_j) = (0)(q) + (1)(p) = p$. Therefore, using Corollary 4, the mean of the binomial distribution is

$$\mu = E(X) = E(I_1) + E(I_2) + \cdots + E(I_n) = \underbrace{p + p + \cdots + p}_{n \text{ terms}} = np.$$

The variance of any I_j is $\sigma_{I_j}^2 = E(I_j^2) - p^2 = (0)^2(q) + (1)^2(p) - p^2 = p(1-p) = pq$. In the case of n, indepenent Bernoulli variables give the variance of the binomial distribution as

$$\sigma_X^2 = \sigma_{I_1}^2 + \sigma_{I_2}^2 + \cdots + \sigma_{I_n}^2 = \underbrace{pq + pq + \cdots + pq}_{n \text{ terms}} = npq.$$

Example 4: It is conjectured that an impurity exists in 30% of all drinking wells in a certain rural community. In order to gain some insight into the true extent of the problem, it is determined that some testing is necessary. It is too expensive to test all of the wells in the area, so 10 are randomly selected for testing.

    (a) Using the binomial distribution, what is the probability that exactly 3 wells have the impurity, assuming that the conjecture is correct?

    (b) What is the probability that more than 3 wells are impure?

Solution: (a) We require

$$b(3; 10, 0.3) = \sum_{x=0}^{3} b(x; 10, 0.3) - \sum_{x=0}^{2} b(x; 10, 0.3) = 0.6496 - 0.3828 = 0.2668.$$

    (b) In this case, $P(X > 3) = 1 - 0.6496 = 0.3504$.

Example 5: Find the mean and variance of the binomial random variable of Example 2, and then use Chebyshev's theorem to interpret the interval $\mu \pm 2\sigma$.

Solution: Since Example 2 was a binomial experiment with $n = 15$ and $p = 0.4$, by Theorem 1, we have

$$\mu = (15)(0.4) = 6 \text{ and } \sigma^2 = (15)(0.4)(0.6) = 3.6.$$

Taking the square root of 3.6, we find that $\sigma = 1.897$. Hence, the required interval is $6 \pm (2)(1.897)$, or from 2.206 to 9.794. Chebyshev's theorem states that the number of recoveries among 15 patients who contracted the disease has a probability of at least 3/4 of falling between 2.206 and 9.794 or, because the data are discrete, between 2 and 10 inclusive.

There are solutions in which the computation of binomial probabilities may allow us to draw a scientific inference about population after data are collected. An illustration is given in the next example.

Example 6: Consider the situation of Example 4. The notion that 30% of the wells are impure is merely a conjecture put forth by the area water board. Suppose 10 wells are randomly selected and 6 are found to contain the impurity. What does this imply about the conjecture? Use a probability statement.

Solution: We must first ask: "If the conjecture is correct, is it likely that we would find 6 or more impure wells?"

$$P(X \geq 6) = \sum_{x=0}^{10} b(x; 10, 0.3) - \sum_{x=0}^{5} b(x; 10, 0.3) = 1 - 0.9527 = 0.0473.$$

As a result, it is very unlikely (4.7% chance) that 6 or more wells would be found impure if only 30% of all are impure. This casts considerable doubt on the conjecture and suggests that the impurity problem is much more severe.

As the reader should realize by now, in many applications there are more than two possible outcomes. To borrow an example from the field of genetics, the color of guinea pigs produced as offspring may be red, black, or white. Often the "defective" or "not defective" dichotomy is truly an oversimplification in engineering situations. Indeed, there are often more than two categories that characterize items or parts coming off an assembly line.

Multinomial Experiments and the Multinomial Distribution

The binomial experiment becomes a **multinomial experiment** if we let each trial have more than two possible outcomes. The classification of a manufactured product as being light, heavy, or acceptable and the recording of accidents at a certain intersection according to the day of the week constitute multinomial experiments. The drawing of a card from a deck *with replacement* is also a multinomial experiment if the 4 suits are the outcomes of interest.

In general, if a given trial can result in any one of k possible outcomes $E_1, E_2, \ldots,$ E_k with probabilities $p_1, p_2, \ldots, p_k$, then the **multinomial distribution** will give the probability that E_1 occurs x_1 times, E_2 occurs x_2 times, $\ldots$, and E_k occurs x_k times in n independent trials, where

$$x_1 + x_2 + \cdots + x_k = n.$$

We shall denote this joint probability distribution by

$$f(x_1, x_2, \ldots, x_k; p_1, p_2, \ldots, p_k, n).$$

Clearly, $p_1 + p_2 + \cdots + p_k = 1$, since the result of each trial must be one of the k possible outcomes.

To derive the general formula, we proceed as in the binomial case. Since the trials are independent, any specified order yielding x_1 outcomes for E_1, x_2 for $E_2, \ldots, x_k$ for E_k will occur with probability $p_1^{x_1} p_2^{x_2} \cdots p_k^{x_k}$. The total number of orders yielding similar outcomes for the n trials is equal to the number of partitions of n items into k groups with x_1 in the first group, x_2 in the second group, $\ldots$, and x_k in the kth group. This can be done in

$$\binom{n}{x_1, x_2, \ldots, x_k} = \frac{n!}{x_1! \, x_2! \cdots x_k!}$$

ways. Since all the partitions are mutually exclusive and occur with equal probability, we obtain the multinomial distribution by multiplying the probability for a specified order by the total number of partitions.

Multinomial Distribution

If a given trial can result in the k outcomes $E_1, E_2, \ldots, E_k$ with probabilities $p_1, p_2, \ldots, p_k$, then the probability distribution of the random variables $X_1, X_2, \ldots, X_k$, representing the number of occurrences for $E_1, E_2, \ldots, E_k$ in n independent trials, is

$$f(x_1, x_2, \ldots, x_k; p_1, p_2, \ldots, p_k, n) = \binom{n}{x_1, x_2, \ldots, x_k} p_1^{x_1} p_2^{x_2} \cdots p_k^{x_k},$$

with

$$\sum_{i=1}^{k} x_i = n \text{ and } \sum_{i=1}^{k} p_i = 1.$$

The multinomial distribution derives its name from the fact that the terms of the multinomial expansion of $(p_1 + p_2 + \cdots + p_k)^n$ correspond to all the possible values of $f(x_1, x_2, \ldots, x_k; p_1, p_2, \ldots, p_k, n)$.

Example 7:   The complexity of arrivals and departures of planes at an airport is such that computer simulation is often used to model the "ideal" conditions. For a certain airport with three runways, it is known that in the ideal setting the following are the probabilities that the individual runways are accessed by a randomly arriving commercial jet:

$$\text{Runway 1:} \quad p_1 = 2/9,$$
$$\text{Runway 2:} \quad p_2 = 1/6,$$
$$\text{Runway 3:} \quad p_3 = 11/18.$$

What is the probability that 6 randomly arriving airplanes are distributed in the following fashion?

$$\text{Runway 1:} \quad \text{2 airplanes,}$$
$$\text{Runway 2:} \quad \text{1 airplane,}$$
$$\text{Runway 3:} \quad \text{3 airplanes}$$

Solution: Using the multinomial distribution, we have

$$f\left(2,1,3; \frac{2}{9}, \frac{1}{6}, \frac{11}{18}, 6\right) = \binom{6}{2,1,3}\left(\frac{2}{9}\right)^2 \left(\frac{1}{6}\right)^1 \left(\frac{11}{18}\right)^3$$

$$= \frac{6!}{2!\,1!\,3!} \cdot \frac{2^2}{9^2} \cdot \frac{1}{6} \cdot \frac{11^3}{18^3} = 0.1127.$$

Exercises

1 A random variable X that assumes the values $x_1, x_2, \ldots, x_k$ is called a discrete uniform random variable if its probability mass function is $f(x) = \frac{1}{k}$ for all of $x_1, x_2, \ldots, x_k$ and 0 otherwise. Find the mean and variance of X.

2 Twelve people are given two identical speakers, which they are asked to listen to for differences, if any. Suppose that these people answer simply by guessing. Find the probability that three people claim to have heard a difference between the two speakers.

3 An employee is selected from a staff of 10 to supervise a certain project by selecting a tag at random from a box containing 10 tags numbered from 1 to 10. Find the formula for the probability distribution of X representing the number on the tag that is drawn. What is the probability that the number drawn is less than 4?

4 In a certain city district, the need for money to buy drugs is stated as the reason for 75% of all thefts. Find the probability that among the next 5 theft cases reported in this district,

(a) exactly 2 resulted from the need for money to buy drugs;

(b) at most 3 resulted from the need for money to buy drugs.

5 According to *Chemical Engineering Progress* (November 1990), approximately 30% of all pipework failures in chemical plants are caused by operator error.

(a) What is the probability that out of the next 20 pipework failures at least 10 are due to operator error?

(b) What is the probability that no more than 4 out of 20 such failures are due to operator error?

(c) Suppose, for a particular plant, that out of the random sample of 20 such failures, exactly 5 are due to operator error. Do you feel that the 30% figure stated above applies to this plant? Comment.

6 According to a survey by the Administrative Management Society, one-half of U.S. companies give employees 4 weeks of vacation after they have been with the company for 15 years. Find the probability that among 6 companies surveyed at random, the number that give employees 4 weeks of vacation after 15 years of employment is

(a) anywhere from 2 to 5;

(b) fewer than 3.

7 One prominent physician claims that 70% of those with lung cancer are chain smokers. If his assertion is correct,

(a) find the probability that of 10 such patients

recently admitted to a hospital, fewer than half are chain smokers;

(b) find the probability that of 20 such patients recently admitted to a hospital, fewer than half are chain smokers.

8   According to a study published by a group of University of Massachusetts sociologists, approximately 60% of the Valium users in the state of Massachusetts first took Valium for psychological problems. Find the probability that among the next 8 users from this state who are interviewed,

(a) exactly 3 began taking Valium for psychological problems;

(b) at least 5 began taking Valium for problems that were not psychological.

9   In testing a certain kind of truck tire over rugged terrain, it is found that 25% of the trucks fail to complete the test run without a blowout. Of the next 15 trucks tested, find the probability that

(a) from 3 to 6 have blowouts;

(b) fewer than 4 have blowouts;

(c) more than 5 have blowouts.

10   A nationwide survey of college seniors by the University of Michigan revealed that almost 70% disapprove of daily pot smoking, according to a report in *Parade*. If 12 seniors are selected at random and asked their opinion, find the probability that the number who disapprove of smoking pot daily is

(a) anywhere from 7 to 9;

(b) at most 5;

(c) not less than 8.

11   The probability that a patient recovers from a delicate heart operation is 0.9. What is the probability that exactly 5 of the next 7 patients having this operation survive?

12   A traffic control engineer reports that 75% of the vehicles passing through a checkpoint are from within the state. What is the probability that fewer than 4 of the next 9 vehicles are from out of state?

13   A national study that examined attitudes about antidepressants revealed that approximately 70% of respondents believe "antidepressants do not really cure anything, they just cover up the real trouble." According to this study, what is the probability that at least 3 of the next 5 people selected at random will hold this opinion?

14   The percentage of wins for the Chicago Bulls basketball team going into the playoffs for the 1996–97 season was 87.7. Round the 87.7 to 90 in order to use Table A.1.

(a) What is the probability that the Bulls sweep (4-0) the initial best-of-7 playoff series?

(b) What is the probability that the Bulls win the initial best-of-7 playoff series?

(c) What very important assumption is made in answering parts (a) and (b)?

15   It is known that 60% of mice inoculated with a serum are protected from a certain disease. If 5 mice are inoculated, find the probability that

(a) none contracts the disease;

(b) fewer than 2 contract the disease;

(c) more than 3 contract the disease.

16   Suppose that airplane engines operate independently and fail with probability equal to 0.4. Assuming that a plane makes a safe flight if at least one-half of its engines run, determine whether a 4-engine plane or a 2-engine plane has the higher probability for a successful flight.

17   If X represents the number of people in Exercise 13 who believe that antidepressants do not cure but only cover up the real problem, find the mean and variance of X when 5 people are selected at random.

5.18 (a) In Exercise 9, how many of the 15 trucks would you expect to have blowouts?

(b) What is the variance of the number of blowouts experienced by the 15 trucks? What does that mean?

19   As a student drives to school, he encounters a traffic signal. This traffic signal stays green for 35 seconds, yellow for 5 seconds, and red for 60 seconds. Assume that the student goes to school each weekday between 8:00 and 8:30 a.m. Let X_1 be the number of times he encounters a green light, X_2 be the number of times he encounters a yellow light, and X_3 be the number of times he encounters a red light. Find the joint distribution of X_1, X_2, and X_3.

20   According to *USA Today* (March 18, 1997), of 4 million workers in the general workforce, 5.8% tested positive for drugs. Of those testing positive, 22.5% were cocaine users and 54.4% marijuana users.

(a) What is the probability that of 10 workers testing positive, 2 are cocaine users, 5 are marijuana users, and 3 are users of other drugs?

(b) What is the probability that of 10 workers testing positive, all are marijuana users?

(c) What is the probability that of 10 workers testing positive, none is a cocaine user?

21 The surface of a circular dart board has a small center circle called the bull's-eye and 20 pie-shaped regions numbered from 1 to 20. Each of the pie-shaped regions is further divided into three parts such that a person throwing a dart that lands in a specific region scores the value of the number, double the number, or triple the number, depending on which of the three parts the dart hits. If a person hits the bull's-eye with probability 0.01, hits a double with probability 0.10, hits a triple with probability 0.05, and misses the dart board with probability 0.02, what is the probability that 7 throws will result in no bull's-eyes, no triples, a double twice, and a complete miss once?

22 According to a genetics theory, a certain cross of guinea pigs will result in red, black, and white offspring in the ratio 8:4:4. Find the probability that among 8 offspring, 5 will be red, 2 black, and 1 white.

23 The probabilities are 0.4, 0.2, 0.3, and 0.1, respectively, that a delegate to a certain convention arrived by air, bus, automobile, or train. What is the probability that among 9 delegates randomly selected at this convention, 3 arrived by air, 3 arrived by bus, 1 arrived by automobile, and 2 arrived by train?

24 A safety engineer claims that only 40% of all workers wear safety helmets when they eat lunch at the workplace. Assuming that this claim is right, find the probability that 4 of 6 workers randomly chosen will be wearing their helmets while having lunch at the workplace.

25 Suppose that for a very large shipment of integrated-circuit chips, the probability of failure for any one chip is 0.10. Assuming that the assumptions underlying the binomial distributions are met, find the probability that at most 3 chips fail in a random sample of 20.

26 Assuming that 6 in 10 automobile accidents are due mainly to a speed violation, find the probability that among 8 automobile accidents, 6 will be due mainly to a speed violation

(a) by using the formula for the binomial distribution;

(b) by using Table Binomial Probability Sums.

27 If the probability that a fluorescent light has a useful life of at least 800 hours is 0.9, find the probabilities that among 20 such lights

(a) exactly 18 will have a useful life of at least 800 hours;

(b) at least 15 will have a useful life of at least 800 hours;

(c) at least 2 will *not* have a useful life of at least 800 hours.

28 A manufacturer knows that on average 20% of the electric toasters produced require repairs within 1 year after they are sold. When 20 toasters are randomly selected, find appropriate numbers x and y such that

(a) the probability that at least x of them will require repairs is less than 0.5;

(b) the probability that at least y of them will *not* require repairs is greater than 0.8.

3 Hypergeometric Distribution

The simplest way to view the distinction between the binomial distribution of Section 2 and the hypergeometric distribution is to note the way the sampling is done. The types of applications for the hypergeometric are very similar to those for the binomial distribution. We are interested in computing probabilities for the number of observations that fall into a particular category. But in the case of the binomial distribution, independence among trials is required. As a result, if that distribution is applied to, say, sampling from a lot of items (deck of cards, batch of production items), the sampling must be done **with replacement** of each item after it is observed. On the other hand, the hypergeometric distribution does not require independence and is based on sampling done **without replacement**.

Applications for the hypergeometric distribution are found in many areas, with heavy use in acceptance sampling, electronic testing, and quality assurance. Obviously, in many of these fields, testing is done at the expense of the item being tested. That is, the item is destroyed and hence cannot be replaced in the sample. Thus, sampling without replacement is necessary. A simple example with playing cards will serve as our first illustration.

If we wish to find the probability of observing 3 red cards in 5 draws from an ordinary deck of 52 playing cards, the binomial distribution of Section 2 does not apply unless each card is replaced and the deck reshuffled before the next draw is made. To solve the problem of sampling without replacement, let us restate the problem. If 5 cards are drawn at random, we are interested in the probability of selecting 3 red cards from the 26 available in the deck and 2 black cards from the 26 available in the deck. There are $\binom{26}{3}$ ways of selecting 3 red cards, and for each of these ways we can choose 2 black cards in $\binom{26}{2}$ ways. Therefore, the total number of ways to select 3 red and 2 black cards in 5 draws is the product $\binom{26}{3}\binom{26}{2}$. The total number of ways to select any 5 cards from the 52 that are available is $\binom{52}{5}$. Hence, the probability of selecting 5 cards without replacement of which 3 are red and 2 are black is given by

$$\frac{\binom{26}{3}\binom{26}{2}}{\binom{52}{5}} = \frac{(26!/3!\,23!)(26!/2!\,24!)}{52!/5!\,47!} = 0.3251.$$

In general, we are interested in the probability of selecting x successes from the k items labeled successes and $n - x$ failures from the $N - k$ items labeled failures when a random sample of size n is selected from N items. This is known as a **hypergeometric experiment**, that is, one that possesses the following two properties:

1. A random sample of size n is selected without replacement from N items.

2. Of the N items, k may be classified as successes and $N - k$ are classified as failures.

The number X of successes of a hypergeometric experiment is called a **hypergeometric random variable**. Accordingly, the probability distribution of the hypergeometric variable is called the **hypergeometric distribution**, and its values are denoted by $h(x; N, n, k)$, since they depend on the number of successes k in the set N from which we select n items.

Hypergeometric Distribution in Acceptance Sampling

Like the binomial distribution, the hypergeometric distribution finds applications in acceptance sampling, where lots of materials or parts are sampled in order to determine whether or not the entire lot is accepted.

Example 8: A particular part that is used as an injection device is sold in lots of 10. The producer deems a lot acceptable if no more than one defective is in the lot. A sampling plan involves random sampling and testing 3 of the parts out of 10. If none of the 3 is defective, the lot is accepted. Comment on the utility of this plan.

Solution: Let us assume that the lot is truly **unacceptable** (i.e., that 2 out of 10 parts are defective). The probability that the sampling plan finds the lot acceptable is

$$P(X = 0) = \frac{\binom{2}{0}\binom{8}{3}}{\binom{10}{3}} = 0.467.$$

Thus, if the lot is truly unacceptable, with 2 defective parts, this sampling plan will allow acceptance roughly 47% of the time. As a result, this plan should be considered faulty.

Let us now generalize in order to find a formula for $h(x; N, n, k)$. The total number of samples of size n chosen from N items is $\binom{N}{n}$. These samples are assumed to be equally likely. There are $\binom{k}{x}$ ways of selecting x successes from the k that are available, and for each of these ways we can choose the $n - x$ failures in $\binom{N-k}{n-x}$ ways. Thus, the total number of favorable samples among the $\binom{N}{n}$ possible samples is given by $\binom{k}{x}\binom{N-k}{n-x}$. Hence, we have the following definition.

Hypergeometric Distribution

The probability distribution of the hypergeometric random variable X, the number of successes in a random sample of size n selected from N items of which k are labeled **success** and $N - k$ labeled **failure**, is

$$h(x; N, n, k) = \frac{\binom{k}{x}\binom{N-k}{n-x}}{\binom{N}{n}}, \quad \max\{0, n - (N - k)\} \leq x \leq \min\{n, k\}.$$

The range of x can be determined by the three binomial coefficients in the definition, where x and $n - x$ are no more than k and $N - k$, respectively, and both of them cannot be less than 0. Usually, when both k (the number of successes) and $N - k$ (the number of failures) are larger than the sample size n, the range of a hypergeometric random variable will be $x = 0, 1, \ldots, n$.

Example 9: Lots of 40 components each are deemed unacceptable if they contain 3 or more defectives. The procedure for sampling a lot is to select 5 components at random and to reject the lot if a defective is found. What is the probability that exactly 1 defective is found in the sample if there are 3 defectives in the entire lot?

Solution: Using the hypergeometric distribution with $n = 5$, $N = 40$, $k = 3$, and $x = 1$, we find the probability of obtaining 1 defective to be

$$h(1; 40, 5, 3) = \frac{\binom{3}{1}\binom{37}{4}}{\binom{40}{5}} = 0.3011.$$

Once again, this plan is not desirable since it detects a bad lot (3 defectives) only about 30% of the time.

Theorem 2: The mean and variance of the hypergeometric distribution $h(x; N, n, k)$ are

$$\mu = \frac{nk}{N} \text{ and } \sigma^2 = \frac{N - n}{N - 1} \cdot n \cdot \frac{k}{N}\left(1 - \frac{k}{N}\right).$$

Example 10: Let us now reinvestigate the following: Statisticians use **sampling plans** to either accept or reject batches or lots of material. Suppose one of these sampling plans involves sampling independently 10 items from a lot of 100 items in which 12 are defective.

Let X be the random variable defined as the number of items found defective in the sample of 10. In this case, the random variable takes on the values $0, 1, 2, \ldots, 9, 10$.

The purpose of this example was to illustrate the notion of a random variable and the corresponding sample space. In the example, we have a lot of 100 items of which 12 are defective. What is the probability that in a sample of 10, 3 are defective?

***Solution*:** Using the hypergeometric probability function, we have

$$h(3; 100, 10, 12) = \frac{\binom{12}{3}\binom{88}{7}}{\binom{100}{10}} = 0.08.$$

Example 11: Find the mean and variance of the random variable of Example 9 and then use Chebyshev's theorem to interpret the interval $\mu \pm 2\sigma$.

***Solution*:** Since Example 9 was a hypergeometric experiment with $N = 40$, $n = 5$, and $k = 3$, by Theorem 2, we have

$$\mu = \frac{(5)(3)}{40} = \frac{3}{8} = 0.375,$$

and

$$\sigma^2 = \left(\frac{40-5}{39}\right)(5)\left(\frac{3}{40}\right)\left(1 - \frac{3}{40}\right) = 0.3113.$$

Taking the square root of 0.3113, we find that $\sigma = 0.558$. Hence, the required interval is $0.375 \pm (2)(0.558)$, or from -0.741 to 1.491. Chebyshev's theorem states that the number of defectives obtained when 5 components are selected at random from a lot of 40 components of which 3 are defective has a probability of at least $3/4$ of falling between -0.741 and 1.491. That is, at least three-fourths of the time, the 5 components include fewer than 2 defectives.

Relationship to the Binomial Distribution

In this chapter, we discuss several important discrete distributions that have wide applicability. Many of these distributions relate nicely to each other. The beginning student should gain a clear understanding of these relationships. There is an interesting relationship between the hypergeometric and the binomial distribution. As one might expect, if n is small compared to N, the nature of the N items changes very little in each draw. So a binomial distribution can be used to approximate the hypergeometric distribution when n is small compared to N. In fact, as a rule of thumb, the approximation is good when $n/N \le 0.05$.

Thus, the quantity k/N plays the role of the binomial parameter p. As a result, the binomial distribution may be viewed as a large-population version of the hypergeometric distribution. The mean and variance then come from the formulas

$$\mu = np = \frac{nk}{N} \text{ and } \sigma^2 = npq = n \cdot \frac{k}{N}\left(1 - \frac{k}{N}\right).$$

Comparing these formulas with those of Theorem 2, we see that the mean is the same but the variance differs by a correction factor of $(N-n)/(N-1)$, which is negligible when n is small relative to N.

Example 12: A manufacturer of automobile tires reports that among a shipment of 5000 sent to a local distributor, 1000 are slightly blemished. If one purchases 10 of these tires at random from the distributor, what is the probability that exactly 3 are blemished?

Solution : Since $N = 5000$ is large relative to the sample size $n = 10$, we shall approximate the desired probability by using the binomial distribution. The probability of obtaining a blemished tire is 0.2. Therefore, the probability of obtaining exactly 3 blemished tires is

$$h(3; 5000, 10, 1000) \approx b(3; 10, 0.2) = 0.8791 - 0.6778 = 0.2013.$$

On the other hand, the exact probability is $h(3; 5000, 10, 1000) = 0.2015$.

The hypergeometric distribution can be extended to treat the case where the N items can be partitioned into k cells $A_1, A_2, \ldots, A_k$ with a_1 elements in the first cell, a_2 elements in the second cell, $\ldots$, a_k elements in the kth cell. We are now interested in the probability that a random sample of size n yields x_1 elements from A_1, x_2 elements from A_2, $\ldots$, and x_k elements from A_k. Let us represent this probability by

$$f(x_1, x_2, \ldots, x_k; a_1, a_2, \ldots, a_k, N, n).$$

To obtain a general formula, we note that the total number of samples of size n that can be chosen from N items is still $\binom{N}{n}$. There are $\binom{a_1}{x_1}$ ways of selecting x_1 items from the items in A_1, and for each of these we can choose x_2 items from the items in A_2 in $\binom{a_2}{x_2}$ ways. Therefore, we can select x_1 items from A_1 and x_2 items from A_2 in $\binom{a_1}{x_1}\binom{a_2}{x_2}$ ways. Continuing in this way, we can select all n items consisting of x_1 from A_1, x_2 from A_2, $\ldots$, and x_k from A_k in

$$\binom{a_1}{x_1}\binom{a_2}{x_2} \cdots \binom{a_k}{x_k} \quad \text{ways}.$$

The required probability distribution is now defined as follows.

Multivariate Hypergeometric Distribution

If N items can be partitioned into the k cells $A_1, A_2, \ldots, A_k$ with $a_1, a_2, \ldots, a_k$ elements, respectively, then the probability distribution of the random variables $X_1, X_2, \ldots, X_k$, representing the number of elements selected from $A_1, A_2, \ldots, A_k$ in a random sample of size n, is

$$f(x_1, x_2, \ldots, x_k; a_1, a_2, \ldots, a_k, N, n) = \frac{\binom{a_1}{x_1}\binom{a_2}{x_2} \cdots \binom{a_k}{x_k}}{\binom{N}{n}},$$

with $\sum_{i=1}^{k} x_i = n$ and $\sum_{i=1}^{k} a_i = N$.

Example 13: A group of 10 individuals is used for a biological case study. The group contains 3 people with blood type O, 4 with blood type A, and 3 with blood type B. What is the probability that a random sample of 5 will contain 1 person with blood type O, 2 people with blood type A, and 2 people with blood type B?

Solution : Using the extension of the hypergeometric distribution with $x_1 = 1$, $x_2 = 2$, $x_3 = 2$, $a_1 = 3$, $a_2 = 4$, $a_3 = 3$, $N = 10$, and $n = 5$, we find that the desired probability is

$$f(1, 2, 2; 3, 4, 3, 10, 5) = \frac{\binom{3}{1}\binom{4}{2}\binom{3}{2}}{\binom{10}{5}} = \frac{3}{14}.$$

Exercises

29 A homeowner plants 6 bulbs selected at random from a box containing 5 tulip bulbs and 4 daffodil bulbs. What is the probability that he planted 2 daffodil bulbs and 4 tulip bulbs?

30 To avoid detection at customs, a traveler places 6 narcotic tablets in a bottle containing 9 vitamin tablets that are similar in appearance. If the customs official selects 3 of the tablets at random for analysis, what is the probability that the traveler will be arrested for illegal possession of narcotics?

31 A random committee of size 3 is selected from 4 doctors and 2 nurses. Write a formula for the probability distribution of the random variable X representing the number of doctors on the committee. Find $P(2 \leq X \leq 3)$.

32 From a lot of 10 missiles, 4 are selected at random and fired. If the lot contains 3 defective missiles that will not fire, what is the probability that

(a) all 4 will fire?

(b) at most 2 will not fire?

33 If 7 cards are dealt from an ordinary deck of 52 playing cards, what is the probability that

(a) exactly 2 of them will be face cards?

(b) at least 1 of them will be a queen?

34 What is the probability that a waitress will refuse to serve alcoholic beverages to only 2 minors if she randomly checks the IDs of 5 among 9 students, 4 of whom are minors?

35 A company is interested in evaluating its current inspection procedure for shipments of 50 identical items. The procedure is to take a sample of 5 and pass the shipment if no more than 2 are found to be defective. What proportion of shipments with 20% defectives will be accepted?

36 A manufacturing company uses an acceptance scheme on items from a production line before they are shipped. The plan is a two-stage one. Boxes of 25 items are readied for shipment, and a sample of 3 items is tested for defectives. If any defectives are found, the entire box is sent back for 100% screening. If no defectives are found, the box is shipped.

(a) What is the probability that a box containing 3 defectives will be shipped?

(b) What is the probability that a box containing only 1 defective will be sent back for screening?

37 Suppose that the manufacturing company of Exercise 36 decides to change its acceptance scheme. Under the new scheme, an inspector takes 1 item at random, inspects it, and then replaces it in the box; a second inspector does likewise. Finally, a third inspector goes through the same procedure. The box is not shipped if any of the three inspectors find a defective. Answer the questions in Exercise 36 for this new plan.

38 Among 150 IRS employees in a large city, only 30 are women. If 10 of the employees are chosen at random to provide free tax assistance for the residents of this city, use the binomial approximation to the hypergeometric distribution to find the probability that at least 3 women are selected.

39 An annexation suit against a county subdivision of 1200 residences is being considered by a neighboring city. If the occupants of half the residences object to being annexed, what is the probability that in a random sample of 10 at least 3 favor the annexation suit?

40 It is estimated that 4000 of the 10,000 voting residents of a town are against a new sales tax. If 15 eligible voters are selected at random and asked their opinion, what is the probability that at most 7 favor the new tax?

41 A nationwide survey of 17,000 college seniors by the University of Michigan revealed that almost 70% disapprove of daily pot smoking. If 18 of these seniors are selected at random and asked their opinion, what is the probability that more than 9 but fewer than 14 disapprove of smoking pot daily?

42 Find the probability of being dealt a bridge hand of 13 cards containing 5 spades, 2 hearts, 3 diamonds, and 3 clubs.

43 A foreign student club lists as its members 2 Canadians, 3 Japanese, 5 Italians, and 2 Germans. If a committee of 4 is selected at random, find the probability that

(a) all nationalities are represented;

(b) all nationalities except Italian are represented.

44 An urn contains 3 green balls, 2 blue balls, and 4 red balls. In a random sample of 5 balls, find the probability that both blue balls and at least 1 red ball are selected.

45 Biologists doing studies in a particular environment often tag and release subjects in order to estimate the size of a population or the prevalence of certain features in the population. Ten animals of a certain population thought to be extinct (or near extinction) are caught, tagged, and released in a certain region. After a period of time, a random sample of 15 of this type of animal is selected in the region. What is the probability that 5 of those selected are tagged if there are 25 animals of this type in the region?

46   A large company has an inspection system for the batches of small compressors purchased from vendors. A batch typically contains 15 compressors. In the inspection system, a random sample of 5 is selected and all are tested. Suppose there are 2 faulty compressors in the batch of 15.

(a) What is the probability that for a given sample there will be 1 faulty compressor?

(b) What is the probability that inspection will discover both faulty compressors?

47   A government task force suspects that some manufacturing companies are in violation of federal pollution regulations with regard to dumping a certain type of product. Twenty firms are under suspicion but not all can be inspected. Suppose that 3 of the firms are in violation.

(a) What is the probability that inspection of 5 firms will find no violations?

(b) What is the probability that the plan above will find two violations?

48   Every hour, 10,000 cans of soda are filled by a machine, among which 300 underfilled cans are produced. Each hour, a sample of 30 cans is randomly selected and the number of ounces of soda per can is checked. Denote by X the number of cans selected that are underfilled. Find the probability that at least 1 underfilled can will be among those sampled.

4   Negative Binomial and Geometric Distributions

Let us consider an experiment where the properties are the same as those listed for a binomial experiment, with the exception that the trials will be repeated until a *fixed* number of successes occur. Therefore, instead of the probability of x successes in n trials, where n is fixed, we are now interested in the probability that the kth success occurs on the xth trial. Experiments of this kind are called **negative binomial experiments**.

As an illustration, consider the use of a drug that is known to be effective in 60% of the cases where it is used. The drug will be considered a success if it is effective in bringing some degree of relief to the patient. We are interested in finding the probability that the fifth patient to experience relief is the seventh patient to receive the drug during a given week. Designating a success by S and a failure by F, a possible order of achieving the desired result is $SFSSSFS$, which occurs with probability

$$(0.6)(0.4)(0.6)(0.6)(0.6)(0.4)(0.6) = (0.6)^5(0.4)^2.$$

We could list all possible orders by rearranging the F's and S's except for the last outcome, which must be the fifth success. The total number of possible orders is equal to the number of partitions of the first six trials into two groups with 2 failures assigned to the one group and 4 successes assigned to the other group. This can be done in $\binom{6}{4} = 15$ mutually exclusive ways. Hence, if X represents the outcome on which the fifth success occurs, then

$$P(X = 7) = \binom{6}{4}(0.6)^5(0.4)^2 = 0.1866.$$

What Is the Negative Binomial Random Variable?

The number X of trials required to produce k successes in a negative binomial experiment is called a **negative binomial random variable**, and its probability distribution is called the **negative binomial distribution**. Since its probabilities depend on the number of successes desired and the probability of a success on a given trial, we shall denote them by $b^*(x; k, p)$. To obtain the general formula for $b^*(x; k, p)$, consider the probability of a success on the xth trial preceded by $k - 1$ successes and $x - k$ failures in some specified order. Since the trials are independent, we can multiply all the probabilities corresponding to each desired outcome. Each success occurs with probability p and each failure with probability $q = 1 - p$. Therefore, the probability for the specified order ending in success is

$$p^{k-1}q^{x-k}p = p^k q^{x-k}.$$

The total number of sample points in the experiment ending in a success, after the occurrence of $k - 1$ successes and $x - k$ failures in any order, is equal to the number of partitions of $x - 1$ trials into two groups with $k - 1$ successes corresponding to one group and $x - k$ failures corresponding to the other group. This number is specified by the term $\binom{x-1}{k-1}$, each mutually exclusive and occurring with equal probability $p^k q^{x-k}$. We obtain the general formula by multiplying $p^k q^{x-k}$ by $\binom{x-1}{k-1}$.

Negative Binomial Distribution	If repeated independent trials can result in a success with probability p and a failure with probability $q = 1 - p$, then the probability distribution of the random variable X, the number of the trial on which the kth success occurs, is

$$b^*(x; k, p) = \binom{x-1}{k-1} p^k q^{x-k}, \quad x = k, k+1, k+2, \ldots.$$

Example 14:

In an NBA (National Basketball Association) championship series, the team that wins four games out of seven is the winner. Suppose that teams A and B face each other in the championship games and that team A has probability 0.55 of winning a game over team B.

(a) What is the probability that team A will win the series in 6 games?

(b) What is the probability that team A will win the series?

(c) If teams A and B were facing each other in a regional playoff series, which is decided by winning three out of five games, what is the probability that team A would win the series?

Solution: (a) $b^*(6; 4, 0.55) = \binom{5}{3} 0.55^4 (1 - 0.55)^{6-4} = 0.1853$

(b) P(team A wins the championship series) is

$$b^*(4; 4, 0.55) + b^*(5; 4, 0.55) + b^*(6; 4, 0.55) + b^*(7; 4, 0.55)$$
$$= 0.0915 + 0.1647 + 0.1853 + 0.1668 = 0.6083.$$

(c) P(team A wins the playoff) is

$$b^*(3; 3, 0.55) + b^*(4; 3, 0.55) + b^*(5; 3, 0.55)$$
$$= 0.1664 + 0.2246 + 0.2021 = 0.5931.$$

The negative binomial distribution derives its name from the fact that each term in the expansion of $p^k(1-q)^{-k}$ corresponds to the values of $b^*(x;k,p)$ for $x = k,\ k+1,\ k+2,\ \ldots$. If we consider the special case of the negative binomial distribution where $k = 1$, we have a probability distribution for the number of trials required for a single success. An example would be the tossing of a coin until a head occurs. We might be interested in the probability that the first head occurs on the fourth toss. The negative binomial distribution reduces to the form

$$b^*(x;1,p) = pq^{x-1}, \quad x = 1,2,3,\ldots.$$

Since the successive terms constitute a geometric progression, it is customary to refer to this special case as the **geometric distribution** and denote its values by $g(x;p)$.

Geometric Distribution   If repeated independent trials can result in a success with probability p and a failure with probability $q = 1 - p$, then the probability distribution of the random variable X, the number of the trial on which the first success occurs, is

$$g(x;p) = pq^{x-1}, \quad x = 1,2,3,\ldots.$$

Example 15: For a certain manufacturing process, it is known that, on the average, 1 in every 100 items is defective. What is the probability that the fifth item inspected is the first defective item found?

Solution: Using the geometric distribution with $x = 5$ and $p = 0.01$, we have

$$g(5;0.01) = (0.01)(0.99)^4 = 0.0096.$$

Example 16: At a "busy time," a telephone exchange is very near capacity, so callers have difficulty placing their calls. It may be of interest to know the number of attempts necessary in order to make a connection. Suppose that we let $p = 0.05$ be the probability of a connection during a busy time. We are interested in knowing the probability that 5 attempts are necessary for a successful call.

Solution: Using the geometric distribution with $x = 5$ and $p = 0.05$ yields

$$P(X = x) = g(5;0.05) = (0.05)(0.95)^4 = 0.041.$$

Quite often, in applications dealing with the geometric distribution, the mean and variance are important. For example, in Example 16, the *expected* number of calls necessary to make a connection is quite important. The following theorem states without proof the mean and variance of the geometric distribution.

Theorem 3: The mean and variance of a random variable following the geometric distribution are

$$\mu = \frac{1}{p} \text{ and } \sigma^2 = \frac{1-p}{p^2}.$$

Applications of Negative Binomial and Geometric Distributions

Areas of application for the negative binomial and geometric distributions become obvious when one focuses on the examples in this section and the exercises devoted to these distributions at the end of Section 5. In the case of the geometric distribution, Example 16 depicts a situation where engineers or managers are attempting to determine how inefficient a telephone exchange system is during busy times. Clearly, in this case, trials occurring prior to a success represent a cost. If there is a high probability of several attempts being required prior to making a connection, then plans should be made to redesign the system.

Applications of the negative binomial distribution are similar in nature. Suppose attempts are costly in some sense and are *occurring in sequence*. A high probability of needing a "large" number of attempts to experience a fixed number of successes is not beneficial to the scientist or engineer. Consider the scenarios of Review Exercises 90 and 91. In Review Exercise 91, the oil driller defines a certain level of success from sequentially drilling locations for oil. If only 6 attempts have been made at the point where the second success is experienced, the profits appear to dominate substantially the investment incurred by the drilling.

5 Poisson Distribution and the Poisson Process

Experiments yielding numerical values of a random variable X, the number of outcomes occurring during a given time interval or in a specified region, are called **Poisson experiments**. The given time interval may be of any length, such as a minute, a day, a week, a month, or even a year. For example, a Poisson experiment can generate observations for the random variable X representing the number of telephone calls received per hour by an office, the number of days school is closed due to snow during the winter, or the number of games postponed due to rain during a baseball season. The specified region could be a line segment, an area, a volume, or perhaps a piece of material. In such instances, X might represent the number of field mice per acre, the number of bacteria in a given culture, or the number of typing errors per page. A Poisson experiment is derived from the **Poisson process** and possesses the following properties.

Properties of the Poisson Process

1. The number of outcomes occurring in one time interval or specified region of space is independent of the number that occur in any other disjoint time interval or region. In this sense we say that the Poisson process has no memory.

2. The probability that a single outcome will occur during a very short time interval or in a small region is proportional to the length of the time interval or the size of the region and does not depend on the number of outcomes occurring outside this time interval or region.

3. The probability that more than one outcome will occur in such a short time interval or fall in such a small region is negligible.

The number X of outcomes occurring during a Poisson experiment is called a **Poisson random variable**, and its probability distribution is called the **Poisson**

distribution. The mean number of outcomes is computed from $\mu = \lambda t$, where t is the specific "time," "distance," "area," or "volume" of interest. Since the probabilities depend on λ, the rate of occurrence of outcomes, we shall denote them by $p(x; \lambda t)$. The derivation of the formula for $p(x; \lambda t)$, based on the three properties of a Poisson process listed above, is beyond the scope of this book. The following formula is used for computing Poisson probabilities.

Poisson Distribution

The probability distribution of the Poisson random variable X, representing the number of outcomes occurring in a given time interval or specified region denoted by t, is

$$p(x; \lambda t) = \frac{e^{-\lambda t}(\lambda t)^x}{x!}, \quad x = 0, 1, 2, \ldots,$$

where λ is the average number of outcomes per unit time, distance, area, or volume and $e = 2.71828 \ldots$.

Table Poisson Probability Sums at the end of this chapter contains,

$$P(r; \lambda t) = \sum_{x=0}^{r} p(x; \lambda t),$$

for selected values of λt ranging from 0.1 to 18.0. We illustrate the use of this table with the following two examples.

Example 17: During a laboratory experiment, the average number of radioactive particles passing through a counter in 1 millisecond is 4. What is the probability that 6 particles enter the counter in a given millisecond?

Solution: Using the Poisson distribution with $x = 6$ and $\lambda t = 4$ and referring to Table Poisson Probability Sums we have

$$p(6; 4) = \frac{e^{-4}4^6}{6!} = \sum_{x=0}^{6} p(x; 4) - \sum_{x=0}^{5} p(x; 4) = 0.8893 - 0.7851 = 0.1042.$$

Example 18: Ten is the average number of oil tankers arriving each day at a certain port. The facilities at the port can handle at most 15 tankers per day. What is the probability that on a given day tankers have to be turned away?

Solution: Let X be the number of tankers arriving each day. Then, using Table Poisson Probability Sums we have

$$P(X > 15) = 1 - P(X \leq 15) = 1 - \sum_{x=0}^{15} p(x; 10) = 1 - 0.9513 = 0.0487.$$

Like the binomial distribution, the Poisson distribution is used for quality control, quality assurance, and acceptance sampling. In addition, certain important continuous distributions used in reliability theory and queuing theory depend on the Poisson process. The following theorem concerning the Poisson random variable is given at the end of this chapter as Proof of Mean and Variance of the Poisson Distribution.

Theorem 4: Both the mean and the variance of the Poisson distribution $p(x; \lambda t)$ are λt.

Nature of the Poisson Probability Function

Like so many discrete and continuous distributions, the form of the Poisson distribution becomes more and more symmetric, even bell-shaped, as the mean grows large. Figure 1 illustrates this, showing plots of the probability function for $\mu = 0.1$, $\mu = 2$, and $\mu = 5$. Note the nearness to symmetry when μ becomes as large as 5. A similar condition exists for the binomial distribution, as will be illustrated later in the text.

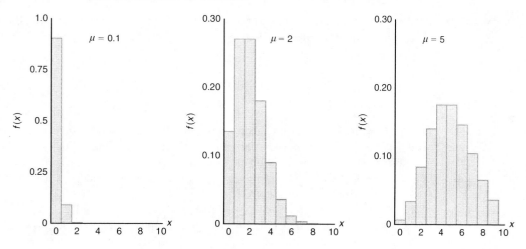

Figure 1: Poisson density functions for different means.

Approximation of Binomial Distribution by a Poisson Distribution

It should be evident from the three principles of the Poisson process that the Poisson distribution is related to the binomial distribution. Although the Poisson usually finds applications in space and time problems, as illustrated by Examples 17 and 18, it can be viewed as a limiting form of the binomial distribution. In the case of the binomial, if n is quite large and p is small, the conditions begin to simulate the *continuous space or time* implications of the Poisson process. The independence among Bernoulli trials in the binomial case is consistent with principle 2 of the Poisson process. Allowing the parameter p to be close to 0 relates to principle 3 of the Poisson process. Indeed, if n is large and p is close to 0, the Poisson distribution can be used, with $\mu = np$, to approximate binomial probabilities. If p is close to 1, we can still use the Poisson distribution to approximate binomial probabilities by interchanging what we have defined to be a success and a failure, thereby changing p to a value close to 0.

Theorem 5:

Let X be a binomial random variable with probability distribution $b(x; n, p)$. When $n \to \infty$, $p \to 0$, and $np \xrightarrow{n \to \infty} \mu$ remains constant,

$$b(x; n, p) \xrightarrow{n \to \infty} p(x; \mu).$$

Example 19: In a certain industrial facility, accidents occur infrequently. It is known that the probability of an accident on any given day is 0.005 and accidents are independent of each other.

(a) What is the probability that in any given period of 400 days there will be an accident on one day?

(b) What is the probability that there are at most three days with an accident?

Solution: Let X be a binomial random variable with $n = 400$ and $p = 0.005$. Thus, $np = 2$. Using the Poisson approximation,

(a) $P(X = 1) = e^{-2}2^1 = 0.271$ and

(b) $P(X \le 3) = \sum_{x=0}^{3} e^{-2}2^x/x! = 0.857.$

Example 20: In a manufacturing process where glass products are made, defects or bubbles occur, occasionally rendering the piece undesirable for marketing. It is known that, on average, 1 in every 1000 of these items produced has one or more bubbles. What is the probability that a random sample of 8000 will yield fewer than 7 items possessing bubbles?

Solution: This is essentially a binomial experiment with $n = 8000$ and $p = 0.001$. Since p is very close to 0 and n is quite large, we shall approximate with the Poisson distribution using

$$\mu = (8000)(0.001) = 8.$$

Hence, if X represents the number of bubbles, we have

$$P(X < 7) = \sum_{x=0}^{6} b(x; 8000, 0.001) \approx p(x; 8) = 0.3134.$$

Exercises

49 The probability that a person living in a certain city owns a dog is estimated to be 0.3. Find the probability that the tenth person randomly interviewed in that city is the fifth one to own a dog.

50 Find the probability that a person flipping a coin gets

(a) the third head on the seventh flip;

(b) the first head on the fourth flip.

51 Three people toss a fair coin and the odd one pays for coffee. If the coins all turn up the same, they are tossed again. Find the probability that fewer than 4 tosses are needed.

52 A scientist inoculates mice, one at a time, with a disease germ until he finds 2 that have contracted the disease. If the probability of contracting the disease is 1/6, what is the probability that 8 mice are required?

53 An inventory study determines that, on average, demands for a particular item at a warehouse are made 5 times per day. What is the probability that on a given day this item is requested

(a) more than 5 times?

(b) not at all?

54 According to a study published by a group of University of Massachusetts sociologists, about two-thirds of the 20 million persons in this country who take Valium are women. Assuming this figure to be a valid estimate, find the probability that on a given day the fifth prescription written by a doctor for Valium is

(a) the first prescribing Valium for a woman;

(b) the third prescribing Valium for a woman.

55 The probability that a student pilot passes the written test for a private pilot's license is 0.7. Find the probability that a given student will pass the test

(a) on the third try;

(b) before the fourth try.

56 On average, 3 traffic accidents per month occur at a certain intersection. What is the probability that in any given month at this intersection

(a) exactly 5 accidents will occur?

(b) fewer than 3 accidents will occur?

(c) at least 2 accidents will occur?

57 On average, a textbook author makes two word-processing errors per page on the first draft of her textbook. What is the probability that on the next page she will make

(a) 4 or more errors?

(b) no errors?

58 A certain area of the eastern United States is, on average, hit by 6 hurricanes a year. Find the probability that in a given year that area will be hit by

(a) fewer than 4 hurricanes;

(b) anywhere from 6 to 8 hurricanes.

59 Suppose the probability that any given person will believe a tale about the transgressions of a famous actress is 0.8. What is the probability that

(a) the sixth person to hear this tale is the fourth one to believe it?

(b) the third person to hear this tale is the first one to believe it?

60 The average number of field mice per acre in a 5-acre wheat field is estimated to be 12. Find the probability that fewer than 7 field mice are found

(a) on a given acre;

(b) on 2 of the next 3 acres inspected.

61 Suppose that, on average, 1 person in 1000 makes a numerical error in preparing his or her income tax return. If 10,000 returns are selected at random and examined, find the probability that 6, 7, or 8 of them contain an error.

62 The probability that a student at a local high school fails the screening test for scoliosis (curvature of the spine) is known to be 0.004. Of the next 1875 students at the school who are screened for scoliosis,

find the probability that

(a) fewer than 5 fail the test;

(b) 8, 9, or 10 fail the test.

63 Find the mean and variance of the random variable X in Exercise 58, representing the number of hurricanes per year to hit a certain area of the eastern United States.

64 Find the mean and variance of the random variable X in Exercise 61, representing the number of persons among 10,000 who make an error in preparing their income tax returns.

65 An automobile manufacturer is concerned about a fault in the braking mechanism of a particular model. The fault can, on rare occasions, cause a catastrophe at high speed. The distribution of the number of cars per year that will experience the catastrophe is a Poisson random variable with $\lambda = 5$.

(a) What is the probability that at most 3 cars per year will experience a catastrophe?

(b) What is the probability that more than 1 car per year will experience a catastrophe?

66 Changes in airport procedures require considerable planning. Arrival rates of aircraft are important factors that must be taken into account. Suppose small aircraft arrive at a certain airport, according to a Poisson process, at the rate of 6 per hour. Thus, the Poisson parameter for arrivals over a period of hours is $\mu = 6t$.

(a) What is the probability that exactly 4 small aircraft arrive during a 1-hour period?

(b) What is the probability that at least 4 arrive during a 1-hour period?

(c) If we define a working day as 12 hours, what is the probability that at least 75 small aircraft arrive during a working day?

67 The number of customers arriving per hour at a certain automobile service facility is assumed to follow a Poisson distribution with mean $\lambda = 7$.

(a) Compute the probability that more than 10 customers will arrive in a 2-hour period.

(b) What is the mean number of arrivals during a 2-hour period?

68 Consider Exercise 62. What is the mean number of students who fail the test?

69 The probability that a person will die when he or she contracts a virus infection is 0.001. Of the next 4000 people infected, what is the mean number who will die?

70 A company purchases large lots of a certain kind of electronic device. A method is used that rejects a lot if 2 or more defective units are found in a random sample of 100 units.

(a) What is the mean number of defective units found in a sample of 100 units if the lot is 1% defective?

(b) What is the variance?

71 For a certain type of copper wire, it is known that, on the average, 1.5 flaws occur per millimeter. Assuming that the number of flaws is a Poisson random variable, what is the probability that no flaws occur in a certain portion of wire of length 5 millimeters? What is the mean number of flaws in a portion of length 5 millimeters?

72 Potholes on a highway can be a serious problem, and are in constant need of repair. With a particular type of terrain and make of concrete, past experience suggests that there are, on the average, 2 potholes per mile after a certain amount of usage. It is assumed that the Poisson process applies to the random variable "number of potholes."

(a) What is the probability that no more than one pothole will appear in a section of 1 mile?

(b) What is the probability that no more than 4 potholes will occur in a given section of 5 miles?

73 Hospital administrators in large cities anguish about traffic in emergency rooms. At a particular hospital in a large city, the staff on hand cannot accommodate the patient traffic if there are more than 10 emergency cases in a given hour. It is assumed that patient arrival follows a Poisson process, and historical data suggest that, on the average, 5 emergencies arrive per hour.

(a) What is the probability that in a given hour the staff cannot accommodate the patient traffic?

(b) What is the probability that more than 20 emergencies arrive during a 3-hour shift?

74 It is known that 3% of people whose luggage is screened at an airport have questionable objects in their luggage. What is the probability that a string of 15 people pass through screening successfully before an individual is caught with a questionable object? What is the expected number of people to pass through before an individual is stopped?

75 Computer technology has produced an environment in which robots operate with the use of microprocessors. The probability that a robot fails during any 6-hour shift is 0.10. What is the probability that a robot will operate through at most 5 shifts before it fails?

76 The refusal rate for telephone polls is known to be approximately 20%. A newspaper report indicates that 50 people were interviewed before the first refusal.

(a) Comment on the validity of the report. Use a probability in your argument.

(b) What is the expected number of people interviewed before a refusal?

Review Exercises

77 During a manufacturing process, 15 units are randomly selected each day from the production line to check the percent defective. From historical information it is known that the probability of a defective unit is 0.05. Any time 2 or more defectives are found in the sample of 15, the process is stopped. This procedure is used to provide a signal in case the probability of a defective has increased.

(a) What is the probability that on any given day the production process will be stopped? (Assume 5% defective.)

(b) Suppose that the probability of a defective has increased to 0.07. What is the probability that on any given day the production process will not be stopped?

78 An automatic welding machine is being considered for use in a production process. It will be considered for purchase if it is successful on 99% of its welds. Otherwise, it will not be considered efficient. A test is to be conducted with a prototype that is to perform 100 welds. The machine will be accepted for manufacture if it misses no more than 3 welds.

(a) What is the probability that a good machine will be rejected?

(b) What is the probability that an inefficient machine with 95% welding success will be accepted?

79 A car rental agency at a local airport has available 5 Fords, 7 Chevrolets, 4 Dodges, 3 Hondas, and 4 Toyotas. If the agency randomly selects 9 of these cars to chauffeur delegates from the airport to the downtown convention center, find the probability that 2 Fords, 3 Chevrolets, 1 Dodge, 1 Honda, and 2 Toyotas are used.

80 Service calls come to a maintenance center according to a Poisson process, and on average, 2.7 calls are received per minute. Find the probability that

(a) no more than 4 calls come in any minute;

(b) fewer than 2 calls come in any minute;

(c) more than 10 calls come in a 5-minute period.

81 An electronics firm claims that the proportion of defective units from a certain process is 5%. A buyer has a standard procedure of inspecting 15 units selected randomly from a large lot. On a particular occasion, the buyer found 5 items defective.

(a) What is the probability of this occurrence, given that the claim of 5% defective is correct?

(b) What would be your reaction if you were the buyer?

82 An electronic switching device occasionally malfunctions, but the device is considered satisfactory if it makes, on average, no more than 0.20 error per hour. A particular 5-hour period is chosen for testing the device. If no more than 1 error occurs during the time period, the device will be considered satisfactory.

(a) What is the probability that a satisfactory device will be considered unsatisfactory on the basis of the test? Assume a Poisson process.

(b) What is the probability that a device will be accepted as satisfactory when, in fact, the mean number of errors is 0.25? Again, assume a Poisson process.

83 A company generally purchases large lots of a certain kind of electronic device. A method is used that rejects a lot if 2 or more defective units are found in a random sample of 100 units.

(a) What is the probability of rejecting a lot that is 1% defective?

(b) What is the probability of accepting a lot that is 5% defective?

84 A local drugstore owner knows that, on average, 100 people enter his store each hour.

(a) Find the probability that in a given 3-minute period nobody enters the store.

(b) Find the probability that in a given 3-minute period more than 5 people enter the store.

85 (a) Suppose that you throw 4 dice. Find the probability that you get at least one 1.

(b) Suppose that you throw 2 dice 24 times. Find the probability that you get at least one (1, 1), that is, "snake-eyes."

86 Suppose that out of 500 lottery tickets sold, 200 pay off at least the cost of the ticket. Now suppose that you buy 5 tickets. Find the probability that you

will win back at least the cost of 3 tickets.

87 Imperfections in computer circuit boards and computer chips lend themselves to statistical treatment. For a particular type of board, the probability of a diode failure is 0.03 and the board contains 200 diodes.

(a) What is the mean number of failures among the diodes?

(b) What is the variance?

(c) The board will work if there are no defective diodes. What is the probability that a board will work?

88 The potential buyer of a particular engine requires (among other things) that the engine start successfully 10 consecutive times. Suppose the probability of a successful start is 0.990. Let us assume that the outcomes of attempted starts are independent.

(a) What is the probability that the engine is accepted after only 10 starts?

(b) What is the probability that 12 attempted starts are made during the acceptance process?

89 The acceptance scheme for purchasing lots containing a large number of batteries is to test no more than 75 randomly selected batteries and to reject a lot if a single battery fails. Suppose the probability of a failure is 0.001.

(a) What is the probability that a lot is accepted?

(b) What is the probability that a lot is rejected on the 20th test?

(c) What is the probability that it is rejected in 10 or fewer trials?

90 An oil drilling company ventures into various locations, and its success or failure is independent from one location to another. Suppose the probability of a success at any specific location is 0.25.

(a) What is the probability that the driller drills at 10 locations and has 1 success?

(b) The driller will go bankrupt if it drills 10 times before the first success occurs. What are the driller's prospects for bankruptcy?

91 Consider the information in Review Exercise 90. The drilling company feels that it will "hit it big" if the second success occurs on or before the sixth attempt. What is the probability that the driller will hit it big?

92 A couple decides to continue to have children until they have two males. Assuming that $P(\text{male}) = 0.5$, what is the probability that their second male is their fourth child?

93 It is known by researchers that 1 in 100 people carries a gene that leads to the inheritance of a certain chronic disease. In a random sample of 1000 individuals, what is the probability that fewer than 7 individuals carry the gene? Use a Poisson approximation. Again, using the approximation, what is the approximate mean number of people out of 1000 carrying the gene?

94 A production process produces electronic component parts. It is presumed that the probability of a defective part is 0.01. During a test of this presumption, 500 parts are sampled randomly and 15 defectives are observed.

(a) What is your response to the presumption that the process is 1% defective? Be sure that a computed probability accompanies your comment.

(b) Under the presumption of a 1% defective process, what is the probability that only 3 parts will be found defective?

(c) Do parts (a) and (b) again using the Poisson approximation.

95 A production process outputs items in lots of 50. Sampling plans exist in which lots are pulled aside periodically and exposed to a certain type of inspection. It is usually assumed that the proportion defective is very small. It is important to the company that lots containing defectives be a rare event. The current inspection plan is to periodically sample randomly 10 out of the 50 items in a lot and, if none are defective, to perform no intervention.

(a) Suppose in a lot chosen at random, 2 out of 50 are defective. What is the probability that at least 1 in the sample of 10 from the lot is defective?

(b) From your answer to part (a), comment on the quality of this sampling plan.

(c) What is the mean number of defects found out of 10 items sampled?

96 Consider the situation of Review Exercise 95. It has been determined that the sampling plan should be extensive enough that there is a high probability, say 0.9, that if as many as 2 defectives exist in the lot of 50 being sampled, at least 1 will be found in the sampling. With these restrictions, how many of the 50 items should be sampled?

97 National security requires that defense technology be able to detect incoming projectiles or missiles. To make the defense system successful, multiple radar screens are required. Suppose that three independent screens are to be operated and the probability that any one screen will detect an incoming missile is 0.8. Obviously, if no screens detect an incoming projectile, the system is unworthy and must be improved.

(a) What is the probability that an incoming missile will not be detected by any of the three screens?

(b) What is the probability that the missile will be detected by only one screen?

(c) What is the probability that it will be detected by at least two out of three screens?

98 Suppose it is important that the overall missile defense system be as near perfect as possible.

(a) Assuming the quality of the screens is as indicated in Review Exercise 97, how many are needed to ensure that the probability that a missile gets through undetected is 0.0001?

(b) Suppose it is decided to stay with only 3 screens and attempt to improve the screen detection ability. What must the individual screen effectiveness (i.e., probability of detection) be in order to achieve the effectiveness required in part (a)?

99 Go back to Review Exercise 95(a). Recompute the probability using the binomial distribution. Comment.

100 There are two vacancies in a certain university statistics department. Five individuals apply. Two have expertise in linear models, and one has expertise in applied probability. The search committee is instructed to choose the two applicants randomly.

(a) What is the probability that the two chosen are those with expertise in linear models?

(b) What is the probability that of the two chosen, one has expertise in linear models and one has expertise in applied probability?

101 The manufacturer of a tricycle for children has received complaints about defective brakes in the product. According to the design of the product and considerable preliminary testing, it had been determined that the probability of the kind of defect in the complaint was 1 in 10,000 (i.e., 0.0001). After a thorough investigation of the complaints, it was determined that during a certain period of time, 200 products were randomly chosen from production and 5 had defective brakes.

(a) Comment on the "1 in 10,000" claim by the manufacturer. Use a probabilistic argument. Use the binomial distribution for your calculations.

(b) Repeat part (a) using the Poisson approximation.

102 **Group Project:** Divide the class into two groups of approximately equal size. The students in group 1 will each toss a coin 10 times (n_1) and count the number of heads obtained. The students in group 2 will each toss a coin 40 times (n_2) and again count the number of heads. The students in each group should individually compute the proportion of heads observed, which is an estimate of p, the probability of observing a head. Thus, there will be a set of values of p_1 (from group 1) and a set of values p_2 (from group 2). All of the values of p_1 and p_2 are estimates of 0.5, which is the true value of the probability of observing a head for a fair coin.

(a) Which set of values is consistently closer to 0.5, the values of p_1 or p_2? Consider the proof of Theorem 5.1 on page 147 with regard to the estimates of the parameter $p = 0.5$. The values of p_1 were obtained with $n = n_1 = 10$, and the values of p_2 were obtained with $n = n_2 = 40$. Using the notation of the proof, the estimates are given by

$$p_1 = \frac{x_1}{n_1} = \frac{I_1 + \cdots + I_{n_1}}{n_1},$$

where $I_1, \ldots, I_{n_1}$ are 0s and 1s and $n_1 = 10$, and

$$p_2 = \frac{x_2}{n_2} = \frac{I_1 + \cdots + I_{n_2}}{n_2},$$

where $I_1, \ldots, I_{n_2}$, again, are 0s and 1s and $n_2 = 40$.

(b) Referring again to Theorem 5.1, show that

$$E(p_1) = E(p_2) = p = 0.5.$$

(c) Show that $\sigma^2_{p_1} = \dfrac{\sigma^2_{X_1}}{n_1}$ is 4 times the value of $\sigma^2_{p_2} = \dfrac{\sigma^2_{X_2}}{n_2}$. Then explain further why the values of p_2 from group 2 are more consistently closer to the true value, $p = 0.5$, than the values of p_1 from group 1.

6   Potential Misconceptions and Hazards

The discrete distributions discussed in this chapter occur with great frequency in engineering and the biological and physical sciences. The exercises and examples certainly suggest this. Industrial sampling plans and many engineering judgments are based on the binomial and Poisson distributions as well as on the hypergeometric distribution. While the geometric and negative binomial distributions are used to a somewhat lesser extent, they also find applications. In particular, a negative binomial random variable can be viewed as a mixture of Poisson and gamma random variables.

Despite the rich heritage that these distributions find in real life, they can be misused unless the scientific practitioner is prudent and cautious. Of course, any probability calculation for the distributions discussed in this chapter is made under the assumption that the parameter value is known. Real-world applications often result in a parameter value that may "move around" due to factors that are difficult to control in the process or because of interventions in the process that have not been taken into account. For example, in Review Exercise 77, "historical information" is used. But is the process that exists now the same as that under which the historical data were collected? The use of the Poisson distribution can suffer even more from this kind of difficulty. For example, in Review Exercise 80, the questions in parts (a), (b), and (c) are based on the use of $\mu = 2.7$ calls per minute. Based on historical records, this is the number of calls that occur "on average." But in this and many other applications of the Poisson distribution, there are slow times and busy times and so there are times in which the conditions for the Poisson process may appear to hold when in fact they do not. Thus, the probability calculations may be incorrect. In the case of the binomial, the assumption that may fail in certain applications (in addition to nonconstancy of p) is the independence assumption, stating that the Bernoulli trials are independent.

One of the most famous misuses of the binomial distribution occurred in the 1961 baseball season, when Mickey Mantle and Roger Maris were engaged in a friendly battle to break Babe Ruth's all-time record of 60 home runs. A famous magazine article made a prediction, based on probability theory, that Mantle would break the record. The prediction was based on probability calculation with the use of the binomial distribution. The classic error made was to estimate the parameter p (one for each player) based on relative historical frequency of home runs throughout the players' careers. Maris, unlike Mantle, had not been a prodigious home run hitter prior to 1961 so his estimate of p was quite low. As a result, the calculated probability of breaking the record was quite high for Mantle and low for Maris. The end result: Mantle failed to break the record and Maris succeeded.

Answers to Odd-Numbered Non-Review Exercises

1 $\mu = \frac{1}{k} \sum_{i=1}^{k} x_i$, $\sigma^2 = \frac{1}{k} \sum_{i=1}^{k} (x_i - \mu)^2$

3 $f(x) = \frac{1}{10}$, for $x = 1, 2, \ldots, 10$, and $f(x) = 0$ elsewhere; $3/10$

5 (a) 0.0480; (b) 0.2375; (c) $P(X = 5 \mid p = 0.3) = 0.1789$, $P = 0.3$ is reasonable.

7 (a) 0.0474; (b) 0.0171

9 (a) 0.7073; (b) 0.4613; (c) 0.1484

11 0.1240

13 0.8369

15 (a) 0.0778; (b) 0.3370; (c) 0.0870

17 $\mu = 3.5$, $\sigma^2 = 1.05$

19 $f(x_1, x_2, x_3) = \binom{n}{x_1, x_2, x_3} 0.35^{x_1} 0.05^{x_2} 0.60^{x_3}$

21 0.0095

23 0.0077

25 0.8670

27 (a) 0.2852; (b) 0.9887; (c) 0.6083

29 5/14

31 $h(x; 6, 3, 4) = \dfrac{\binom{4}{x}\binom{2}{3-x}}{\binom{6}{3}}$, for $x = 1, 2, 3$;

$P(2 \le X \le 3) = 4/5$

33 (a) 0.3246; (b) 0.4496

35 0.9517

37 (a) 0.6815; (b) 0.1153

39 0.9453

41 0.6077

43 (a) 4/33; (b) 8/165

45 0.2315

47 (a) 0.3991; (b) 0.1316

49 0.0515

51 63/64

53 (a) 0.3840; (b) 0.0067

55 (a) 0.0630; (b) 0.9730

57 (a) 0.1429; (b) 0.1353

59 (a) 0.1638; (b) 0.032

61 0.2657

63 $\mu = 6$, $\sigma^2 = 6$

65 (a) 0.2650; (b) 0.9596

67 (a) 0.8243; (b) 14

69 4

71 5.53×10^{-4}; $\mu = 7.5$

73 (a) 0.0137; (b) 0.0830

75 0.4686

Table Binomial Probability Sums $\sum_{x=0}^{r} b(x; n, p)$

		p									
n	r	0.10	0.20	0.25	0.30	0.40	0.50	0.60	0.70	0.80	0.90
1	0	0.9000	0.8000	0.7500	0.7000	0.6000	0.5000	0.4000	0.3000	0.2000	0.1000
	1	1.0000	1.0000	1.0000	1.0000	1.0000	1.0000	1.0000	1.0000	1.0000	1.0000
2	0	0.8100	0.6400	0.5625	0.4900	0.3600	0.2500	0.1600	0.0900	0.0400	0.0100
	1	0.9900	0.9600	0.9375	0.9100	0.8400	0.7500	0.6400	0.5100	0.3600	0.1900
	2	1.0000	1.0000	1.0000	1.0000	1.0000	1.0000	1.0000	1.0000	1.0000	1.0000
3	0	0.7290	0.5120	0.4219	0.3430	0.2160	0.1250	0.0640	0.0270	0.0080	0.0010
	1	0.9720	0.8960	0.8438	0.7840	0.6480	0.5000	0.3520	0.2160	0.1040	0.0280
	2	0.9990	0.9920	0.9844	0.9730	0.9360	0.8750	0.7840	0.6570	0.4880	0.2710
	3	1.0000	1.0000	1.0000	1.0000	1.0000	1.0000	1.0000	1.0000	1.0000	1.0000
4	0	0.6561	0.4096	0.3164	0.2401	0.1296	0.0625	0.0256	0.0081	0.0016	0.0001
	1	0.9477	0.8192	0.7383	0.6517	0.4752	0.3125	0.1792	0.0837	0.0272	0.0037
	2	0.9963	0.9728	0.9492	0.9163	0.8208	0.6875	0.5248	0.3483	0.1808	0.0523
	3	0.9999	0.9984	0.9961	0.9919	0.9744	0.9375	0.8704	0.7599	0.5904	0.3439
	4	1.0000	1.0000	1.0000	1.0000	1.0000	1.0000	1.0000	1.0000	1.0000	1.0000
5	0	0.5905	0.3277	0.2373	0.1681	0.0778	0.0313	0.0102	0.0024	0.0003	0.0000
	1	0.9185	0.7373	0.6328	0.5282	0.3370	0.1875	0.0870	0.0308	0.0067	0.0005
	2	0.9914	0.9421	0.8965	0.8369	0.6826	0.5000	0.3174	0.1631	0.0579	0.0086
	3	0.9995	0.9933	0.9844	0.9692	0.9130	0.8125	0.6630	0.4718	0.2627	0.0815
	4	1.0000	0.9997	0.9990	0.9976	0.9898	0.9688	0.9222	0.8319	0.6723	0.4095
	5	1.0000	1.0000	1.0000	1.0000	1.0000	1.0000	1.0000	1.0000	1.0000	1.0000
6	0	0.5314	0.2621	0.1780	0.1176	0.0467	0.0156	0.0041	0.0007	0.0001	0.0000
	1	0.8857	0.6554	0.5339	0.4202	0.2333	0.1094	0.0410	0.0109	0.0016	0.0001
	2	0.9842	0.9011	0.8306	0.7443	0.5443	0.3438	0.1792	0.0705	0.0170	0.0013
	3	0.9987	0.9830	0.9624	0.9295	0.8208	0.6563	0.4557	0.2557	0.0989	0.0159
	4	0.9999	0.9984	0.9954	0.9891	0.9590	0.8906	0.7667	0.5798	0.3446	0.1143
	5	1.0000	0.9999	0.9998	0.9993	0.9959	0.9844	0.9533	0.8824	0.7379	0.4686
	6	1.0000	1.0000	1.0000	1.0000	1.0000	1.0000	1.0000	1.0000	1.0000	1.0000
7	0	0.4783	0.2097	0.1335	0.0824	0.0280	0.0078	0.0016	0.0002	0.0000	
	1	0.8503	0.5767	0.4449	0.3294	0.1586	0.0625	0.0188	0.0038	0.0004	0.0000
	2	0.9743	0.8520	0.7564	0.6471	0.4199	0.2266	0.0963	0.0288	0.0047	0.0002
	3	0.9973	0.9667	0.9294	0.8740	0.7102	0.5000	0.2898	0.1260	0.0333	0.0027
	4	0.9998	0.9953	0.9871	0.9712	0.9037	0.7734	0.5801	0.3529	0.1480	0.0257
	5	1.0000	0.9996	0.9987	0.9962	0.9812	0.9375	0.8414	0.6706	0.4233	0.1497
	6		1.0000	0.9999	0.9998	0.9984	0.9922	0.9720	0.9176	0.7903	0.5217
	7			1.0000	1.0000	1.0000	1.0000	1.0000	1.0000	1.0000	1.0000

Table (continued) Binomial Probability Sums $\sum_{x=0}^{r} b(x;n,p)$

		p									
n	r	0.10	0.20	0.25	0.30	0.40	0.50	0.60	0.70	0.80	0.90
8	0	0.4305	0.1678	0.1001	0.0576	0.0168	0.0039	0.0007	0.0001	0.0000	
	1	0.8131	0.5033	0.3671	0.2553	0.1064	0.0352	0.0085	0.0013	0.0001	
	2	0.9619	0.7969	0.6785	0.5518	0.3154	0.1445	0.0498	0.0113	0.0012	0.0000
	3	0.9950	0.9437	0.8862	0.8059	0.5941	0.3633	0.1737	0.0580	0.0104	0.0004
	4	0.9996	0.9896	0.9727	0.9420	0.8263	0.6367	0.4059	0.1941	0.0563	0.0050
	5	1.0000	0.9988	0.9958	0.9887	0.9502	0.8555	0.6846	0.4482	0.2031	0.0381
	6		0.9999	0.9996	0.9987	0.9915	0.9648	0.8936	0.7447	0.4967	0.1869
	7		1.0000	1.0000	0.9999	0.9993	0.9961	0.9832	0.9424	0.8322	0.5695
	8				1.0000	1.0000	1.0000	1.0000	1.0000	1.0000	1.0000
9	0	0.3874	0.1342	0.0751	0.0404	0.0101	0.0020	0.0003	0.0000		
	1	0.7748	0.4362	0.3003	0.1960	0.0705	0.0195	0.0038	0.0004	0.0000	
	2	0.9470	0.7382	0.6007	0.4628	0.2318	0.0898	0.0250	0.0043	0.0003	0.0000
	3	0.9917	0.9144	0.8343	0.7297	0.4826	0.2539	0.0994	0.0253	0.0031	0.0001
	4	0.9991	0.9804	0.9511	0.9012	0.7334	0.5000	0.2666	0.0988	0.0196	0.0009
	5	0.9999	0.9969	0.9900	0.9747	0.9006	0.7461	0.5174	0.2703	0.0856	0.0083
	6	1.0000	0.9997	0.9987	0.9957	0.9750	0.9102	0.7682	0.5372	0.2618	0.0530
	7		1.0000	0.9999	0.9996	0.9962	0.9805	0.9295	0.8040	0.5638	0.2252
	8			1.0000	1.0000	0.9997	0.9980	0.9899	0.9596	0.8658	0.6126
	9					1.0000	1.0000	1.0000	1.0000	1.0000	1.0000
10	0	0.3487	0.1074	0.0563	0.0282	0.0060	0.0010	0.0001	0.0000		
	1	0.7361	0.3758	0.2440	0.1493	0.0464	0.0107	0.0017	0.0001	0.0000	
	2	0.9298	0.6778	0.5256	0.3828	0.1673	0.0547	0.0123	0.0016	0.0001	
	3	0.9872	0.8791	0.7759	0.6496	0.3823	0.1719	0.0548	0.0106	0.0009	0.0000
	4	0.9984	0.9672	0.9219	0.8497	0.6331	0.3770	0.1662	0.0473	0.0064	0.0001
	5	0.9999	0.9936	0.9803	0.9527	0.8338	0.6230	0.3669	0.1503	0.0328	0.0016
	6	1.0000	0.9991	0.9965	0.9894	0.9452	0.8281	0.6177	0.3504	0.1209	0.0128
	7		0.9999	0.9996	0.9984	0.9877	0.9453	0.8327	0.6172	0.3222	0.0702
	8		1.0000	1.0000	0.9999	0.9983	0.9893	0.9536	0.8507	0.6242	0.2639
	9				1.0000	0.9999	0.9990	0.9940	0.9718	0.8926	0.6513
	10					1.0000	1.0000	1.0000	1.0000	1.0000	1.0000
11	0	0.3138	0.0859	0.0422	0.0198	0.0036	0.0005	0.0000			
	1	0.6974	0.3221	0.1971	0.1130	0.0302	0.0059	0.0007	0.0000		
	2	0.9104	0.6174	0.4552	0.3127	0.1189	0.0327	0.0059	0.0006	0.0000	
	3	0.9815	0.8389	0.7133	0.5696	0.2963	0.1133	0.0293	0.0043	0.0002	
	4	0.9972	0.9496	0.8854	0.7897	0.5328	0.2744	0.0994	0.0216	0.0020	0.0000
	5	0.9997	0.9883	0.9657	0.9218	0.7535	0.5000	0.2465	0.0782	0.0117	0.0003
	6	1.0000	0.9980	0.9924	0.9784	0.9006	0.7256	0.4672	0.2103	0.0504	0.0028
	7		0.9998	0.9988	0.9957	0.9707	0.8867	0.7037	0.4304	0.1611	0.0185
	8		1.0000	0.9999	0.9994	0.9941	0.9673	0.8811	0.6873	0.3826	0.0896
	9			1.0000	1.0000	0.9993	0.9941	0.9698	0.8870	0.6779	0.3026
	10					1.0000	0.9995	0.9964	0.9802	0.9141	0.6862
	11						1.0000	1.0000	1.0000	1.0000	1.0000

Table (continued) Binomial Probability Sums $\sum_{x=0}^{r} b(x; n, p)$

						p					
n	r	0.10	0.20	0.25	0.30	0.40	0.50	0.60	0.70	0.80	0.90
12	0	0.2824	0.0687	0.0317	0.0138	0.0022	0.0002	0.0000			
	1	0.6590	0.2749	0.1584	0.0850	0.0196	0.0032	0.0003	0.0000		
	2	0.8891	0.5583	0.3907	0.2528	0.0834	0.0193	0.0028	0.0002	0.0000	
	3	0.9744	0.7946	0.6488	0.4925	0.2253	0.0730	0.0153	0.0017	0.0001	
	4	0.9957	0.9274	0.8424	0.7237	0.4382	0.1938	0.0573	0.0095	0.0006	0.0000
	5	0.9995	0.9806	0.9456	0.8822	0.6652	0.3872	0.1582	0.0386	0.0039	0.0001
	6	0.9999	0.9961	0.9857	0.9614	0.8418	0.6128	0.3348	0.1178	0.0194	0.0005
	7	1.0000	0.9994	0.9972	0.9905	0.9427	0.8062	0.5618	0.2763	0.0726	0.0043
	8		0.9999	0.9996	0.9983	0.9847	0.9270	0.7747	0.5075	0.2054	0.0256
	9		1.0000	1.0000	0.9998	0.9972	0.9807	0.9166	0.7472	0.4417	0.1109
	10				1.0000	0.9997	0.9968	0.9804	0.9150	0.7251	0.3410
	11					1.0000	0.9998	0.9978	0.9862	0.9313	0.7176
	12						1.0000	1.0000	1.0000	1.0000	1.0000
13	0	0.2542	0.0550	0.0238	0.0097	0.0013	0.0001	0.0000			
	1	0.6213	0.2336	0.1267	0.0637	0.0126	0.0017	0.0001	0.0000		
	2	0.8661	0.5017	0.3326	0.2025	0.0579	0.0112	0.0013	0.0001		
	3	0.9658	0.7473	0.5843	0.4206	0.1686	0.0461	0.0078	0.0007	0.0000	
	4	0.9935	0.9009	0.7940	0.6543	0.3530	0.1334	0.0321	0.0040	0.0002	
	5	0.9991	0.9700	0.9198	0.8346	0.5744	0.2905	0.0977	0.0182	0.0012	0.0000
	6	0.9999	0.9930	0.9757	0.9376	0.7712	0.5000	0.2288	0.0624	0.0070	0.0001
	7	1.0000	0.9988	0.9944	0.9818	0.9023	0.7095	0.4256	0.1654	0.0300	0.0009
	8		0.9998	0.9990	0.9960	0.9679	0.8666	0.6470	0.3457	0.0991	0.0065
	9		1.0000	0.9999	0.9993	0.9922	0.9539	0.8314	0.5794	0.2527	0.0342
	10			1.0000	0.9999	0.9987	0.9888	0.9421	0.7975	0.4983	0.1339
	11				1.0000	0.9999	0.9983	0.9874	0.9363	0.7664	0.3787
	12					1.0000	0.9999	0.9987	0.9903	0.9450	0.7458
	13						1.0000	1.0000	1.0000	1.0000	1.0000
14	0	0.2288	0.0440	0.0178	0.0068	0.0008	0.0001	0.0000			
	1	0.5846	0.1979	0.1010	0.0475	0.0081	0.0009	0.0001			
	2	0.8416	0.4481	0.2811	0.1608	0.0398	0.0065	0.0006	0.0000		
	3	0.9559	0.6982	0.5213	0.3552	0.1243	0.0287	0.0039	0.0002		
	4	0.9908	0.8702	0.7415	0.5842	0.2793	0.0898	0.0175	0.0017	0.0000	
	5	0.9985	0.9561	0.8883	0.7805	0.4859	0.2120	0.0583	0.0083	0.0004	
	6	0.9998	0.9884	0.9617	0.9067	0.6925	0.3953	0.1501	0.0315	0.0024	0.0000
	7	1.0000	0.9976	0.9897	0.9685	0.8499	0.6047	0.3075	0.0933	0.0116	0.0002
	8		0.9996	0.9978	0.9917	0.9417	0.7880	0.5141	0.2195	0.0439	0.0015
	9		1.0000	0.9997	0.9983	0.9825	0.9102	0.7207	0.4158	0.1298	0.0092
	10			1.0000	0.9998	0.9961	0.9713	0.8757	0.6448	0.3018	0.0441
	11				1.0000	0.9994	0.9935	0.9602	0.8392	0.5519	0.1584
	12					0.9999	0.9991	0.9919	0.9525	0.8021	0.4154
	13					1.0000	0.9999	0.9992	0.9932	0.9560	0.7712
	14						1.0000	1.0000	1.0000	1.0000	1.0000

Table (continued) Binomial Probability Sums $\sum_{x=0}^{r} b(x; n, p)$

						p					
n	r	0.10	0.20	0.25	0.30	0.40	0.50	0.60	0.70	0.80	0.90
15	0	0.2059	0.0352	0.0134	0.0047	0.0005	0.0000				
	1	0.5490	0.1671	0.0802	0.0353	0.0052	0.0005	0.0000			
	2	0.8159	0.3980	0.2361	0.1268	0.0271	0.0037	0.0003	0.0000		
	3	0.9444	0.6482	0.4613	0.2969	0.0905	0.0176	0.0019	0.0001		
	4	0.9873	0.8358	0.6865	0.5155	0.2173	0.0592	0.0093	0.0007	0.0000	
	5	0.9978	0.9389	0.8516	0.7216	0.4032	0.1509	0.0338	0.0037	0.0001	
	6	0.9997	0.9819	0.9434	0.8689	0.6098	0.3036	0.0950	0.0152	0.0008	
	7	1.0000	0.9958	0.9827	0.9500	0.7869	0.5000	0.2131	0.0500	0.0042	0.0000
	8		0.9992	0.9958	0.9848	0.9050	0.6964	0.3902	0.1311	0.0181	0.0003
	9		0.9999	0.9992	0.9963	0.9662	0.8491	0.5968	0.2784	0.0611	0.0022
	10		1.0000	0.9999	0.9993	0.9907	0.9408	0.7827	0.4845	0.1642	0.0127
	11			1.0000	0.9999	0.9981	0.9824	0.9095	0.7031	0.3518	0.0556
	12				1.0000	0.9997	0.9963	0.9729	0.8732	0.6020	0.1841
	13					1.0000	0.9995	0.9948	0.9647	0.8329	0.4510
	14						1.0000	0.9995	0.9953	0.9648	0.7941
	15							1.0000	1.0000	1.0000	1.0000
16	0	0.1853	0.0281	0.0100	0.0033	0.0003	0.0000				
	1	0.5147	0.1407	0.0635	0.0261	0.0033	0.0003	0.0000			
	2	0.7892	0.3518	0.1971	0.0994	0.0183	0.0021	0.0001			
	3	0.9316	0.5981	0.4050	0.2459	0.0651	0.0106	0.0009	0.0000		
	4	0.9830	0.7982	0.6302	0.4499	0.1666	0.0384	0.0049	0.0003		
	5	0.9967	0.9183	0.8103	0.6598	0.3288	0.1051	0.0191	0.0016	0.0000	
	6	0.9995	0.9733	0.9204	0.8247	0.5272	0.2272	0.0583	0.0071	0.0002	
	7	0.9999	0.9930	0.9729	0.9256	0.7161	0.4018	0.1423	0.0257	0.0015	0.0000
	8	1.0000	0.9985	0.9925	0.9743	0.8577	0.5982	0.2839	0.0744	0.0070	0.0001
	9		0.9998	0.9984	0.9929	0.9417	0.7728	0.4728	0.1753	0.0267	0.0005
	10		1.0000	0.9997	0.9984	0.9809	0.8949	0.6712	0.3402	0.0817	0.0033
	11			1.0000	0.9997	0.9951	0.9616	0.8334	0.5501	0.2018	0.0170
	12				1.0000	0.9991	0.9894	0.9349	0.7541	0.4019	0.0684
	13					0.9999	0.9979	0.9817	0.9006	0.6482	0.2108
	14					1.0000	0.9997	0.9967	0.9739	0.8593	0.4853
	15						1.0000	0.9997	0.9967	0.9719	0.8147
	16							1.0000	1.0000	1.0000	1.0000

Table (continued) Binomial Probability Sums $\sum_{x=0}^{r} b(x; n, p)$

						p					
n	r	0.10	0.20	0.25	0.30	0.40	0.50	0.60	0.70	0.80	0.90
17	0	0.1668	0.0225	0.0075	0.0023	0.0002	0.0000				
	1	0.4818	0.1182	0.0501	0.0193	0.0021	0.0001	0.0000			
	2	0.7618	0.3096	0.1637	0.0774	0.0123	0.0012	0.0001			
	3	0.9174	0.5489	0.3530	0.2019	0.0464	0.0064	0.0005	0.0000		
	4	0.9779	0.7582	0.5739	0.3887	0.1260	0.0245	0.0025	0.0001		
	5	0.9953	0.8943	0.7653	0.5968	0.2639	0.0717	0.0106	0.0007	0.0000	
	6	0.9992	0.9623	0.8929	0.7752	0.4478	0.1662	0.0348	0.0032	0.0001	
	7	0.9999	0.9891	0.9598	0.8954	0.6405	0.3145	0.0919	0.0127	0.0005	
	8	1.0000	0.9974	0.9876	0.9597	0.8011	0.5000	0.1989	0.0403	0.0026	0.0000
	9		0.9995	0.9969	0.9873	0.9081	0.6855	0.3595	0.1046	0.0109	0.0001
	10		0.9999	0.9994	0.9968	0.9652	0.8338	0.5522	0.2248	0.0377	0.0008
	11		1.0000	0.9999	0.9993	0.9894	0.9283	0.7361	0.4032	0.1057	0.0047
	12			1.0000	0.9999	0.9975	0.9755	0.8740	0.6113	0.2418	0.0221
	13				1.0000	0.9995	0.9936	0.9536	0.7981	0.4511	0.0826
	14					0.9999	0.9988	0.9877	0.9226	0.6904	0.2382
	15					1.0000	0.9999	0.9979	0.9807	0.8818	0.5182
	16						1.0000	0.9998	0.9977	0.9775	0.8332
	17							1.0000	1.0000	1.0000	1.0000
18	0	0.1501	0.0180	0.0056	0.0016	0.0001	0.0000				
	1	0.4503	0.0991	0.0395	0.0142	0.0013	0.0001				
	2	0.7338	0.2713	0.1353	0.0600	0.0082	0.0007	0.0000			
	3	0.9018	0.5010	0.3057	0.1646	0.0328	0.0038	0.0002			
	4	0.9718	0.7164	0.5187	0.3327	0.0942	0.0154	0.0013	0.0000		
	5	0.9936	0.8671	0.7175	0.5344	0.2088	0.0481	0.0058	0.0003		
	6	0.9988	0.9487	0.8610	0.7217	0.3743	0.1189	0.0203	0.0014	0.0000	
	7	0.9998	0.9837	0.9431	0.8593	0.5634	0.2403	0.0576	0.0061	0.0002	
	8	1.0000	0.9957	0.9807	0.9404	0.7368	0.4073	0.1347	0.0210	0.0009	
	9		0.9991	0.9946	0.9790	0.8653	0.5927	0.2632	0.0596	0.0043	0.0000
	10		0.9998	0.9988	0.9939	0.9424	0.7597	0.4366	0.1407	0.0163	0.0002
	11		1.0000	0.9998	0.9986	0.9797	0.8811	0.6257	0.2783	0.0513	0.0012
	12			1.0000	0.9997	0.9942	0.9519	0.7912	0.4656	0.1329	0.0064
	13				1.0000	0.9987	0.9846	0.9058	0.6673	0.2836	0.0282
	14					0.9998	0.9962	0.9672	0.8354	0.4990	0.0982
	15					1.0000	0.9993	0.9918	0.9400	0.7287	0.2662
	16						0.9999	0.9987	0.9858	0.9009	0.5497
	17						1.0000	0.9999	0.9984	0.9820	0.8499
	18							1.0000	1.0000	1.0000	1.0000

Table (continued) Binomial Probability Sums $\sum_{x=0}^{r} b(x; n, p)$

						p					
n	r	0.10	0.20	0.25	0.30	0.40	0.50	0.60	0.70	0.80	0.90
19	0	0.1351	0.0144	0.0042	0.0011	0.0001					
	1	0.4203	0.0829	0.0310	0.0104	0.0008	0.0000				
	2	0.7054	0.2369	0.1113	0.0462	0.0055	0.0004	0.0000			
	3	0.8850	0.4551	0.2631	0.1332	0.0230	0.0022	0.0001			
	4	0.9648	0.6733	0.4654	0.2822	0.0696	0.0096	0.0006	0.0000		
	5	0.9914	0.8369	0.6678	0.4739	0.1629	0.0318	0.0031	0.0001		
	6	0.9983	0.9324	0.8251	0.6655	0.3081	0.0835	0.0116	0.0006		
	7	0.9997	0.9767	0.9225	0.8180	0.4878	0.1796	0.0352	0.0028	0.0000	
	8	1.0000	0.9933	0.9713	0.9161	0.6675	0.3238	0.0885	0.0105	0.0003	
	9		0.9984	0.9911	0.9674	0.8139	0.5000	0.1861	0.0326	0.0016	
	10		0.9997	0.9977	0.9895	0.9115	0.6762	0.3325	0.0839	0.0067	0.0000
	11		1.0000	0.9995	0.9972	0.9648	0.8204	0.5122	0.1820	0.0233	0.0003
	12			0.9999	0.9994	0.9884	0.9165	0.6919	0.3345	0.0676	0.0017
	13			1.0000	0.9999	0.9969	0.9682	0.8371	0.5261	0.1631	0.0086
	14				1.0000	0.9994	0.9904	0.9304	0.7178	0.3267	0.0352
	15					0.9999	0.9978	0.9770	0.8668	0.5449	0.1150
	16					1.0000	0.9996	0.9945	0.9538	0.7631	0.2946
	17						1.0000	0.9992	0.9896	0.9171	0.5797
	18							0.9999	0.9989	0.9856	0.8649
	19							1.0000	1.0000	1.0000	1.0000
20	0	0.1216	0.0115	0.0032	0.0008	0.0000					
	1	0.3917	0.0692	0.0243	0.0076	0.0005	0.0000				
	2	0.6769	0.2061	0.0913	0.0355	0.0036	0.0002				
	3	0.8670	0.4114	0.2252	0.1071	0.0160	0.0013	0.0000			
	4	0.9568	0.6296	0.4148	0.2375	0.0510	0.0059	0.0003			
	5	0.9887	0.8042	0.6172	0.4164	0.1256	0.0207	0.0016	0.0000		
	6	0.9976	0.9133	0.7858	0.6080	0.2500	0.0577	0.0065	0.0003		
	7	0.9996	0.9679	0.8982	0.7723	0.4159	0.1316	0.0210	0.0013	0.0000	
	8	0.9999	0.9900	0.9591	0.8867	0.5956	0.2517	0.0565	0.0051	0.0001	
	9	1.0000	0.9974	0.9861	0.9520	0.7553	0.4119	0.1275	0.0171	0.0006	
	10		0.9994	0.9961	0.9829	0.8725	0.5881	0.2447	0.0480	0.0026	0.0000
	11		0.9999	0.9991	0.9949	0.9435	0.7483	0.4044	0.1133	0.0100	0.0001
	12		1.0000	0.9998	0.9987	0.9790	0.8684	0.5841	0.2277	0.0321	0.0004
	13			1.0000	0.9997	0.9935	0.9423	0.7500	0.3920	0.0867	0.0024
	14				1.0000	0.9984	0.9793	0.8744	0.5836	0.1958	0.0113
	15					0.9997	0.9941	0.9490	0.7625	0.3704	0.0432
	16					1.0000	0.9987	0.9840	0.8929	0.5886	0.1330
	17						0.9998	0.9964	0.9645	0.7939	0.3231
	18						1.0000	0.9995	0.9924	0.9308	0.6083
	19							1.0000	0.9992	0.9885	0.8784
	20								1.0000	1.0000	1.0000

Table Poisson Probability Sums $\sum_{x=0}^{r} p(x;\mu)$

	μ								
r	0.1	0.2	0.3	0.4	0.5	0.6	0.7	0.8	0.9
0	0.9048	0.8187	0.7408	0.6703	0.6065	0.5488	0.4966	0.4493	0.4066
1	0.9953	0.9825	0.9631	0.9384	0.9098	0.8781	0.8442	0.8088	0.7725
2	0.9998	0.9989	0.9964	0.9921	0.9856	0.9769	0.9659	0.9526	0.9371
3	1.0000	0.9999	0.9997	0.9992	0.9982	0.9966	0.9942	0.9909	0.9865
4		1.0000	1.0000	0.9999	0.9998	0.9996	0.9992	0.9986	0.9977
5				1.0000	1.0000	1.0000	0.9999	0.9998	0.9997
6							1.0000	1.0000	1.0000

	μ								
r	1.0	1.5	2.0	2.5	3.0	3.5	4.0	4.5	5.0
0	0.3679	0.2231	0.1353	0.0821	0.0498	0.0302	0.0183	0.0111	0.0067
1	0.7358	0.5578	0.4060	0.2873	0.1991	0.1359	0.0916	0.0611	0.0404
2	0.9197	0.8088	0.6767	0.5438	0.4232	0.3208	0.2381	0.1736	0.1247
3	0.9810	0.9344	0.8571	0.7576	0.6472	0.5366	0.4335	0.3423	0.2650
4	0.9963	0.9814	0.9473	0.8912	0.8153	0.7254	0.6288	0.5321	0.4405
5	0.9994	0.9955	0.9834	0.9580	0.9161	0.8576	0.7851	0.7029	0.6160
6	0.9999	0.9991	0.9955	0.9858	0.9665	0.9347	0.8893	0.8311	0.7622
7	1.0000	0.9998	0.9989	0.9958	0.9881	0.9733	0.9489	0.9134	0.8666
8		1.0000	0.9998	0.9989	0.9962	0.9901	0.9786	0.9597	0.9319
9			1.0000	0.9997	0.9989	0.9967	0.9919	0.9829	0.9682
10				0.9999	0.9997	0.9990	0.9972	0.9933	0.9863
11				1.0000	0.9999	0.9997	0.9991	0.9976	0.9945
12					1.0000	0.9999	0.9997	0.9992	0.9980
13						1.0000	0.9999	0.9997	0.9993
14							1.0000	0.9999	0.9998
15								1.0000	0.9999
16									1.0000

Table (continued) Poisson Probability Sums $\sum_{x=0}^{r} p(x;\mu)$

					μ				
r	5.5	6.0	6.5	7.0	7.5	8.0	8.5	9.0	9.5
0	0.0041	0.0025	0.0015	0.0009	0.0006	0.0003	0.0002	0.0001	0.0001
1	0.0266	0.0174	0.0113	0.0073	0.0047	0.0030	0.0019	0.0012	0.0008
2	0.0884	0.0620	0.0430	0.0296	0.0203	0.0138	0.0093	0.0062	0.0042
3	0.2017	0.1512	0.1118	0.0818	0.0591	0.0424	0.0301	0.0212	0.0149
4	0.3575	0.2851	0.2237	0.1730	0.1321	0.0996	0.0744	0.0550	0.0403
5	0.5289	0.4457	0.3690	0.3007	0.2414	0.1912	0.1496	0.1157	0.0885
6	0.6860	0.6063	0.5265	0.4497	0.3782	0.3134	0.2562	0.2068	0.1649
7	0.8095	0.7440	0.6728	0.5987	0.5246	0.4530	0.3856	0.3239	0.2687
8	0.8944	0.8472	0.7916	0.7291	0.6620	0.5925	0.5231	0.4557	0.3918
9	0.9462	0.9161	0.8774	0.8305	0.7764	0.7166	0.6530	0.5874	0.5218
10	0.9747	0.9574	0.9332	0.9015	0.8622	0.8159	0.7634	0.7060	0.6453
11	0.9890	0.9799	0.9661	0.9467	0.9208	0.8881	0.8487	0.8030	0.7520
12	0.9955	0.9912	0.9840	0.9730	0.9573	0.9362	0.9091	0.8758	0.8364
13	0.9983	0.9964	0.9929	0.9872	0.9784	0.9658	0.9486	0.9261	0.8981
14	0.9994	0.9986	0.9970	0.9943	0.9897	0.9827	0.9726	0.9585	0.9400
15	0.9998	0.9995	0.9988	0.9976	0.9954	0.9918	0.9862	0.9780	0.9665
16	0.9999	0.9998	0.9996	0.9990	0.9980	0.9963	0.9934	0.9889	0.9823
17	1.0000	0.9999	0.9998	0.9996	0.9992	0.9984	0.9970	0.9947	0.9911
18		1.0000	0.9999	0.9999	0.9997	0.9993	0.9987	0.9976	0.9957
19			1.0000	1.0000	0.9999	0.9997	0.9995	0.9989	0.9980
20						0.9999	0.9998	0.9996	0.9991
21						1.0000	0.9999	0.9998	0.9996
22							1.0000	0.9999	0.9999
23								1.0000	0.9999
24									1.0000

Table (continued) Poisson Probability Sums $\sum\limits_{x=0}^{r} p(x; \mu)$

r	10.0	11.0	12.0	13.0	14.0	15.0	16.0	17.0	18.0
0	0.0000	0.0000	0.0000						
1	0.0005	0.0002	0.0001	0.0000	0.0000				
2	0.0028	0.0012	0.0005	0.0002	0.0001	0.0000	0.0000		
3	0.0103	0.0049	0.0023	0.0011	0.0005	0.0002	0.0001	0.0000	0.0000
4	0.0293	0.0151	0.0076	0.0037	0.0018	0.0009	0.0004	0.0002	0.0001
5	0.0671	0.0375	0.0203	0.0107	0.0055	0.0028	0.0014	0.0007	0.0003
6	0.1301	0.0786	0.0458	0.0259	0.0142	0.0076	0.0040	0.0021	0.0010
7	0.2202	0.1432	0.0895	0.0540	0.0316	0.0180	0.0100	0.0054	0.0029
8	0.3328	0.2320	0.1550	0.0998	0.0621	0.0374	0.0220	0.0126	0.0071
9	0.4579	0.3405	0.2424	0.1658	0.1094	0.0699	0.0433	0.0261	0.0154
10	0.5830	0.4599	0.3472	0.2517	0.1757	0.1185	0.0774	0.0491	0.0304
11	0.6968	0.5793	0.4616	0.3532	0.2600	0.1848	0.1270	0.0847	0.0549
12	0.7916	0.6887	0.5760	0.4631	0.3585	0.2676	0.1931	0.1350	0.0917
13	0.8645	0.7813	0.6815	0.5730	0.4644	0.3632	0.2745	0.2009	0.1426
14	0.9165	0.8540	0.7720	0.6751	0.5704	0.4657	0.3675	0.2808	0.2081
15	0.9513	0.9074	0.8444	0.7636	0.6694	0.5681	0.4667	0.3715	0.2867
16	0.9730	0.9441	0.8987	0.8355	0.7559	0.6641	0.5660	0.4677	0.3751
17	0.9857	0.9678	0.9370	0.8905	0.8272	0.7489	0.6593	0.5640	0.4686
18	0.9928	0.9823	0.9626	0.9302	0.8826	0.8195	0.7423	0.6550	0.5622
19	0.9965	0.9907	0.9787	0.9573	0.9235	0.8752	0.8122	0.7363	0.6509
20	0.9984	0.9953	0.9884	0.9750	0.9521	0.9170	0.8682	0.8055	0.7307
21	0.9993	0.9977	0.9939	0.9859	0.9712	0.9469	0.9108	0.8615	0.7991
22	0.9997	0.9990	0.9970	0.9924	0.9833	0.9673	0.9418	0.9047	0.8551
23	0.9999	0.9995	0.9985	0.9960	0.9907	0.9805	0.9633	0.9367	0.8989
24	1.0000	0.9998	0.9993	0.9980	0.9950	0.9888	0.9777	0.9594	0.9317
25		0.9999	0.9997	0.9990	0.9974	0.9938	0.9869	0.9748	0.9554
26		1.0000	0.9999	0.9995	0.9987	0.9967	0.9925	0.9848	0.9718
27			0.9999	0.9998	0.9994	0.9983	0.9959	0.9912	0.9827
28			1.0000	0.9999	0.9997	0.9991	0.9978	0.9950	0.9897
29				1.0000	0.9999	0.9996	0.9989	0.9973	0.9941
30					0.9999	0.9998	0.9994	0.9986	0.9967
31					1.0000	0.9999	0.9997	0.9993	0.9982
32						1.0000	0.9999	0.9996	0.9990
33							0.9999	0.9998	0.9995
34							1.0000	0.9999	0.9998
35								1.0000	0.9999
36									0.9999
37									1.0000

Some Discrete Probability Distributions

Proof of Mean and Variance of the Poisson Distribution

Let $\mu = \lambda t$.

$$E(X) = \sum_{x=0}^{\infty} x \cdot \frac{e^{-\mu}\mu^x}{x!} = \sum_{x=1}^{\infty} x \cdot \frac{e^{-\mu}\mu^x}{x!} = \mu \sum_{x=1}^{\infty} \frac{e^{-\mu}\mu^{x-1}}{(x-1)!}.$$

Since the summation in the last term above is the total probability of a Poisson random variable with mean μ, which can be easily seen by letting $y = x - 1$, it equals 1. Therefore, $E(X) = \mu$. To calculate the variance of X, note that

$$E[X(X-1)] = \sum_{x=0}^{\infty} x(x-1)\frac{e^{-\mu}\mu^x}{x!} = \mu^2 \sum_{x=2}^{\infty} \frac{e^{-\mu}\mu^{x-2}}{(x_2)!}.$$

Again, letting $y = x - 2$, the summation in the last term above is the total probability of a Poisson random variable with mean μ. Hence, we obtain

$$\sigma^2 = E(X^2) - [E(X)]^2 = E[X(X-1)] + E(X) - [E(X)]^2 = \mu^2 + \mu - \mu^2 = \mu = \lambda t.$$

186

Some Continuous Probability Distributions

1   Continuous Uniform Distribution

One of the simplest continuous distributions in all of statistics is the **continuous uniform distribution**. This distribution is characterized by a density function that is "flat," and thus the probability is uniform in a closed interval, say $[A, B]$. Although applications of the continuous uniform distribution are not as abundant as those for other distributions discussed in this chapter, it is appropriate for the novice to begin this introduction to continuous distributions with the uniform distribution.

Uniform Distribution

The density function of the continuous uniform random variable X on the interval $[A, B]$ is

$$f(x; A, B) = \begin{cases} \frac{1}{B-A}, & A \le x \le B, \\ 0, & \text{elsewhere.} \end{cases}$$

The density function forms a rectangle with base $B-A$ and **constant height** $\frac{1}{B-A}$. As a result, the uniform distribution is often called the **rectangular distribution**. Note, however, that the interval may not always be closed: $[A, B]$. It can be (A, B) as well. The density function for a uniform random variable on the interval $[1, 3]$ is shown in Figure 1.

Probabilities are simple to calculate for the uniform distribution because of the simple nature of the density function. However, note that the application of this distribution is based on the assumption that the probability of falling in an interval of fixed length within $[A, B]$ is constant.

Example 1:   Suppose that a large conference room at a certain company can be reserved for no more than 4 hours. Both long and short conferences occur quite often. In fact, it can be assumed that the length X of a conference has a uniform distribution on the interval $[0, 4]$.

From Chapter 6 of *Probability & Statistics for Engineers & Scientists*, Ninth Edition, Ronald E. Walpole, Raymond H. Myers, Sharon L. Myers, Keying Ye. Copyright © 2012 by Pearson Education, Inc. Published by Pearson Prentice Hall. All rights reserved.

Figure 1: The density function for a random variable on the interval $[1, 3]$.

(a) What is the probability density function?

(b) What is the probability that any given conference lasts at least 3 hours?

Solution: (a) The appropriate density function for the uniformly distributed random variable X in this situation is

$$f(x) = \begin{cases} \frac{1}{4}, & 0 \le x \le 4, \\ 0, & \text{elsewhere.} \end{cases}$$

(b) $P[X \ge 3] = \int_3^4 \frac{1}{4}\, dx = \frac{1}{4}$.

Theorem 1: | The mean and variance of the uniform distribution are

$$\mu = \frac{A+B}{2} \quad \text{and} \quad \sigma^2 = \frac{(B-A)^2}{12}.$$

The proofs of the theorems are left to the reader. See Exercise 1.

2 Normal Distribution

The most important continuous probability distribution in the entire field of statistics is the **normal distribution**. Its graph, called the **normal curve**, is the bell-shaped curve of Figure 2, which approximately describes many phenomena that occur in nature, industry, and research. For example, physical measurements in areas such as meteorological experiments, rainfall studies, and measurements of manufactured parts are often more than adequately explained with a normal distribution. In addition, errors in scientific measurements are extremely well approximated by a normal distribution. In 1733, Abraham DeMoivre developed the mathematical equation of the normal curve. It provided a basis from which much of the theory of inductive statistics is founded. The normal distribution is often referred to as the **Gaussian distribution**, in honor of Karl Friedrich Gauss

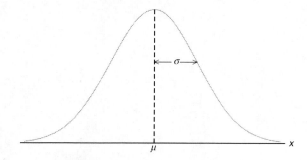

Figure 2: The normal curve.

(1777–1855), who also derived its equation from a study of errors in repeated measurements of the same quantity.

A continuous random variable X having the bell-shaped distribution of Figure 2 is called a **normal random variable**. The mathematical equation for the probability distribution of the normal variable depends on the two parameters μ and σ, its mean and standard deviation, respectively. Hence, we denote the values of the density of X by $n(x; \mu, \sigma)$.

Normal Distribution	The density of the normal random variable X, with mean μ and variance σ^2, is $$n(x; \mu, \sigma) = \frac{1}{\sqrt{2\pi}\sigma} e^{-\frac{1}{2\sigma^2}(x-\mu)^2}, \quad -\infty < x < \infty,$$ where $\pi = 3.14159\dots$ and $e = 2.71828\dots$.

Once μ and σ are specified, the normal curve is completely determined. For example, if $\mu = 50$ and $\sigma = 5$, then the ordinates $n(x; 50, 5)$ can be computed for various values of x and the curve drawn. In Figure 3, we have sketched two normal curves having the same standard deviation but different means. The two curves are identical in form but are centered at different positions along the horizontal axis.

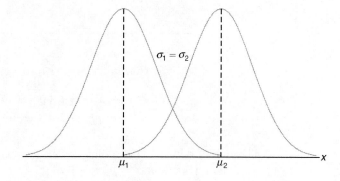

Figure 3: Normal curves with $\mu_1 < \mu_2$ and $\sigma_1 = \sigma_2$.

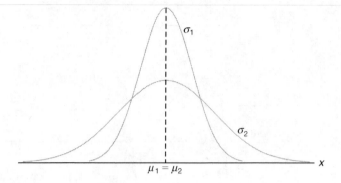

Figure 4: Normal curves with $\mu_1 = \mu_2$ and $\sigma_1 < \sigma_2$.

In Figure 4, we have sketched two normal curves with the same mean but different standard deviations. This time we see that the two curves are centered at exactly the same position on the horizontal axis, but the curve with the larger standard deviation is lower and spreads out farther. Remember that the area under a probability curve must be equal to 1, and therefore the more variable the set of observations, the lower and wider the corresponding curve will be.

Figure 5 shows two normal curves having different means and different standard deviations. Clearly, they are centered at different positions on the horizontal axis and their shapes reflect the two different values of σ.

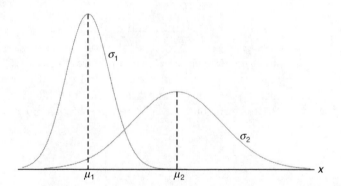

Figure 5: Normal curves with $\mu_1 < \mu_2$ and $\sigma_1 < \sigma_2$.

Based on inspection of Figures 2 through 5 and examination of the first and second derivatives of $n(x; \mu, \sigma)$, we list the following properties of the normal curve:

1. The mode, which is the point on the horizontal axis where the curve is a maximum, occurs at $x = \mu$.

2. The curve is symmetric about a vertical axis through the mean μ.

3. The curve has its points of inflection at $x = \mu \pm \sigma$; it is concave downward if $\mu - \sigma < X < \mu + \sigma$ and is concave upward otherwise.

4. The normal curve approaches the horizontal axis asymptotically as we proceed in either direction away from the mean.

5. The total area under the curve and above the horizontal axis is equal to 1.

Theorem 2: The mean and variance of $n(x; \mu, \sigma)$ are μ and σ^2, respectively. Hence, the standard deviation is σ.

Proof: To evaluate the mean, we first calculate

$$E(X - \mu) = \int_{-\infty}^{\infty} \frac{x - \mu}{\sqrt{2\pi}\sigma} e^{-\frac{1}{2}\left(\frac{x-\mu}{\sigma}\right)^2} \, dx.$$

Setting $z = (x - \mu)/\sigma$ and $dx = \sigma \, dz$, we obtain

$$E(X - \mu) = \frac{1}{\sqrt{2\pi}} \int_{-\infty}^{\infty} z e^{-\frac{1}{2}z^2} \, dz = 0,$$

since the integrand above is an odd function of z.
We conclude that

$$E(X) = \mu.$$

The variance of the normal distribution is given by

$$E[(X - \mu)^2] = \frac{1}{\sqrt{2\pi}\sigma} \int_{-\infty}^{\infty} (x - \mu)^2 e^{-\frac{1}{2}[(x-\mu)/\sigma]^2} \, dx.$$

Again setting $z = (x - \mu)/\sigma$ and $dx = \sigma \, dz$, we obtain

$$E[(X - \mu)^2] = \frac{\sigma^2}{\sqrt{2\pi}} \int_{-\infty}^{\infty} z^2 e^{-\frac{z^2}{2}} \, dz.$$

Integrating by parts with $u = z$ and $dv = ze^{-z^2/2} \, dz$ so that $du = dz$ and $v = -e^{-z^2/2}$, we find that

$$E[(X - \mu)^2] = \frac{\sigma^2}{\sqrt{2\pi}} \left(-ze^{-z^2/2} \Big|_{-\infty}^{\infty} + \int_{-\infty}^{\infty} e^{-z^2/2} \, dz \right) = \sigma^2(0 + 1) = \sigma^2.$$

Many random variables have probability distributions that can be described adequately by the normal curve once μ and σ^2 are specified. In this chapter, we shall assume that these two parameters are known, perhaps from previous investigations. Later, we shall make statistical inferences when μ and σ^2 are unknown and have been estimated from the available experimental data.

We pointed out earlier the role that the normal distribution plays as a reasonable approximation of scientific variables in real-life experiments. There are other applications of the normal distribution that the reader will appreciate as he or she moves on in the book. The normal distribution finds enormous application as a *limiting distribution*. Under certain conditions, the normal distribution provides a good continuous approximation to the binomial and hypergeometric distributions. The case of the approximation to the binomial is covered in Section 6. It turns out that the limiting distribution of sample averages is normal. This provides a broad base for statistical inference that proves very valuable to the data analyst interested in estimation and hypothesis testing. Theory in the important areas such as analysis of variance and quality control is based on assumptions that make use of the normal distribution.

In Section 3, examples demonstrate the use of tables of the normal distribution. Section 4 follows with examples of applications of the normal distribution.

3   Areas under the Normal Curve

The curve of any continuous probability distribution or density function is constructed so that the area under the curve bounded by the two ordinates $x = x_1$ and $x = x_2$ equals the probability that the random variable X assumes a value between $x = x_1$ and $x = x_2$. Thus, for the normal curve in Figure 6,

$$P(x_1 < X < x_2) = \int_{x_1}^{x_2} n(x; \mu, \sigma) \, dx = \frac{1}{\sqrt{2\pi}\sigma} \int_{x_1}^{x_2} e^{-\frac{1}{2\sigma^2}(x-\mu)^2} dx$$

is represented by the area of the shaded region.

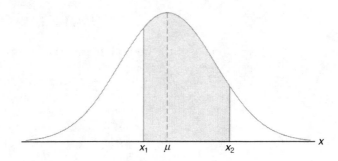

Figure 6: $P(x_1 < X < x_2) =$ area of the shaded region.

In Figures 3, 4, and 5 we saw how the normal curve is dependent on the mean and the standard deviation of the distribution under investigation. The area under the curve between any two ordinates must then also depend on the values μ and σ. This is evident in Figure 7, where we have shaded regions corresponding to $P(x_1 < X < x_2)$ for two curves with different means and variances. $P(x_1 < X < x_2)$, where X is the random variable describing distribution A, is indicated by the shaded area below the curve of A. If X is the random variable describing distribution B, then $P(x_1 < X < x_2)$ is given by the entire shaded region. Obviously, the two shaded regions are different in size; therefore, the probability associated with each distribution will be different for the two given values of X.

There are many types of statistical software that can be used in calculating areas under the normal curve. The difficulty encountered in solving integrals of normal density functions necessitates the tabulation of normal curve areas for quick reference. However, it would be a hopeless task to attempt to set up separate tables for every conceivable value of μ and σ. Fortunately, we are able to transform all the observations of any normal random variable X into a new set of observations

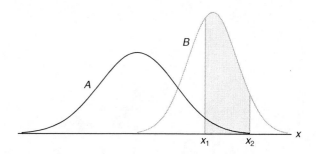

Figure 7: $P(x_1 < X < x_2)$ for different normal curves.

of a normal random variable Z with mean 0 and variance 1. This can be done by means of the transformation

$$Z = \frac{X - \mu}{\sigma}.$$

Whenever X assumes a value x, the corresponding value of Z is given by $z = (x - \mu)/\sigma$. Therefore, if X falls between the values $x = x_1$ and $x = x_2$, the random variable Z will fall between the corresponding values $z_1 = (x_1 - \mu)/\sigma$ and $z_2 = (x_2 - \mu)/\sigma$. Consequently, we may write

$$P(x_1 < X < x_2) = \frac{1}{\sqrt{2\pi}\sigma} \int_{x_1}^{x_2} e^{-\frac{1}{2\sigma^2}(x-\mu)^2} dx = \frac{1}{\sqrt{2\pi}} \int_{z_1}^{z_2} e^{-\frac{1}{2}z^2} \, dz$$

$$= \int_{z_1}^{z_2} n(z; 0, 1) \, dz = P(z_1 < Z < z_2),$$

where Z is seen to be a normal random variable with mean 0 and variance 1.

Definition 1:

> The distribution of a normal random variable with mean 0 and variance 1 is called a **standard normal distribution**.

The original and transformed distributions are illustrated in Figure 6.8. Since all the values of X falling between x_1 and x_2 have corresponding z values between z_1 and z_2, the area under the X-curve between the ordinates $x = x_1$ and $x = x_2$ in Figure 8 equals the area under the Z-curve between the transformed ordinates $z = z_1$ and $z = z_2$.

We have now reduced the required number of tables of normal-curve areas to one, that of the standard normal distribution. Table Areas under the Normal Curve at the end of this chapter indicates the area under the standard normal curve corresponding to $P(Z < z)$ for values of z ranging from -3.49 to 3.49. To illustrate the use of this table, let us find the probability that Z is less than 1.74. First, we locate a value of z equal to 1.7 in the left column; then we move across the row to the column under 0.04, where we read 0.9591. Therefore, $P(Z < 1.74) = 0.9591$. To find a z value corresponding to a given probability, the process is reversed. For example, the z value leaving an area of 0.2148 under the curve to the left of z is seen to be -0.79.

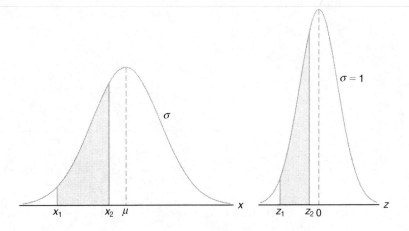

Figure 8: The original and transformed normal distributions.

Example 2: Given a standard normal distribution, find the area under the curve that lies

(a) to the right of $z = 1.84$ and

(b) between $z = -1.97$ and $z = 0.86$.

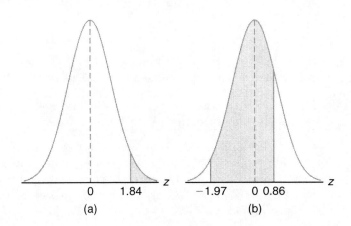

Figure 9: Areas for Example 2.

Solution: See Figure 9 for the specific areas.

(a) The area in Figure 9(a) to the right of $z = 1.84$ is equal to 1 minus the area in Table Areas under the Normal Curve to the left of $z = 1.84$, namely, $1 - 0.9671 = 0.0329$.

(b) The area in Figure 9(b) between $z = -1.97$ and $z = 0.86$ is equal to the area to the left of $z = 0.86$ minus the area to the left of $z = -1.97$. From Table Areas under the Normal Curve we find the desired area to be $0.8051 - 0.0244 = 0.7807$.

Example 3: Given a standard normal distribution, find the value of k such that

(a) $P(Z > k) = 0.3015$ and

(b) $P(k < Z < -0.18) = 0.4197$.

 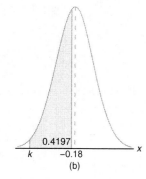

Figure 10: Areas for Example 3.

Solution: Distributions and the desired areas are shown in Figure 10.

(a) In Figure 10(a), we see that the k value leaving an area of 0.3015 to the right must then leave an area of 0.6985 to the left. From Table Areas under the Normal Curve it follows that $k = 0.52$.

(b) From Table Areas under the Normal Curve we note that the total area to the left of -0.18 is equal to 0.4286. In Figure 10(b), we see that the area between k and -0.18 is 0.4197, so the area to the left of k must be $0.4286 - 0.4197 = 0.0089$. Hence, from Table Areas under the Normal Curve, we have $k = -2.37$.

Example 4: Given a random variable X having a normal distribution with $\mu = 50$ and $\sigma = 10$, find the probability that X assumes a value between 45 and 62.

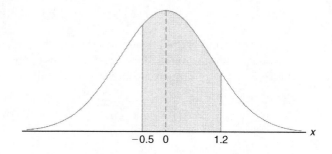

Figure 11: Area for Example 4.

Solution: The z values corresponding to $x_1 = 45$ and $x_2 = 62$ are

$$z_1 = \frac{45 - 50}{10} = -0.5 \text{ and } z_2 = \frac{62 - 50}{10} = 1.2.$$

Therefore,

$$P(45 < X < 62) = P(-0.5 < Z < 1.2).$$

$P(-0.5 < Z < 1.2)$ is shown by the area of the shaded region in Figure 11. This area may be found by subtracting the area to the left of the ordinate $z = -0.5$ from the entire area to the left of $z = 1.2$. Using Table Areas under the Normal Curve, we have

$$P(45 < X < 62) = P(-0.5 < Z < 1.2) = P(Z < 1.2) - P(Z < -0.5)$$
$$= 0.8849 - 0.3085 = 0.5764.$$

Example 5: Given that X has a normal distribution with $\mu = 300$ and $\sigma = 50$, find the probability that X assumes a value greater than 362.

Solution: The normal probability distribution with the desired area shaded is shown in Figure 12. To find $P(X > 362)$, we need to evaluate the area under the normal curve to the right of $x = 362$. This can be done by transforming $x = 362$ to the corresponding z value, obtaining the area to the left of z from Table Areas under the Normal Curve, and then subtracting this area from 1. We find that

$$z = \frac{362 - 300}{50} = 1.24.$$

Hence,

$$P(X > 362) = P(Z > 1.24) = 1 - P(Z < 1.24) = 1 - 0.8925 = 0.1075.$$

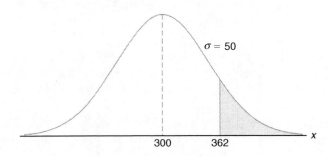

Figure 12: Area for Example 5.

According to Chebyshev's theorem, the probability that a random variable assumes a value within 2 standard deviations of the mean is at least 3/4. If the random variable has a normal distribution, the z values corresponding to $x_1 = \mu - 2\sigma$ and $x_2 = \mu + 2\sigma$ are easily computed to be

$$z_1 = \frac{(\mu - 2\sigma) - \mu}{\sigma} = -2 \text{ and } z_2 = \frac{(\mu + 2\sigma) - \mu}{\sigma} = 2.$$

Hence,

$$P(\mu - 2\sigma < X < \mu + 2\sigma) = P(-2 < Z < 2) = P(Z < 2) - P(Z < -2)$$
$$= 0.9772 - 0.0228 = 0.9544,$$

which is a much stronger statement than that given by Chebyshev's theorem.

Using the Normal Curve in Reverse

Sometimes, we are required to find the value of z corresponding to a specified probability that falls between values listed in Table Areas under the Normal Curve (see Example 6). For convenience, we shall always choose the z value corresponding to the tabular probability that comes closest to the specified probability.

The preceding two examples were solved by going first from a value of x to a z value and then computing the desired area. In Example 6, we reverse the process and begin with a known area or probability, find the z value, and then determine x by rearranging the formula

$$z = \frac{x - \mu}{\sigma} \quad \text{to give} \quad x = \sigma z + \mu.$$

Example 6: Given a normal distribution with $\mu = 40$ and $\sigma = 6$, find the value of x that has

(a) 45% of the area to the left and

(b) 14% of the area to the right.

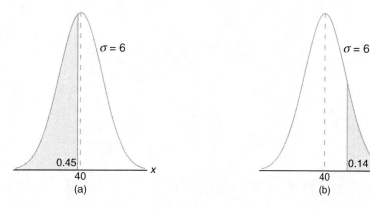

Figure 13: Areas for Example 6.

Solution: (a) An area of 0.45 to the left of the desired x value is shaded in Figure 13(a). We require a z value that leaves an area of 0.45 to the left. From Table Areas under the Normal Curve we find $P(Z < -0.13) = 0.45$, so the desired z value is -0.13. Hence,

$$x = (6)(-0.13) + 40 = 39.22.$$

(b) In Figure 13(b), we shade an area equal to 0.14 to the right of the desired x value. This time we require a z value that leaves 0.14 of the area to the right and hence an area of 0.86 to the left. Again, from Table Areas under the Normal Curve, we find $P(Z < 1.08) = 0.86$, so the desired z value is 1.08 and

$$x = (6)(1.08) + 40 = 46.48.$$

4   Applications of the Normal Distribution

Some of the many problems for which the normal distribution is applicable are treated in the following examples. The use of the normal curve to approximate binomial probabilities is considered in Section 5.

Example 7: A certain type of storage battery lasts, on average, 3.0 years with a standard deviation of 0.5 year. Assuming that battery life is normally distributed, find the probability that a given battery will last less than 2.3 years.

Solution: First construct a diagram such as Figure 14, showing the given distribution of battery lives and the desired area. To find $P(X < 2.3)$, we need to evaluate the area under the normal curve to the left of 2.3. This is accomplished by finding the area to the left of the corresponding z value. Hence, we find that

$$z = \frac{2.3 - 3}{0.5} = -1.4,$$

and then, using Table Areas under the Normal Curve, we have

$$P(X < 2.3) = P(Z < -1.4) = 0.0808.$$

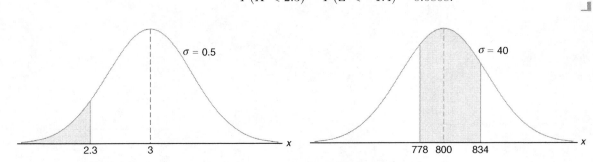

Figure 14: Area for Example 7.   Figure 15: Area for Example 8.

Example 8: An electrical firm manufactures light bulbs that have a life, before burn-out, that is normally distributed with mean equal to 800 hours and a standard deviation of 40 hours. Find the probability that a bulb burns between 778 and 834 hours.

Solution: The distribution of light bulb life is illustrated in Figure 15. The z values corresponding to $x_1 = 778$ and $x_2 = 834$ are

$$z_1 = \frac{778 - 800}{40} = -0.55 \text{ and } z_2 = \frac{834 - 800}{40} = 0.85.$$

Hence,

$$P(778 < X < 834) = P(-0.55 < Z < 0.85) = P(Z < 0.85) - P(Z < -0.55)$$
$$= 0.8023 - 0.2912 = 0.5111.$$

Example 9: In an industrial process, the diameter of a ball bearing is an important measurement. The buyer sets specifications for the diameter to be 3.0 ± 0.01 cm. The implication is that no part falling outside these specifications will be accepted. It is known that in the process the diameter of a ball bearing has a normal distribution with mean $\mu = 3.0$ and standard deviation $\sigma = 0.005$. On average, how many manufactured ball bearings will be scrapped?

Solution: The distribution of diameters is illustrated by Figure 16. The values corresponding to the specification limits are $x_1 = 2.99$ and $x_2 = 3.01$. The corresponding z values are

$$z_1 = \frac{2.99 - 3.0}{0.005} = -2.0 \text{ and } z_2 = \frac{3.01 - 3.0}{0.005} = +2.0.$$

Hence,

$$P(2.99 < X < 3.01) = P(-2.0 < Z < 2.0).$$

From Table Areas under the Normal Curve, $P(Z < 2.0) = 0.0228$. Due to symmetry of the normal distribution, we find that

$$P(Z < -2.0) + P(Z > 2.0) = 2(0.0228) = 0.0456.$$

As a result, it is anticipated that, on average, 4.56% of manufactured ball bearings will be scrapped.

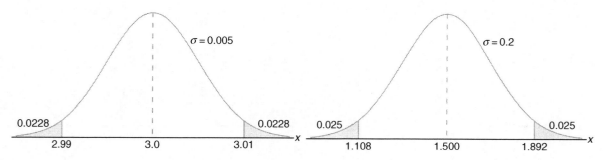

Figure 16: Area for Example 9.   Figure 17: Specifications for Example 10.

Example 10: Gauges are used to reject all components for which a certain dimension is not within the specification $1.50 \pm d$. It is known that this measurement is normally distributed with mean 1.50 and standard deviation 0.2. Determine the value d such that the specifications "cover" 95% of the measurements.

Solution: From Table Areas under the Normal Curve, we know that

$$P(-1.96 < Z < 1.96) = 0.95.$$

Therefore,

$$1.96 = \frac{(1.50 + d) - 1.50}{0.2},$$

from which we obtain

$$d = (0.2)(1.96) = 0.392.$$

An illustration of the specifications is shown in Figure 17.

Example 11: A certain machine makes electrical resistors having a mean resistance of 40 ohms and a standard deviation of 2 ohms. Assuming that the resistance follows a normal distribution and can be measured to any degree of accuracy, what percentage of resistors will have a resistance exceeding 43 ohms?

Solution: A percentage is found by multiplying the relative frequency by 100%. Since the relative frequency for an interval is equal to the probability of a value falling in the interval, we must find the area to the right of $x = 43$ in Figure 18. This can be done by transforming $x = 43$ to the corresponding z value, obtaining the area to the left of z from Table Areas under the Normal Curve, and then subtracting this area from 1. We find

$$z = \frac{43 - 40}{2} = 1.5.$$

Therefore,

$$P(X > 43) = P(Z > 1.5) = 1 - P(Z < 1.5) = 1 - 0.9332 = 0.0668.$$

Hence, 6.68% of the resistors will have a resistance exceeding 43 ohms.

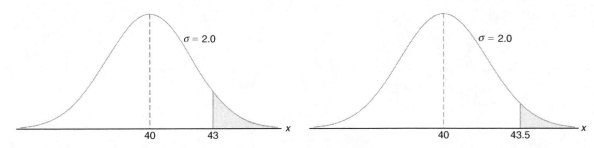

Figure 18: Area for Example 11.   Figure 19: Area for Example 12.

Example 12: Find the percentage of resistances exceeding 43 ohms for Example 11 if resistance is measured to the nearest ohm.

Solution: This problem differs from that in Example 11 in that we now assign a measurement of 43 ohms to all resistors whose resistances are greater than 42.5 and less than 43.5. We are actually approximating a discrete distribution by means of a continuous normal distribution. The required area is the region shaded to the right of 43.5 in Figure 19. We now find that

$$z = \frac{43.5 - 40}{2} = 1.75.$$

Hence,

$$P(X > 43.5) = P(Z > 1.75) = 1 - P(Z < 1.75) = 1 - 0.9599 = 0.0401.$$

Therefore, 4.01% of the resistances exceed 43 ohms when measured to the nearest ohm. The difference 6.68% − 4.01% = 2.67% between this answer and that of Example 11 represents all those resistance values greater than 43 and less than 43.5 that are now being recorded as 43 ohms.

Example 13: The average grade for an exam is 74, and the standard deviation is 7. If 12% of the class is given *A*s, and the grades are curved to follow a normal distribution, what is the lowest possible *A* and the highest possible *B*?

Solution: In this example, we begin with a known area of probability, find the *z* value, and then determine *x* from the formula $x = \sigma z + \mu$. An area of 0.12, corresponding to the fraction of students receiving *A*s, is shaded in Figure 20. We require a *z* value that leaves 0.12 of the area to the right and, hence, an area of 0.88 to the left. From Table Areas under the Normal Curve, $P(Z < 1.18)$ has the closest value to 0.88, so the desired *z* value is 1.18. Hence,

$$x = (7)(1.18) + 74 = 82.26.$$

Therefore, the lowest *A* is 83 and the highest *B* is 82.

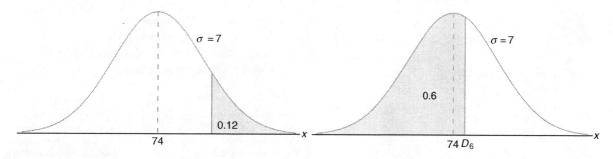

Figure 20: Area for Example 13.   Figure 21: Area for Example 14.

Example 14: Refer to Example 13 and find the sixth decile.

Solution: The sixth decile, written D_6, is the *x* value that leaves 60% of the area to the left, as shown in Figure 21. From Table Areas under the Normal Curve we find $P(Z < 0.25) \approx 0.6$, so the desired *z* value is 0.25. Now $x = (7)(0.25) + 74 = 75.75$. Hence, $D_6 = 75.75$. That is, 60% of the grades are 75 or less.

Exercises

1 Given a continuous uniform distribution, show that
(a) $\mu = \frac{A+B}{2}$ and
(b) $\sigma^2 = \frac{(B-A)^2}{12}$.

2 Suppose *X* follows a continuous uniform distribution from 1 to 5. Determine the conditional probability $P(X > 2.5 \mid X \le 4)$.

3 The daily amount of coffee, in liters, dispensed by a machine located in an airport lobby is a random variable *X* having a continuous uniform distribution with $A = 7$ and $B = 10$. Find the probability that on a given day the amount of coffee dispensed by this machine will be
(a) at most 8.8 liters;
(b) more than 7.4 liters but less than 9.5 liters;
(c) at least 8.5 liters.

4 A bus arrives every 10 minutes at a bus stop. It is assumed that the waiting time for a particular individual is a random variable with a continuous uniform distribution.

(a) What is the probability that the individual waits more than 7 minutes?

(b) What is the probability that the individual waits between 2 and 7 minutes?

5   Given a standard normal distribution, find the area under the curve that lies

(a) to the left of $z = -1.39$;

(b) to the right of $z = 1.96$;

(c) between $z = -2.16$ and $z = -0.65$;

(d) to the left of $z = 1.43$;

(e) to the right of $z = -0.89$;

(f) between $z = -0.48$ and $z = 1.74$.

6   Find the value of z if the area under a standard normal curve

(a) to the right of z is 0.3622;

(b) to the left of z is 0.1131;

(c) between 0 and z, with $z > 0$, is 0.4838;

(d) between $-z$ and z, with $z > 0$, is 0.9500.

7   Given a standard normal distribution, find the value of k such that

(a) $P(Z > k) = 0.2946$;

(b) $P(Z < k) = 0.0427$;

(c) $P(-0.93 < Z < k) = 0.7235$.

8   Given a normal distribution with $\mu = 30$ and $\sigma = 6$, find

(a) the normal curve area to the right of $x = 17$;

(b) the normal curve area to the left of $x = 22$;

(c) the normal curve area between $x = 32$ and $x = 41$;

(d) the value of x that has 80% of the normal curve area to the left;

(e) the two values of x that contain the middle 75% of the normal curve area.

9   Given the normally distributed variable X with mean 18 and standard deviation 2.5, find

(a) $P(X < 15)$;

(b) the value of k such that $P(X < k) = 0.2236$;

(c) the value of k such that $P(X > k) = 0.1814$;

(d) $P(17 < X < 21)$.

10   According to Chebyshev's theorem, the probability that any random variable assumes a value within 3 standard deviations of the mean is at least 8/9. If it is known that the probability distribution of a random variable X is normal with mean μ and variance σ^2, what is the exact value of $P(\mu - 3\sigma < X < \mu + 3\sigma)$?

11   A soft-drink machine is regulated so that it discharges an average of 200 milliliters per cup. If the amount of drink is normally distributed with a standard deviation equal to 15 milliliters,

(a) what fraction of the cups will contain more than 224 milliliters?

(b) what is the probability that a cup contains between 191 and 209 milliliters?

(c) how many cups will probably overflow if 230-milliliter cups are used for the next 1000 drinks?

(d) below what value do we get the smallest 25% of the drinks?

12   The loaves of rye bread distributed to local stores by a certain bakery have an average length of 30 centimeters and a standard deviation of 2 centimeters. Assuming that the lengths are normally distributed, what percentage of the loaves are

(a) longer than 31.7 centimeters?

(b) between 29.3 and 33.5 centimeters in length?

(c) shorter than 25.5 centimeters?

13   A research scientist reports that mice will live an average of 40 months when their diets are sharply restricted and then enriched with vitamins and proteins. Assuming that the lifetimes of such mice are normally distributed with a standard deviation of 6.3 months, find the probability that a given mouse will live

(a) more than 32 months;

(b) less than 28 months;

(c) between 37 and 49 months.

14   The finished inside diameter of a piston ring is normally distributed with a mean of 10 centimeters and a standard deviation of 0.03 centimeter.

(a) What proportion of rings will have inside diameters exceeding 10.075 centimeters?

(b) What is the probability that a piston ring will have an inside diameter between 9.97 and 10.03 centimeters?

(c) Below what value of inside diameter will 15% of the piston rings fall?

15   A lawyer commutes daily from his suburban home to his midtown office. The average time for a one-way trip is 24 minutes, with a standard deviation of 3.8 minutes. Assume the distribution of trip times to be normally distributed.

(a) What is the probability that a trip will take at least 1/2 hour?

(b) If the office opens at 9:00 A.M. and the lawyer leaves his house at 8:45 A.M. daily, what percentage of the time is he late for work?

(c) If he leaves the house at 8:35 A.M. and coffee is served at the office from 8:50 A.M. until 9:00 A.M., what is the probability that he misses coffee?

(d) Find the length of time above which we find the slowest 15% of the trips.

(e) Find the probability that 2 of the next 3 trips will take at least 1/2 hour.

16   In the November 1990 issue of *Chemical Engineering Progress*, a study discussed the percent purity of oxygen from a certain supplier. Assume that the mean was 99.61 with a standard deviation of 0.08. Assume that the distribution of percent purity was approximately normal.

(a) What percentage of the purity values would you expect to be between 99.5 and 99.7?

(b) What purity value would you expect to exceed exactly 5% of the population?

17   The average life of a certain type of small motor is 10 years with a standard deviation of 2 years. The manufacturer replaces free all motors that fail while under guarantee. If she is willing to replace only 3% of the motors that fail, how long a guarantee should be offered? Assume that the lifetime of a motor follows a normal distribution.

18   The heights of 1000 students are normally distributed with a mean of 174.5 centimeters and a standard deviation of 6.9 centimeters. Assuming that the heights are recorded to the nearest half-centimeter, how many of these students would you expect to have heights

(a) less than 160.0 centimeters?

(b) between 171.5 and 182.0 centimeters inclusive?

(c) equal to 175.0 centimeters?

(d) greater than or equal to 188.0 centimeters?

19   A company pays its employees an average wage of $15.90 an hour with a standard deviation of $1.50. If the wages are approximately normally distributed and paid to the nearest cent,

(a) what percentage of the workers receive wages between $13.75 and $16.22 an hour inclusive?

(b) the highest 5% of the employee hourly wages is greater than what amount?

20   The weights of a large number of miniature poodles are approximately normally distributed with a mean of 8 kilograms and a standard deviation of 0.9 kilogram. If measurements are recorded to the nearest tenth of a kilogram, find the fraction of these poodles with weights

(a) over 9.5 kilograms;

(b) of at most 8.6 kilograms;

(c) between 7.3 and 9.1 kilograms inclusive.

21   The tensile strength of a certain metal component is normally distributed with a mean of 10,000 kilograms per square centimeter and a standard deviation of 100 kilograms per square centimeter. Measurements are recorded to the nearest 50 kilograms per square centimeter.

(a) What proportion of these components exceed 10,150 kilograms per square centimeter in tensile strength?

(b) If specifications require that all components have tensile strength between 9800 and 10,200 kilograms per square centimeter inclusive, what proportion of pieces would we expect to scrap?

22   If a set of observations is normally distributed, what percent of these differ from the mean by

(a) more than 1.3σ?

(b) less than 0.52σ?

23   The IQs of 600 applicants to a certain college are approximately normally distributed with a mean of 115 and a standard deviation of 12. If the college requires an IQ of at least 95, how many of these students will be rejected on this basis of IQ, regardless of their other qualifications? Note that IQs are recorded to the nearest integers.

5   Normal Approximation to the Binomial

Probabilities associated with binomial experiments are readily obtainable from the formula $b(x; n, p)$ of the binomial distribution or from Table Binomial Probability Sums at the end of this chapter when n is small. In addition, binomial probabilities are readily available in many computer software packages. However, it is instructive to learn the relationship between the binomial and the normal distribution. In Section 5, we illustrated how the Poisson distribution can be used to approximate binomial probabilities when n is quite large and p is very close to 0 or 1. Both the binomial and the Poisson distributions are discrete. The first application of a continuous probability distribution to approximate probabilities over a discrete sample space was demonstrated in Example 12, where the normal curve was used. The normal distribution is often a good approximation to a discrete distribution when the latter takes on a symmetric bell shape. From a theoretical point of view, some distributions converge to the normal as their parameters approach certain limits. The normal distribution is a convenient approximating distribution because the cumulative distribution function is so easily tabled. The binomial distribution is nicely approximated by the normal in practical problems when one works with the cumulative distribution function. We now state a theorem that allows us to use areas under the normal curve to approximate binomial properties when n is sufficiently large.

Theorem 3:

If X is a binomial random variable with mean $\mu = np$ and variance $\sigma^2 = npq$, then the limiting form of the distribution of

$$Z = \frac{X - np}{\sqrt{npq}},$$

as $n \to \infty$, is the standard normal distribution $n(z; 0, 1)$.

It turns out that the normal distribution with $\mu = np$ and $\sigma^2 = np(1 - p)$ not only provides a very accurate approximation to the binomial distribution when n is large and p is not extremely close to 0 or 1 but also provides a fairly good approximation even when n is small and p is reasonably close to $1/2$.

To illustrate the normal approximation to the binomial distribution, we first draw the histogram for $b(x; 15, 0.4)$ and then superimpose the particular normal curve having the same mean and variance as the binomial variable X. Hence, we draw a normal curve with

$$\mu = np = (15)(0.4) = 6 \text{ and } \sigma^2 = npq = (15)(0.4)(0.6) = 3.6.$$

The histogram of $b(x; 15, 0.4)$ and the corresponding superimposed normal curve, which is completely determined by its mean and variance, are illustrated in Figure 22.

Figure 22: Normal approximation of $b(x; 15, 0.4)$.

The exact probability that the binomial random variable X assumes a given value x is equal to the area of the bar whose base is centered at x. For example, the exact probability that X assumes the value 4 is equal to the area of the rectangle with base centered at $x = 4$. Using Table Binomial Probability Sums, we find this area to be

$$P(X = 4) = b(4; 15, 0.4) = 0.1268,$$

which is approximately equal to the area of the shaded region under the normal curve between the two ordinates $x_1 = 3.5$ and $x_2 = 4.5$ in Figure 23. Converting to z values, we have

$$z_1 = \frac{3.5 - 6}{1.897} = -1.32 \quad \text{and} \quad z_2 = \frac{4.5 - 6}{1.897} = -0.79.$$

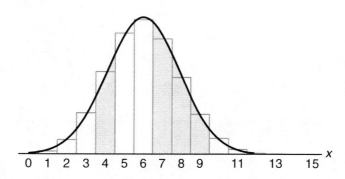

Figure 23: Normal approximation of $b(x; 15, 0.4)$ and $\sum_{x=7}^{9} b(x; 15, 0.4)$.

If X is a binomial random variable and Z a standard normal variable, then

$$P(X = 4) = b(4; 15, 0.4) \approx P(-1.32 < Z < -0.79)$$
$$= P(Z < -0.79) - P(Z < -1.32) = 0.2148 - 0.0934 = 0.1214.$$

This agrees very closely with the exact value of 0.1268.

The normal approximation is most useful in calculating binomial sums for large values of n. Referring to Figure 23, we might be interested in the probability that X assumes a value from 7 to 9 inclusive. The exact probability is given by

$$P(7 \leq X \leq 9) = \sum_{x=0}^{9} b(x; 15, 0.4) - \sum_{x=0}^{6} b(x; 15, 0.4)$$
$$= 0.9662 - 0.6098 = 0.3564,$$

which is equal to the sum of the areas of the rectangles with bases centered at $x = 7$, 8, and 9. For the normal approximation, we find the area of the shaded region under the curve between the ordinates $x_1 = 6.5$ and $x_2 = 9.5$ in Figure 23. The corresponding z values are

$$z_1 = \frac{6.5 - 6}{1.897} = 0.26 \quad \text{and} \quad z_2 = \frac{9.5 - 6}{1.897} = 1.85.$$

Now,

$$P(7 \leq X \leq 9) \approx P(0.26 < Z < 1.85) = P(Z < 1.85) - P(Z < 0.26)$$
$$= 0.9678 - 0.6026 = 0.3652.$$

Once again, the normal curve approximation provides a value that agrees very closely with the exact value of 0.3564. The degree of accuracy, which depends on how well the curve fits the histogram, will increase as n increases. This is particularly true when p is not very close to $1/2$ and the histogram is no longer symmetric. Figures 24 and 25 show the histograms for $b(x; 6, 0.2)$ and $b(x; 15, 0.2)$, respectively. It is evident that a normal curve would fit the histogram considerably better when $n = 15$ than when $n = 6$.

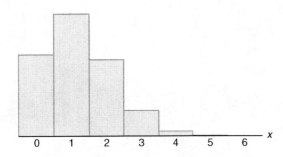

Figure 24: Histogram for $b(x; 6, 0.2)$.   Figure 25: Histogram for $b(x; 15, 0.2)$.

In our illustrations of the normal approximation to the binomial, it became apparent that if we seek the area under the normal curve to the left of, say, x, it is more accurate to use $x + 0.5$. This is a correction to accommodate the fact that a discrete distribution is being approximated by a continuous distribution. The correction $+0.5$ is called a **continuity correction**. The foregoing discussion leads to the following formal normal approximation to the binomial.

Normal Approximation to the Binomial Distribution

Let X be a binomial random variable with parameters n and p. For large n, X has approximately a normal distribution with $\mu = np$ and $\sigma^2 = npq = np(1-p)$ and

$$
\begin{aligned}
P(X \leq x) &= \sum_{k=0}^{x} b(k; n, p) \\
&\approx \text{ area under normal curve to the left of } x + 0.5 \\
&= P\left(Z \leq \frac{x + 0.5 - np}{\sqrt{npq}}\right),
\end{aligned}
$$

and the approximation will be good if np and $n(1-p)$ are greater than or equal to 5.

As we indicated earlier, the quality of the approximation is quite good for large n. If p is close to $1/2$, a moderate or small sample size will be sufficient for a reasonable approximation. We offer Table 1 as an indication of the quality of the approximation. Both the normal approximation and the true binomial cumulative probabilities are given. Notice that at $p = 0.05$ and $p = 0.10$, the approximation is fairly crude for $n = 10$. However, even for $n = 10$, note the improvement for $p = 0.50$. On the other hand, when p is fixed at $p = 0.05$, note the improvement of the approximation as we go from $n = 20$ to $n = 100$.

Table 1: Normal Approximation and True Cumulative Binomial Probabilities

	$p = 0.05$, $n = 10$		$p = 0.10$, $n = 10$		$p = 0.50$, $n = 10$	
r	**Binomial**	**Normal**	**Binomial**	**Normal**	**Binomial**	**Normal**
0	0.5987	0.5000	0.3487	0.2981	0.0010	0.0022
1	0.9139	0.9265	0.7361	0.7019	0.0107	0.0136
2	0.9885	0.9981	0.9298	0.9429	0.0547	0.0571
3	0.9990	1.0000	0.9872	0.9959	0.1719	0.1711
4	1.0000	1.0000	0.9984	0.9999	0.3770	0.3745
5			1.0000	1.0000	0.6230	0.6255
6					0.8281	0.8289
7					0.9453	0.9429
8					0.9893	0.9864
9					0.9990	0.9978
10					1.0000	0.9997

	$p = 0.05$					
	$n = 20$		$n = 50$		$n = 100$	
r	**Binomial**	**Normal**	**Binomial**	**Normal**	**Binomial**	**Normal**
0	0.3585	0.3015	0.0769	0.0968	0.0059	0.0197
1	0.7358	0.6985	0.2794	0.2578	0.0371	0.0537
2	0.9245	0.9382	0.5405	0.5000	0.1183	0.1251
3	0.9841	0.9948	0.7604	0.7422	0.2578	0.2451
4	0.9974	0.9998	0.8964	0.9032	0.4360	0.4090
5	0.9997	1.0000	0.9622	0.9744	0.6160	0.5910
6	1.0000	1.0000	0.9882	0.9953	0.7660	0.7549
7			0.9968	0.9994	0.8720	0.8749
8			0.9992	0.9999	0.9369	0.9463
9			0.9998	1.0000	0.9718	0.9803
10			1.0000	1.0000	0.9885	0.9941

Example 15: The probability that a patient recovers from a rare blood disease is 0.4. If 100 people are known to have contracted this disease, what is the probability that fewer than 30 survive?

Solution: Let the binomial variable X represent the number of patients who survive. Since $n = 100$, we should obtain fairly accurate results using the normal-curve approximation with

$$\mu = np = (100)(0.4) = 40 \text{ and } \sigma = \sqrt{npq} = \sqrt{(100)(0.4)(0.6)} = 4.899.$$

To obtain the desired probability, we have to find the area to the left of $x = 29.5$.

The z value corresponding to 29.5 is

$$z = \frac{29.5 - 40}{4.899} = -2.14,$$

and the probability of fewer than 30 of the 100 patients surviving is given by the shaded region in Figure 26. Hence,

$$P(X < 30) \approx P(Z < -2.14) = 0.0162.$$

Figure 26: Area for Example 15.　　　　Figure 27: Area for Example 16.

Example 16:　A multiple-choice quiz has 200 questions, each with 4 possible answers of which only 1 is correct. What is the probability that sheer guesswork yields from 25 to 30 correct answers for the 80 of the 200 problems about which the student has no knowledge?

Solution: The probability of guessing a correct answer for each of the 80 questions is $p = 1/4$. If X represents the number of correct answers resulting from guesswork, then

$$P(25 \le X \le 30) = \sum_{x=25}^{30} b(x; 80, 1/4).$$

Using the normal curve approximation with

$$\mu = np = (80)\left(\frac{1}{4}\right) = 20$$

and

$$\sigma = \sqrt{npq} = \sqrt{(80)(1/4)(3/4)} = 3.873,$$

we need the area between $x_1 = 24.5$ and $x_2 = 30.5$. The corresponding z values are

$$z_1 = \frac{24.5 - 20}{3.873} = 1.16 \text{ and } z_2 = \frac{30.5 - 20}{3.873} = 2.71.$$

The probability of correctly guessing from 25 to 30 questions is given by the shaded region in Figure 27. From Table Areas under the Normal Curve we find that

$$P(25 \le X \le 30) = \sum_{x=25}^{30} b(x; 80, 0.25) \approx P(1.16 < Z < 2.71)$$

$$= P(Z < 2.71) - P(Z < 1.16) = 0.9966 - 0.8770 = 0.1196.$$

Exercises

24 A coin is tossed 400 times. Use the normal curve approximation to find the probability of obtaining

(a) between 185 and 210 heads inclusive;

(b) exactly 205 heads;

(c) fewer than 176 or more than 227 heads.

25 A process for manufacturing an electronic component yields items of which 1% are defective. A quality control plan is to select 100 items from the process, and if none are defective, the process continues. Use the normal approximation to the binomial to find

(a) the probability that the process continues given the sampling plan described;

(b) the probability that the process continues even if the process has gone bad (i.e., if the frequency of defective components has shifted to 5.0% defective).

26 A process yields 10% defective items. If 100 items are randomly selected from the process, what is the probability that the number of defectives

(a) exceeds 13?

(b) is less than 8?

27 The probability that a patient recovers from a delicate heart operation is 0.9. Of the next 100 patients having this operation, what is the probability that

(a) between 84 and 95 inclusive survive?

(b) fewer than 86 survive?

28 Researchers at George Washington University and the National Institutes of Health claim that approximately 75% of people believe "tranquilizers work very well to make a person more calm and relaxed." Of the next 80 people interviewed, what is the probability that

(a) at least 50 are of this opinion?

(b) at most 56 are of this opinion?

29 If 20% of the residents in a U.S. city prefer a white telephone over any other color available, what is the probability that among the next 1000 telephones installed in that city

(a) between 170 and 185 inclusive will be white?

(b) at least 210 but not more than 225 will be white?

30 A drug manufacturer claims that a certain drug cures a blood disease, on the average, 80% of the time. To check the claim, government testers use the drug on a sample of 100 individuals and decide to accept the claim if 75 or more are cured.

(a) What is the probability that the claim will be rejected when the cure probability is, in fact, 0.8?

(b) What is the probability that the claim will be accepted by the government when the cure probability is as low as 0.7?

31 One-sixth of the male freshmen entering a large state school are out-of-state students. If the students are assigned at random to dormitories, 180 to a building, what is the probability that in a given dormitory at least one-fifth of the students are from out of state?

32 A pharmaceutical company knows that approximately 5% of its birth-control pills have an ingredient that is below the minimum strength, thus rendering the pill ineffective. What is the probability that fewer than 10 in a sample of 200 pills will be ineffective?

33 Statistics released by the National Highway Traffic Safety Administration and the National Safety Council show that on an average weekend night, 1 out of every 10 drivers on the road is drunk. If 400 drivers are randomly checked next Saturday night, what is the probability that the number of drunk drivers will be

(a) less than 32?

(b) more than 49?

(c) at least 35 but less than 47?

34 A pair of dice is rolled 180 times. What is the probability that a total of 7 occurs

(a) at least 25 times?

(b) between 33 and 41 times inclusive?

(c) exactly 30 times?

35 A company produces component parts for an engine. Parts specifications suggest that 95% of items meet specifications. The parts are shipped to customers in lots of 100.

(a) What is the probability that more than 2 items in a given lot will be defective?

(b) What is the probability that more than 10 items in a lot will be defective?

36 A common practice of airline companies is to sell more tickets for a particular flight than there are seats on the plane, because customers who buy tickets do not always show up for the flight. Suppose that the percentage of no-shows at flight time is 2%. For a particular flight with 197 seats, a total of 200 tickets were sold. What is the probability that the airline overbooked this flight?

37 The serum cholesterol level X in 14-year-old boys has approximately a normal distribution with mean 170 and standard deviation 30.

(a) Find the probability that the serum cholesterol level of a randomly chosen 14-year-old boy exceeds 230.

(b) In a middle school there are 300 14-year-old boys. Find the probability that at least 8 boys have a serum cholesterol level that exceeds 230.

38 A telemarketing company has a special letter-opening machine that opens and removes the contents of an envelope. If the envelope is fed improperly into the machine, the contents of the envelope may not be removed or may be damaged. In this case, the machine is said to have "failed."

(a) If the machine has a probability of failure of 0.01, what is the probability of more than 1 failure occurring in a batch of 20 envelopes?

(b) If the probability of failure of the machine is 0.01 and a batch of 500 envelopes is to be opened, what is the probability that more than 8 failures will occur?

6   Gamma and Exponential Distributions

Although the normal distribution can be used to solve many problems in engineering and science, there are still numerous situations that require different types of density functions. Two such density functions, the **gamma** and **exponential distributions**, are discussed in this section.

It turns out that the exponential distribution is a special case of the gamma distribution. Both find a large number of applications. The exponential and gamma distributions play an important role in both queuing theory and reliability problems. Time between arrivals at service facilities and time to failure of component parts and electrical systems often are nicely modeled by the exponential distribution. The relationship between the gamma and the exponential allows the gamma to be used in similar types of problems. More details and illustrations will be supplied later in the section.

The gamma distribution derives its name from the well-known **gamma function**, studied in many areas of mathematics. Before we proceed to the gamma distribution, let us review this function and some of its important properties.

Definition 2:

> The **gamma function** is defined by
>
> $$\Gamma(\alpha) = \int_0^\infty x^{\alpha-1} e^{-x} \, dx, \qquad \text{for } \alpha > 0.$$

The following are a few simple properties of the gamma function.

(a) $\Gamma(n) = (n-1)(n-2)\cdots(1)\Gamma(1)$, for a positive integer n.

To see the proof, integrating by parts with $u = x^{\alpha-1}$ and $dv = e^{-x} \, dx$, we obtain

$$\Gamma(\alpha) = -e^{-x} \, x^{\alpha-1}\big|_0^\infty + \int_0^\infty e^{-x}(\alpha-1)x^{\alpha-2} \, dx = (\alpha-1)\int_0^\infty x^{\alpha-2}e^{-x} \, dx,$$

for $\alpha > 1$, which yields the recursion formula

$$\Gamma(\alpha) = (\alpha-1)\Gamma(\alpha-1).$$

The result follows after repeated application of the recursion formula. Using this result, we can easily show the following two properties.

(b) $\Gamma(n) = (n-1)!$ for a positive integer n.

(c) $\Gamma(1) = 1$.

Furthermore, we have the following property of $\Gamma(\alpha)$, which is left for the reader to verify (see Exercise 39).

(d) $\Gamma(1/2) = \sqrt{\pi}$.

The following is the definition of the **gamma distribution**.

Gamma Distribution

The continuous random variable X has a **gamma distribution**, with parameters α and β, if its density function is given by

$$f(x; \alpha, \beta) = \begin{cases} \frac{1}{\beta^\alpha \Gamma(\alpha)} x^{\alpha-1} e^{-x/\beta}, & x > 0, \\ 0, & \text{elsewhere,} \end{cases}$$

where $\alpha > 0$ and $\beta > 0$.

Graphs of several gamma distributions are shown in Figure 28 for certain specified values of the parameters α and β. The special gamma distribution for which $\alpha = 1$ is called the **exponential distribution**.

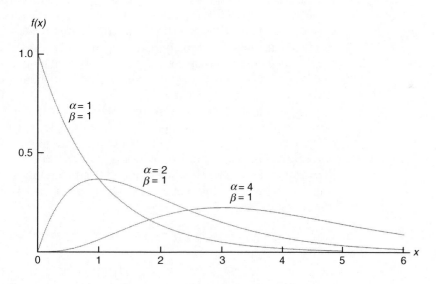

Figure 28: Gamma distributions.

Exponential Distribution

The continuous random variable X has an **exponential distribution**, with parameter β, if its density function is given by

$$f(x; \beta) = \begin{cases} \frac{1}{\beta} e^{-x/\beta}, & x > 0, \\ 0, & \text{elsewhere,} \end{cases}$$

where $\beta > 0$.

The following theorem and corollary give the mean and variance of the gamma and exponential distributions.

Theorem 4:

> The mean and variance of the gamma distribution are
>
> $$\mu = \alpha\beta \text{ and } \sigma^2 = \alpha\beta^2.$$

The proof of this theorem is found in Appendix A.26.

Corollary 1:

> The mean and variance of the exponential distribution are
>
> $$\mu = \beta \text{ and } \sigma^2 = \beta^2.$$

Relationship to the Poisson Process

We shall pursue applications of the exponential distribution and then return to the gamma distribution. The most important applications of the exponential distribution are situations where the Poisson process applies. The reader should recall that the Poisson process allows for the use of the discrete distribution called the Poisson distribution. Recall that the Poisson distribution is used to compute the probability of specific numbers of "events" during a particular *period of time or span of space*. In many applications, the time period or span of space is the random variable. For example, an industrial engineer may be interested in modeling the time T between arrivals at the congested intersection during rush hour in a large city. An arrival represents the Poisson event.

The relationship between the exponential distribution (often called the negative exponential) and the Poisson process is quite simple. The Poisson distribution can be developed as a single-parameter distribution with parameter λ, where λ may be interpreted as the mean number of events *per unit "time."* Consider now the *random variable* described by the time required for the first event to occur. Using the Poisson distribution, we find that the probability of no events occurring in the span up to time t is given by

$$p(0; \lambda t) = \frac{e^{-\lambda t}(\lambda t)^0}{0!} = e^{-\lambda t}.$$

We can now make use of the above and let X be the time to the first Poisson event. The probability that the length of time until the first event will exceed x is the same as the probability that no Poisson events will occur in x. The latter, of course, is given by $e^{-\lambda x}$. As a result,

$$P(X > x) = e^{-\lambda x}.$$

Thus, the cumulative distribution function for X is given by

$$P(0 \leq X \leq x) = 1 - e^{-\lambda x}.$$

Now, in order that we may recognize the presence of the exponential distribution, we differentiate the cumulative distribution function above to obtain the density function

$$f(x) = \lambda e^{-\lambda x},$$

which is the density function of the exponential distribution with $\lambda = 1/\beta$.

Applications of the Exponential and Gamma Distributions

In the foregoing, we provided the foundation for the application of the exponential distribution in "time to arrival" or time to Poisson event problems. We will illustrate some applications here and then proceed to discuss the role of the gamma distribution in these modeling applications. Notice that the mean of the exponential distribution is the parameter β, the reciprocal of the parameter in the Poisson distribution. The reader should recall that it is often said that the Poisson distribution has no memory, implying that occurrences in successive time periods are independent. The important parameter β is the mean time between events. In reliability theory, where equipment failure often conforms to this Poisson process, β is called **mean time between failures**. Many equipment breakdowns do follow the Poisson process, and thus the exponential distribution does apply. Other applications include survival times in biomedical experiments and computer response time.

In the following example, we show a simple application of the exponential distribution to a problem in reliability. The binomial distribution also plays a role in the solution.

Example 17: Suppose that a system contains a certain type of component whose time, in years, to failure is given by T. The random variable T is modeled nicely by the exponential distribution with mean time to failure $\beta = 5$. If 5 of these components are installed in different systems, what is the probability that at least 2 are still functioning at the end of 8 years?

Solution: The probability that a given component is still functioning after 8 years is given by

$$P(T > 8) = \frac{1}{5} \int_8^\infty e^{-t/5} \, dt = e^{-8/5} \approx 0.2.$$

Let X represent the number of components functioning after 8 years. Then using the binomial distribution, we have

$$P(X \geq 2) = \sum_{x=2}^{5} b(x; 5, 0.2) = 1 - \sum_{x=0}^{1} b(x; 5, 0.2) = 1 - 0.7373 = 0.2627.$$

There are exercises where the reader can encounter the exponential distribution. Others involving waiting time and reliability include Example 24 and some of the exercises and review exercises at the end of this chapter.

The Memoryless Property and Its Effect on the Exponential Distribution

The types of applications of the exponential distribution in reliability and component or machine lifetime problems are influenced by the **memoryless** (or lack-of-memory) **property** of the exponential distribution. For example, in the case of, say, an electronic component where lifetime has an exponential distribution, the probability that the component lasts, say, t hours, that is, $P(X \geq t)$, is the same as the conditional probability

$$P(X \geq t_0 + t \mid X \geq t_0).$$

So if the component "makes it" to t_0 hours, the probability of lasting an additional t hours is the same as the probability of lasting t hours. There is no "punishment" through wear that may have ensued for lasting the first t_0 hours. Thus, the exponential distribution is more appropriate when the memoryless property is justified. But if the failure of the component is a result of gradual or slow wear (as in mechanical wear), then the exponential does not apply and either the gamma or the Weibull distribution (Section 10) may be more appropriate.

The importance of the gamma distribution lies in the fact that it defines a family of which other distributions are special cases. But the gamma itself has important applications in waiting time and reliability theory. Whereas the exponential distribution describes the time until the occurrence of a Poisson event (or the time between Poisson events), the time (or space) occurring until a *specified number of Poisson events occur* is a random variable whose density function is described by the gamma distribution. This specific number of events is the parameter α in the gamma density function. Thus, it becomes easy to understand that when $\alpha = 1$, the special case of the exponential distribution occurs. The gamma density can be developed from its relationship to the Poisson process in much the same manner as we developed the exponential density. The details are left to the reader. The following is a numerical example of the use of the gamma distribution in a waiting-time application.

Example 18: Suppose that telephone calls arriving at a particular switchboard follow a Poisson process with an average of 5 calls coming per minute. What is the probability that up to a minute will elapse by the time 2 calls have come in to the switchboard?

Solution: The Poisson process applies, with time until 2 Poisson events following a gamma distribution with $\beta = 1/5$ and $\alpha = 2$. Denote by X the time in minutes that transpires before 2 calls come. The required probability is given by

$$P(X \leq 1) = \int_0^1 \frac{1}{\beta^2} x e^{-x/\beta} \, dx = 25 \int_0^1 x e^{-5x} \, dx = 1 - e^{-5}(1 + 5) = 0.96.$$

While the origin of the gamma distribution deals in time (or space) until the occurrence of α Poisson events, there are many instances where a gamma distribution works very well even though there is no clear Poisson structure. This is particularly true for **survival time** problems in both engineering and biomedical applications.

Example 19: In a biomedical study with rats, a dose-response investigation is used to determine the effect of the dose of a toxicant on their survival time. The toxicant is one that is frequently discharged into the atmosphere from jet fuel. For a certain dose of the toxicant, the study determines that the survival time, in weeks, has a gamma distribution with $\alpha = 5$ and $\beta = 10$. What is the probability that a rat survives no longer than 60 weeks?

Solution: Let the random variable X be the survival time (time to death). The required probability is

$$P(X \leq 60) = \frac{1}{\beta^5} \int_0^{60} \frac{x^{\alpha-1}e^{-x/\beta}}{\Gamma(5)} \, dx.$$

The integral above can be solved through the use of the **incomplete gamma function**, which becomes the cumulative distribution function for the gamma distribution. This function is written as

$$F(x;\alpha) = \int_0^x \frac{y^{\alpha-1}e^{-y}}{\Gamma(\alpha)} \, dy.$$

If we let $y = x/\beta$, so $x = \beta y$, we have

$$P(X \leq 60) = \int_0^6 \frac{y^4 e^{-y}}{\Gamma(5)} \, dy,$$

which is denoted as $F(6;5)$ function in The Incomplete Gamma Function table at the end of this chapter. Note that this allows a quick computation of probabilities for the gamma distribution. Indeed, for this problem, the probability that the rat survives no longer than 60 days is given by

$$P(X \leq 60) = F(6;5) = 0.715.$$

Example 20: It is known, from previous data, that the length of time in months between customer complaints about a certain product is a gamma distribution with $\alpha = 2$ and $\beta = 4$. Changes were made to tighten quality control requirements. Following these changes, 20 months passed before the first complaint. Does it appear as if the quality control tightening was effective?

Solution: Let X be the time to the first complaint, which, under conditions prior to the changes, followed a gamma distribution with $\alpha = 2$ and $\beta = 4$. The question centers around how rare $X \geq 20$ is, given that α and β remain at values 2 and 4, respectively. In other words, under the prior conditions is a "time to complaint" as large as 20 months reasonable? Thus, following the solution to Example 19,

$$P(X \geq 20) = 1 - \frac{1}{\beta^\alpha} \int_0^{20} \frac{x^{\alpha-1}e^{-x/\beta}}{\Gamma(\alpha)} dx.$$

Again, using $y = x/\beta$, we have

$$P(X \geq 20) = 1 - \int_0^5 \frac{ye^{-y}}{\Gamma(2)} \, dy = 1 - F(5;2) = 1 - 0.96 = 0.04,$$

where $F(5;2) = 0.96$ is found from Table The Incomplete Gamma Function.

As a result, we could conclude that the conditions of the gamma distribution with $\alpha = 2$ and $\beta = 4$ are not supported by the data that an observed time to complaint is as large as 20 months. Thus, it is reasonable to conclude that the quality control work was effective.

Example 21: Based on extensive testing, it is determined that the time Y in years before a major repair is required for a certain washing machine is characterized by the density function

$$f(y) = \begin{cases} \frac{1}{4}e^{-y/4}, & y \geq 0, \\ 0, & \text{elsewhere.} \end{cases}$$

Note that Y is an exponential random variable with $\mu = 4$ years. The machine is considered a bargain if it is unlikely to require a major repair before the sixth year. What is the probability $P(Y > 6)$? What is the probability that a major repair is required in the first year?

Solution: Consider the cumulative distribution function $F(y)$ for the exponential distribution,

$$F(y) = \frac{1}{\beta} \int_0^y e^{-t/\beta} \, dt = 1 - e^{-y/\beta}.$$

Then

$$P(Y > 6) = 1 - F(6) = e^{-3/2} = 0.2231.$$

Thus, the probability that the washing machine will require major repair after year six is 0.223. Of course, it will require repair before year six with probability 0.777. Thus, one might conclude the machine is not really a bargain. The probability that a major repair is necessary in the first year is

$$P(Y < 1) = 1 - e^{-1/4} = 1 - 0.779 = 0.221.$$

7 Chi-Squared Distribution

Another very important special case of the gamma distribution is obtained by letting $\alpha = v/2$ and $\beta = 2$, where v is a positive integer. The result is called **the chi-squared distribution**. The distribution has a single parameter, v, called the **degrees of freedom**.

Chi-Squared Distribution

The continuous random variable X has a **chi-squared distribution**, with v **degrees of freedom**, if its density function is given by

$$f(x; v) = \begin{cases} \frac{1}{2^{v/2}\Gamma(v/2)} x^{v/2-1} e^{-x/2}, & x > 0, \\ 0, & \text{elsewhere,} \end{cases}$$

where v is a positive integer.

The chi-squared distribution plays a vital role in statistical inference. It has considerable applications in both methodology and theory. The chi-squared distribution is an important component of statistical hypothesis testing and estimation.

Topics dealing with sampling distributions, analysis of variance, and nonparametric statistics involve extensive use of the chi-squared distribution.

Theorem 5:

The mean and variance of the chi-squared distribution are

$$\mu = v \text{ and } \sigma^2 = 2v.$$

8   Beta Distribution

An extension to the uniform distribution is a beta distribution. Let us start by defining a **beta function**.

Definition 3:

> A **beta function** is defined by
>
> $$B(\alpha, \beta) = \int_0^1 x^{\alpha-1}(1-x)^{\beta-1}dx = \frac{\Gamma(\alpha)\Gamma(\beta)}{\Gamma(\alpha+\beta)}, \text{ for } \alpha, \beta > 0,$$
>
> where $\Gamma(\alpha)$ is the gamma function.

Beta Distribution

The continuous random variable X has a **beta distribution** with parameters $\alpha > 0$ and $\beta > 0$ if its density function is given by

$$f(x) = \begin{cases} \frac{1}{B(\alpha,\beta)}x^{\alpha-1}(1-x)^{\beta-1}, & 0 < x < 1, \\ 0, & \text{elsewhere.} \end{cases}$$

Note that the uniform distribution on $(0,1)$ is a beta distribution with parameters $\alpha = 1$ and $\beta = 1$.

Theorem 6:

> The mean and variance of a beta distribution with parameters α and β are
>
> $$\mu = \frac{\alpha}{\alpha+\beta} \text{ and } \sigma^2 = \frac{\alpha\beta}{(\alpha+\beta)^2(\alpha+\beta+1)},$$
>
> respectively.

For the uniform distribution on $(0,1)$, the mean and variance are

$$\mu = \frac{1}{1+1} = \frac{1}{2} \text{ and } \sigma^2 = \frac{(1)(1)}{(1+1)^2(1+1+1)} = \frac{1}{12},$$

respectively.

9   Lognormal Distribution

The lognormal distribution is used for a wide variety of applications. The distribution applies in cases where a natural log transformation results in a normal distribution.

Lognormal Distribution

The continuous random variable X has a **lognormal distribution** if the random variable $Y = \ln(X)$ has a normal distribution with mean μ and standard deviation σ. The resulting density function of X is

$$f(x; \mu, \sigma) = \begin{cases} \frac{1}{\sqrt{2\pi}\sigma x}e^{-\frac{1}{2\sigma^2}[\ln(x)-\mu]^2}, & x \geq 0, \\ 0, & x < 0. \end{cases}$$

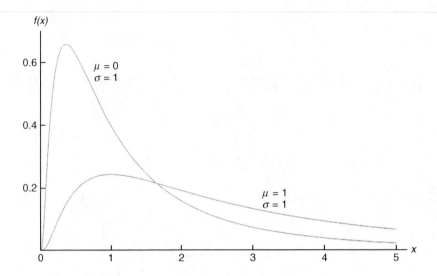

Figure 29: Lognormal distributions.

The graphs of the lognormal distributions are illustrated in Figure 29.

Theorem 7:

The mean and variance of the lognormal distribution are

$$\mu = e^{\mu+\sigma^2/2} \text{ and } \sigma^2 = e^{2\mu+\sigma^2}(e^{\sigma^2} - 1).$$

The cumulative distribution function is quite simple due to its relationship to the normal distribution. The use of the distribution function is illustrated by the following example.

Example 22:

Concentrations of pollutants produced by chemical plants historically are known to exhibit behavior that resembles a lognormal distribution. This is important when one considers issues regarding compliance with government regulations. Suppose it is assumed that the concentration of a certain pollutant, in parts per million, has a lognormal distribution with parameters $\mu = 3.2$ and $\sigma = 1$. What is the probability that the concentration exceeds 8 parts per million?

Solution: Let the random variable X be pollutant concentration. Then

$$P(X > 8) = 1 - P(X \le 8).$$

Since $\ln(X)$ has a normal distribution with mean $\mu = 3.2$ and standard deviation $\sigma = 1$,

$$P(X \le 8) = \Phi\left[\frac{\ln(8) - 3.2}{1}\right] = \Phi(-1.12) = 0.1314.$$

Here, we use Φ to denote the cumulative distribution function of the standard normal distribution. As a result, the probability that the pollutant concentration exceeds 8 parts per million is 0.1314.

Example 23: The life, in thousands of miles, of a certain type of electronic control for locomotives has an approximately lognormal distribution with $\mu = 5.149$ and $\sigma = 0.737$. Find the 5th percentile of the life of such an electronic control.

Solution: From Table Areas under the Normal Curve, we know that $P(Z < -1.645) = 0.05$. Denote by X the life of such an electronic control. Since $\ln(X)$ has a normal distribution with mean $\mu = 5.149$ and $\sigma = 0.737$, the 5th percentile of X can be calculated as

$$\ln(x) = 5.149 + (0.737)(-1.645) = 3.937.$$

Hence, $x = 51.265$. This means that only 5% of the controls will have lifetimes less than 51,265 miles.

10   Weibull Distribution (Optional)

Modern technology has enabled engineers to design many complicated systems whose operation and safety depend on the reliability of the various components making up the systems. For example, a fuse may burn out, a steel column may buckle, or a heat-sensing device may fail. Identical components subjected to identical environmental conditions will fail at different and unpredictable times. We have seen the role that the gamma and exponential distributions play in these types of problems. Another distribution that has been used extensively in recent years to deal with such problems is the **Weibull distribution**, introduced by the Swedish physicist Waloddi Weibull in 1939.

Weibull Distribution — The continuous random variable X has a **Weibull distribution**, with parameters α and β, if its density function is given by

$$f(x; \alpha, \beta) = \begin{cases} \alpha\beta x^{\beta-1} e^{-\alpha x^{\beta}}, & x > 0, \\ 0, & \text{elsewhere,} \end{cases}$$

where $\alpha > 0$ and $\beta > 0$.

The graphs of the Weibull distribution for $\alpha = 1$ and various values of the parameter β are illustrated in Figure 6.30. We see that the curves change considerably in shape for different values of the parameter β. If we let $\beta = 1$, the Weibull distribution reduces to the exponential distribution. For values of $\beta > 1$, the curves become somewhat bell shaped and resemble the normal curve but display some skewness.

The mean and variance of the Weibull distribution are stated in the following theorem. The reader is asked to provide the proof in Exercise 52.

Theorem 8: The mean and variance of the Weibull distribution are

$$\mu = \alpha^{-1/\beta}\Gamma\left(1 + \frac{1}{\beta}\right) \quad \text{and} \quad \sigma^2 = \alpha^{-2/\beta}\left\{\Gamma\left(1 + \frac{2}{\beta}\right) - \left[\Gamma\left(1 + \frac{1}{\beta}\right)\right]^2\right\}.$$

Like the gamma and exponential distributions, the Weibull distribution is also applied to reliability and life-testing problems such as the **time to failure** or

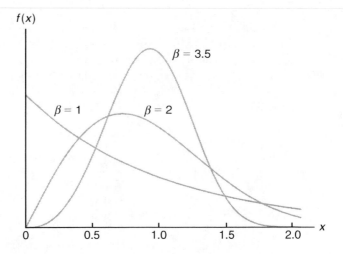

Figure 30: Weibull distributions ($\alpha = 1$).

life length of a component, measured from some specified time until it fails. Let us represent this time to failure by the continuous random variable T, with probability density function $f(t)$, where $f(t)$ is the Weibull distribution. The Weibull distribution has inherent flexibility in that it does not require the lack of memory property of the exponential distribution. The cumulative distribution function (cdf) for the Weibull can be written in closed form and certainly is useful in computing probabilities.

---

cdf for Weibull Distribution

The **cumulative distribution function for the Weibull distribution** is given by

$$F(x) = 1 - e^{-\alpha x^{\beta}}, \qquad \text{for } x \geq 0,$$

for $\alpha > 0$ and $\beta > 0$.

Example 24: The length of life X, in hours, of an item in a machine shop has a Weibull distribution with $\alpha = 0.01$ and $\beta = 2$. What is the probability that it fails before eight hours of usage?

Solution: $P(X < 8) = F(8) = 1 - e^{-(0.01)8^{2}} = 1 - 0.527 = 0.473.$

The Failure Rate for the Weibull Distribution

When the Weibull distribution applies, it is often helpful to determine the **failure rate** (sometimes called the hazard rate) in order to get a sense of wear or deterioration of the component. Let us first define the reliability of a component or product as the *probability that it will function properly for at least a specified time under specified experimental conditions*. Therefore, if $R(t)$ is defined to be the reliability of the given component at time t, we may write

$$R(t) = P(T > t) = \int_t^\infty f(t)\, dt = 1 - F(t),$$

where $F(t)$ is the cumulative distribution function of T. The conditional probability that a component will fail in the interval from $T = t$ to $T = t + \Delta t$, given that it survived to time t, is

$$\frac{F(t + \Delta t) - F(t)}{R(t)}.$$

Dividing this ratio by Δt and taking the limit as $\Delta t \to 0$, we get the **failure rate**, denoted by $Z(t)$. Hence,

$$Z(t) = \lim_{\Delta t \to 0} \frac{F(t + \Delta t) - F(t)}{\Delta t} \frac{1}{R(t)} = \frac{F'(t)}{R(t)} = \frac{f(t)}{R(t)} = \frac{f(t)}{1 - F(t)},$$

which expresses the failure rate in terms of the distribution of the time to failure. Since $Z(t) = f(t)/[1 - F(t)]$, the failure rate is given as follows:

Failure Rate for Weibull Distribution   The **failure rate** at time t for the Weibull distribution is given by

$$Z(t) = \alpha \beta t^{\beta - 1}, \qquad t > 0.$$

Interpretation of the Failure Rate

The quantity $Z(t)$ is aptly named as a failure rate since it does quantify the rate of change over time of the conditional probability that the component lasts an additional Δt *given that it has lasted to time t*. The rate of decrease (or increase) with time is important. The following are crucial points.

(a) If $\beta = 1$, the failure rate $= \alpha$, a constant. This, as indicated earlier, is the special case of the exponential distribution in which lack of memory prevails.

(b) If $\beta > 1$, $Z(t)$ is an increasing function of time t, which indicates that the component wears over time.

(c) If $\beta < 1$, $Z(t)$ is a decreasing function of time t and hence the component strengthens or hardens over time.

For example, the item in the machine shop in Example 24 has $\beta = 2$, and hence it wears over time. In fact, the failure rate function is given by $Z(t) = 0.02t$. On the other hand, suppose the parameters were $\beta = 3/4$ and $\alpha = 2$. In that case, $Z(t) = 1.5/t^{1/4}$ and hence the component gets stronger over time.

Exercises

39 Use the gamma function with $y = \sqrt{2x}$ to show that $\Gamma(1/2) = \sqrt{\pi}$.

40 In a certain city, the daily consumption of water (in millions of liters) follows approximately a gamma distribution with $\alpha = 2$ and $\beta = 3$. If the daily capacity of that city is 9 million liters of water, what is the probability that on any given day the water supply is inadequate?

41 If a random variable X has the gamma distribution with $\alpha = 2$ and $\beta = 1$, find $P(1.8 < X < 2.4)$.

42 Suppose that the time, in hours, required to repair a heat pump is a random variable X having a gamma distribution with parameters $\alpha = 2$ and $\beta = 1/2$. What is the probability that on the next service call

(a) at most 1 hour will be required to repair the heat pump?

(b) at least 2 hours will be required to repair the heat pump?

43 (a) Find the mean and variance of the daily water consumption in Exercise 40.

(b) According to Chebyshev's theorem, there is a probability of at least 3/4 that the water consumption on any given day will fall within what interval?

44 In a certain city, the daily consumption of electric power, in millions of kilowatt-hours, is a random variable X having a gamma distribution with mean $\mu = 6$ and variance $\sigma^2 = 12$.

(a) Find the values of α and β.

(b) Find the probability that on any given day the daily power consumption will exceed 12 million kilowatt-hours.

45 The length of time for one individual to be served at a cafeteria is a random variable having an exponential distribution with a mean of 4 minutes. What is the probability that a person is served in less than 3 minutes on at least 4 of the next 6 days?

46 The life, in years, of a certain type of electrical switch has an exponential distribution with an average life $\beta = 2$. If 100 of these switches are installed in different systems, what is the probability that at most 30 fail during the first year?

47 Suppose that the service life, in years, of a hearing aid battery is a random variable having a Weibull distribution with $\alpha = 1/2$ and $\beta = 2$.

(a) How long can such a battery be expected to last?

(b) What is the probability that such a battery will be operating after 2 years?

48 Derive the mean and variance of the beta distribution.

49 Suppose the random variable X follows a beta distribution with $\alpha = 1$ and $\beta = 3$.

(a) Determine the mean and median of X.

(b) Determine the variance of X.

(c) Find the probability that $X > 1/3$.

50 If the proportion of a brand of television set requiring service during the first year of operation is a random variable having a beta distribution with $\alpha = 3$ and $\beta = 2$, what is the probability that at least 80% of the new models of this brand sold this year will require service during their first year of operation?

51 The lives of a certain automobile seal have the Weibull distribution with failure rate $Z(t) = 1/\sqrt{t}$. Find the probability that such a seal is still intact after 4 years.

52 Derive the mean and variance of the Weibull distribution.

53 In a biomedical research study, it was determined that the survival time, in weeks, of an animal subjected to a certain exposure of gamma radiation has a gamma distribution with $\alpha = 5$ and $\beta = 10$.

(a) What is the mean survival time of a randomly selected animal of the type used in the experiment?

(b) What is the standard deviation of survival time?

(c) What is the probability that an animal survives more than 30 weeks?

54 The lifetime, in weeks, of a certain type of transistor is known to follow a gamma distribution with mean 10 weeks and standard deviation $\sqrt{50}$ weeks.

(a) What is the probability that a transistor of this type will last at most 50 weeks?

(b) What is the probability that a transistor of this type will not survive the first 10 weeks?

55 Computer response time is an important application of the gamma and exponential distributions. Suppose that a study of a certain computer system reveals that the response time, in seconds, has an exponential distribution with a mean of 3 seconds.

(a) What is the probability that response time exceeds 5 seconds?

(b) What is the probability that response time exceeds 10 seconds?

56 Rate data often follow a lognormal distribution. Average power usage (dB per hour) for a particular company is studied and is known to have a lognormal distribution with parameters $\mu = 4$ and $\sigma = 2$. What is the probability that the company uses more than 270 dB during any particular hour?

57 For Exercise 56, what is the mean power usage (average dB per hour)? What is the variance?

58 The number of automobiles that arrive at a certain intersection per minute has a Poisson distribution with a mean of 5. Interest centers around the time that elapses before 10 automobiles appear at the intersection.

(a) What is the probability that more than 10 automobiles appear at the intersection during any given minute of time?

(b) What is the probability that more than 2 minutes elapse before 10 cars arrive?

59 Consider the information in Exercise 58.

(a) What is the probability that more than 1 minute elapses between arrivals?

(b) What is the mean number of minutes that elapse between arrivals?

60 Show that the failure-rate function is given by

$$Z(t) = \alpha\beta t^{\beta-1}, \quad t > 0,$$

if and only if the time to failure distribution is the Weibull distribution

$$f(t) = \alpha\beta t^{\beta-1}e^{-\alpha t^{\beta}}, \quad t > 0.$$

Review Exercises

61 According to a study published by a group of sociologists at the University of Massachusetts, approximately 49% of the Valium users in the state of Massachusetts are white-collar workers. What is the probability that between 482 and 510, inclusive, of the next 1000 randomly selected Valium users from this state are white-collar workers?

62 The exponential distribution is frequently applied to the waiting times between successes in a Poisson process. If the number of calls received per hour by a telephone answering service is a Poisson random variable with parameter $\lambda = 6$, we know that the time, in hours, between successive calls has an exponential distribution with parameter $\beta = 1/6$. What is the probability of waiting more than 15 minutes between any two successive calls?

63 When α is a positive integer n, the gamma distribution is also known as the **Erlang distribution**. Setting $\alpha = n$ in the gamma distribution, the Erlang distribution is

$$f(x) = \begin{cases} \frac{x^{n-1}e^{-x/\beta}}{\beta^n (n-1)!}, & x > 0, \\ 0, & \text{elsewhere.} \end{cases}$$

It can be shown that if the times between successive events are independent, each having an exponential distribution with parameter β, then the total elapsed waiting time X until all n events occur has the Erlang distribution. Referring to Review Exercise 62, what

is the probability that the next 3 calls will be received within the next 30 minutes?

64 A manufacturer of a certain type of large machine wishes to buy rivets from one of two manufacturers. It is important that the breaking strength of each rivet exceed 10,000 psi. Two manufacturers (A and B) offer this type of rivet and both have rivets whose breaking strength is normally distributed. The mean breaking strengths for manufacturers A and B are 14,000 psi and 13,000 psi, respectively. The standard deviations are 2000 psi and 1000 psi, respectively. Which manufacturer will produce, on the average, the fewest number of defective rivets?

65 According to a recent census, almost 65% of all households in the United States were composed of only one or two persons. Assuming that this percentage is still valid today, what is the probability that between 590 and 625, inclusive, of the next 1000 randomly selected households in America consist of either one or two persons?

66 A certain type of device has an advertised failure rate of 0.01 per hour. The failure rate is constant and the exponential distribution applies.

(a) What is the mean time to failure?

(b) What is the probability that 200 hours will pass before a failure is observed?

67 In a chemical processing plant, it is important that the yield of a certain type of batch product stay above 80%. If it stays below 80% for an extended period of time, the company loses money. Occasional defective batches are of little concern. But if several batches per day are defective, the plant shuts down and adjustments are made. It is known that the yield is normally distributed with standard deviation 4%.

(a) What is the probability of a "false alarm" (yield below 80%) when the mean yield is 85%?

(b) What is the probability that a batch will have a yield that exceeds 80% when in fact the mean yield is 79%?

68 For an electrical component with a failure rate of once every 5 hours, it is important to consider the time that it takes for 2 components to fail.

(a) Assuming that the gamma distribution applies, what is the mean time that it takes for 2 components to fail?

(b) What is the probability that 12 hours will elapse before 2 components fail?

69 The elongation of a steel bar under a particular load has been established to be normally distributed with a mean of 0.05 inch and $\sigma = 0.01$ inch. Find the probability that the elongation is

(a) above 0.1 inch;

(b) below 0.04 inch;

(c) between 0.025 and 0.065 inch.

70 A controlled satellite is known to have an error (distance from target) that is normally distributed with mean zero and standard deviation 4 feet. The manufacturer of the satellite defines a success as a firing in which the satellite comes within 10 feet of the target. Compute the probability that the satellite fails.

71 A technician plans to test a certain type of resin developed in the laboratory to determine the nature of the time required before bonding takes place. It is known that the mean time to bonding is 3 hours and the standard deviation is 0.5 hour. It will be considered an undesirable product if the bonding time is either less than 1 hour or more than 4 hours. Comment on the utility of the resin. How often would its performance be considered undesirable? Assume that time to bonding is normally distributed.

72 Consider the information in Review Exercise 66. What is the probability that less than 200 hours will elapse before 2 failures occur?

73 For Review Exercise 72, what are the mean and variance of the time that elapses before 2 failures occur?

74 The average rate of water usage (thousands of gallons per hour) by a certain community is known to involve the lognormal distribution with parameters $\mu = 5$ and $\sigma = 2$. It is important for planning purposes to get a sense of periods of high usage. What is the probability that, for any given hour, 50,000 gallons of water are used?

75 For Review Exercise 74, what is the mean of the average water usage per hour in thousands of gallons?

76 In Exercise 54, the lifetime of a transistor is assumed to have a gamma distribution with mean 10 weeks and standard deviation $\sqrt{50}$ weeks. Suppose that the gamma distribution assumption is incorrect. Assume that the distribution is normal.

(a) What is the probability that a transistor will last at most 50 weeks?

(b) What is the probability that a transistor will not survive for the first 10 weeks?

(c) Comment on the difference between your results here and those found in Exercise 54.

77 The beta distribution has considerable application in reliability problems in which the basic random variable is a proportion, as in the practical scenario illustrated in Exercise 50. Impurities in batches of product of a chemical process reflect a serious problem. It is known that the proportion of impurities Y in a batch has the density function

$$f(y) = \begin{cases} 10(1-y)^9, & 0 \le y \le 1, \\ 0, & \text{elsewhere.} \end{cases}$$

(a) Verify that the above is a valid density function.

(b) What is the probability that a batch is considered not acceptable (i.e., $Y > 0.6$)?

(c) What are the parameters α and β of the beta distribution illustrated here?

(d) The mean of the beta distribution is $\frac{\alpha}{\alpha+\beta}$. What is the mean proportion of impurities in the batch?

(e) The variance of a beta distributed random variable is

$$\sigma^2 = \frac{\alpha\beta}{(\alpha+\beta)^2(\alpha+\beta+1)}.$$

What is the variance of Y in this problem?

78
The density function of the time Z in minutes between calls to an electrical supply store is given by

$$f(z) = \begin{cases} \frac{1}{10}e^{-z/10}, & 0 < z < \infty, \\ 0, & \text{elsewhere.} \end{cases}$$

(a) What is the mean time between calls?

(b) What is the variance in the time between calls?

(c) What is the probability that the time between calls exceeds the mean?

79 Consider Review Exercise 78. Given the assumption of the exponential distribution, what is the mean number of calls per hour? What is the variance in the number of calls per hour?

80 In a human factor experimental project, it has been determined that the reaction time of a pilot to a visual stimulus is normally distributed with a mean of $1/2$ second and standard deviation of $2/5$ second.

(a) What is the probability that a reaction from the pilot takes more than 0.3 second?

(b) What reaction time is that which is exceeded 95% of the time?

81 The length of time between breakdowns of an essential piece of equipment is important in the decision of the use of auxiliary equipment. An engineer thinks that the best model for time between breakdowns of a generator is the exponential distribution with a mean of 15 days.

(a) If the generator has just broken down, what is the probability that it will break down in the next 21 days?

(b) What is the probability that the generator will operate for 30 days without a breakdown?

82 The length of life, in hours, of a drill bit in a mechanical operation has a Weibull distribution with $\alpha = 2$ and $\beta = 50$. Find the probability that the bit will fail before 10 hours of usage.

83 Derive the cdf for the Weibull distribution. [*Hint*: In the definition of a cdf, make the transformation $z = y^{\beta}$.]

84 Explain why the nature of the scenario in Review Exercise 82 would likely not lend itself to the exponential distribution.

85 From the relationship between the chi-squared random variable and the gamma random variable, prove that the mean of the chi-squared random variable is v and the variance is $2v$.

86 The length of time, in seconds, that a computer user takes to read his or her e-mail is distributed as a lognormal random variable with $\mu = 1.8$ and $\sigma^2 = 4.0$.

(a) What is the probability that a user reads e-mail for more than 20 seconds? More than a minute?

(b) What is the probability that a user reads e-mail for a length of time that is equal to the mean of the underlying lognormal distribution?

87 **Group Project**: Have groups of students observe the number of people who enter a specific coffee shop or fast food restaurant over the course of an hour, beginning at the same time every day, for two weeks. The hour should be a time of peak traffic at the shop or restaurant. The data collected will be the number of customers who enter the shop in each half hour of time. Thus, two data points will be collected each day. Let us assume that the random variable X, the number of people entering each half hour, follows a Poisson distribution. The students should calculate the sample mean and variance of X using the 28 data points collected.

(a) What evidence indicates that the Poisson distribution assumption may or may not be correct?

(b) Given that X is Poisson, what is the distribution of T, the time between arrivals into the shop during a half hour period? Give a numerical estimate of the parameter of that distribution.

(c) Give an estimate of the probability that the time between two arrivals is less than 15 minutes.

(d) What is the estimated probability that the time between two arrivals is more than 10 minutes?

(e) What is the estimated probability that 20 minutes after the start of data collection not one customer has appeared?

11 Potential Misconceptions and Hazards

One of the biggest misuses of statistics is the assumption of an underlying normal distribution in carrying out a type of statistical inference when indeed it is not normal.

A warning should be conveyed regarding assumptions that are often made concerning other distributions, apart from the normal. This chapter has presented examples in which one is required to calculate probabilities to failure of a certain item or the probability that one observes a complaint during a certain time period. Assumptions are made concerning a certain distribution type as well as values of parameters of the distributions. Note that parameter values (for example, the value of β for the exponential distribution) were given in the example problems. However, in real-life problems, parameter values must be estimates from real-life experience or data.

Answers to Odd-Numbered Non-Review Exercises

3 (a) 0.6; (b) 0.7; (c) 0.5

5 (a) 0.0823; (b) 0.0250; (c) 0.2424; (d) 0.9236; (e) 0.8133; (f) 0.6435

7 (a) 0.54; (b) -1.72; (c) 1.28

9 (a) 0.1151; (b) 16.1; (c) 20.275; (d) 0.5403

11 (a) 0.0548; (b) 0.4514; (c) 23 cups; (d) 189.95 milliliters

13 (a) 0.8980; (b) 0.0287; (c) 0.6080

15 (a) 0.0571; (b) 99.11%; (c) 0.3974; (d) 27.952 minutes; (e) 0.0092

17 6.24 years

19 (a) 51%; (b) $18.37

21 (a) 0.0401; (b) 0.0244

23 26 students

25 (a) 0.3085; (b) 0.0197

27 (a) 0.9514; (b) 0.0668

29 (a) 0.1171; (b) 0.2049

31 0.1357

33 (a) 0.0778; (b) 0.0571; (c) 0.6811

35 (a) 0.8749; (b) 0.0059

37 (a) 0.0228; (b) 0.3974

41 $2.8e^{-1.8} - 3.4e^{-2.4} = 0.1545$

43 (a) $\mu = 6$; $\sigma^2 = 18$; (b) between 0 and 14.485 million liters

45 $\sum_{x=4}^{6} \binom{6}{x} (1 - e^{-3/4})^x (e^{-3/4})^{6-x} = 0.3968$

47 (a) $\sqrt{\pi/2} = 1.2533$ years; (b) e^{-2}

49 (a) Mean $= 0.25$, median $= 0.206$; (b) variance $= 0.0375$; (c) 0.2963

51 $e^{-4} = 0.0183$

53 (a) $\mu = \alpha\beta = 50$; (b) $\sigma^2 = \alpha\beta^2 = 500$; $\sigma = \sqrt{500}$; (c) 0.815

55 (a) 0.1889; (b) 0.0357

57 Mean $= e^6$, variance $= e^{12}(e^4 - 1)$

59 (a) e^{-5}; (b) $\beta = 0.2$

Table Areas under the Normal Curve

z	.00	.01	.02	.03	.04	.05	.06	.07	.08	.09
−3.4	0.0003	0.0003	0.0003	0.0003	0.0003	0.0003	0.0003	0.0003	0.0003	0.0002
−3.3	0.0005	0.0005	0.0005	0.0004	0.0004	0.0004	0.0004	0.0004	0.0004	0.0003
−3.2	0.0007	0.0007	0.0006	0.0006	0.0006	0.0006	0.0006	0.0005	0.0005	0.0005
−3.1	0.0010	0.0009	0.0009	0.0009	0.0008	0.0008	0.0008	0.0008	0.0007	0.0007
−3.0	0.0013	0.0013	0.0013	0.0012	0.0012	0.0011	0.0011	0.0011	0.0010	0.0010
−2.9	0.0019	0.0018	0.0018	0.0017	0.0016	0.0016	0.0015	0.0015	0.0014	0.0014
−2.8	0.0026	0.0025	0.0024	0.0023	0.0023	0.0022	0.0021	0.0021	0.0020	0.0019
−2.7	0.0035	0.0034	0.0033	0.0032	0.0031	0.0030	0.0029	0.0028	0.0027	0.0026
−2.6	0.0047	0.0045	0.0044	0.0043	0.0041	0.0040	0.0039	0.0038	0.0037	0.0036
−2.5	0.0062	0.0060	0.0059	0.0057	0.0055	0.0054	0.0052	0.0051	0.0049	0.0048
−2.4	0.0082	0.0080	0.0078	0.0075	0.0073	0.0071	0.0069	0.0068	0.0066	0.0064
−2.3	0.0107	0.0104	0.0102	0.0099	0.0096	0.0094	0.0091	0.0089	0.0087	0.0084
−2.2	0.0139	0.0136	0.0132	0.0129	0.0125	0.0122	0.0119	0.0116	0.0113	0.0110
−2.1	0.0179	0.0174	0.0170	0.0166	0.0162	0.0158	0.0154	0.0150	0.0146	0.0143
−2.0	0.0228	0.0222	0.0217	0.0212	0.0207	0.0202	0.0197	0.0192	0.0188	0.0183
−1.9	0.0287	0.0281	0.0274	0.0268	0.0262	0.0256	0.0250	0.0244	0.0239	0.0233
−1.8	0.0359	0.0351	0.0344	0.0336	0.0329	0.0322	0.0314	0.0307	0.0301	0.0294
−1.7	0.0446	0.0436	0.0427	0.0418	0.0409	0.0401	0.0392	0.0384	0.0375	0.0367
−1.6	0.0548	0.0537	0.0526	0.0516	0.0505	0.0495	0.0485	0.0475	0.0465	0.0455
−1.5	0.0668	0.0655	0.0643	0.0630	0.0618	0.0606	0.0594	0.0582	0.0571	0.0559
−1.4	0.0808	0.0793	0.0778	0.0764	0.0749	0.0735	0.0721	0.0708	0.0694	0.0681
−1.3	0.0968	0.0951	0.0934	0.0918	0.0901	0.0885	0.0869	0.0853	0.0838	0.0823
−1.2	0.1151	0.1131	0.1112	0.1093	0.1075	0.1056	0.1038	0.1020	0.1003	0.0985
−1.1	0.1357	0.1335	0.1314	0.1292	0.1271	0.1251	0.1230	0.1210	0.1190	0.1170
−1.0	0.1587	0.1562	0.1539	0.1515	0.1492	0.1469	0.1446	0.1423	0.1401	0.1379
−0.9	0.1841	0.1814	0.1788	0.1762	0.1736	0.1711	0.1685	0.1660	0.1635	0.1611
−0.8	0.2119	0.2090	0.2061	0.2033	0.2005	0.1977	0.1949	0.1922	0.1894	0.1867
−0.7	0.2420	0.2389	0.2358	0.2327	0.2296	0.2266	0.2236	0.2206	0.2177	0.2148
−0.6	0.2743	0.2709	0.2676	0.2643	0.2611	0.2578	0.2546	0.2514	0.2483	0.2451
−0.5	0.3085	0.3050	0.3015	0.2981	0.2946	0.2912	0.2877	0.2843	0.2810	0.2776
−0.4	0.3446	0.3409	0.3372	0.3336	0.3300	0.3264	0.3228	0.3192	0.3156	0.3121
−0.3	0.3821	0.3783	0.3745	0.3707	0.3669	0.3632	0.3594	0.3557	0.3520	0.3483
−0.2	0.4207	0.4168	0.4129	0.4090	0.4052	0.4013	0.3974	0.3936	0.3897	0.3859
−0.1	0.4602	0.4562	0.4522	0.4483	0.4443	0.4404	0.4364	0.4325	0.4286	0.4247
−0.0	0.5000	0.4960	0.4920	0.4880	0.4840	0.4801	0.4761	0.4721	0.4681	0.4641

z	.00	.01	.02	.03	.04	.05	.06	.07	.08	.09
0.0	0.5000	0.5040	0.5080	0.5120	0.5160	0.5199	0.5239	0.5279	0.5319	0.5359
0.1	0.5398	0.5438	0.5478	0.5517	0.5557	0.5596	0.5636	0.5675	0.5714	0.5753
0.2	0.5793	0.5832	0.5871	0.5910	0.5948	0.5987	0.6026	0.6064	0.6103	0.6141
0.3	0.6179	0.6217	0.6255	0.6293	0.6331	0.6368	0.6406	0.6443	0.6480	0.6517
0.4	0.6554	0.6591	0.6628	0.6664	0.6700	0.6736	0.6772	0.6808	0.6844	0.6879
0.5	0.6915	0.6950	0.6985	0.7019	0.7054	0.7088	0.7123	0.7157	0.7190	0.7224
0.6	0.7257	0.7291	0.7324	0.7357	0.7389	0.7422	0.7454	0.7486	0.7517	0.7549
0.7	0.7580	0.7611	0.7642	0.7673	0.7704	0.7734	0.7764	0.7794	0.7823	0.7852
0.8	0.7881	0.7910	0.7939	0.7967	0.7995	0.8023	0.8051	0.8078	0.8106	0.8133
0.9	0.8159	0.8186	0.8212	0.8238	0.8264	0.8289	0.8315	0.8340	0.8365	0.8389
1.0	0.8413	0.8438	0.8461	0.8485	0.8508	0.8531	0.8554	0.8577	0.8599	0.8621
1.1	0.8643	0.8665	0.8686	0.8708	0.8729	0.8749	0.8770	0.8790	0.8810	0.8830
1.2	0.8849	0.8869	0.8888	0.8907	0.8925	0.8944	0.8962	0.8980	0.8997	0.9015
1.3	0.9032	0.9049	0.9066	0.9082	0.9099	0.9115	0.9131	0.9147	0.9162	0.9177
1.4	0.9192	0.9207	0.9222	0.9236	0.9251	0.9265	0.9279	0.9292	0.9306	0.9319
1.5	0.9332	0.9345	0.9357	0.9370	0.9382	0.9394	0.9406	0.9418	0.9429	0.9441
1.6	0.9452	0.9463	0.9474	0.9484	0.9495	0.9505	0.9515	0.9525	0.9535	0.9545
1.7	0.9554	0.9564	0.9573	0.9582	0.9591	0.9599	0.9608	0.9616	0.9625	0.9633
1.8	0.9641	0.9649	0.9656	0.9664	0.9671	0.9678	0.9686	0.9693	0.9699	0.9706
1.9	0.9713	0.9719	0.9726	0.9732	0.9738	0.9744	0.9750	0.9756	0.9761	0.9767
2.0	0.9772	0.9778	0.9783	0.9788	0.9793	0.9798	0.9803	0.9808	0.9812	0.9817
2.1	0.9821	0.9826	0.9830	0.9834	0.9838	0.9842	0.9846	0.9850	0.9854	0.9857
2.2	0.9861	0.9864	0.9868	0.9871	0.9875	0.9878	0.9881	0.9884	0.9887	0.9890
2.3	0.9893	0.9896	0.9898	0.9901	0.9904	0.9906	0.9909	0.9911	0.9913	0.9916
2.4	0.9918	0.9920	0.9922	0.9925	0.9927	0.9929	0.9931	0.9932	0.9934	0.9936
2.5	0.9938	0.9940	0.9941	0.9943	0.9945	0.9946	0.9948	0.9949	0.9951	0.9952
2.6	0.9953	0.9955	0.9956	0.9957	0.9959	0.9960	0.9961	0.9962	0.9963	0.9964
2.7	0.9965	0.9966	0.9967	0.9968	0.9969	0.9970	0.9971	0.9972	0.9973	0.9974
2.8	0.9974	0.9975	0.9976	0.9977	0.9977	0.9978	0.9979	0.9979	0.9980	0.9981
2.9	0.9981	0.9982	0.9982	0.9983	0.9984	0.9984	0.9985	0.9985	0.9986	0.9986
3.0	0.9987	0.9987	0.9987	0.9988	0.9988	0.9989	0.9989	0.9989	0.9990	0.9990
3.1	0.9990	0.9991	0.9991	0.9991	0.9992	0.9992	0.9992	0.9992	0.9993	0.9993
3.2	0.9993	0.9993	0.9994	0.9994	0.9994	0.9994	0.9994	0.9995	0.9995	0.9995
3.3	0.9995	0.9995	0.9995	0.9996	0.9996	0.9996	0.9996	0.9996	0.9996	0.9997
3.4	0.9997	0.9997	0.9997	0.9997	0.9997	0.9997	0.9997	0.9997	0.9997	0.9998

Table Binomial Probability Sums $\sum_{x=0}^{r} b(x; n, p)$

						p					
n	r	0.10	0.20	0.25	0.30	0.40	0.50	0.60	0.70	0.80	0.90
1	0	0.9000	0.8000	0.7500	0.7000	0.6000	0.5000	0.4000	0.3000	0.2000	0.1000
	1	1.0000	1.0000	1.0000	1.0000	1.0000	1.0000	1.0000	1.0000	1.0000	1.0000
2	0	0.8100	0.6400	0.5625	0.4900	0.3600	0.2500	0.1600	0.0900	0.0400	0.0100
	1	0.9900	0.9600	0.9375	0.9100	0.8400	0.7500	0.6400	0.5100	0.3600	0.1900
	2	1.0000	1.0000	1.0000	1.0000	1.0000	1.0000	1.0000	1.0000	1.0000	1.0000
3	0	0.7290	0.5120	0.4219	0.3430	0.2160	0.1250	0.0640	0.0270	0.0080	0.0010
	1	0.9720	0.8960	0.8438	0.7840	0.6480	0.5000	0.3520	0.2160	0.1040	0.0280
	2	0.9990	0.9920	0.9844	0.9730	0.9360	0.8750	0.7840	0.6570	0.4880	0.2710
	3	1.0000	1.0000	1.0000	1.0000	1.0000	1.0000	1.0000	1.0000	1.0000	1.0000
4	0	0.6561	0.4096	0.3164	0.2401	0.1296	0.0625	0.0256	0.0081	0.0016	0.0001
	1	0.9477	0.8192	0.7383	0.6517	0.4752	0.3125	0.1792	0.0837	0.0272	0.0037
	2	0.9963	0.9728	0.9492	0.9163	0.8208	0.6875	0.5248	0.3483	0.1808	0.0523
	3	0.9999	0.9984	0.9961	0.9919	0.9744	0.9375	0.8704	0.7599	0.5904	0.3439
	4	1.0000	1.0000	1.0000	1.0000	1.0000	1.0000	1.0000	1.0000	1.0000	1.0000
5	0	0.5905	0.3277	0.2373	0.1681	0.0778	0.0313	0.0102	0.0024	0.0003	0.0000
	1	0.9185	0.7373	0.6328	0.5282	0.3370	0.1875	0.0870	0.0308	0.0067	0.0005
	2	0.9914	0.9421	0.8965	0.8369	0.6826	0.5000	0.3174	0.1631	0.0579	0.0086
	3	0.9995	0.9933	0.9844	0.9692	0.9130	0.8125	0.6630	0.4718	0.2627	0.0815
	4	1.0000	0.9997	0.9990	0.9976	0.9898	0.9688	0.9222	0.8319	0.6723	0.4095
	5	1.0000	1.0000	1.0000	1.0000	1.0000	1.0000	1.0000	1.0000	1.0000	1.0000
6	0	0.5314	0.2621	0.1780	0.1176	0.0467	0.0156	0.0041	0.0007	0.0001	0.0000
	1	0.8857	0.6554	0.5339	0.4202	0.2333	0.1094	0.0410	0.0109	0.0016	0.0001
	2	0.9842	0.9011	0.8306	0.7443	0.5443	0.3438	0.1792	0.0705	0.0170	0.0013
	3	0.9987	0.9830	0.9624	0.9295	0.8208	0.6563	0.4557	0.2557	0.0989	0.0159
	4	0.9999	0.9984	0.9954	0.9891	0.9590	0.8906	0.7667	0.5798	0.3446	0.1143
	5	1.0000	0.9999	0.9998	0.9993	0.9959	0.9844	0.9533	0.8824	0.7379	0.4686
	6	1.0000	1.0000	1.0000	1.0000	1.0000	1.0000	1.0000	1.0000	1.0000	1.0000
7	0	0.4783	0.2097	0.1335	0.0824	0.0280	0.0078	0.0016	0.0002	0.0000	
	1	0.8503	0.5767	0.4449	0.3294	0.1586	0.0625	0.0188	0.0038	0.0004	0.0000
	2	0.9743	0.8520	0.7564	0.6471	0.4199	0.2266	0.0963	0.0288	0.0047	0.0002
	3	0.9973	0.9667	0.9294	0.8740	0.7102	0.5000	0.2898	0.1260	0.0333	0.0027
	4	0.9998	0.9953	0.9871	0.9712	0.9037	0.7734	0.5801	0.3529	0.1480	0.0257
	5	1.0000	0.9996	0.9987	0.9962	0.9812	0.9375	0.8414	0.6706	0.4233	0.1497
	6		1.0000	0.9999	0.9998	0.9984	0.9922	0.9720	0.9176	0.7903	0.5217
	7			1.0000	1.0000	1.0000	1.0000	1.0000	1.0000	1.0000	1.0000

Table (continued) Binomial Probability Sums $\sum_{x=0}^{r} b(x; n, p)$

						p					
n	r	0.10	0.20	0.25	0.30	0.40	0.50	0.60	0.70	0.80	0.90
8	0	0.4305	0.1678	0.1001	0.0576	0.0168	0.0039	0.0007	0.0001	0.0000	
	1	0.8131	0.5033	0.3671	0.2553	0.1064	0.0352	0.0085	0.0013	0.0001	
	2	0.9619	0.7969	0.6785	0.5518	0.3154	0.1445	0.0498	0.0113	0.0012	0.0000
	3	0.9950	0.9437	0.8862	0.8059	0.5941	0.3633	0.1737	0.0580	0.0104	0.0004
	4	0.9996	0.9896	0.9727	0.9420	0.8263	0.6367	0.4059	0.1941	0.0563	0.0050
	5	1.0000	0.9988	0.9958	0.9887	0.9502	0.8555	0.6846	0.4482	0.2031	0.0381
	6		0.9999	0.9996	0.9987	0.9915	0.9648	0.8936	0.7447	0.4967	0.1869
	7		1.0000	1.0000	0.9999	0.9993	0.9961	0.9832	0.9424	0.8322	0.5695
	8				1.0000	1.0000	1.0000	1.0000	1.0000	1.0000	1.0000
9	0	0.3874	0.1342	0.0751	0.0404	0.0101	0.0020	0.0003	0.0000		
	1	0.7748	0.4362	0.3003	0.1960	0.0705	0.0195	0.0038	0.0004	0.0000	
	2	0.9470	0.7382	0.6007	0.4628	0.2318	0.0898	0.0250	0.0043	0.0003	0.0000
	3	0.9917	0.9144	0.8343	0.7297	0.4826	0.2539	0.0994	0.0253	0.0031	0.0001
	4	0.9991	0.9804	0.9511	0.9012	0.7334	0.5000	0.2666	0.0988	0.0196	0.0009
	5	0.9999	0.9969	0.9900	0.9747	0.9006	0.7461	0.5174	0.2703	0.0856	0.0083
	6	1.0000	0.9997	0.9987	0.9957	0.9750	0.9102	0.7682	0.5372	0.2618	0.0530
	7		1.0000	0.9999	0.9996	0.9962	0.9805	0.9295	0.8040	0.5638	0.2252
	8			1.0000	1.0000	0.9997	0.9980	0.9899	0.9596	0.8658	0.6126
	9					1.0000	1.0000	1.0000	1.0000	1.0000	1.0000
10	0	0.3487	0.1074	0.0563	0.0282	0.0060	0.0010	0.0001	0.0000		
	1	0.7361	0.3758	0.2440	0.1493	0.0464	0.0107	0.0017	0.0001	0.0000	
	2	0.9298	0.6778	0.5256	0.3828	0.1673	0.0547	0.0123	0.0016	0.0001	
	3	0.9872	0.8791	0.7759	0.6496	0.3823	0.1719	0.0548	0.0106	0.0009	0.0000
	4	0.9984	0.9672	0.9219	0.8497	0.6331	0.3770	0.1662	0.0473	0.0064	0.0001
	5	0.9999	0.9936	0.9803	0.9527	0.8338	0.6230	0.3669	0.1503	0.0328	0.0016
	6	1.0000	0.9991	0.9965	0.9894	0.9452	0.8281	0.6177	0.3504	0.1209	0.0128
	7		0.9999	0.9996	0.9984	0.9877	0.9453	0.8327	0.6172	0.3222	0.0702
	8		1.0000	1.0000	0.9999	0.9983	0.9893	0.9536	0.8507	0.6242	0.2639
	9				1.0000	0.9999	0.9990	0.9940	0.9718	0.8926	0.6513
	10					1.0000	1.0000	1.0000	1.0000	1.0000	1.0000
11	0	0.3138	0.0859	0.0422	0.0198	0.0036	0.0005	0.0000			
	1	0.6974	0.3221	0.1971	0.1130	0.0302	0.0059	0.0007	0.0000		
	2	0.9104	0.6174	0.4552	0.3127	0.1189	0.0327	0.0059	0.0006	0.0000	
	3	0.9815	0.8389	0.7133	0.5696	0.2963	0.1133	0.0293	0.0043	0.0002	
	4	0.9972	0.9496	0.8854	0.7897	0.5328	0.2744	0.0994	0.0216	0.0020	0.0000
	5	0.9997	0.9883	0.9657	0.9218	0.7535	0.5000	0.2465	0.0782	0.0117	0.0003
	6	1.0000	0.9980	0.9924	0.9784	0.9006	0.7256	0.4672	0.2103	0.0504	0.0028
	7		0.9998	0.9988	0.9957	0.9707	0.8867	0.7037	0.4304	0.1611	0.0185
	8		1.0000	0.9999	0.9994	0.9941	0.9673	0.8811	0.6873	0.3826	0.0896
	9			1.0000	1.0000	0.9993	0.9941	0.9698	0.8870	0.6779	0.3026
	10					1.0000	0.9995	0.9964	0.9802	0.9141	0.6862
	11						1.0000	1.0000	1.0000	1.0000	1.0000

Table (continued) Binomial Probability Sums $\sum_{x=0}^{r} b(x; n, p)$

						p					
n	r	0.10	0.20	0.25	0.30	0.40	0.50	0.60	0.70	0.80	0.90
12	0	0.2824	0.0687	0.0317	0.0138	0.0022	0.0002	0.0000			
	1	0.6590	0.2749	0.1584	0.0850	0.0196	0.0032	0.0003	0.0000		
	2	0.8891	0.5583	0.3907	0.2528	0.0834	0.0193	0.0028	0.0002	0.0000	
	3	0.9744	0.7946	0.6488	0.4925	0.2253	0.0730	0.0153	0.0017	0.0001	
	4	0.9957	0.9274	0.8424	0.7237	0.4382	0.1938	0.0573	0.0095	0.0006	0.0000
	5	0.9995	0.9806	0.9456	0.8822	0.6652	0.3872	0.1582	0.0386	0.0039	0.0001
	6	0.9999	0.9961	0.9857	0.9614	0.8418	0.6128	0.3348	0.1178	0.0194	0.0005
	7	1.0000	0.9994	0.9972	0.9905	0.9427	0.8062	0.5618	0.2763	0.0726	0.0043
	8		0.9999	0.9996	0.9983	0.9847	0.9270	0.7747	0.5075	0.2054	0.0256
	9		1.0000	1.0000	0.9998	0.9972	0.9807	0.9166	0.7472	0.4417	0.1109
	10				1.0000	0.9997	0.9968	0.9804	0.9150	0.7251	0.3410
	11					1.0000	0.9998	0.9978	0.9862	0.9313	0.7176
	12						1.0000	1.0000	1.0000	1.0000	1.0000
13	0	0.2542	0.0550	0.0238	0.0097	0.0013	0.0001	0.0000			
	1	0.6213	0.2336	0.1267	0.0637	0.0126	0.0017	0.0001	0.0000		
	2	0.8661	0.5017	0.3326	0.2025	0.0579	0.0112	0.0013	0.0001		
	3	0.9658	0.7473	0.5843	0.4206	0.1686	0.0461	0.0078	0.0007	0.0000	
	4	0.9935	0.9009	0.7940	0.6543	0.3530	0.1334	0.0321	0.0040	0.0002	
	5	0.9991	0.9700	0.9198	0.8346	0.5744	0.2905	0.0977	0.0182	0.0012	0.0000
	6	0.9999	0.9930	0.9757	0.9376	0.7712	0.5000	0.2288	0.0624	0.0070	0.0001
	7	1.0000	0.9988	0.9944	0.9818	0.9023	0.7095	0.4256	0.1654	0.0300	0.0009
	8		0.9998	0.9990	0.9960	0.9679	0.8666	0.6470	0.3457	0.0991	0.0065
	9		1.0000	0.9999	0.9993	0.9922	0.9539	0.8314	0.5794	0.2527	0.0342
	10			1.0000	0.9999	0.9987	0.9888	0.9421	0.7975	0.4983	0.1339
	11				1.0000	0.9999	0.9983	0.9874	0.9363	0.7664	0.3787
	12					1.0000	0.9999	0.9987	0.9903	0.9450	0.7458
	13						1.0000	1.0000	1.0000	1.0000	1.0000
14	0	0.2288	0.0440	0.0178	0.0068	0.0008	0.0001	0.0000			
	1	0.5846	0.1979	0.1010	0.0475	0.0081	0.0009	0.0001			
	2	0.8416	0.4481	0.2811	0.1608	0.0398	0.0065	0.0006	0.0000		
	3	0.9559	0.6982	0.5213	0.3552	0.1243	0.0287	0.0039	0.0002		
	4	0.9908	0.8702	0.7415	0.5842	0.2793	0.0898	0.0175	0.0017	0.0000	
	5	0.9985	0.9561	0.8883	0.7805	0.4859	0.2120	0.0583	0.0083	0.0004	
	6	0.9998	0.9884	0.9617	0.9067	0.6925	0.3953	0.1501	0.0315	0.0024	0.0000
	7	1.0000	0.9976	0.9897	0.9685	0.8499	0.6047	0.3075	0.0933	0.0116	0.0002
	8		0.9996	0.9978	0.9917	0.9417	0.7880	0.5141	0.2195	0.0439	0.0015
	9		1.0000	0.9997	0.9983	0.9825	0.9102	0.7207	0.4158	0.1298	0.0092
	10			1.0000	0.9998	0.9961	0.9713	0.8757	0.6448	0.3018	0.0441
	11				1.0000	0.9994	0.9935	0.9602	0.8392	0.5519	0.1584
	12					0.9999	0.9991	0.9919	0.9525	0.8021	0.4154
	13					1.0000	0.9999	0.9992	0.9932	0.9560	0.7712
	14						1.0000	1.0000	1.0000	1.0000	1.0000

Table (continued) Binomial Probability Sums $\sum_{x=0}^{r} b(x; n, p)$

						p					
n	r	0.10	0.20	0.25	0.30	0.40	0.50	0.60	0.70	0.80	0.90
15	0	0.2059	0.0352	0.0134	0.0047	0.0005	0.0000				
	1	0.5490	0.1671	0.0802	0.0353	0.0052	0.0005	0.0000			
	2	0.8159	0.3980	0.2361	0.1268	0.0271	0.0037	0.0003	0.0000		
	3	0.9444	0.6482	0.4613	0.2969	0.0905	0.0176	0.0019	0.0001		
	4	0.9873	0.8358	0.6865	0.5155	0.2173	0.0592	0.0093	0.0007	0.0000	
	5	0.9978	0.9389	0.8516	0.7216	0.4032	0.1509	0.0338	0.0037	0.0001	
	6	0.9997	0.9819	0.9434	0.8689	0.6098	0.3036	0.0950	0.0152	0.0008	
	7	1.0000	0.9958	0.9827	0.9500	0.7869	0.5000	0.2131	0.0500	0.0042	0.0000
	8		0.9992	0.9958	0.9848	0.9050	0.6964	0.3902	0.1311	0.0181	0.0003
	9		0.9999	0.9992	0.9963	0.9662	0.8491	0.5968	0.2784	0.0611	0.0022
	10		1.0000	0.9999	0.9993	0.9907	0.9408	0.7827	0.4845	0.1642	0.0127
	11			1.0000	0.9999	0.9981	0.9824	0.9095	0.7031	0.3518	0.0556
	12				1.0000	0.9997	0.9963	0.9729	0.8732	0.6020	0.1841
	13					1.0000	0.9995	0.9948	0.9647	0.8329	0.4510
	14						1.0000	0.9995	0.9953	0.9648	0.7941
	15							1.0000	1.0000	1.0000	1.0000
16	0	0.1853	0.0281	0.0100	0.0033	0.0003	0.0000				
	1	0.5147	0.1407	0.0635	0.0261	0.0033	0.0003	0.0000			
	2	0.7892	0.3518	0.1971	0.0994	0.0183	0.0021	0.0001			
	3	0.9316	0.5981	0.4050	0.2459	0.0651	0.0106	0.0009	0.0000		
	4	0.9830	0.7982	0.6302	0.4499	0.1666	0.0384	0.0049	0.0003		
	5	0.9967	0.9183	0.8103	0.6598	0.3288	0.1051	0.0191	0.0016	0.0000	
	6	0.9995	0.9733	0.9204	0.8247	0.5272	0.2272	0.0583	0.0071	0.0002	
	7	0.9999	0.9930	0.9729	0.9256	0.7161	0.4018	0.1423	0.0257	0.0015	0.0000
	8	1.0000	0.9985	0.9925	0.9743	0.8577	0.5982	0.2839	0.0744	0.0070	0.0001
	9		0.9998	0.9984	0.9929	0.9417	0.7728	0.4728	0.1753	0.0267	0.0005
	10		1.0000	0.9997	0.9984	0.9809	0.8949	0.6712	0.3402	0.0817	0.0033
	11			1.0000	0.9997	0.9951	0.9616	0.8334	0.5501	0.2018	0.0170
	12				1.0000	0.9991	0.9894	0.9349	0.7541	0.4019	0.0684
	13					0.9999	0.9979	0.9817	0.9006	0.6482	0.2108
	14					1.0000	0.9997	0.9967	0.9739	0.8593	0.4853
	15						1.0000	0.9997	0.9967	0.9719	0.8147
	16							1.0000	1.0000	1.0000	1.0000

Table (continued) Binomial Probability Sums $\sum_{x=0}^{r} b(x; n, p)$

							p				
n	r	0.10	0.20	0.25	0.30	0.40	0.50	0.60	0.70	0.80	0.90
17	0	0.1668	0.0225	0.0075	0.0023	0.0002	0.0000				
	1	0.4818	0.1182	0.0501	0.0193	0.0021	0.0001	0.0000			
	2	0.7618	0.3096	0.1637	0.0774	0.0123	0.0012	0.0001			
	3	0.9174	0.5489	0.3530	0.2019	0.0464	0.0064	0.0005	0.0000		
	4	0.9779	0.7582	0.5739	0.3887	0.1260	0.0245	0.0025	0.0001		
	5	0.9953	0.8943	0.7653	0.5968	0.2639	0.0717	0.0106	0.0007	0.0000	
	6	0.9992	0.9623	0.8929	0.7752	0.4478	0.1662	0.0348	0.0032	0.0001	
	7	0.9999	0.9891	0.9598	0.8954	0.6405	0.3145	0.0919	0.0127	0.0005	
	8	1.0000	0.9974	0.9876	0.9597	0.8011	0.5000	0.1989	0.0403	0.0026	0.0000
	9		0.9995	0.9969	0.9873	0.9081	0.6855	0.3595	0.1046	0.0109	0.0001
	10		0.9999	0.9994	0.9968	0.9652	0.8338	0.5522	0.2248	0.0377	0.0008
	11		1.0000	0.9999	0.9993	0.9894	0.9283	0.7361	0.4032	0.1057	0.0047
	12			1.0000	0.9999	0.9975	0.9755	0.8740	0.6113	0.2418	0.0221
	13				1.0000	0.9995	0.9936	0.9536	0.7981	0.4511	0.0826
	14					0.9999	0.9988	0.9877	0.9226	0.6904	0.2382
	15					1.0000	0.9999	0.9979	0.9807	0.8818	0.5182
	16						1.0000	0.9998	0.9977	0.9775	0.8332
	17							1.0000	1.0000	1.0000	1.0000
18	0	0.1501	0.0180	0.0056	0.0016	0.0001	0.0000				
	1	0.4503	0.0991	0.0395	0.0142	0.0013	0.0001				
	2	0.7338	0.2713	0.1353	0.0600	0.0082	0.0007	0.0000			
	3	0.9018	0.5010	0.3057	0.1646	0.0328	0.0038	0.0002			
	4	0.9718	0.7164	0.5187	0.3327	0.0942	0.0154	0.0013	0.0000		
	5	0.9936	0.8671	0.7175	0.5344	0.2088	0.0481	0.0058	0.0003		
	6	0.9988	0.9487	0.8610	0.7217	0.3743	0.1189	0.0203	0.0014	0.0000	
	7	0.9998	0.9837	0.9431	0.8593	0.5634	0.2403	0.0576	0.0061	0.0002	
	8	1.0000	0.9957	0.9807	0.9404	0.7368	0.4073	0.1347	0.0210	0.0009	
	9		0.9991	0.9946	0.9790	0.8653	0.5927	0.2632	0.0596	0.0043	0.0000
	10		0.9998	0.9988	0.9939	0.9424	0.7597	0.4366	0.1407	0.0163	0.0002
	11		1.0000	0.9998	0.9986	0.9797	0.8811	0.6257	0.2783	0.0513	0.0012
	12			1.0000	0.9997	0.9942	0.9519	0.7912	0.4656	0.1329	0.0064
	13				1.0000	0.9987	0.9846	0.9058	0.6673	0.2836	0.0282
	14					0.9998	0.9962	0.9672	0.8354	0.4990	0.0982
	15					1.0000	0.9993	0.9918	0.9400	0.7287	0.2662
	16						0.9999	0.9987	0.9858	0.9009	0.5497
	17						1.0000	0.9999	0.9984	0.9820	0.8499
	18							1.0000	1.0000	1.0000	1.0000

Table (continued) Binomial Probability Sums $\sum_{x=0}^{r} b(x; n, p)$

						p					
n	r	0.10	0.20	0.25	0.30	0.40	0.50	0.60	0.70	0.80	0.90
19	0	0.1351	0.0144	0.0042	0.0011	0.0001					
	1	0.4203	0.0829	0.0310	0.0104	0.0008	0.0000				
	2	0.7054	0.2369	0.1113	0.0462	0.0055	0.0004	0.0000			
	3	0.8850	0.4551	0.2631	0.1332	0.0230	0.0022	0.0001			
	4	0.9648	0.6733	0.4654	0.2822	0.0696	0.0096	0.0006	0.0000		
	5	0.9914	0.8369	0.6678	0.4739	0.1629	0.0318	0.0031	0.0001		
	6	0.9983	0.9324	0.8251	0.6655	0.3081	0.0835	0.0116	0.0006		
	7	0.9997	0.9767	0.9225	0.8180	0.4878	0.1796	0.0352	0.0028	0.0000	
	8	1.0000	0.9933	0.9713	0.9161	0.6675	0.3238	0.0885	0.0105	0.0003	
	9		0.9984	0.9911	0.9674	0.8139	0.5000	0.1861	0.0326	0.0016	
	10		0.9997	0.9977	0.9895	0.9115	0.6762	0.3325	0.0839	0.0067	0.0000
	11		1.0000	0.9995	0.9972	0.9648	0.8204	0.5122	0.1820	0.0233	0.0003
	12			0.9999	0.9994	0.9884	0.9165	0.6919	0.3345	0.0676	0.0017
	13			1.0000	0.9999	0.9969	0.9682	0.8371	0.5261	0.1631	0.0086
	14				1.0000	0.9994	0.9904	0.9304	0.7178	0.3267	0.0352
	15					0.9999	0.9978	0.9770	0.8668	0.5449	0.1150
	16					1.0000	0.9996	0.9945	0.9538	0.7631	0.2946
	17						1.0000	0.9992	0.9896	0.9171	0.5797
	18							0.9999	0.9989	0.9856	0.8649
	19							1.0000	1.0000	1.0000	1.0000
20	0	0.1216	0.0115	0.0032	0.0008	0.0000					
	1	0.3917	0.0692	0.0243	0.0076	0.0005	0.0000				
	2	0.6769	0.2061	0.0913	0.0355	0.0036	0.0002				
	3	0.8670	0.4114	0.2252	0.1071	0.0160	0.0013	0.0000			
	4	0.9568	0.6296	0.4148	0.2375	0.0510	0.0059	0.0003			
	5	0.9887	0.8042	0.6172	0.4164	0.1256	0.0207	0.0016	0.0000		
	6	0.9976	0.9133	0.7858	0.6080	0.2500	0.0577	0.0065	0.0003		
	7	0.9996	0.9679	0.8982	0.7723	0.4159	0.1316	0.0210	0.0013	0.0000	
	8	0.9999	0.9900	0.9591	0.8867	0.5956	0.2517	0.0565	0.0051	0.0001	
	9	1.0000	0.9974	0.9861	0.9520	0.7553	0.4119	0.1275	0.0171	0.0006	
	10		0.9994	0.9961	0.9829	0.8725	0.5881	0.2447	0.0480	0.0026	0.0000
	11		0.9999	0.9991	0.9949	0.9435	0.7483	0.4044	0.1133	0.0100	0.0001
	12		1.0000	0.9998	0.9987	0.9790	0.8684	0.5841	0.2277	0.0321	0.0004
	13			1.0000	0.9997	0.9935	0.9423	0.7500	0.3920	0.0867	0.0024
	14				1.0000	0.9984	0.9793	0.8744	0.5836	0.1958	0.0113
	15					0.9997	0.9941	0.9490	0.7625	0.3704	0.0432
	16					1.0000	0.9987	0.9840	0.8929	0.5886	0.1330
	17						0.9998	0.9964	0.9645	0.7939	0.3231
	18						1.0000	0.9995	0.9924	0.9308	0.6083
	19							1.0000	0.9992	0.9885	0.8784
	20								1.0000	1.0000	1.0000

Table The Incomplete Gamma Function: $F(x; \alpha) = \int_0^x \frac{1}{\Gamma(\alpha)} y^{\alpha-1} e^{-y} \, dy$

	α									
x	1	2	3	4	5	6	7	8	9	10
1	0.6320	0.2640	0.0800	0.0190	0.0040	0.0010	0.0000	0.0000	0.0000	0.0000
2	0.8650	0.5940	0.3230	0.1430	0.0530	0.0170	0.0050	0.0010	0.0000	0.0000
3	0.9500	0.8010	0.5770	0.3530	0.1850	0.0840	0.0340	0.0120	0.0040	0.0010
4	0.9820	0.9080	0.7620	0.5670	0.3710	0.2150	0.1110	0.0510	0.0210	0.0080
5	0.9930	0.9600	0.8750	0.7350	0.5600	0.3840	0.2380	0.1330	0.0680	0.0320
6	0.9980	0.9830	0.9380	0.8490	0.7150	0.5540	0.3940	0.2560	0.1530	0.0840
7	0.9990	0.9930	0.9700	0.9180	0.8270	0.6990	0.5500	0.4010	0.2710	0.1700
8	1.0000	0.9970	0.9860	0.9580	0.9000	0.8090	0.6870	0.5470	0.4070	0.2830
9		0.9990	0.9940	0.9790	0.9450	0.8840	0.7930	0.6760	0.5440	0.4130
10		1.0000	0.9970	0.9900	0.9710	0.9330	0.8700	0.7800	0.6670	0.5420
11			0.9990	0.9950	0.9850	0.9620	0.9210	0.8570	0.7680	0.6590
12			1.0000	0.9980	0.9920	0.9800	0.9540	0.9110	0.8450	0.7580
13				0.9990	0.9960	0.9890	0.9740	0.9460	0.9000	0.8340
14				1.0000	0.9980	0.9940	0.9860	0.9680	0.9380	0.8910
15					0.9990	0.9970	0.9920	0.9820	0.9630	0.9300

Fundamental Sampling Distributions and Data Descriptions

1 Random Sampling

The outcome of a statistical experiment may be recorded either as a numerical value or as a descriptive representation. When a pair of dice is tossed and the total is the outcome of interest, we record a numerical value. However, if the students of a certain school are given blood tests and the type of blood is of interest, then a descriptive representation might be more useful. A person's blood can be classified in 8 ways: AB, A, B, or O, each with a plus or minus sign, depending on the presence or absence of the Rh antigen.

In this chapter, we focus on sampling from distributions or populations and study such important quantities as the *sample mean* and *sample variance*, which will be of vital importance in future chapters. In addition, we attempt to give the reader an introduction to the role that the sample mean and variance will play in statistical inference in later chapters. The use of modern high-speed computers allows the scientist or engineer to greatly enhance his or her use of formal statistical inference with graphical techniques. Much of the time, formal inference appears quite dry and perhaps even abstract to the practitioner or to the manager who wishes to let statistical analysis be a guide to decision-making.

Populations and Samples

We begin this section by discussing the notions of *populations* and *samples*. The totality of observations with which we are concerned, whether their number be finite or infinite, constitutes what we call a **population**. There was a time when the word *population* referred to observations obtained from statistical studies about people. Today, statisticians use the term to refer to observations relevant to anything of interest, whether it be groups of people, animals, or all possible outcomes from some complicated biological or engineering system.

From Chapter 8 of *Probability & Statistics for Engineers & Scientists*, Ninth Edition, Ronald E. Walpole, Raymond H. Myers, Sharon L. Myers, Keying Ye. Copyright © 2012 by Pearson Education, Inc. Published by Pearson Prentice Hall. All rights reserved.

Definition 1: | A **population** consists of the totality of the observations with which we are concerned.

The number of observations in the population is defined to be the size of the population. If there are 600 students in the school whom we classified according to blood type, we say that we have a population of size 600. The numbers on the cards in a deck, the heights of residents in a certain city, and the lengths of fish in a particular lake are examples of populations with finite size. In each case, the total number of observations is a finite number. The observations obtained by measuring the atmospheric pressure every day, from the past on into the future, or all measurements of the depth of a lake, from any conceivable position, are examples of populations whose sizes are infinite. Some finite populations are so large that in theory we assume them to be infinite. This is true in the case of the population of lifetimes of a certain type of storage battery being manufactured for mass distribution throughout the country.

Each observation in a population is a value of a random variable X having some probability distribution $f(x)$. If one is inspecting items coming off an assembly line for defects, then each observation in the population might be a value 0 or 1 of the Bernoulli random variable X with probability distribution

$$b(x; 1, p) = p^x q^{1-x}, \qquad x = 0, 1$$

where 0 indicates a nondefective item and 1 indicates a defective item. Of course, it is assumed that p, the probability of any item being defective, remains constant from trial to trial. In the blood-type experiment, the random variable X represents the type of blood and is assumed to take on values from 1 to 8. Each student is given one of the values of the discrete random variable. The lives of the storage batteries are values assumed by a continuous random variable having perhaps a normal distribution. When we refer hereafter to a "binomial population," a "normal population," or, in general, the "population $f(x)$," we shall mean a population whose observations are values of a random variable having a binomial distribution, a normal distribution, or the probability distribution $f(x)$. Hence, the mean and variance of a random variable or probability distribution are also referred to as the mean and variance of the corresponding population.

In the field of statistical inference, statisticians are interested in arriving at conclusions concerning a population when it is impossible or impractical to observe the entire set of observations that make up the population. For example, in attempting to determine the average length of life of a certain brand of light bulb, it would be impossible to test all such bulbs if we are to have any left to sell. Exorbitant costs can also be a prohibitive factor in studying an entire population. Therefore, we must depend on a subset of observations from the population to help us make inferences concerning that same population. This brings us to consider the notion of sampling.

Definition 2: | A **sample** is a subset of a population.

If our inferences from the sample to the population are to be valid, we must obtain samples that are representative of the population. All too often we are tempted to choose a sample by selecting the most convenient members of the population. Such a procedure may lead to erroneous inferences concerning the population. Any sampling procedure that produces inferences that consistently overestimate or consistently underestimate some characteristic of the population is said to be **biased**. To eliminate any possibility of bias in the sampling procedure, it is desirable to choose a **random sample** in the sense that the observations are made independently and at random.

In selecting a random sample of size n from a population $f(x)$, let us define the random variable X_i, $i = 1, 2, \ldots, n$, to represent the ith measurement or sample value that we observe. The random variables $X_1, X_2, \ldots, X_n$ will then constitute a random sample from the population $f(x)$ with numerical values $x_1, x_2, \ldots, x_n$ if the measurements are obtained by repeating the experiment n independent times under essentially the same conditions. Because of the identical conditions under which the elements of the sample are selected, it is reasonable to assume that the n random variables $X_1, X_2, \ldots, X_n$ are independent and that each has the same probability distribution $f(x)$. That is, the probability distributions of $X_1, X_2, \ldots, X_n$ are, respectively, $f(x_1), f(x_2), \ldots, f(x_n)$, and their joint probability distribution is $f(x_1, x_2, \ldots, x_n) = f(x_1)f(x_2) \cdots f(x_n)$. The concept of a random sample is described formally by the following definition.

Definition 3:

Let $X_1, X_2, \ldots, X_n$ be n independent random variables, each having the same probability distribution $f(x)$. Define $X_1, X_2, \ldots, X_n$ to be a **random sample** of size n from the population $f(x)$ and write its joint probability distribution as

$$f(x_1, x_2, \ldots, x_n) = f(x_1)f(x_2) \cdots f(x_n).$$

If one makes a random selection of $n = 8$ storage batteries from a manufacturing process that has maintained the same specification throughout and records the length of life for each battery, with the first measurement x_1 being a value of X_1, the second measurement x_2 a value of X_2, and so forth, then $x_1, x_2, \ldots, x_8$ are the values of the random sample $X_1, X_2, \ldots, X_8$. If we assume the population of battery lives to be normal, the possible values of any X_i, $i = 1, 2, \ldots, 8$, will be precisely the same as those in the original population, and hence X_i has the same identical normal distribution as X.

2   Some Important Statistics

Our main purpose in selecting random samples is to elicit information about the unknown population parameters. Suppose, for example, that we wish to arrive at a conclusion concerning the proportion of coffee-drinkers in the United States who prefer a certain brand of coffee. It would be impossible to question every coffee-drinking American in order to compute the value of the parameter p representing the population proportion. Instead, a large random sample is selected and the proportion $\hat{p}$ of people in this sample favoring the brand of coffee in question is calculated. The value $\hat{p}$ is now used to make an inference concerning the true proportion p.

Now, $\hat{p}$ is a function of the observed values in the random sample; since many

random samples are possible from the same population, we would expect $\hat{p}$ to vary somewhat from sample to sample. That is, $\hat{p}$ is a value of a random variable that we represent by P. Such a random variable is called a **statistic**.

Definition 4: Any function of the random variables constituting a random sample is called a **statistic**.

Location Measures of a Sample: The Sample Mean, Median, and Mode

The two parameters μ and σ^2 measure the center of location and the variability of a probability distribution. These are constant population parameters and are in no way affected or influenced by the observations of a random sample. We shall, however, define some important statistics that describe corresponding measures of a random sample. The most commonly used statistics for measuring the center of a set of data, arranged in order of magnitude, are the **mean**, **median**, and **mode**. Let $X_1, X_2, \ldots, X_n$ represent n random variables.

(a) Sample mean:

$$\bar{X} = \frac{1}{n}\sum_{i=1}^{n} X_i.$$

Note that the statistic $\bar{X}$ assumes the value $\bar{x} = \frac{1}{n}\sum_{i=1}^{n} x_i$ when X_1 assumes the value x_1, X_2 assumes the value x_2, and so forth. The term *sample mean* is applied to both the statistic $\bar{X}$ and its computed value $\bar{x}$.

(b) Sample median:

$$\tilde{x} = \begin{cases} x_{(n+1)/2}, & \text{if } n \text{ is odd,} \\ \frac{1}{2}(x_{n/2} + x_{n/2+1}), & \text{if } n \text{ is even.} \end{cases}$$

The sample median is also a location measure that shows the middle value of the sample. The sample mode is defined as follows.

(c) The sample mode is the value of the sample that occurs most often.

Example 1: Suppose a data set consists of the following observations:

0.32 0.53 0.28 0.37 0.47 0.43 0.36 0.42 0.38 0.43.

The sample mode is 0.43, since this value occurs more than any other value.

A measure of location or central tendency in a sample does not by itself give a clear indication of the nature of the sample. Thus, a measure of variability in the sample must also be considered.

Variability Measures of a Sample: The Sample Variance, Standard Deviation, and Range

The variability in a sample displays how the observations spread out from the average. It is possible to have two sets of observations with the same mean or median that differ considerably in the variability of their measurements about the average.

Consider the following measurements, in liters, for two samples of orange juice bottled by companies A and B:

Sample A	0.97	1.00	0.94	1.03	1.06
Sample B	1.06	1.01	0.88	0.91	1.14

Both samples have the same mean, 1.00 liter. It is obvious that company A bottles orange juice with a more uniform content than company B. We say that the **variability**, or the **dispersion**, of the observations from the average is less for sample A than for sample B. Therefore, in buying orange juice, we would feel more confident that the bottle we select will be close to the advertised average if we buy from company A.

There are several measures of sample variability, including the **sample variance**, **sample standard deviation**, and **sample range**. In this chapter, we will focus mainly on the sample variance. Again, let $X_1, \ldots, X_n$ represent n random variables.

(a) Sample variance:

$$S^2 = \frac{1}{n-1} \sum_{i=1}^{n} (X_i - \bar{X})^2. \qquad (2.1)$$

The computed value of S^2 for a given sample is denoted by s^2. Note that S^2 is essentially defined to be the average of the squares of the deviations of the observations from their mean. The reason for using $n-1$ as a divisor rather than the more obvious choice n will become apparent.

Example 2: A comparison of coffee prices at 4 randomly selected grocery stores in San Diego showed increases from the previous month of 12, 15, 17, and 20 cents for a 1-pound bag. Find the variance of this random sample of price increases.

Solution: Calculating the sample mean, we get

$$\bar{x} = \frac{12 + 15 + 17 + 20}{4} = 16 \text{ cents.}$$

Therefore,

$$s^2 = \frac{1}{3} \sum_{i=1}^{4} (x_i - 16)^2 = \frac{(12-16)^2 + (15-16)^2 + (17-16)^2 + (20-16)^2}{3}$$
$$= \frac{(-4)^2 + (-1)^2 + (1)^2 + (4)^2}{3} = \frac{34}{3}.$$

Whereas the expression for the sample variance best illustrates that S^2 is a measure of variability, an alternative expression does have some merit and thus the reader should be aware of it. The following theorem contains this expression.

Theorem 1:

If S^2 is the variance of a random sample of size n, we may write

$$S^2 = \frac{1}{n(n-1)}\left[n\sum_{i=1}^{n}X_i^2 - \left(\sum_{i=1}^{n}X_i\right)^2\right].$$

Proof: By definition,

$$S^2 = \frac{1}{n-1}\sum_{i=1}^{n}(X_i - \bar{X})^2 = \frac{1}{n-1}\sum_{i=1}^{n}(X_i^2 - 2\bar{X}X_i + \bar{X}^2)$$

$$= \frac{1}{n-1}\left[\sum_{i=1}^{n}X_i^2 - 2\bar{X}\sum_{i=1}^{n}X_i + n\bar{X}^2\right].$$

The **sample standard deviation** and the **sample range** are defined below.

(b) Sample standard deviation:

$$S = \sqrt{S^2},$$

where S^2 is the sample variance.

Let $X_{\max}$ denote the largest of the X_i values and $X_{\min}$ the smallest.

(c) Sample range:

$$R = X_{\max} - X_{\min}.$$

Example 3:

Find the variance of the data 3, 4, 5, 6, 6, and 7, representing the number of trout caught by a random sample of 6 fishermen on June 19, 1996, at Lake Muskoka.

Solution: We find that $\sum_{i=1}^{6}x_i^2 = 171$, $\sum_{i=1}^{6}x_i = 31$, and $n = 6$. Hence,

$$s^2 = \frac{1}{(6)(5)}[(6)(171) - (31)^2] = \frac{13}{6}.$$

Thus, the sample standard deviation $s = \sqrt{13/6} = 1.47$ and the sample range is $7 - 3 = 4$.

Exercises

1 Define suitable populations from which the following samples are selected:

(a) Persons in 200 homes in the city of Richmond are called on the phone and asked to name the candidate they favor for election to the school board.

(b) A coin is tossed 100 times and 34 tails are recorded.

(c) Two hundred pairs of a new type of tennis shoe were tested on the professional tour and, on average, lasted 4 months.

(d) On five different occasions it took a lawyer 21, 26, 24, 22, and 21 minutes to drive from her suburban home to her midtown office.

2 The lengths of time, in minutes, that 10 patients waited in a doctor's office before receiving treatment were recorded as follows: 5, 11, 9, 5, 10, 15, 6, 10, 5, and 10. Treating the data as a random sample, find

(a) the mean;

(b) the median;

(c) the mode.

3 The reaction times for a random sample of 9 subjects to a stimulant were recorded as 2.5, 3.6, 3.1, 4.3, 2.9. 2.3, 2.6, 4.1, and 3.4 seconds. Calculate

(a) the mean;

(b) the median.

4 The number of tickets issued for traffic violations by 8 state troopers during the Memorial Day weekend are 5, 4, 7, 7, 6, 3, 8, and 6.

(a) If these values represent the number of tickets issued by a random sample of 8 state troopers from Montgomery County in Virginia, define a suitable population.

(b) If the values represent the number of tickets issued by a random sample of 8 state troopers from South Carolina, define a suitable population.

5 The numbers of incorrect answers on a true-false competency test for a random sample of 15 students were recorded as follows: 2, 1, 3, 0, 1, 3, 6, 0, 3, 3, 5, 2, 1, 4, and 2. Find

(a) the mean;

(b) the median;

(c) the mode.

6 Find the mean, median, and mode for the sample whose observations, 15, 7, 8, 95, 19, 12, 8, 22, and 14, represent the number of sick days claimed on 9 federal income tax returns. Which value appears to be the best measure of the center of these data? State reasons for your preference.

7 A random sample of employees from a local manufacturing plant pledged the following donations, in dollars, to the United Fund: 100, 40, 75, 15, 20, 100, 75, 50, 30, 10, 55, 75, 25, 50, 90, 80, 15, 25, 45, and 100. Calculate

(a) the mean;

(b) the mode.

8 According to ecology writer Jacqueline Killeen, phosphates contained in household detergents pass right through our sewer systems, causing lakes to turn into swamps that eventually dry up into deserts. The following data show the amount of phosphates per load

of laundry, in grams, for a random sample of various types of detergents used according to the prescribed directions:

Laundry Detergent	Phosphates per Load (grams)
A & P Blue Sail	48
Dash	47
Concentrated All	42
Cold Water All	42
Breeze	41
Oxydol	34
Ajax	31
Sears	30
Fab	29
Cold Power	29
Bold	29
Rinso	26

For the given phosphate data, find

(a) the mean;

(b) the median;

(c) the mode.

9 Consider the data in Exercise 2, find

(a) the range;

(b) the standard deviation.

10 For the sample of reaction times in Exercise 3, calculate

(a) the range;

(b) the variance, using the formula of form (2.1).

11 For the data of Exercise 5, calculate the variance using the formula

(a) of form (2.1);

(b) in Theorem 1.

12 The tar contents of 8 brands of cigarettes selected at random from the latest list released by the Federal Trade Commission are as follows: 7.3, 8.6, 10.4, 16.1, 12.2, 15.1, 14.5, and 9.3 milligrams. Calculate

(a) the mean;

(b) the variance.

13 The grade-point averages of 20 college seniors selected at random from a graduating class are as follows:

3.2	1.9	2.7	2.4	2.8
2.9	3.8	3.0	2.5	3.3
1.8	2.5	3.7	2.8	2.0
3.2	2.3	2.1	2.5	1.9

Calculate the standard deviation.

14 (a) Show that the sample variance is unchanged if a constant c is added to or subtracted from each value in the sample.

(b) Show that the sample variance becomes c^2 times its original value if each observation in the sample is multiplied by c.

15 Verify that the variance of the sample 4, 9, 3, 6, 4, and 7 is 5.1, and using this fact, along with the results of Exercise 14, find

(a) the variance of the sample 12, 27, 9, 18, 12, and 21;

(b) the variance of the sample 9, 14, 8, 11, 9, and 12.

16 In the 2004-05 football season, University of Southern California had the following score differences for the 13 games it played.

$$11\ 49\ 32\ 3\ 6\ 38\ 38\ 30\ 8\ 40\ 31\ 5\ 36$$

Find

(a) the mean score difference;

(b) the median score difference.

3   Sampling Distributions

The field of statistical inference is basically concerned with generalizations and predictions. For example, we might claim, based on the opinions of several people interviewed on the street, that in a forthcoming election 60% of the eligible voters in the city of Detroit favor a certain candidate. In this case, we are dealing with a random sample of opinions from a very large finite population. As a second illustration we might state that the average cost to build a residence in Charleston, South Carolina, is between $330,000 and $335,000, based on the estimates of 3 contractors selected at random from the 30 now building in this city. The population being sampled here is again finite but very small. Finally, let us consider a soft-drink machine designed to dispense, on average, 240 milliliters per drink. A company official who computes the mean of 40 drinks obtains $\bar{x} = 236$ milliliters and, on the basis of this value, decides that the machine is still dispensing drinks with an average content of $\mu = 240$ milliliters. The 40 drinks represent a sample from the infinite population of possible drinks that will be dispensed by this machine.

Inference about the Population from Sample Information

In each of the examples above, we computed a statistic from a sample selected from the population, and from this statistic we made various statements concerning the values of population parameters that may or may not be true. The company official made the decision that the soft-drink machine dispenses drinks with an average content of 240 milliliters, even though the sample mean was 236 milliliters, because he knows from sampling theory that, if $\mu = 240$ milliliters, such a sample value could easily occur. In fact, if he ran similar tests, say every hour, he would expect the values of the statistic $\bar{x}$ to fluctuate above and below $\mu = 240$ milliliters. Only when the value of $\bar{x}$ is substantially different from 240 milliliters will the company official initiate action to adjust the machine.

Since a statistic is a random variable that depends only on the observed sample, it must have a probability distribution.

Definition 5: | The probability distribution of a statistic is called a **sampling distribution**.

The sampling distribution of a statistic depends on the distribution of the population, the size of the samples, and the method of choosing the samples. In the remainder of this chapter we study several of the important sampling distributions of frequently used statistics. Applications of these sampling distributions to problems of statistical inference are considered throughout most of the remaining chapters. The probability distribution of $\bar{X}$ is called the **sampling distribution of the mean**.

What Is the Sampling Distribution of $\bar{X}$?

We should view the sampling distributions of $\bar{X}$ and S^2 as the mechanisms from which we will be able to make inferences on the parameters μ and σ^2. The sampling distribution of $\bar{X}$ with sample size n is the distribution that results when an **experiment is conducted over and over** (always with sample size n) **and the many values of $\bar{X}$ result**. This sampling distribution, then, describes the variability of sample averages around the population mean μ. In the case of the soft-drink machine, knowledge of the sampling distribution of $\bar{X}$ arms the analyst with the knowledge of a "typical" discrepancy between an observed $\bar{x}$ value and true μ. The same principle applies in the case of the distribution of S^2. The sampling distribution produces information about the variability of s^2 values around σ^2 in repeated experiments.

4   Sampling Distribution of Means and the Central Limit Theorem

The first important sampling distribution to be considered is that of the mean $\bar{X}$. Suppose that a random sample of n observations is taken from a normal population with mean μ and variance σ^2. Each observation X_i, $i = 1, 2, \ldots, n$, of the random sample will then have the same normal distribution as the population being sampled. Hence, by the reproductive property of the normal distribution, we conclude that

$$\bar{X} = \frac{1}{n}(X_1 + X_2 + \cdots + X_n)$$

has a normal distribution with mean

$$\mu_{\bar{X}} = \frac{1}{n}\underbrace{(\mu + \mu + \cdots + \mu)}_{n \text{ terms}} = \mu \text{ and variance } \sigma_{\bar{X}}^2 = \frac{1}{n^2}\underbrace{(\sigma^2 + \sigma^2 + \cdots + \sigma^2)}_{n \text{ terms}} = \frac{\sigma^2}{n}.$$

If we are sampling from a population with unknown distribution, either finite or infinite, the sampling distribution of $\bar{X}$ will still be approximately normal with mean μ and variance σ^2/n, provided that the sample size is large. This amazing result is an immediate consequence of the following theorem, called the Central Limit Theorem.

The Central Limit Theorem

Theorem 2:

> **Central Limit Theorem:** If $\bar{X}$ is the mean of a random sample of size n taken from a population with mean μ and finite variance σ^2, then the limiting form of the distribution of
>
> $$Z = \frac{\bar{X} - \mu}{\sigma/\sqrt{n}},$$
>
> as $n \to \infty$, is the standard normal distribution $n(z; 0, 1)$.

The normal approximation for $\bar{X}$ will generally be good if $n \geq 30$, provided the population distribution is not terribly skewed. If $n < 30$, the approximation is good only if the population is not too different from a normal distribution and, as stated above, if the population is known to be normal, the sampling distribution of $\bar{X}$ will follow a normal distribution exactly, no matter how small the size of the samples.

The sample size $n = 30$ is a guideline to use for the Central Limit Theorem. However, as the statement of the theorem implies, the presumption of normality on the distribution of $\bar{X}$ becomes more accurate as n grows larger. In fact, Figure 1 illustrates how the theorem works. It shows how the distribution of $\bar{X}$ becomes closer to normal as n grows larger, beginning with the clearly nonsymmetric distribution of an individual observation ($n = 1$). It also illustrates that the mean of $\bar{X}$ remains μ for any sample size and the variance of $\bar{X}$ gets smaller as n increases.

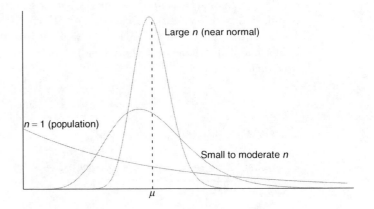

Figure 1: Illustration of the Central Limit Theorem (distribution of $\bar{X}$ for $n = 1$, moderate n, and large n).

Example 4: An electrical firm manufactures light bulbs that have a length of life that is approximately normally distributed, with mean equal to 800 hours and a standard deviation of 40 hours. Find the probability that a random sample of 16 bulbs will have an average life of less than 775 hours.

Solution: The sampling distribution of $\bar{X}$ will be approximately normal, with $\mu_{\bar{X}} = 800$ and $\sigma_{\bar{X}} = 40/\sqrt{16} = 10$. The desired probability is given by the area of the shaded region in Figure 2.

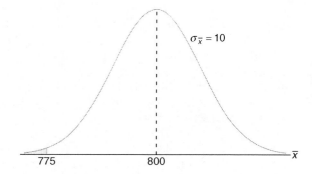

Figure 2: Area for Example 4.

Corresponding to $\bar{x} = 775$, we find that

$$z = \frac{775 - 800}{10} = -2.5,$$

and therefore

$$P(\bar{X} < 775) = P(Z < -2.5) = 0.0062.$$

Inferences on the Population Mean

One very important application of the Central Limit Theorem is the determination of reasonable values of the population mean μ. Topics such as hypothesis testing, estimation, quality control, and many others make use of the Central Limit Theorem. The following example illustrates the use of the Central Limit Theorem with regard to its relationship with μ, the mean of the population, although the formal application to the foregoing topics is relegated to future chapters.

In the following case study, an illustration is given which draws an inference that makes use of the sampling distribution of $\bar{X}$. In this simple illustration, μ and σ are both known. The Central Limit Theorem and the general notion of sampling distributions are often used to produce evidence about some important aspect of a distribution such as a parameter of the distribution. In the case of the Central Limit Theorem, the parameter of interest is the mean μ. The inference made concerning μ may take one of many forms. Often there is a desire on the part of the analyst that the data (in the form of $\bar{x}$) support (or not) some predetermined conjecture concerning the value of μ. The use of what we know about the sampling distribution can contribute to answering this type of question. In the following case study, the concept of hypothesis testing leads to a formal objective that we will highlight in future chapters.

Case Study 1: **Automobile Parts:** An important manufacturing process produces cylindrical component parts for the automotive industry. It is important that the process produce parts having a mean diameter of 5.0 millimeters. The engineer involved conjectures that the population mean is 5.0 millimeters. An experiment is conducted in which 100 parts produced by the process are selected randomly and the diameter measured on each. It is known that the population standard deviation is $\sigma = 0.1$ millimeter. The experiment indicates a sample average diameter of $\bar{x} = 5.027$ millimeters. Does this sample information appear to support or refute the engineer's conjecture?

Solution: This example reflects the kind of problem often posed and solved with hypothesis testing machinery introduced in future chapters. We will not use the formality associated with hypothesis testing here, but we will illustrate the principles and logic used.

Whether the data support or refute the conjecture depends on the probability that data similar to those obtained in this experiment ($\bar{x} = 5.027$) can readily occur when in fact $\mu = 5.0$ (Figure 3). In other words, how likely is it that one can obtain $\bar{x} \geq 5.027$ with $n = 100$ if the population mean is $\mu = 5.0$? If this probability suggests that $\bar{x} = 5.027$ is not unreasonable, the conjecture is not refuted. If the probability is quite low, one can certainly argue that the data do not support the conjecture that $\mu = 5.0$. The probability that we choose to compute is given by $P(|\bar{X} - 5| \geq 0.027)$.

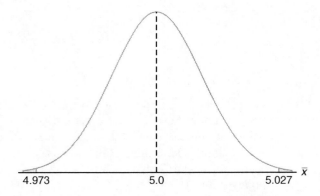

Figure 3: Area for Case Study 1.

In other words, if the mean μ is 5, what is the chance that $\bar{X}$ will deviate by as much as 0.027 millimeter?

$$P(|\bar{X} - 5| \geq 0.027) = P(\bar{X} - 5 \geq 0.027) + P(\bar{X} - 5 \leq -0.027)$$

$$= 2P\left(\frac{\bar{X} - 5}{0.1/\sqrt{100}} \geq 2.7\right).$$

Here we are simply standardizing $\bar{X}$ according to the Central Limit Theorem. If the conjecture $\mu = 5.0$ is true, $\frac{\bar{X}-5}{0.1/\sqrt{100}}$ should follow $N(0,1)$. Thus,

$$2P\left(\frac{\bar{X} - 5}{0.1/\sqrt{100}} \geq 2.7\right) = 2P(Z \geq 2.7) = 2(0.0035) = 0.007.$$

Therefore, one would experience by chance that an $\bar{x}$ would be 0.027 millimeter from the mean in only 7 in 1000 experiments. As a result, this experiment with $\bar{x} = 5.027$ certainly does not give supporting evidence to the conjecture that $\mu = 5.0$. In fact, it strongly refutes the conjecture!

Example 5: Traveling between two campuses of a university in a city via shuttle bus takes, on average, 28 minutes with a standard deviation of 5 minutes. In a given week, a bus transported passengers 40 times. What is the probability that the average transport time was more than 30 minutes? Assume the mean time is measured to the nearest minute.

Solution: In this case, $\mu = 28$ and $\sigma = 3$. We need to calculate the probability $P(\bar{X} > 30)$ with $n = 40$. Since the time is measured on a continuous scale to the nearest minute, an $\bar{x}$ greater than 30 is equivalent to $\bar{x} \geq 30.5$. Hence,

$$P(\bar{X} > 30) = P\left(\frac{\bar{X} - 28}{5/\sqrt{40}} \geq \frac{30.5 - 28}{5/\sqrt{40}}\right) = P(Z \geq 3.16) = 0.0008.$$

There is only a slight chance that the average time of one bus trip will exceed 30 minutes. An illustrative graph is shown in Figure 4.

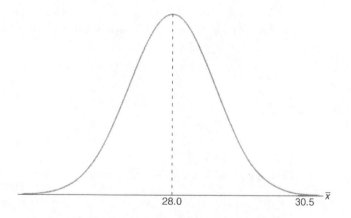

Figure 4: Area for Example 5.

Sampling Distribution of the Difference between Two Means

The illustration in Case Study 1 deals with notions of statistical inference on a single mean μ. The engineer was interested in supporting a conjecture regarding a single population mean. A far more important application involves two populations. A scientist or engineer may be interested in a comparative experiment in which two manufacturing methods, 1 and 2, are to be compared. The basis for that comparison is $\mu_1 - \mu_2$, the difference in the population means.

Suppose that we have two populations, the first with mean μ_1 and variance σ_1^2, and the second with mean μ_2 and variance σ_2^2. Let the statistic $\bar{X}_1$ represent the mean of a random sample of size n_1 selected from the first population, and the statistic $\bar{X}_2$ represent the mean of a random sample of size n_2 selected from the second population, independent of the sample from the first population. What can we say about the sampling distribution of the difference $\bar{X}_1 - \bar{X}_2$ for repeated samples of size n_1 and n_2? According to Theorem 2, the variables $\bar{X}_1 - \bar{X}_2$ are both approximately normally distributed with means μ_1 and μ_2 and variances σ_1^2/n_1 and σ_2^2/n_2, respectively. This approximation improves as n_1 and n_2 increase. By choosing independent samples from the two populations we ensure that the variables $\bar{X}_1$ and $\bar{X}_2$ will be independent, with $a_1 = 1$ and $a_2 = -1$, we can conclude that $\bar{X}_1 - \bar{X}_2$ is approximately normally distributed with mean

$$\mu_{\bar{X}_1 - \bar{X}_2} = \mu_{\bar{X}_1} - \mu_{\bar{X}_2} = \mu_1 - \mu_2$$

and variance

$$\sigma_{\bar{X}_1 - \bar{X}_2}^2 = \sigma_{\bar{X}_1}^2 + \sigma_{\bar{X}_2}^2 = \frac{\sigma_1^2}{n_1} + \frac{\sigma_2^2}{n_2}.$$

The Central Limit Theorem can be easily extended to the two-sample, two-population case.

Theorem 3:	If independent samples of size n_1 and n_2 are drawn at random from two populations, discrete or continuous, with means μ_1 and μ_2 and variances σ_1^2 and σ_2^2, respectively, then the sampling distribution of the differences of means, $\bar{X}_1 - \bar{X}_2$, is approximately normally distributed with mean and variance given by $$\mu_{\bar{X}_1 - \bar{X}_2} = \mu_1 - \mu_2 \text{ and } \sigma_{\bar{X}_1 - \bar{X}_2}^2 = \frac{\sigma_1^2}{n_1} + \frac{\sigma_2^2}{n_2}.$$ Hence, $$Z = \frac{(\bar{X}_1 - \bar{X}_2) - (\mu_1 - \mu_2)}{\sqrt{(\sigma_1^2/n_1) + (\sigma_2^2/n_2)}}$$ is approximately a standard normal variable.

If both n_1 and n_2 are greater than or equal to 30, the normal approximation for the distribution of $\bar{X}_1 - \bar{X}_2$ is very good when the underlying distributions are not too far away from normal. However, even when n_1 and n_2 are less than 30, the normal approximation is reasonably good except when the populations are decidedly nonnormal. Of course, if both populations are normal, then $\bar{X}_1 - \bar{X}_2$ has a normal distribution no matter what the sizes of n_1 and n_2 are.

The utility of the sampling distribution of the difference between two sample averages is very similar to that described in Case Study 1 for the case of a single mean. Case Study 2 that follows focuses on the use of the difference between two sample means to support (or not) the conjecture that two population means are the same.

Case Study 2:	**Paint Drying Time**: Two independent experiments are run in which two different types of paint are compared. Eighteen specimens are painted using type A, and the drying time, in hours, is recorded for each. The same is done with type B. The population standard deviations are both known to be 1.0.

Assuming that the mean drying time is equal for the two types of paint, find $P(\bar{X}_A - \bar{X}_B > 1.0)$, where $\bar{X}_A$ and $\bar{X}_B$ are average drying times for samples of size $n_A = n_B = 18$.

Solution: From the sampling distribution of $\bar{X}_A - \bar{X}_B$, we know that the distribution is approximately normal with mean

$$\mu_{\bar{X}_A - \bar{X}_B} = \mu_A - \mu_B = 0$$

and variance

$$\sigma^2_{\bar{X}_A - \bar{X}_B} = \frac{\sigma^2_A}{n_A} + \frac{\sigma^2_B}{n_B} = \frac{1}{18} + \frac{1}{18} = \frac{1}{9}.$$

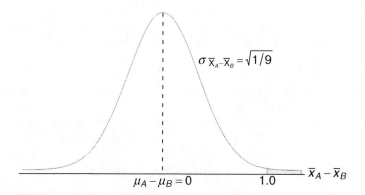

Figure 5: Area for Case Study 2.

The desired probability is given by the shaded region in Figure 5. Corresponding to the value $\bar{X}_A - \bar{X}_B = 1.0$, we have

$$z = \frac{1 - (\mu_A - \mu_B)}{\sqrt{1/9}} = \frac{1 - 0}{\sqrt{1/9}} = 3.0;$$

so

$$P(Z > 3.0) = 1 - P(Z < 3.0) = 1 - 0.9987 = 0.0013.$$

What Do We Learn from Case Study 2?

The machinery in the calculation is based on the presumption that $\mu_A = \mu_B$. Suppose, however, that the experiment is actually conducted for the purpose of drawing an inference regarding the equality of μ_A and μ_B, the two population mean drying times. If the two averages differ by as much as 1 hour (or more), this clearly is evidence that would lead one to conclude that the population mean drying time is not equal for the two types of paint. On the other hand, suppose that the difference in the two sample averages is as small as, say, 15 minutes. If $\mu_A = \mu_B$,

$$P[(\bar{X}_A - \bar{X}_B) > 0.25 \text{ hour}] = P\left(\frac{\bar{X}_A - \bar{X}_B - 0}{\sqrt{1/9}} > \frac{3}{4}\right)$$

$$= P\left(Z > \frac{3}{4}\right) = 1 - P(Z < 0.75) = 1 - 0.7734 = 0.2266.$$

Since this probability is not low, one would conclude that a difference in sample means of 15 minutes can happen by chance (i.e., it happens frequently even though $\mu_A = \mu_B$). As a result, that type of difference in average drying times certainly *is not a clear signal* that $\mu_A \neq \mu_B$.

As we indicated earlier, a more detailed formalism regarding this and other types of statistical inference (e.g., hypothesis testing) will be supplied in future chapters. The Central Limit Theorem and sampling distributions discussed in the next three sections will also play a vital role.

Example 6: The television picture tubes of manufacturer A have a mean lifetime of 6.5 years and a standard deviation of 0.9 year, while those of manufacturer B have a mean lifetime of 6.0 years and a standard deviation of 0.8 year. What is the probability that a random sample of 36 tubes from manufacturer A will have a mean lifetime that is at least 1 year more than the mean lifetime of a sample of 49 tubes from manufacturer B?

Solution: We are given the following information:

Population 1	Population 2
$\mu_1 = 6.5$	$\mu_2 = 6.0$
$\sigma_1 = 0.9$	$\sigma_2 = 0.8$
$n_1 = 36$	$n_2 = 49$

If we use Theorem 3, the sampling distribution of $\bar{X}_1 - \bar{X}_2$ will be approximately normal and will have a mean and standard deviation

$$\mu_{\bar{X}_1 - \bar{X}_2} = 6.5 - 6.0 = 0.5 \quad \text{and} \quad \sigma_{\bar{X}_1 - \bar{X}_2} = \sqrt{\frac{0.81}{36} + \frac{0.64}{49}} = 0.189.$$

The probability that the mean lifetime for 36 tubes from manufacturer A will be at least 1 year longer than the mean lifetime for 49 tubes from manufacturer B is given by the area of the shaded region in Figure 6. Corresponding to the value $\bar{x}_1 - \bar{x}_2 = 1.0$, we find that

$$z = \frac{1.0 - 0.5}{0.189} = 2.65,$$

and hence

$$P(\bar{X}_1 - \bar{X}_2 \geq 1.0) = P(Z > 2.65) = 1 - P(Z < 2.65)$$
$$= 1 - 0.9960 = 0.0040.$$

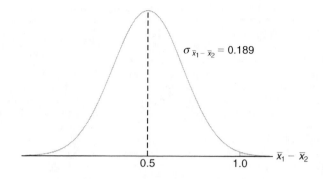

Figure 6: Area for Example 6.

More on Sampling Distribution of Means—Normal Approximation to the Binomial Distribution

The Central Limit Theorem sheds light on how and why "normal approximation" works. We certainly know that a binomial random variable is the number X of successes in n independent trials, where the outcome of each trial is binary. The proportion computed in such an experiment is an average of a set of 0s and 1s. Indeed, while the proportion X/n is an average, X is the sum of this set of 0s and 1s, and both X and X/n are approximately normal if n is sufficiently large. We know that there are conditions on n and p that affect the quality of the approximation, namely $np \geq 5$ and $nq \geq 5$.

Exercises

17 If all possible samples of size 16 are drawn from a normal population with mean equal to 50 and standard deviation equal to 5, what is the probability that a sample mean $\bar{X}$ will fall in the interval from $\mu_{\bar{X}} - 1.9\sigma_{\bar{X}}$ to $\mu_{\bar{X}} - 0.4\sigma_{\bar{X}}$? Assume that the sample means can be measured to any degree of accuracy.

18 If the standard deviation of the mean for the sampling distribution of random samples of size 36 from a large or infinite population is 2, how large must the sample size become if the standard deviation is to be reduced to 1.2?

19 A certain type of thread is manufactured with a mean tensile strength of 78.3 kilograms and a standard deviation of 5.6 kilograms. How is the variance of the sample mean changed when the sample size is

(a) increased from 64 to 196?

(b) decreased from 784 to 49?

20 Given the discrete uniform population

$$f(x) = \begin{cases} \frac{1}{3}, & x = 2, 4, 6, \\ 0, & \text{elsewhere,} \end{cases}$$

find the probability that a random sample of size 54, selected with replacement, will yield a sample mean greater than 4.1 but less than 4.4. Assume the means are measured to the nearest tenth.

21 A soft-drink machine is regulated so that the amount of drink dispensed averages 240 milliliters with a standard deviation of 15 milliliters. Periodically, the machine is checked by taking a sample of 40 drinks and computing the average content. If the mean of the 40 drinks is a value within the interval $\mu_{\bar{X}} \pm 2\sigma_{\bar{X}}$, the machine is thought to be operating satisfactorily; otherwise, adjustments are made. In Section 3, the company official found the mean of 40 drinks to be $\bar{x} = 236$ milliliters and concluded that the machine needed no adjustment. Was this a reasonable decision?

22 The heights of 1000 students are approximately normally distributed with a mean of 174.5 centimeters and a standard deviation of 6.9 centimeters. Suppose 200 random samples of size 25 are drawn from this population and the means recorded to the nearest tenth of a centimeter. Determine

(a) the mean and standard deviation of the sampling distribution of $\bar{X}$;

(b) the number of sample means that fall between 172.5 and 175.8 centimeters inclusive;

(c) the number of sample means falling below 172.0 centimeters.

23 The random variable X, representing the number of cherries in a cherry puff, has the following probability distribution:

x	4	5	6	7
$P(X = x)$	0.2	0.4	0.3	0.1

(a) Find the mean μ and the variance σ^2 of X.

(b) Find the mean $\mu_{\bar{X}}$ and the variance $\sigma_{\bar{X}}^2$ of the mean $\bar{X}$ for random samples of 36 cherry puffs.

(c) Find the probability that the average number of cherries in 36 cherry puffs will be less than 5.5.

24 If a certain machine makes electrical resistors having a mean resistance of 40 ohms and a standard deviation of 2 ohms, what is the probability that a random sample of 36 of these resistors will have a combined resistance of more than 1458 ohms?

25 The average life of a bread-making machine is 7 years, with a standard deviation of 1 year. Assuming that the lives of these machines follow approximately a normal distribution, find

(a) the probability that the mean life of a random sample of 9 such machines falls between 6.4 and 7.2 years;

(b) the value of x to the right of which 15% of the means computed from random samples of size 9 would fall.

26 The amount of time that a drive-through bank teller spends on a customer is a random variable with a mean $\mu = 3.2$ minutes and a standard deviation $\sigma = 1.6$ minutes. If a random sample of 64 customers is observed, find the probability that their mean time at the teller's window is

(a) at most 2.7 minutes;

(b) more than 3.5 minutes;

(c) at least 3.2 minutes but less than 3.4 minutes.

27 In a chemical process, the amount of a certain type of impurity in the output is difficult to control and is thus a random variable. Speculation is that the population mean amount of the impurity is 0.20 gram per gram of output. It is known that the standard deviation is 0.1 gram per gram. An experiment is conducted to gain more insight regarding the speculation that $\mu = 0.2$. The process is run on a lab scale 50 times and the sample average $\bar{x}$ turns out to be 0.23 gram per gram. Comment on the speculation that the mean amount of impurity is 0.20 gram per gram. Make use of the Central Limit Theorem in your work.

28 A random sample of size 25 is taken from a normal population having a mean of 80 and a standard deviation of 5. A second random sample of size 36 is taken from a different normal population having a mean of 75 and a standard deviation of 3. Find the probability that the sample mean computed from the 25 measurements will exceed the sample mean computed from the 36 measurements by at least 3.4 but less than 5.9. Assume the difference of the means to be measured to the nearest tenth.

29 The distribution of heights of a certain breed of terrier has a mean of 72 centimeters and a standard deviation of 10 centimeters, whereas the distribution of heights of a certain breed of poodle has a mean of 28 centimeters with a standard deviation of 5 centimeters. Assuming that the sample means can be measured to any degree of accuracy, find the probability that the sample mean for a random sample of heights of 64 terriers exceeds the sample mean for a random sample of heights of 100 poodles by at most 44.2 centimeters.

30 The mean score for freshmen on an aptitude test at a certain college is 540, with a standard deviation of 50. Assume the means to be measured to any degree of accuracy. What is the probability that two groups selected at random, consisting of 32 and 50 students, respectively, will differ in their mean scores by

(a) more than 20 points?

(b) an amount between 5 and 10 points?

31 Consider Case Study 2. Suppose 18 specimens were used for each type of paint in an experiment and $\bar{x}_A - \bar{x}_B$, the actual difference in mean drying time, turned out to be 1.0.

(a) Does this seem to be a reasonable result if the

two population mean drying times truly are equal? Make use of the result in the solution to Case Study 8.2.

(b) If someone did the experiment 10,000 times under the condition that $\mu_A = \mu_B$, in how many of those 10,000 experiments would there be a difference $\bar{x}_A - \bar{x}_B$ that was as large as (or larger than) 1.0?

32 Two different box-filling machines are used to fill cereal boxes on an assembly line. The critical measurement influenced by these machines is the weight of the product in the boxes. Engineers are quite certain that the variance of the weight of product is $\sigma^2 = 1$ ounce. Experiments are conducted using both machines with sample sizes of 36 each. The sample averages for machines A and B are $\bar{x}_A = 4.5$ ounces and $\bar{x}_B = 4.7$ ounces. Engineers are surprised that the two sample averages for the filling machines are so different.

(a) Use the Central Limit Theorem to determine

$$P(\bar{X}_B - \bar{X}_A \geq 0.2)$$

under the condition that $\mu_A = \mu_B$.

(b) Do the aforementioned experiments seem to, in any way, strongly support a conjecture that the population means for the two machines are different? Explain using your answer in (a).

33 The chemical benzene is highly toxic to humans. However, it is used in the manufacture of many medicine dyes, leather, and coverings. Government regulations dictate that for any production process involving benzene, the water in the output of the process must not exceed 7950 parts per million (ppm) of benzene. For a particular process of concern, the water sample was collected by a manufacturer 25 times randomly and the sample average $\bar{x}$ was 7960 ppm. It is known from historical data that the standard deviation σ is 100 ppm.

(a) What is the probability that the sample average in this experiment would exceed the government limit if the population mean is equal to the limit? Use the Central Limit Theorem.

(b) Is an observed $\bar{x} = 7960$ in this experiment firm evidence that the population mean for the process

exceeds the government limit? Answer your question by computing

$$P(\bar{X} \geq 7960 \mid \mu = 7950).$$

Assume that the distribution of benzene concentration is normal.

34 Two alloys A and B are being used to manufacture a certain steel product. An experiment needs to be designed to compare the two in terms of maximum load capacity in tons (the maximum weight that can be tolerated without breaking). It is known that the two standard deviations in load capacity are equal at 5 tons each. An experiment is conducted in which 30 specimens of each alloy (A and B) are tested and the results recorded as follows:

$$\bar{x}_A = 49.5, \quad \bar{x}_B = 45.5; \quad \bar{x}_A - \bar{x}_B = 4.$$

The manufacturers of alloy A are convinced that this evidence shows conclusively that $\mu_A > \mu_B$ and strongly supports the claim that their alloy is superior. Manufacturers of alloy B claim that the experiment could easily have given $\bar{x}_A - \bar{x}_B = 4$ *even if* the two population means are equal. In other words, "the results are inconclusive!"

(a) Make an argument that manufacturers of alloy B are wrong. Do it by computing

$$P(\bar{X}_A - \bar{X}_B > 4 \mid \mu_A = \mu_B).$$

(b) Do you think these data strongly support alloy A?

35 Consider the situation described in Example 4. Do these results prompt you to question the premise that $\mu = 800$ hours? Give a probabilistic result that indicates how *rare* an event $\bar{X} \leq 775$ is when $\mu = 800$. On the other hand, how rare would it be if μ truly were, say, 760 hours?

36 Let $X_1, X_2, \ldots, X_n$ be a random sample from a distribution that can take on only positive values. Use the Central Limit Theorem to produce an argument that if n is sufficiently large, then $Y = X_1 X_2 \cdots X_n$ has approximately a lognormal distribution.

5   Sampling Distribution of S^2

In the preceding section we learned about the sampling distribution of $\bar{X}$. The Central Limit Theorem allowed us to make use of the fact that

$$\frac{\bar{X} - \mu}{\sigma/\sqrt{n}}$$

tends toward $N(0,1)$ as the sample size grows large. *Sampling distributions of important statistics* allow us to learn information about parameters. Usually, the parameters are the counterpart to the statistics in question. For example, if an engineer is interested in the population mean resistance of a certain type of resistor, the sampling distribution of $\bar{X}$ will be exploited once the sample information is gathered. On the other hand, if the variability in resistance is to be studied, clearly the sampling distribution of S^2 will be used in learning about the parametric counterpart, the population variance σ^2.

If a random sample of size n is drawn from a normal population with mean μ and variance σ^2, and the sample variance is computed, we obtain a value of the statistic S^2. We shall proceed to consider the distribution of the statistic $(n-1)S^2/\sigma^2$.

By the addition and subtraction of the sample mean $\bar{X}$, it is easy to see that

$$\sum_{i=1}^{n}(X_i - \mu)^2 = \sum_{i=1}^{n}[(X_i - \bar{X}) + (\bar{X} - \mu)]^2$$

$$= \sum_{i=1}^{n}(X_i - \bar{X})^2 + \sum_{i=1}^{n}(\bar{X} - \mu)^2 + 2(\bar{X} - \mu)\sum_{i=1}^{n}(X_i - \bar{X})$$

$$= \sum_{i=1}^{n}(X_i - \bar{X})^2 + n(\bar{X} - \mu)^2.$$

Dividing each term of the equality by σ^2 and substituting $(n-1)S^2$ for $\sum_{i=1}^{n}(X_i-\bar{X})^2$, we obtain

$$\frac{1}{\sigma^2}\sum_{i=1}^{n}(X_i - \mu)^2 = \frac{(n-1)S^2}{\sigma^2} + \frac{(\bar{X} - \mu)^2}{\sigma^2/n}.$$

Now, we know that

$$\sum_{i=1}^{n}\frac{(X_i - \mu)^2}{\sigma^2}$$

is a chi-squared random variable with n degrees of freedom. We have a chi-squared random variable with n degrees of freedom partitioned into two components. The second term on the right-hand side is Z^2, which is a chi-squared random variable 1 degree of freedom, and it turns out that $(n-1)S^2/\sigma^2$ is a chi-squared random variable with $n-1$ degree of freedom. We formalize this in the following theorem.

Theorem 4: If S^2 is the variance of a random sample of size n taken from a normal population having the variance σ^2, then the statistic

$$\chi^2 = \frac{(n-1)S^2}{\sigma^2} = \sum_{i=1}^{n}\frac{(X_i - \bar{X})^2}{\sigma^2}$$

has a chi-squared distribution with $v = n - 1$ degrees of freedom.

The values of the random variable χ^2 are calculated from each sample by the formula

$$\chi^2 = \frac{(n-1)s^2}{\sigma^2}.$$

The probability that a random sample produces a χ^2 value greater than some specified value is equal to the area under the curve to the right of this value. It is customary to let χ_α^2 represent the χ^2 value above which we find an area of α. This is illustrated by the shaded region in Figure 7.

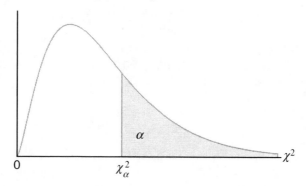

Figure 7: The chi-squared distribution.

Table Critical Values of the Chi-Squared Distribution at the end of this chapter gives values of χ_α^2 for various values of α and ν. The areas, α, are the column headings; the degrees of freedom, ν, are given in the left column; and the table entries are the χ^2 values. Hence, the χ^2 value with 7 degrees of freedom, leaving an area of 0.05 to the right, is $\chi_{0.05}^2 = 14.067$. Owing to lack of symmetry, we must also use the tables to find $\chi_{0.95}^2 = 2.167$ for $\nu = 7$.

Exactly 95% of a chi-squared distribution lies between $\chi_{0.975}^2$ and $\chi_{0.025}^2$. A χ^2 value falling to the right of $\chi_{0.025}^2$ is not likely to occur unless our assumed value of σ^2 is too small. Similarly, a χ^2 value falling to the left of $\chi_{0.975}^2$ is unlikely unless our assumed value of σ^2 is too large. In other words, it is possible to have a χ^2 value to the left of $\chi_{0.975}^2$ or to the right of $\chi_{0.025}^2$ when σ^2 is correct, but if this should occur, it is more probable that the assumed value of σ^2 is in error.

Example 7: A manufacturer of car batteries guarantees that the batteries will last, on average, 3 years with a standard deviation of 1 year. If five of these batteries have lifetimes of 1.9, 2.4, 3.0, 3.5, and 4.2 years, should the manufacturer still be convinced that the batteries have a standard deviation of 1 year? Assume that the battery lifetime follows a normal distribution.

Solution: We first find the sample variance using Theorem 1,

$$s^2 = \frac{(5)(48.26) - (15)^2}{(5)(4)} = 0.815.$$

Then

$$\chi^2 = \frac{(4)(0.815)}{1} = 3.26$$

is a value from a chi-squared distribution with 4 degrees of freedom. Since 95% of the χ^2 values with 4 degrees of freedom fall between 0.484 and 11.143, the computed value with $\sigma^2 = 1$ is reasonable, and therefore the manufacturer has no reason to suspect that the standard deviation is other than 1 year.

Degrees of Freedom as a Measure of Sample Information

Recall that

$$\sum_{i=1}^{n} \frac{(X_i - \mu)^2}{\sigma^2}$$

has a χ^2-distribution with *n degrees of freedom*. Note also Theorem 4, which indicates that the random variable

$$\frac{(n-1)S^2}{\sigma^2} = \sum_{i=1}^{n} \frac{(X_i - \bar{X})^2}{\sigma^2}$$

has a χ^2-distribution with $n-1$ *degrees of freedom*.

As we indicated earlier, the proof of Theorem 4 will not be given. However, the reader can view Theorem 4 as indicating that when μ is not known and one considers the distribution of

$$\sum_{i=1}^{n} \frac{(X_i - \bar{X})^2}{\sigma^2},$$

there is **1 less degree of freedom**, or a degree of freedom is lost in the estimation of μ (i.e., when μ is replaced by $\bar{x}$). In other words, there are n degrees of freedom, or independent *pieces of information*, in the random sample from the normal distribution. When the data (the values in the sample) are used to compute the mean, there is 1 less degree of freedom in the information used to estimate σ^2.

6   *t*-Distribution

In Section 4, we discussed the utility of the Central Limit Theorem. Its applications revolve around inferences on a population mean or the difference between two population means. Use of the Central Limit Theorem and the normal distribution is certainly helpful in this context. However, it was assumed that the population standard deviation is known. This assumption may not be unreasonable in situations where the engineer is quite familiar with the system or process. However, in many experimental scenarios, knowledge of σ is certainly no more reasonable than knowledge of the population mean μ. Often, in fact, an estimate of σ must be supplied by the same sample information that produced the sample average $\bar{x}$. As a result, a natural statistic to consider to deal with inferences on μ is

$$T = \frac{\bar{X} - \mu}{S/\sqrt{n}},$$

since S is the sample analog to σ. If the sample size is small, the values of S^2 fluctuate considerably from sample to sample (see Exercise 43) and the distribution of T deviates appreciably from that of a standard normal distribution.

If the sample size is large enough, say $n \geq 30$, the distribution of T does not differ considerably from the standard normal. However, for $n < 30$, it is useful to deal with the exact distribution of T. In developing the sampling distribution of T, we shall assume that our random sample was selected from a normal population. We can then write

$$T = \frac{(\bar{X} - \mu)/(\sigma/\sqrt{n})}{\sqrt{S^2/\sigma^2}} = \frac{Z}{\sqrt{V/(n-1)}},$$

where

$$Z = \frac{\bar{X} - \mu}{\sigma/\sqrt{n}}$$

has the standard normal distribution and

$$V = \frac{(n-1)S^2}{\sigma^2}$$

has a chi-squared distribution with $v = n - 1$ degrees of freedom. In sampling from normal populations, we can show that $\bar{X}$ and S^2 are independent, and consequently so are Z and V. The following theorem gives the definition of a random variable T as a function of Z (standard normal) and χ^2. For completeness, the density function of the t-distribution is given.

Theorem 5: Let Z be a standard normal random variable and V a chi-squared random variable with v degrees of freedom. If Z and V are independent, then the distribution of the random variable T, where

$$T = \frac{Z}{\sqrt{V/v}},$$

is given by the density function

$$h(t) = \frac{\Gamma[(v+1)/2]}{\Gamma(v/2)\sqrt{\pi v}} \left(1 + \frac{t^2}{v}\right)^{-(v+1)/2}, \quad -\infty < t < \infty.$$

This is known as the **t-distribution** with v degrees of freedom.

From the foregoing and the theorem above we have the following corollary.

Corollary 1:

Let $X_1, X_2, \ldots, X_n$ be independent random variables that are all normal with mean μ and standard deviation σ. Let

$$\bar{X} = \frac{1}{n} \sum_{i=1}^{n} X_i \quad \text{and} \quad S^2 = \frac{1}{n-1} \sum_{i=1}^{n} (X_i - \bar{X})^2.$$

Then the random variable $T = \frac{\bar{X} - \mu}{S/\sqrt{n}}$ has a t-distribution with $v = n - 1$ degrees of freedom.

The probability distribution of T was first published in 1908 in a paper written by W. S. Gosset. At the time, Gosset was employed by an Irish brewery that prohibited publication of research by members of its staff. To circumvent this restriction, he published his work secretly under the name "Student." Consequently, the distribution of T is usually called the Student t-distribution or simply the t-distribution. In deriving the equation of this distribution, Gosset assumed that the samples were selected from a normal population. Although this would seem to be a very restrictive assumption, it can be shown that nonnormal populations possessing nearly bell-shaped distributions will still provide values of T that approximate the t-distribution very closely.

What Does the *t*-Distribution Look Like?

The distribution of T is similar to the distribution of Z in that they both are symmetric about a mean of zero. Both distributions are bell shaped, but the t-distribution is more variable, owing to the fact that the T-values depend on the fluctuations of two quantities, $\bar{X}$ and S^2, whereas the Z-values depend only on the changes in $\bar{X}$ from sample to sample. The distribution of T differs from that of Z in that the variance of T depends on the sample size n and is always greater than 1. Only when the sample size $n \to \infty$ will the two distributions become the same. In Figure 8, we show the relationship between a standard normal distribution ($v = \infty$) and t-distributions with 2 and 5 degrees of freedom. The percentage points of the t-distribution are given in Table Critical Values of the t-Distribution.

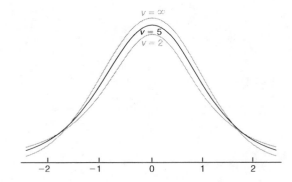

Figure 8: The t-distribution curves for $v = 2, 5$, and ∞.

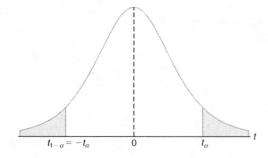

Figure 9: Symmetry property (about 0) of the t-distribution.

It is customary to let t_α represent the t-value above which we find an area equal to α. Hence, the t-value with 10 degrees of freedom leaving an area of 0.025 to the right is $t = 2.228$. Since the t-distribution is symmetric about a mean of zero, we have $t_{1-\alpha} = -t_\alpha$; that is, the t-value leaving an area of $1 - \alpha$ to the right and therefore an area of α to the left is equal to the negative t-value that leaves an area of α in the right tail of the distribution (see Figure 9). That is, $t_{0.95} = -t_{0.05}$, $t_{0.99} = -t_{0.01}$, and so forth.

Example 8: The t-value with $v = 14$ degrees of freedom that leaves an area of 0.025 to the left, and therefore an area of 0.975 to the right, is

$$t_{0.975} = -t_{0.025} = -2.145.$$

Example 9: Find $P(-t_{0.025} < T < t_{0.05})$.

Solution: Since $t_{0.05}$ leaves an area of 0.05 to the right, and $-t_{0.025}$ leaves an area of 0.025 to the left, we find a total area of

$$1 - 0.05 - 0.025 = 0.925$$

between $-t_{0.025}$ and $t_{0.05}$. Hence

$$P(-t_{0.025} < T < t_{0.05}) = 0.925.$$

Example 10: Find k such that $P(k < T < -1.761) = 0.045$ for a random sample of size 15 selected from a normal distribution and $\frac{\overline{X} - \mu}{s/\sqrt{n}}$.

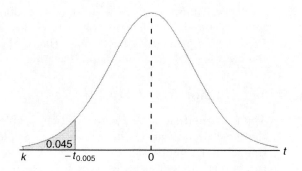

Figure 10: The t-values for Example 10.

Solution: From Table Critical Values of the t-Distribution we note that 1.761 corresponds to $t_{0.05}$ when $v = 14$. Therefore, $-t_{0.05} = -1.761$. Since k in the original probability statement is to the left of $-t_{0.05} = -1.761$, let $k = -t_\alpha$. Then, from Figure 10, we have

$$0.045 = 0.05 - \alpha, \text{ or } \alpha = 0.005.$$

Hence, from Table Critical Values of the t-Distribution with $v = 14$,
$$k = -t_{0.005} = -2.977 \text{ and } P(-2.977 < T < -1.761) = 0.045.$$

Exactly 95% of the values of a t-distribution with $\nu = n - 1$ degrees of freedom lie between $-t_{0.025}$ and $t_{0.025}$. Of course, there are other t-values that contain 95% of the distribution, such as $-t_{0.02}$ and $t_{0.03}$, but these values do not appear in Table Critical Values of the t-Distribution, and furthermore, the shortest possible interval is obtained by choosing t-values that leave exactly the same area in the two tails of our distribution. A t-value that falls below $-t_{0.025}$ or above $t_{0.025}$ would tend to make us believe either that a very rare event has taken place or that our assumption about μ is in error. Should this happen, we shall make the decision that our assumed value of μ is in error. In fact, a t-value falling below $-t_{0.01}$ or above $t_{0.01}$ would provide even stronger evidence that our assumed value of μ is quite unlikely. A preliminary look into the foundation of these procedures is illustrated by the following example.

Example 11: A chemical engineer claims that the population mean yield of a certain batch process is 500 grams per milliliter of raw material. To check this claim he samples 25 batches each month. If the computed t-value falls between $-t_{0.05}$ and $t_{0.05}$, he is satisfied with this claim. What conclusion should he draw from a sample that has a mean $\bar{x} = 518$ grams per milliliter and a sample standard deviation $s = 40$ grams? Assume the distribution of yields to be approximately normal.

Solution: From Table Critical Values of the t-Distribution we find that $t_{0.05} = 1.711$ for 24 degrees of freedom. Therefore, the engineer can be satisfied with his claim if a sample of 25 batches yields a t-value between -1.711 and 1.711. If $\mu = 500$, then

$$t = \frac{518 - 500}{40/\sqrt{25}} = 2.25,$$

a value well above 1.711. The probability of obtaining a t-value, with $\nu = 24$, equal to or greater than 2.25 is approximately 0.02. If $\mu > 500$, the value of t computed from the sample is more reasonable. Hence, the engineer is likely to conclude that the process produces a better product than he thought.

What Is the t-Distribution Used For?

The t-distribution is used extensively in problems that deal with inference about the population mean (as illustrated in Example 11) or in problems that involve comparative samples (i.e., in cases where one is trying to determine if means from two samples are significantly different). The reader should note that use of the t-distribution for the statistic

$$T = \frac{\bar{X} - \mu}{S/\sqrt{n}}$$

requires that $X_1, X_2, \ldots, X_n$ be normal. The use of the t-distribution and the sample size consideration do not relate to the Central Limit Theorem. The use of the standard normal distribution rather than T for $n \geq 30$ merely implies that S is a sufficiently good estimator of σ in this case. In chapters that follow the t-distribution finds extensive usage.

7   F-Distribution

We have motivated the t-distribution in part by its application to problems in which there is comparative sampling (i.e., a comparison between two sample means). For example, some of our examples in future chapters will take a more formal approach, chemical engineer collects data on two catalysts, biologist collects data on two growth media, or chemist gathers data on two methods of coating material to inhibit corrosion. While it is of interest to let sample information shed light on two population means, it is often the case that a comparison of variability is equally important, if not more so. The F-distribution finds enormous application in comparing sample variances. Applications of the F-distribution are found in problems involving two or more samples.

The statistic F is defined to be the ratio of two independent chi-squared random variables, each divided by its number of degrees of freedom. Hence, we can write

$$F = \frac{U/v_1}{V/v_2},$$

where U and V are independent random variables having chi-squared distributions with v_1 and v_2 degrees of freedom, respectively. We shall now state the sampling distribution of F.

Theorem 6:

Let U and V be two independent random variables having chi-squared distributions with v_1 and v_2 degrees of freedom, respectively. Then the distribution of the random variable $F = \frac{U/v_1}{V/v_2}$ is given by the density function

$$h(f) = \begin{cases} \frac{\Gamma[(v_1+v_2)/2](v_1/v_2)^{v_1/2}}{\Gamma(v_1/2)\Gamma(v_2/2)} \frac{f^{(v_1/2)-1}}{(1+v_1 f/v_2)^{(v_1+v_2)/2}}, & f > 0, \\ 0, & f \leq 0. \end{cases}$$

This is known as the **F-distribution** with v_1 and v_2 degrees of freedom (d.f.).

We will make considerable use of the random variable F in future chapters. However, the density function will not be used and is given only for completeness. The curve of the F-distribution depends not only on the two parameters v_1 and v_2 but also on the order in which we state them. Once these two values are given, we can identify the curve. Typical F-distributions are shown in Figure 11.

Let f_α be the f-value above which we find an area equal to α. This is illlustrated by the shaded region in Figure 12. Table Critical Values of the F-Distribution gives values of f_α only for $\alpha = 0.05$ and $\alpha = 0.01$ for various combinations of the degrees of freedom v_1 and v_2. Hence, the f-value with 6 and 10 degrees of freedom, leaving an area of 0.05 to the right, if $f_{0.05} = 3.22$. By means of the following theorem, Table Critical Values of the F-Distribution can also be used to find values of $f_{0.95}$ and $f_{0.99}$. The proof is left for the reader.

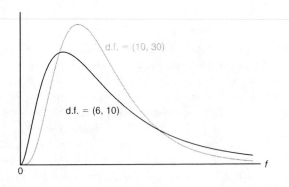

Figure 11: Typical F-distributions.

Figure 12: Illustration of the f_α for the F-distribution.

Theorem 7:

Writing $f_\alpha(v_1, v_2)$ for f_α with v_1 and v_2 degrees of freedom, we obtain

$$f_{1-\alpha}(v_1, v_2) = \frac{1}{f_\alpha(v_2, v_1)}.$$

Thus, the f-value with 6 and 10 degrees of freedom, leaving an area of 0.95 to the right, is

$$f_{0.95}(6, 10) = \frac{1}{f_{0.05}(10, 6)} = \frac{1}{4.06} = 0.246.$$

The F-Distribution with Two Sample Variances

Suppose that random samples of size n_1 and n_2 are selected from two normal populations with variances σ_1^2 and σ_2^2, respectively. From Theorem 4, we know that

$$\chi_1^2 = \frac{(n_1 - 1)S_1^2}{\sigma_1^2} \text{ and } \chi_2^2 = \frac{(n_2 - 1)S_2^2}{\sigma_2^2}$$

are random variables having chi-squared distributions with $v_1 = n_1 - 1$ and $v_2 = n_2 - 1$ degrees of freedom. Furthermore, since the samples are selected at random, we are dealing with independent random variables. Then, using Theorem 6 with $\chi_1^2 = U$ and $\chi_2^2 = V$, we obtain the following result.

Theorem 8:

If S_1^2 and S_2^2 are the variances of independent random samples of size n_1 and n_2 taken from normal populations with variances σ_1^2 and σ_2^2, respectively, then

$$F = \frac{S_1^2/\sigma_1^2}{S_2^2/\sigma_2^2} = \frac{\sigma_2^2 S_1^2}{\sigma_1^2 S_2^2}$$

has an F-distribution with $v_1 = n_1 - 1$ and $v_2 = n_2 - 1$ degrees of freedom.

What Is the *F*-Distribution Used For?

We answered this question, in part, at the beginning of this section. The *F*-distribution is used in two-sample situations to draw inferences about the population variances. This involves the application of Theorem 8. However, the *F*-distribution can also be applied to many other types of problems involving sample variances. In fact, the *F*-distribution is called the *variance ratio distribution*. As an illustration, consider Case Study 2, in which two paints, *A* and *B*, were compared with regard to mean drying time. The normal distribution applies nicely (assuming that σ_A and σ_B are known). However, suppose that there are three types of paints to compare, say *A*, *B*, and *C*. We wish to determine if the population means are equivalent. Suppose that important summary information from the experiment is as follows:

Paint	Sample Mean	Sample Variance	Sample Size
A	$\bar{X}_A = 4.5$	$s_A^2 = 0.20$	10
B	$\bar{X}_B = 5.5$	$s_B^2 = 0.14$	10
C	$\bar{X}_C = 6.5$	$s_C^2 = 0.11$	10

The problem centers around whether or not the sample averages ($\bar{x}_A$, $\bar{x}_B$, $\bar{x}_C$) are far enough apart. The implication of "far enough apart" is very important. It would seem reasonable that if the variability between sample averages is larger than what one would expect by chance, the data do not support the conclusion that $\mu_A = \mu_B = \mu_C$. Whether these sample averages could have occurred by chance depends on the *variability within samples*, as quantified by s_A^2, s_B^2, and s_C^2. The notion of the important components of variability is best seen through some simple graphics. Consider the plot of raw data from samples *A*, *B*, and *C*, shown in Figure 13. These data could easily have generated the above summary information.

Figure 13: Data from three distinct samples.

It appears evident that the data came from distributions with different population means, although there is some overlap between the samples. An analysis that involves all of the data would attempt to determine if the variability between the sample averages *and* the variability within the samples could have occurred jointly *if in fact the populations have a common mean*. Notice that the key to this analysis centers around the two following sources of variability.

(1) Variability within samples (between observations in distinct samples)

(2) Variability between samples (between sample averages)

Clearly, if the variability in (1) is considerably larger than that in (2), there will be considerable overlap in the sample data, a signal that the data could all have come from a common distribution. An example is found in the data set shown in Figure 14. On the other hand, it is very unlikely that data from distributions with a common mean could have variability between sample averages that is considerably larger than the variability within samples.

$$A \quad B\ C \quad A\ CB\ AC \quad CAB \quad C \quad ACBA \quad BABABCACBBABCC$$
$$\uparrow \quad \uparrow \quad \uparrow$$
$$\bar{x}_A \quad \bar{x}_C \quad \bar{x}_B$$

Figure 14: Data that easily could have come from the same population.

The sources of variability in (1) and (2) above generate important ratios of *sample variances*, and ratios are used in conjunction with the F-distribution. The general procedure involved is called **analysis of variance**. It is interesting that in the paint example described here, we are dealing with inferences on three population means, but two sources of variability are used.

8 Quantile and Probability Plots

We introduce the reader to empirical distributions. The motivation is to use creative displays to extract information about properties of a set of data. For example, stem-and-leaf plots provide the viewer with a look at symmetry and other properties of the data. In this chapter we deal with samples, which, of course, are collections of experimental data from which we draw conclusions about populations. Often the appearance of the sample provides information about the distribution from which the data are taken.

We often make the assumption that a distribution is normal. Graphical information regarding the validity of this assumption can be retrieved from displays like stem-and-leaf plots and frequency histograms. In addition, we will introduce the notion of *normal probability plots* and *quantile plots* in this section. These plots are used in studies that have varying degrees of complexity, with the main objective of the plots being to provide a diagnostic check on the assumption that the data came from a normal distribution.

We can characterize statistical analysis as the process of drawing conclusions about systems in the presence of system variability. For example, an engineer's attempt to learn about a chemical process is often clouded by *process variability*. A study involving the number of defective items in a production process is often made more difficult by variability in the method of manufacture of the items. In what has preceded, we have learned about samples and statistics that express center of location and variability in the sample. These statistics provide single measures, whereas a graphical display adds additional information through a picture.

One type of plot that can be particularly useful in characterizing the nature of a data set is the *quantile plot*. As in the case of the box-and-whisker plot one can use the basic ideas in the quantile plot to *compare samples of data*, where the goal of the analyst is to draw distinctions.

Quantile Plot

The purpose of the quantile plot is to depict, in sample form, the cumulative distribution function.

Definition 6: | A **quantile** of a sample, $q(f)$, is a value for which a specified fraction f of the data values is less than or equal to $q(f)$.

Obviously, a quantile represents an estimate of a characteristic of a population, or rather, the theoretical distribution. The sample median is $q(0.5)$. The 75th percentile (upper quartile) is $q(0.75)$ and the lower quartile is $q(0.25)$.

A **quantile plot** simply *plots the data values on the vertical axis against an empirical assessment of the fraction of observations exceeded by the data value.* For theoretical purposes, this fraction is computed as

$$f_i = \frac{i - \frac{3}{8}}{n + \frac{1}{4}},$$

where i is the order of the observations when they are ranked from low to high. In other words, if we denote the ranked observations as

$$y_{(1)} \leq y_{(2)} \leq y_{(3)} \leq \cdots \leq y_{(n-1)} \leq y_{(n)},$$

then the quantile plot depicts a plot of $y_{(i)}$ against f_i. In Figure 15, the quantile plot is given for the paint can ear data discussed previously.

Unlike the box-and-whisker plot, the quantile plot actually shows all observations. All quantiles, including the median and the upper and lower quantile, can be approximated visually. For example, we readily observe a median of 35 and an upper quartile of about 36. Relatively large clusters around specific values are indicated by slopes near zero, while sparse data in certain areas produce steeper slopes. Figure 15 depicts sparsity of data from the values 28 through 30 but relatively high density at 36 through 38.

It should be somewhat evident to the reader that detection of whether or not a data set came from a normal distribution can be an important tool for the data analyst. As we indicated earlier in this section, we often make the assumption that all or subsets of observations in a data set are realizations of independent identically distributed normal random variables. Once again, the diagnostic plot can often nicely augment (for display purposes) a formal *goodness-of-fit test* on the data. Readers of a scientific paper or report tend to find diagnostic information much clearer, less dry, and perhaps less boring than a formal analysis.

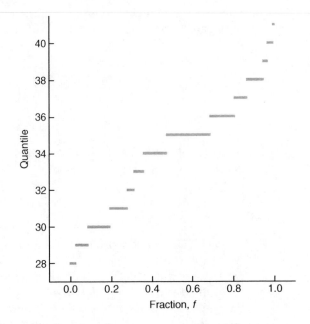

Figure 15: Quantile plot for paint data.

Quantile plots are useful in detection of distribution types. There are also situations in both model building and design of experiments in which the plots are used to detect important **model terms** or **effects** that are active. In other situations, they are used to determine whether or not the underlying assumptions made by the scientist or engineer in building the model are reasonable. The following subsection provides a discussion and illustration of a diagnostic plot called the *normal quantile-quantile plot*.

Normal Quantile-Quantile Plot

The normal quantile-quantile plot takes advantage of what is known about the quantiles of the normal distribution. The methodology involves a plot of the empirical quantiles recently discussed against the corresponding quantile of the normal distribution. Now, the expression for a quantile of an $N(\mu, \sigma)$ random variable is very complicated. However, a good approximation is given by

$$q_{\mu,\sigma}(f) = \mu + \sigma\{4.91[f^{0.14} - (1 - f)^{0.14}]\}.$$

The expression in braces (the multiple of σ) is the approximation for the corresponding quantile for the $N(0, 1)$ random variable, that is,

$$q_{0,1}(f) = 4.91[f^{0.14} - (1 - f)^{0.14}].$$

Definition 7:

> The **normal quantile-quantile plot** is a plot of $y_{(i)}$ (ordered observations) against $q_{0,1}(f_i)$, where $f_i = \frac{i - \frac{3}{8}}{n + \frac{1}{4}}$.

A nearly straight-line relationship suggests that the data came from a normal distribution. The intercept on the vertical axis is an estimate of the population mean μ and the slope is an estimate of the standard deviation σ. Figure 16 shows a normal quantile-quantile plot for the paint can data.

Figure 16: Normal quantile-quantile plot for paint data.

Normal Probability Plotting

Notice how the deviation from normality becomes clear from the appearance of the plot. The asymmetry exhibited in the data results in changes in the slope.

The ideas of probability plotting are manifested in plots other than the normal quantile-quantile plot discussed here. For example, much attention is given to the so-called **normal probability plot**, in which f is plotted against the ordered data values on special paper and the scale used results in a straight line. In addition, an alternative plot makes use of the expected values of the ranked observations for the normal distribution and plots the ranked observations against their expected value, under the assumption of data from $N(\mu, \sigma)$. Once again, the straight line is the graphical yardstick used. We continue to suggest that the foundation in graphical analytical methods developed in this section will aid in understanding formal methods of distinguishing between distinct samples of data.

Example 12: In a study "Nutrient Retention and Macro Invertebrate Community Response to Sewage Stress in a Stream Ecosystem," conducted in the Department of Zoology at the Virginia Polytechnic Institute and State University, data were collected on density measurements (number of organisms per square meter) at two different collecting stations. The data are given in Table 1.

Table 1: Data for Example 12

Number of Organisms per Square Meter			
Station 1		Station 2	
5,030	4,980	2,800	2,810
13,700	11,910	4,670	1,330
10,730	8,130	6,890	3,320
11,400	26,850	7,720	1,230
860	17,660	7,030	2,130
2,200	22,800	7,330	2,190
4,250	1,130		
15,040	1,690		

Construct a normal quantile-quantile plot and draw conclusions regarding whether or not it is reasonable to assume that the two samples are from the same $n(x; \mu, \sigma)$ distribution.

Figure 17: Normal quantile-quantile plot for density data of Example 12.

Solution: Figure 17 shows the normal quantile-quantile plot for the density measurements. The plot is far from a single straight line. In fact, the data from station 1 reflect a few values in the lower tail of the distribution and several in the upper tail. The "clustering" of observations would make it seem unlikely that the two samples came from a common $N(\mu, \sigma)$ distribution.

Although we have concentrated our development and illustration on probability plotting for the normal distribution, we could focus on any distribution. We would merely need to compute quantities analytically for the theoretical distribution in question.

Exercises

37 For a chi-squared distribution, find
(a) $\chi^2_{0.025}$ when $v = 15$;
(b) $\chi^2_{0.01}$ when $v = 7$;
(c) $\chi^2_{0.05}$ when $v = 24$.

38 For a chi-squared distribution, find
(a) $\chi^2_{0.005}$ when $v = 5$;
(b) $\chi^2_{0.05}$ when $v = 19$;
(c) $\chi^2_{0.01}$ when $v = 12$.

39 For a chi-squared distribution, find χ^2_α such that
(a) $P(X^2 > \chi^2_\alpha) = 0.99$ when $v = 4$;
(b) $P(X^2 > \chi^2_\alpha) = 0.025$ when $v = 19$;
(c) $P(37.652 < X^2 < \chi^2_\alpha) = 0.045$ when $v = 25$.

40 For a chi-squared distribution, find χ^2_α such that
(a) $P(X^2 > \chi^2_\alpha) = 0.01$ when $v = 21$;
(b) $P(X^2 < \chi^2_\alpha) = 0.95$ when $v = 6$;
(c) $P(\chi^2_\alpha < X^2 < 23.209) = 0.015$ when $v = 10$.

41 Assume the sample variances to be continuous measurements. Find the probability that a random sample of 25 observations, from a normal population with variance $\sigma^2 = 6$, will have a sample variance S^2
(a) greater than 9.1;
(b) between 3.462 and 10.745.

42 The scores on a placement test given to college freshmen for the past five years are approximately normally distributed with a mean $\mu = 74$ and a variance $\sigma^2 = 8$. Would you still consider $\sigma^2 = 8$ to be a valid value of the variance if a random sample of 20 students who take the placement test this year obtain a value of $s^2 = 20$?

43 Show that the variance of S^2 for random samples of size n from a normal population decreases as n becomes large. [*Hint*: First find the variance of $(n-1)S^2/\sigma^2$.]

44 (a) Find $t_{0.025}$ when $v = 14$.
(b) Find $-t_{0.10}$ when $v = 10$.
(c) Find $t_{0.995}$ when $v = 7$.

45 (a) Find $P(T < 2.365)$ when $v = 7$.
(b) Find $P(T > 1.318)$ when $v = 24$.
(c) Find $P(-1.356 < T < 2.179)$ when $v = 12$.
(d) Find $P(T > -2.567)$ when $v = 17$.

46 (a) Find $P(-t_{0.005} < T < t_{0.01})$ for $v = 20$.
(b) Find $P(T > -t_{0.025})$.

47 Given a random sample of size 24 from a normal distribution, find k such that
(a) $P(-2.069 < T < k) = 0.965$;
(b) $P(k < T < 2.807) = 0.095$;
(c) $P(-k < T < k) = 0.90$.

48 A manufacturing firm claims that the batteries used in their electronic games will last an average of 30 hours. To maintain this average, 16 batteries are tested each month. If the computed t-value falls between $-t_{0.025}$ and $t_{0.025}$, the firm is satisfied with its claim. What conclusion should the firm draw from a sample that has a mean of $\bar{x} = 27.5$ hours and a standard deviation of $s = 5$ hours? Assume the distribution of battery lives to be approximately normal.

49 A normal population with unknown variance has a mean of 20. Is one likely to obtain a random sample of size 9 from this population with a mean of 24 and a standard deviation of 4.1? If not, what conclusion would you draw?

50 A maker of a certain brand of low-fat cereal bars claims that the average saturated fat content is 0.5 gram. In a random sample of 8 cereal bars of this brand, the saturated fat content was 0.6, 0.7, 0.7, 0.3, 0.4, 0.5, 0.4, and 0.2. Would you agree with the claim? Assume a normal distribution.

51 For an F-distribution, find
(a) $f_{0.05}$ with $v_1 = 7$ and $v_2 = 15$;
(b) $f_{0.05}$ with $v_1 = 15$ and $v_2 = 7$:
(c) $f_{0.01}$ with $v_1 = 24$ and $v_2 = 19$;
(d) $f_{0.95}$ with $v_1 = 19$ and $v_2 = 24$;
(e) $f_{0.99}$ with $v_1 = 28$ and $v_2 = 12$.

52 Pull-strength tests on 10 soldered leads for a semiconductor device yield the following results, in pounds of force required to rupture the bond:

19.8	12.7	13.2	16.9	10.6
18.8	11.1	14.3	17.0	12.5

Another set of 8 leads was tested after encapsulation to determine whether the pull strength had been increased by encapsulation of the device, with the following results:

24.9 22.8 23.6 22.1 20.4 21.6 21.8 22.5

Comment on the evidence available concerning equality of the two population variances.

53 Consider the following measurements of the heat-producing capacity of the coal produced by two mines (in millions of calories per ton):

Mine 1: 8260 8130 8350 8070 8340
Mine 2: 7950 7890 7900 8140 7920 7840

Can it be concluded that the two population variances are equal?

54 Construct a quantile plot of these data, which represent the lifetimes, in hours, of fifty 40-watt, 110-volt internally frosted incandescent lamps taken from forced life tests:

919	1196	785	1126	936	918
1156	920	948	1067	1092	1162
1170	929	950	905	972	1035
1045	855	1195	1195	1340	1122
938	970	1237	956	1102	1157
978	832	1009	1157	1151	1009
765	958	902	1022	1333	811
1217	1085	896	958	1311	1037
702	923				

55 Construct a normal quantile-quantile plot of these data, which represent the diameters of 36 rivet heads in 1/100 of an inch:

6.72	6.77	6.82	6.70	6.78	6.70	6.62
6.75	6.66	6.66	6.64	6.76	6.73	6.80
6.72	6.76	6.76	6.68	6.66	6.62	6.72
6.76	6.70	6.78	6.76	6.67	6.70	6.72
6.74	6.81	6.79	6.78	6.66	6.76	6.76
6.72						

Review Exercises

56 Consider the data displayed in Exercise 20 Chapter **Introduction to Statistics and Data Analysis**. Construct a box-and-whisker plot and comment on the nature of the sample. Compute the sample mean and sample standard deviation.

57 If $X_1, X_2, \ldots, X_n$ are independent random variables having identical exponential distributions with parameter θ, show that the density function of the random variable $Y = X_1 + X_2 + \cdots + X_n$ is that of a gamma distribution with parameters $\alpha = n$ and $\beta = \theta$.

58 In testing for carbon monoxide in a certain brand of cigarette, the data, in milligrams per cigarette, were coded by subtracting 12 from each observation. Use the results of Exercise 14 to find the standard deviation for the carbon monoxide content of a random sample of 15 cigarettes of this brand if the coded measurements are 3.8, −0.9, 5.4, 4.5, 5.2, 5.6, 2.7, −0.1, −0.3, −1.7, 5.7, 3.3, 4.4, −0.5, and 1.9.

59 If S_1^2 and S_2^2 represent the variances of indepen-dent random samples of size $n_1 = 8$ and $n_2 = 12$, taken from normal populations with equal variances, find $P(S_1^2/S_2^2 < 4.89)$.

60 A random sample of 5 bank presidents indicated annual salaries of $395,000, $521,000, $483,000, $479,000, and $510,000. Find the variance of this set.

61 If the number of hurricanes that hit a certain area of the eastern United States per year is a random variable having a Poisson distribution with $\mu = 6$, find the probability that this area will be hit by
(a) exactly 15 hurricanes in 2 years;
(b) at most 9 hurricanes in 2 years.

62 A taxi company tests a random sample of 10 steel-belted radial tires of a certain brand and records the following tread wear: 48,000, 53,000, 45,000, 61,000, 59,000, 56,000, 63,000, 49,000, 53,000, and 54,000 kilometers. Use the results of Exercise 14 to find the standard deviation of this set of data by first dividing each observation by 1000 and then subtracting 55.

63 Consider the data of Exercise 19. Construct a box-and-whisker plot. Comment. Compute the sample mean and sample standard deviation.

64 If S_1^2 and S_2^2 represent the variances of independent random samples of size $n_1 = 25$ and $n_2 = 31$, taken from normal populations with variances $\sigma_1^2 = 10$ and $\sigma_2^2 = 15$, respectively, find

$$P(S_1^2/S_2^2 > 1.26).$$

65 Consider Example 5. Comment on any outliers.

66 Consider Review Exercise 56. Comment on any outliers in the data.

67 The breaking strength X of a certain rivet used in a machine engine has a mean 5000 psi and standard deviation 400 psi. A random sample of 36 rivets is taken. Consider the distribution of $\bar{X}$, the sample mean breaking strength.

(a) What is the probability that the sample mean falls between 4800 psi and 5200 psi?

(b) What sample n would be necessary in order to have

$$P(4900 < \bar{X} < 5100) = 0.99?$$

68 Consider the situation of Review Exercise 62. If the population from which the sample was taken has population mean $\mu = 53,000$ kilometers, does the sample information here seem to support that claim? In your answer, compute

$$t = \frac{\bar{x} - 53,000}{s/\sqrt{10}}$$

and determine from Table Critical Values of the t-Distribution (with 9 d.f.) whether the computed t-value is reasonable or appears to be a rare event.

69 Two distinct solid fuel propellants, type A and type B, are being considered for a space program activity. Burning rates of the propellant are crucial. Random samples of 20 specimens of the two propellants are taken with sample means 20.5 cm/sec for propellant A and 24.50 cm/sec for propellant B. It is generally assumed that the variability in burning rate is roughly the same for the two propellants and is given by a population standard deviation of 5 cm/sec. Assume that the burning rates for each propellant are approximately normal and hence make use of the Central Limit Theorem. Nothing is known about the two

population mean burning rates, and it is hoped that this experiment might shed some light on them.

(a) If, indeed, $\mu_A = \mu_B$, what is $P(\bar{X}_B - \bar{X}_A \geq 4.0)$?

(b) Use your answer in (a) to shed some light on the proposition that $\mu_A = \mu_B$.

70 The concentration of an active ingredient in the output of a chemical reaction is strongly influenced by the catalyst that is used in the reaction. It is felt that when catalyst A is used, the population mean concentration exceeds 65%. The standard deviation is known to be $\sigma = 5\%$. A sample of outputs from 30 independent experiments gives the average concentration of $\bar{x}_A = 64.5\%$.

(a) Does this sample information with an average concentration of $\bar{x}_A = 64.5\%$ provide disturbing information that perhaps μ_A is not 65%, but less than 65%? Support your answer with a probability statement.

(b) Suppose a similar experiment is done with the use of another catalyst, catalyst B. The standard deviation σ is still assumed to be 5% and $\bar{x}_B$ turns out to be 70%. Comment on whether or not the sample information on catalyst B strongly suggests that μ_B is truly greater than μ_A. Support your answer by computing

$$P(\bar{X}_B - \bar{X}_A \geq 5.5 \mid \mu_B = \mu_A).$$

(c) Under the condition that $\mu_A = \mu_B = 65\%$, give the approximate distribution of the following quantities (with mean and variance of each). Make use of the Central Limit Theorem.
  i) $\bar{X}_B$;
  ii) $\bar{X}_A - \bar{X}_B$;
  iii) $\frac{\bar{X}_A - \bar{X}_B}{\sigma\sqrt{2/30}}$.

71 From the information in Review Exercise 70, compute (assuming $\mu_B = 65\%$) $P(\bar{X}_B \geq 70)$.

72 Given a normal random variable X with mean 20 and variance 9, and a random sample of size n taken from the distribution, what sample size n is necessary in order that

$$P(19.9 \leq \bar{X} \leq 20.1) = 0.95?$$

73 Suppose X is a random variable with mean μ and variance $\sigma^2 = 1.0$. Suppose also that a random sample of size n is to be taken and $\bar{x}$ is to be used as an *estmate of* μ. When the data are taken and the sample mean is measured, we wish it to be within 0.05 unit of the true mean with probability 0.99. That is, we want there to be a good chance that the computed $\bar{x}$ from the sample is "very close" to the population mean (wherever it is!), so we wish

$$P(|\bar{X} - \mu| > 0.05) = 0.99.$$

What sample size is required?

74 Suppose a filling machine is used to fill cartons with a liquid product. The specification that is strictly enforced for the filling machine is 9 ± 1.5 oz. If any carton is produced with weight outside these bounds, it is considered by the supplier to be defective. It is hoped that at least 99% of cartons will meet these specifications. With the conditions $\mu = 9$ and $\sigma = 1$, what proportion of cartons from the process are defective? If changes are made to reduce variability, what must σ be reduced to in order to meet specifications with probability 0.99? Assume a normal distribution for the weight.

75 Consider the situation in Review Exercise 74. Suppose a considerable effort is conducted to "tighten" the variability in the system. Following the effort, a random sample of size 40 is taken from the new assembly line and the sample variance is $s^2 = 0.188$ ounces^2.

Do we have strong numerical evidence that σ^2 has been reduced below 1.0? Consider the probability

$$P(S^2 \le 0.188 \mid \sigma^2 = 1.0),$$

and give your conclusion.

76 **Group Project**: The class should be divided into groups of four people. The four students in each group should go to the college gym or a local fitness center. The students should ask each person who comes through the door his or her height in inches. Each group will then divide the height data by gender and work together to answer the following questions.

(a) Construct a normal quantile-quantile plot of the data. Based on the plot, do the data appear to follow a normal distribution?

(b) Use the estimated sample variance as the true variance for each gender. Assume that the population mean height for male students is actually three inches larger than that of female students. What is the probability that the average height of the male students will be 4 inches larger than that of the female students in your sample?

(c) What factors could render these results misleading?

9 Potential Misconceptions and Hazards; Relationship to Material in Other Chapters

The Central Limit Theorem is one of the most powerful tools in all of statistics, and even though this chapter is relatively short, it contains a wealth of fundamental information about tools that can be used.

The notion of a sampling distribution is one of the most important fundamental concepts in all of statistics, and the student at this point in his or her training should gain a clear understanding of it before proceeding beyond this chapter. Suppose one wants to use the statistic $\bar{X}$ to draw inferences about the population mean μ. This will be done by using the observed value $\bar{x}$ from a single sample of size n. Then any inference made must be accomplished by taking into account not just the single value but rather the theoretical structure, or **distribution of all $\bar{x}$ values that could be observed from samples of size n.** Thus, the concept of a *sampling distribution* comes to the surface. This distribution is the basis for the Central Limit Theorem. The t, χ^2, and F-distributions are also used in the context of sampling distributions. For example, the t-distribution, pictured in Figure 8, represents the structure that occurs if all of the values of $\frac{\bar{x} - \mu}{s/\sqrt{n}}$ are formed, where $\bar{x}$ and s are taken from samples of size n from a $n(x; \mu, \sigma)$ distribution. Similar remarks can be made about χ^2 and F, and the reader should not forget that the sample information forming the statistics for all of these distributions is the normal. So it can be said that **where there is a t, F, or χ^2, the source was a sample from a normal distribution.**

The three distributions described above may appear to have been introduced in a rather self-contained fashion with no indication of what they are about. However, they will appear in practical problem-solving throughout the balance of the text.

Now, there are three things that one must bear in mind, lest confusion set in regarding these fundamental sampling distributions:

(i) One cannot use the Central Limit Theorem unless σ is known. When σ is not known, it should be replaced by s, the sample standard deviation, in order to use the Central Limit Theorem.

(ii) The T statistic is **not** a result of the Central Limit Theorem and $x_1, x_2, \ldots, x_n$ must come from a $n(x; \mu, \sigma)$ distribution in order for $\frac{\bar{x}-\mu}{s/\sqrt{n}}$ to be a t-distribution; s is, of course, merely an estimate of σ.

(iii) While the notion of **degrees of freedom** is new at this point, the concept should be very intuitive, since it is reasonable that the nature of the distribution of S and also t should depend on the amount of information in the sample $x_1, x_2, \ldots, x_n$.

Answers to Odd-Numbered Non-Review Exercises

1 (a) Responses of all people in Richmond who have a telephone;
   (b) Outcomes for a large or infinite number of tosses of a coin;
   (c) Length of life of such tennis shoes when worn on the professional tour;
   (d) All possible time intervals for this lawyer to drive from her home to her office.

3 (a) $\bar{x} = 3.2$ seconds; (b) $\tilde{x} = 3.1$ seconds

5 (a) $\bar{x} = 2.4$; (b) $\tilde{x} = 2$; (c) $m = 3$

7 (a) 53.75; (b) 75 and 100

9 (a) Range is 10; (b) $s = 3.307$

11 (a) 2.971; (b) 2.971

13 $s = 0.585$

15 (a) 45.9; (b) 5.1

17 0.3159

19 (a) Variance is reduced from 0.49 to 0.16.
    (b) Variance is increased from 0.04 to 0.64.

21 Yes

23 (a) $\mu = 5.3$; $\sigma^2 = 0.81$;
    (b) $\mu_{\bar{X}} = 5.3$; $\sigma_{\bar{X}}^2 = 0.0225$;
    (c) 0.9082

25 (a) 0.6898; (b) 7.35

29 0.5596

31 (a) The chance that the difference in mean drying time is larger than 1.0 is 0.0013; (b) 13

33 (a) 1/2; (b) 0.3085

35 $P(\bar{X} \leq 775 \mid \mu = 760) = 0.9332$

37 (a) 27.488; (b) 18.475; (c) 36.415

39 (a) 0.297; (b) 32.852; (c) 46.928

41 (a) 0.05; (b) 0.94

45 (a) 0.975; (b) 0.10; (c) 0.875; (d) 0.99

47 (a) 2.500; (b) 1.319; (c) 1.714

49 No; $\mu > 20$

51 (a) 2.71; (b) 3.51; (c) 2.92;
    (d) 0.47; (e) 0.34

53 The F-ratio is 1.44. The variances are not significantly different.

Table Critical Values of the Chi-Squared Distribution

					α					
v	0.995	0.99	0.98	0.975	0.95	0.90	0.80	0.75	0.70	0.50
1	0.0^4393	0.0^3157	0.0^3628	0.0^3982	0.00393	0.0158	0.0642	0.102	0.148	0.455
2	0.0100	0.0201	0.0404	0.0506	0.103	0.211	0.446	0.575	0.713	1.386
3	0.0717	0.115	0.185	0.216	0.352	0.584	1.005	1.213	1.424	2.366
4	0.207	0.297	0.429	0.484	0.711	1.064	1.649	1.923	2.195	3.357
5	0.412	0.554	0.752	0.831	1.145	1.610	2.343	2.675	3.000	4.351
6	0.676	0.872	1.134	1.237	1.635	2.204	3.070	3.455	3.828	5.348
7	0.989	1.239	1.564	1.690	2.167	2.833	3.822	4.255	4.671	6.346
8	1.344	1.647	2.032	2.180	2.733	3.490	4.594	5.071	5.527	7.344
9	1.735	2.088	2.532	2.700	3.325	4.168	5.380	5.899	6.393	8.343
10	2.156	2.558	3.059	3.247	3.940	4.865	6.179	6.737	7.267	9.342
11	2.603	3.053	3.609	3.816	4.575	5.578	6.989	7.584	8.148	10.341
12	3.074	3.571	4.178	4.404	5.226	6.304	7.807	8.438	9.034	11.340
13	3.565	4.107	4.765	5.009	5.892	7.041	8.634	9.299	9.926	12.340
14	4.075	4.660	5.368	5.629	6.571	7.790	9.467	10.165	10.821	13.339
15	4.601	5.229	5.985	6.262	7.261	8.547	10.307	11.037	11.721	14.339
16	5.142	5.812	6.614	6.908	7.962	9.312	11.152	11.912	12.624	15.338
17	5.697	6.408	7.255	7.564	8.672	10.085	12.002	12.792	13.531	16.338
18	6.265	7.015	7.906	8.231	9.390	10.865	12.857	13.675	14.440	17.338
19	6.844	7.633	8.567	8.907	10.117	11.651	13.716	14.562	15.352	18.338
20	7.434	8.260	9.237	9.591	10.851	12.443	14.578	15.452	16.266	19.337
21	8.034	8.897	9.915	10.283	11.591	13.240	15.445	16.344	17.182	20.337
22	8.643	9.542	10.600	10.982	12.338	14.041	16.314	17.240	18.101	21.337
23	9.260	10.196	11.293	11.689	13.091	14.848	17.187	18.137	19.021	22.337
24	9.886	10.856	11.992	12.401	13.848	15.659	18.062	19.037	19.943	23.337
25	10.520	11.524	12.697	13.120	14.611	16.473	18.940	19.939	20.867	24.337
26	11.160	12.198	13.409	13.844	15.379	17.292	19.820	20.843	21.792	25.336
27	11.808	12.878	14.125	14.573	16.151	18.114	20.703	21.749	22.719	26.336
28	12.461	13.565	14.847	15.308	16.928	18.939	21.588	22.657	23.647	27.336
29	13.121	14.256	15.574	16.047	17.708	19.768	22.475	23.567	24.577	28.336
30	13.787	14.953	16.306	16.791	18.493	20.599	23.364	24.478	25.508	29.336
40	20.707	22.164	23.838	24.433	26.509	29.051	32.345	33.66	34.872	39.335
50	27.991	29.707	31.664	32.357	34.764	37.689	41.449	42.942	44.313	49.335
60	35.534	37.485	39.699	40.482	43.188	46.459	50.641	52.294	53.809	59.335

Table (continued) Critical Values of the Chi-Squared Distribution

v	α									
	0.30	0.25	0.20	0.10	0.05	0.025	0.02	0.01	0.005	0.001
1	1.074	1.323	1.642	2.706	3.841	5.024	5.412	6.635	7.879	10.827
2	2.408	2.773	3.219	4.605	5.991	7.378	7.824	9.210	10.597	13.815
3	3.665	4.108	4.642	6.251	7.815	9.348	9.837	11.345	12.838	16.266
4	4.878	5.385	5.989	7.779	9.488	11.143	11.668	13.277	14.860	18.466
5	6.064	6.626	7.289	9.236	11.070	12.832	13.388	15.086	16.750	20.515
6	7.231	7.841	8.558	10.645	12.592	14.449	15.033	16.812	18.548	22.457
7	8.383	9.037	9.803	12.017	14.067	16.013	16.622	18.475	20.278	24.321
8	9.524	10.219	11.030	13.362	15.507	17.535	18.168	20.090	21.955	26.124
9	10.656	11.389	12.242	14.684	16.919	19.023	19.679	21.666	23.589	27.877
10	11.781	12.549	13.442	15.987	18.307	20.483	21.161	23.209	25.188	29.588
11	12.899	13.701	14.631	17.275	19.675	21.920	22.618	24.725	26.757	31.264
12	14.011	14.845	15.812	18.549	21.026	23.337	24.054	26.217	28.300	32.909
13	15.119	15.984	16.985	19.812	22.362	24.736	25.471	27.688	29.819	34.527
14	16.222	17.117	18.151	21.064	23.685	26.119	26.873	29.141	31.319	36.124
15	17.322	18.245	19.311	22.307	24.996	27.488	28.259	30.578	32.801	37.698
16	18.418	19.369	20.465	23.542	26.296	28.845	29.633	32.000	34.267	39.252
17	19.511	20.489	21.615	24.769	27.587	30.191	30.995	33.409	35.718	40.791
18	20.601	21.605	22.760	25.989	28.869	31.526	32.346	34.805	37.156	42.312
19	21.689	22.718	23.900	27.204	30.144	32.852	33.687	36.191	38.582	43.819
20	22.775	23.828	25.038	28.412	31.410	34.170	35.020	37.566	39.997	45.314
21	23.858	24.935	26.171	29.615	32.671	35.479	36.343	38.932	41.401	46.796
22	24.939	26.039	27.301	30.813	33.924	36.781	37.659	40.289	42.796	48.268
23	26.018	27.141	28.429	32.007	35.172	38.076	38.968	41.638	44.181	49.728
24	27.096	28.241	29.553	33.196	36.415	39.364	40.270	42.980	45.558	51.179
25	28.172	29.339	30.675	34.382	37.652	40.646	41.566	44.314	46.928	52.619
26	29.246	30.435	31.795	35.563	38.885	41.923	42.856	45.642	48.290	54.051
27	30.319	31.528	32.912	36.741	40.113	43.195	44.140	46.963	49.645	55.475
28	31.391	32.620	34.027	37.916	41.337	44.461	45.419	48.278	50.994	56.892
29	32.461	33.711	35.139	39.087	42.557	45.722	46.693	49.588	52.335	58.301
30	33.530	34.800	36.250	40.256	43.773	46.979	47.962	50.892	53.672	59.702
40	44.165	45.616	47.269	51.805	55.758	59.342	60.436	63.691	66.766	73.403
50	54.723	56.334	58.164	63.167	67.505	71.420	72.613	76.154	79.490	86.660
60	65.226	66.981	68.972	74.397	79.082	83.298	84.58	88.379	91.952	99.608

Table Critical Values of the *t*-Distribution

				α			
v	0.40	0.30	0.20	0.15	0.10	0.05	0.025
1	0.325	0.727	1.376	1.963	3.078	6.314	12.706
2	0.289	0.617	1.061	1.386	1.886	2.920	4.303
3	0.277	0.584	0.978	1.250	1.638	2.353	3.182
4	0.271	0.569	0.941	1.190	1.533	2.132	2.776
5	0.267	0.559	0.920	1.156	1.476	2.015	2.571
6	0.265	0.553	0.906	1.134	1.440	1.943	2.447
7	0.263	0.549	0.896	1.119	1.415	1.895	2.365
8	0.262	0.546	0.889	1.108	1.397	1.860	2.306
9	0.261	0.543	0.883	1.100	1.383	1.833	2.262
10	0.260	0.542	0.879	1.093	1.372	1.812	2.228
11	0.260	0.540	0.876	1.088	1.363	1.796	2.201
12	0.259	0.539	0.873	1.083	1.356	1.782	2.179
13	0.259	0.538	0.870	1.079	1.350	1.771	2.160
14	0.258	0.537	0.868	1.076	1.345	1.761	2.145
15	0.258	0.536	0.866	1.074	1.341	1.753	2.131
16	0.258	0.535	0.865	1.071	1.337	1.746	2.120
17	0.257	0.534	0.863	1.069	1.333	1.740	2.110
18	0.257	0.534	0.862	1.067	1.330	1.734	2.101
19	0.257	0.533	0.861	1.066	1.328	1.729	2.093
20	0.257	0.533	0.860	1.064	1.325	1.725	2.086
21	0.257	0.532	0.859	1.063	1.323	1.721	2.080
22	0.256	0.532	0.858	1.061	1.321	1.717	2.074
23	0.256	0.532	0.858	1.060	1.319	1.714	2.069
24	0.256	0.531	0.857	1.059	1.318	1.711	2.064
25	0.256	0.531	0.856	1.058	1.316	1.708	2.060
26	0.256	0.531	0.856	1.058	1.315	1.706	2.056
27	0.256	0.531	0.855	1.057	1.314	1.703	2.052
28	0.256	0.530	0.855	1.056	1.313	1.701	2.048
29	0.256	0.530	0.854	1.055	1.311	1.699	2.045
30	0.256	0.530	0.854	1.055	1.310	1.697	2.042
40	0.255	0.529	0.851	1.050	1.303	1.684	2.021
60	0.254	0.527	0.848	1.045	1.296	1.671	2.000
120	0.254	0.526	0.845	1.041	1.289	1.658	1.980
∞	0.253	0.524	0.842	1.036	1.282	1.645	1.960

Table (continued) Critical Values of the *t*-Distribution

	α						
v	0.02	0.015	0.01	0.0075	0.005	0.0025	0.0005
1	15.894	21.205	31.821	42.433	63.656	127.321	636.578
2	4.849	5.643	6.965	8.073	9.925	14.089	31.600
3	3.482	3.896	4.541	5.047	5.841	7.453	12.924
4	2.999	3.298	3.747	4.088	4.604	5.598	8.610
5	2.757	3.003	3.365	3.634	4.032	4.773	6.869
6	2.612	2.829	3.143	3.372	3.707	4.317	5.959
7	2.517	2.715	2.998	3.203	3.499	4.029	5.408
8	2.449	2.634	2.896	3.085	3.355	3.833	5.041
9	2.398	2.574	2.821	2.998	3.250	3.690	4.781
10	2.359	2.527	2.764	2.932	3.169	3.581	4.587
11	2.328	2.491	2.718	2.879	3.106	3.497	4.437
12	2.303	2.461	2.681	2.836	3.055	3.428	4.318
13	2.282	2.436	2.650	2.801	3.012	3.372	4.221
14	2.264	2.415	2.624	2.771	2.977	3.326	4.140
15	2.249	2.397	2.602	2.746	2.947	3.286	4.073
16	2.235	2.382	2.583	2.724	2.921	3.252	4.015
17	2.224	2.368	2.567	2.706	2.898	3.222	3.965
18	2.214	2.356	2.552	2.689	2.878	3.197	3.922
19	2.205	2.346	2.539	2.674	2.861	3.174	3.883
20	2.197	2.336	2.528	2.661	2.845	3.153	3.850
21	2.189	2.328	2.518	2.649	2.831	3.135	3.819
22	2.183	2.320	2.508	2.639	2.819	3.119	3.792
23	2.177	2.313	2.500	2.629	2.807	3.104	3.768
24	2.172	2.307	2.492	2.620	2.797	3.091	3.745
25	2.167	2.301	2.485	2.612	2.787	3.078	3.725
26	2.162	2.296	2.479	2.605	2.779	3.067	3.707
27	2.158	2.291	2.473	2.598	2.771	3.057	3.689
28	2.154	2.286	2.467	2.592	2.763	3.047	3.674
29	2.150	2.282	2.462	2.586	2.756	3.038	3.660
30	2.147	2.278	2.457	2.581	2.750	3.030	3.646
40	2.123	2.250	2.423	2.542	2.704	2.971	3.551
60	2.099	2.223	2.390	2.504	2.660	2.915	3.460
120	2.076	2.196	2.358	2.468	2.617	2.860	3.373
∞	2.054	2.170	2.326	2.432	2.576	2.807	3.290

$$f_{0.05}(v_1, v_2)$$

v_2	v_1								
	1	**2**	**3**	**4**	**5**	**6**	**7**	**8**	**9**
1	161.45	199.50	215.71	224.58	230.16	233.99	236.77	238.88	240.54
2	18.51	19.00	19.16	19.25	19.30	19.33	19.35	19.37	19.38
3	10.13	9.55	9.28	9.12	9.01	8.94	8.89	8.85	8.81
4	7.71	6.94	6.59	6.39	6.26	6.16	6.09	6.04	6.00
5	6.61	5.79	5.41	5.19	5.05	4.95	4.88	4.82	4.77
6	5.99	5.14	4.76	4.53	4.39	4.28	4.21	4.15	4.10
7	5.59	4.74	4.35	4.12	3.97	3.87	3.79	3.73	3.68
8	5.32	4.46	4.07	3.84	3.69	3.58	3.50	3.44	3.39
9	5.12	4.26	3.86	3.63	3.48	3.37	3.29	3.23	3.18
10	4.96	4.10	3.71	3.48	3.33	3.22	3.14	3.07	3.02
11	4.84	3.98	3.59	3.36	3.20	3.09	3.01	2.95	2.90
12	4.75	3.89	3.49	3.26	3.11	3.00	2.91	2.85	2.80
13	4.67	3.81	3.41	3.18	3.03	2.92	2.83	2.77	2.71
14	4.60	3.74	3.34	3.11	2.96	2.85	2.76	2.70	2.65
15	4.54	3.68	3.29	3.06	2.90	2.79	2.71	2.64	2.59
16	4.49	3.63	3.24	3.01	2.85	2.74	2.66	2.59	2.54
17	4.45	3.59	3.20	2.96	2.81	2.70	2.61	2.55	2.49
18	4.41	3.55	3.16	2.93	2.77	2.66	2.58	2.51	2.46
19	4.38	3.52	3.13	2.90	2.74	2.63	2.54	2.48	2.42
20	4.35	3.49	3.10	2.87	2.71	2.60	2.51	2.45	2.39
21	4.32	3.47	3.07	2.84	2.68	2.57	2.49	2.42	2.37
22	4.30	3.44	3.05	2.82	2.66	2.55	2.46	2.40	2.34
23	4.28	3.42	3.03	2.80	2.64	2.53	2.44	2.37	2.32
24	4.26	3.40	3.01	2.78	2.62	2.51	2.42	2.36	2.30
25	4.24	3.39	2.99	2.76	2.60	2.49	2.40	2.34	2.28
26	4.23	3.37	2.98	2.74	2.59	2.47	2.39	2.32	2.27
27	4.21	3.35	2.96	2.73	2.57	2.46	2.37	2.31	2.25
28	4.20	3.34	2.95	2.71	2.56	2.45	2.36	2.29	2.24
29	4.18	3.33	2.93	2.70	2.55	2.43	2.35	2.28	2.22
30	4.17	3.32	2.92	2.69	2.53	2.42	2.33	2.27	2.21
40	4.08	3.23	2.84	2.61	2.45	2.34	2.25	2.18	2.12
60	4.00	3.15	2.76	2.53	2.37	2.25	2.17	2.10	2.04
120	3.92	3.07	2.68	2.45	2.29	2.18	2.09	2.02	1.96
∞	3.84	3.00	2.60	2.37	2.21	2.10	2.01	1.94	1.88

Table (continued) Critical Values of the *F*-Distribution

					$f_{0.05}(v_1, v_2)$					
					v_1					
v_2	10	12	15	20	24	30	40	60	120	∞
1	241.88	243.91	245.95	248.01	249.05	250.10	251.14	252.20	253.25	254.31
2	19.40	19.41	19.43	19.45	19.45	19.46	19.47	19.48	19.49	19.50
3	8.79	8.74	8.70	8.66	8.64	8.62	8.59	8.57	8.55	8.53
4	5.96	5.91	5.86	5.80	5.77	5.75	5.72	5.69	5.66	5.63
5	4.74	4.68	4.62	4.56	4.53	4.50	4.46	4.43	4.40	4.36
6	4.06	4.00	3.94	3.87	3.84	3.81	3.77	3.74	3.70	3.67
7	3.64	3.57	3.51	3.44	3.41	3.38	3.34	3.30	3.27	3.23
8	3.35	3.28	3.22	3.15	3.12	3.08	3.04	3.01	2.97	2.93
9	3.14	3.07	3.01	2.94	2.90	2.86	2.83	2.79	2.75	2.71
10	2.98	2.91	2.85	2.77	2.74	2.70	2.66	2.62	2.58	2.54
11	2.85	2.79	2.72	2.65	2.61	2.57	2.53	2.49	2.45	2.40
12	2.75	2.69	2.62	2.54	2.51	2.47	2.43	2.38	2.34	2.30
13	2.67	2.60	2.53	2.46	2.42	2.38	2.34	2.30	2.25	2.21
14	2.60	2.53	2.46	2.39	2.35	2.31	2.27	2.22	2.18	2.13
15	2.54	2.48	2.40	2.33	2.29	2.25	2.20	2.16	2.11	2.07
16	2.49	2.42	2.35	2.28	2.24	2.19	2.15	2.11	2.06	2.01
17	2.45	2.38	2.31	2.23	2.19	2.15	2.10	2.06	2.01	1.96
18	2.41	2.34	2.27	2.19	2.15	2.11	2.06	2.02	1.97	1.92
19	2.38	2.31	2.23	2.16	2.11	2.07	2.03	1.98	1.93	1.88
20	2.35	2.28	2.20	2.12	2.08	2.04	1.99	1.95	1.90	1.84
21	2.32	2.25	2.18	2.10	2.05	2.01	1.96	1.92	1.87	1.81
22	2.30	2.23	2.15	2.07	2.03	1.98	1.94	1.89	1.84	1.78
23	2.27	2.20	2.13	2.05	2.01	1.96	1.91	1.86	1.81	1.76
24	2.25	2.18	2.11	2.03	1.98	1.94	1.89	1.84	1.79	1.73
25	2.24	2.16	2.09	2.01	1.96	1.92	1.87	1.82	1.77	1.71
26	2.22	2.15	2.07	1.99	1.95	1.90	1.85	1.80	1.75	1.69
27	2.20	2.13	2.06	1.97	1.93	1.88	1.84	1.79	1.73	1.67
28	2.19	2.12	2.04	1.96	1.91	1.87	1.82	1.77	1.71	1.65
29	2.18	2.10	2.03	1.94	1.90	1.85	1.81	1.75	1.70	1.64
30	2.16	2.09	2.01	1.93	1.89	1.84	1.79	1.74	1.68	1.62
40	2.08	2.00	1.92	1.84	1.79	1.74	1.69	1.64	1.58	1.51
60	1.99	1.92	1.84	1.75	1.70	1.65	1.59	1.53	1.47	1.39
120	1.91	1.83	1.75	1.66	1.61	1.55	1.50	1.43	1.35	1.25
∞	1.83	1.75	1.67	1.57	1.52	1.46	1.39	1.32	1.22	1.00

Table (continued) Critical Values of the F-Distribution

$$f_{0.01}(v_1, v_2)$$

v_2	v_1								
	1	2	3	4	5	6	7	8	9
1	4052.18	4999.50	5403.35	5624.58	5763.65	5858.99	5928.36	5981.07	6022.47
2	98.50	99.00	99.17	99.25	99.30	99.33	99.36	99.37	99.39
3	34.12	30.82	29.46	28.71	28.24	27.91	27.67	27.49	27.35
4	21.20	18.00	16.69	15.98	15.52	15.21	14.98	14.80	14.66
5	16.26	13.27	12.06	11.39	10.97	10.67	10.46	10.29	10.16
6	13.75	10.92	9.78	9.15	8.75	8.47	8.26	8.10	7.98
7	12.25	9.55	8.45	7.85	7.46	7.19	6.99	6.84	6.72
8	11.26	8.65	7.59	7.01	6.63	6.37	6.18	6.03	5.91
9	10.56	8.02	6.99	6.42	6.06	5.80	5.61	5.47	5.35
10	10.04	7.56	6.55	5.99	5.64	5.39	5.20	5.06	4.94
11	9.65	7.21	6.22	5.67	5.32	5.07	4.89	4.74	4.63
12	9.33	6.93	5.95	5.41	5.06	4.82	4.64	4.50	4.39
13	9.07	6.70	5.74	5.21	4.86	4.62	4.44	4.30	4.19
14	8.86	6.51	5.56	5.04	4.69	4.46	4.28	4.14	4.03
15	8.68	6.36	5.42	4.89	4.56	4.32	4.14	4.00	3.89
16	8.53	6.23	5.29	4.77	4.44	4.20	4.03	3.89	3.78
17	8.40	6.11	5.18	4.67	4.34	4.10	3.93	3.79	3.68
18	8.29	6.01	5.09	4.58	4.25	4.01	3.84	3.71	3.60
19	8.18	5.93	5.01	4.50	4.17	3.94	3.77	3.63	3.52
20	8.10	5.85	4.94	4.43	4.10	3.87	3.70	3.56	3.46
21	8.02	5.78	4.87	4.37	4.04	3.81	3.64	3.51	3.40
22	7.95	5.72	4.82	4.31	3.99	3.76	3.59	3.45	3.35
23	7.88	5.66	4.76	4.26	3.94	3.71	3.54	3.41	3.30
24	7.82	5.61	4.72	4.22	3.90	3.67	3.50	3.36	3.26
25	7.77	5.57	4.68	4.18	3.85	3.63	3.46	3.32	3.22
26	7.72	5.53	4.64	4.14	3.82	3.59	3.42	3.29	3.18
27	7.68	5.49	4.60	4.11	3.78	3.56	3.39	3.26	3.15
28	7.64	5.45	4.57	4.07	3.75	3.53	3.36	3.23	3.12
29	7.60	5.42	4.54	4.04	3.73	3.50	3.33	3.20	3.09
30	7.56	5.39	4.51	4.02	3.70	3.47	3.30	3.17	3.07
40	7.31	5.18	4.31	3.83	3.51	3.29	3.12	2.99	2.89
60	7.08	4.98	4.13	3.65	3.34	3.12	2.95	2.82	2.72
120	6.85	4.79	3.95	3.48	3.17	2.96	2.79	2.66	2.56
∞	6.63	4.61	3.78	3.32	3.02	2.80	2.64	2.51	2.41

Table (continued) Critical Values of the *F*-Distribution

$$f_{0.01}(v_1, v_2)$$

v_2	v_1									
	10	**12**	**15**	**20**	**24**	**30**	**40**	**60**	**120**	**∞**
1	6055.85	6106.32	6157.28	6208.73	6234.63	6260.65	6286.78	6313.03	6339.39	6365.86
2	99.40	99.42	99.43	99.45	99.46	99.47	99.47	99.48	99.49	99.50
3	27.23	27.05	26.87	26.69	26.60	26.50	26.41	26.32	26.22	26.13
4	14.55	14.37	14.20	14.02	13.93	13.84	13.75	13.65	13.56	13.46
5	10.05	9.89	9.72	9.55	9.47	9.38	9.29	9.20	9.11	9.02
6	7.87	7.72	7.56	7.40	7.31	7.23	7.14	7.06	6.97	6.88
7	6.62	6.47	6.31	6.16	6.07	5.99	5.91	5.82	5.74	5.65
8	5.81	5.67	5.52	5.36	5.28	5.20	5.12	5.03	4.95	4.86
9	5.26	5.11	4.96	4.81	4.73	4.65	4.57	4.48	4.40	4.31
10	4.85	4.71	4.56	4.41	4.33	4.25	4.17	4.08	4.00	3.91
11	4.54	4.40	4.25	4.10	4.02	3.94	3.86	3.78	3.69	3.60
12	4.30	4.16	4.01	3.86	3.78	3.70	3.62	3.54	3.45	3.36
13	4.10	3.96	3.82	3.66	3.59	3.51	3.43	3.34	3.25	3.17
14	3.94	3.80	3.66	3.51	3.43	3.35	3.27	3.18	3.09	3.00
15	3.80	3.67	3.52	3.37	3.29	3.21	3.13	3.05	2.96	2.87
16	3.69	3.55	3.41	3.26	3.18	3.10	3.02	2.93	2.84	2.75
17	3.59	3.46	3.31	3.16	3.08	3.00	2.92	2.83	2.75	2.65
18	3.51	3.37	3.23	3.08	3.00	2.92	2.84	2.75	2.66	2.57
19	3.43	3.30	3.15	3.00	2.92	2.84	2.76	2.67	2.58	2.49
20	3.37	3.23	3.09	2.94	2.86	2.78	2.69	2.61	2.52	2.42
21	3.31	3.17	3.03	2.88	2.80	2.72	2.64	2.55	2.46	2.36
22	3.26	3.12	2.98	2.83	2.75	2.67	2.58	2.50	2.40	2.31
23	3.21	3.07	2.93	2.78	2.70	2.62	2.54	2.45	2.35	2.26
24	3.17	3.03	2.89	2.74	2.66	2.58	2.49	2.40	2.31	2.21
25	3.13	2.99	2.85	2.70	2.62	2.54	2.45	2.36	2.27	2.17
26	3.09	2.96	2.81	2.66	2.58	2.50	2.42	2.33	2.23	2.13
27	3.06	2.93	2.78	2.63	2.55	2.47	2.38	2.29	2.20	2.10
28	3.03	2.90	2.75	2.60	2.52	2.44	2.35	2.26	2.17	2.06
29	3.00	2.87	2.73	2.57	2.49	2.41	2.33	2.23	2.14	2.03
30	2.98	2.84	2.70	2.55	2.47	2.39	2.30	2.21	2.11	2.01
40	2.80	2.66	2.52	2.37	2.29	2.20	2.11	2.02	1.92	1.80
60	2.63	2.50	2.35	2.20	2.12	2.03	1.94	1.84	1.73	1.60
120	2.47	2.34	2.19	2.03	1.95	1.86	1.76	1.66	1.53	1.38
∞	2.32	2.18	2.04	1.88	1.79	1.70	1.59	1.47	1.32	1.00

One- and Two-Sample Estimation Problems

1 Introduction

The Central Limit Theorem provides information about the distribution of the sample mean $\bar{X}$. The distribution involves the population mean μ. Thus, any conclusions concerning μ drawn from an observed sample average must depend on knowledge of this sampling distribution. Similar comments apply to S^2 and σ^2. Clearly, any conclusions we draw about the variance of a normal distribution will likely involve the sampling distribution of S^2.

In this chapter, we begin by formally outlining the purpose of statistical inference. We follow this by discussing the problem of **estimation of population parameters**. We confine our formal developments of specific estimation procedures to problems involving one and two samples.

2 Statistical Inference

Statistical inference consists of those methods by which one makes inferences or generalizations about a population. The trend today is to distinguish between the **classical method** of estimating a population parameter, whereby inferences are based strictly on information obtained from a random sample selected from the population, and the **Bayesian method**, which utilizes prior subjective knowledge about the probability distribution of the unknown parameters in conjunction with the information provided by the sample data. Throughout most of this chapter, we shall use classical methods to estimate unknown population parameters such as the mean, the proportion, and the variance by computing statistics from random

From Chapter 9 of *Probability & Statistics for Engineers & Scientists*, Ninth Edition, Ronald E. Walpole, Raymond H. Myers, Sharon L. Myers, Keying Ye. Copyright © 2012 by Pearson Education, Inc. Published by Pearson Prentice Hall. All rights reserved.

samples and applying the theory of sampling distributions.

Statistical inferrence may be divided into two major areas: **estimation** and **tests of hypotheses.** We will deal with theory and applications of estimation in this chapter. To distinguish clearly between the two areas, consider the following examples. A candidate for public office may wish to estimate the true proportion of voters favoring him by obtaining opinions from a random sample of 100 eligible voters. The fraction of voters in the sample favoring the candidate could be used as an estimate of the true proportion in the population of voters. A knowledge of the sampling distribution of a proportion enables one to establish the degree of accuracy of such an estimate. This problem falls in the area of estimation.

Now consider the case in which one is interested in finding out whether brand *A* floor wax is more scuff-resistant than brand *B* floor wax. He or she might hypothesize that brand *A* is better than brand *B* and, after proper testing, accept or reject this hypothesis. In this example, we do not attempt to estimate a parameter, but instead we try to arrive at a correct decision about a prestated hypothesis. Once again we are dependent on sampling theory and the use of data to provide us with some measure of accuracy for our decision.

3   Classical Methods of Estimation

A **point estimate** of some population parameter θ is a single value $\hat{\theta}$ of a statistic $\hat{\Theta}$. For example, the value $\bar{x}$ of the statistic $\bar{X}$, computed from a sample of size n, is a point estimate of the population parameter μ. Similarly, $\hat{p} = x/n$ is a point estimate of the true proportion p for a binomial experiment.

An estimator is not expected to estimate the population parameter without error. We do not expect $\bar{X}$ to estimate μ exactly, but we certainly hope that it is not far off. For a particular sample, it is possible to obtain a closer estimate of μ by using the sample median $\tilde{X}$ as an estimator. Consider, for instance, a sample consisting of the values 2, 5, and 11 from a population whose mean is 4 but is supposedly unknown. We would estimate μ to be $\bar{x} = 6$, using the sample mean as our estimate, or $\tilde{x} = 5$, using the sample median as our estimate. In this case, the estimator $\tilde{X}$ produces an estimate closer to the true parameter than does the estimator $\bar{X}$. On the other hand, if our random sample contains the values 2, 6, and 7, then $\bar{x} = 5$ and $\tilde{x} = 6$, so $\bar{X}$ is the better estimator. Not knowing the true value of μ, we must decide in advance whether to use $\bar{X}$ or $\tilde{X}$ as our estimator.

Unbiased Estimator

What are the desirable properties of a "good" decision function that would influence us to choose one estimator rather than another? Let $\hat{\Theta}$ be an estimator whose value $\hat{\theta}$ is a point estimate of some unknown population parameter θ. Certainly, we would like the sampling distribution of $\hat{\Theta}$ to have a mean equal to the parameter estimated. An estimator possessing this property is said to be **unbiased**.

Definition 1:

A statistic $\hat{\Theta}$ is said to be an **unbiased estimator** of the parameter θ if

$$\mu_{\hat{\Theta}} = E(\hat{\Theta}) = \theta.$$

Example 1: Show that S^2 is an unbiased estimator of the parameter σ^2.

Solution: Note that

$$\sum_{i=1}^{n}(X_i - \bar{X})^2 = \sum_{i=1}^{n}(X_i - \mu)^2 - n(\bar{X} - \mu)^2.$$

Now

$$E(S^2) = E\left[\frac{1}{n-1}\sum_{i=1}^{n}(X_i - \bar{X})^2\right]$$

$$= \frac{1}{n-1}\left[\sum_{i=1}^{n}E(X_i - \mu)^2 - nE(\bar{X} - \mu)^2\right] = \frac{1}{n-1}\left(\sum_{i=1}^{n}\sigma_{X_i}^2 - n\sigma_{\bar{X}}^2\right).$$

However,

$$\sigma_{X_i}^2 = \sigma^2, \text{ for } i = 1, 2, \ldots, n, \text{ and } \sigma_{\bar{X}}^2 = \frac{\sigma^2}{n}.$$

Therefore,

$$E(S^2) = \frac{1}{n-1}\left(n\sigma^2 - n\frac{\sigma^2}{n}\right) = \sigma^2.$$

Although S^2 is an unbiased estimator of σ^2, S, on the other hand, is usually a biased estimator of σ, with the bias becoming insignificant for large samples. This example illustrates **why we divide by $n - 1$** rather than n when the variance is estimated.

Variance of a Point Estimator

If $\hat{\Theta}_1$ and $\hat{\Theta}_2$ are two unbiased estimators of the same population parameter θ, we want to choose the estimator whose sampling distribution has the smaller variance. Hence, if $\sigma_{\hat{\theta}_1}^2 < \sigma_{\hat{\theta}_2}^2$, we say that $\hat{\Theta}_1$ is a **more efficient estimator** of θ than $\hat{\Theta}_2$.

Definition 2:

If we consider all possible unbiased estimators of some parameter θ, the one with the smallest variance is called the **most efficient estimator** of θ.

Figure 1 illustrates the sampling distributions of three different estimators, $\hat{\Theta}_1$, $\hat{\Theta}_2$, and $\hat{\Theta}_3$, all estimating θ. It is clear that only $\hat{\Theta}_1$ and $\hat{\Theta}_2$ are unbiased, since their distributions are centered at θ. The estimator $\hat{\Theta}_1$ has a smaller variance than $\hat{\Theta}_2$ and is therefore more efficient. Hence, our choice for an estimator of θ, among the three considered, would be $\hat{\Theta}_1$.

For normal populations, one can show that both $\bar{X}$ and $\tilde{X}$ are unbiased estimators of the population mean μ, but the variance of $\bar{X}$ is smaller than the variance

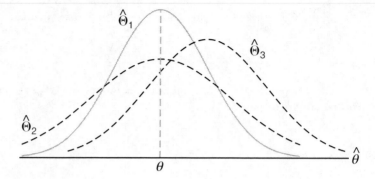

Figure 1: Sampling distributions of different estimators of θ.

of $\tilde{X}$. Thus, both estimates $\bar{x}$ and $\tilde{x}$ will, on average, equal the population mean μ, but $\bar{x}$ is likely to be closer to μ for a given sample, and thus $\bar{X}$ is more efficient than $\tilde{X}$.

Interval Estimation

Even the most efficient unbiased estimator is unlikely to estimate the population parameter exactly. It is true that estimation accuracy increases with large samples, but there is still no reason we should expect a **point estimate** from a given sample to be exactly equal to the population parameter it is supposed to estimate. There are many situations in which it is preferable to determine an interval within which we would expect to find the value of the parameter. Such an interval is called an **interval estimate**.

An interval estimate of a population parameter θ is an interval of the form $\hat{\theta}_L < \theta < \hat{\theta}_U$, where $\hat{\theta}_L$ and $\hat{\theta}_U$ depend on the value of the statistic $\hat{\Theta}$ for a particular sample and also on the sampling distribution of $\hat{\Theta}$. For example, a random sample of SAT verbal scores for students in the entering freshman class might produce an interval from 530 to 550, within which we expect to find the true average of all SAT verbal scores for the freshman class. The values of the endpoints, 530 and 550, will depend on the computed sample mean $\bar{x}$ and the sampling distribution of $\bar{X}$. As the sample size increases, we know that $\sigma_{\bar{X}}^2 = \sigma^2/n$ decreases, and consequently our estimate is likely to be closer to the parameter μ, resulting in a shorter interval. Thus, the interval estimate indicates, by its length, the accuracy of the point estimate. An engineer will gain some insight into the population proportion defective by taking a sample and computing the *sample proportion defective*. But an interval estimate might be more informative.

Interpretation of Interval Estimates

Since different samples will generally yield different values of $\hat{\Theta}$ and, therefore, different values for $\hat{\theta}_L$ and $\hat{\theta}_U$, these endpoints of the interval are values of corresponding random variables $\hat{\Theta}_L$ and $\hat{\Theta}_U$. From the sampling distribution of $\hat{\Theta}$ we shall be able to determine $\hat{\Theta}_L$ and $\hat{\Theta}_U$ such that $P(\hat{\Theta}_L < \theta < \hat{\Theta}_U)$ is equal to any positive fractional value we care to specify. If, for instance, we find $\hat{\Theta}_L$ and $\hat{\Theta}_U$ such that

$$P(\hat{\Theta}_L < \theta < \hat{\Theta}_U) = 1 - \alpha,$$

for $0 < \alpha < 1$, then we have a probability of $1-\alpha$ of selecting a random sample that will produce an interval containing θ. The interval $\hat{\theta}_L < \theta < \hat{\theta}_U$, computed from the selected sample, is called a $100(1 - \alpha)\%$ **confidence interval**, the fraction $1 - \alpha$ is called the **confidence coefficient** or the **degree of confidence**, and the endpoints, $\hat{\theta}_L$ and $\hat{\theta}_U$, are called the lower and upper **confidence limits**. Thus, when $\alpha = 0.05$, we have a 95% confidence interval, and when $\alpha = 0.01$, we obtain a wider 99% confidence interval. The wider the confidence interval is, the more confident we can be that the interval contains the unknown parameter. Of course, it is better to be 95% confident that the average life of a certain television transistor is between 6 and 7 years than to be 99% confident that it is between 3 and 10 years. Ideally, we prefer a short interval with a high degree of confidence. Sometimes, restrictions on the size of our sample prevent us from achieving short intervals without sacrificing some degree of confidence.

In the sections that follow, we pursue the notions of point and interval estimation, with each section presenting a different special case. The reader should notice that while point and interval estimation represent different approaches to gaining information regarding a parameter, they are related in the sense that confidence interval estimators are based on point estimators. In the following section, for example, we will see that $\bar{X}$ is a very reasonable point estimator of μ. As a result, the important confidence interval estimator of μ depends on knowledge of the sampling distribution of $\bar{X}$.

We begin the following section with the simplest case of a confidence interval. The scenario is simple and yet unrealistic. We are interested in estimating a population mean μ and yet σ is known. Clearly, if μ is unknown, it is quite unlikely that σ is known. Any historical results that produced enough information to allow the assumption that σ is known would likely have produced similar information about μ. Despite this argument, we begin with this case because the concepts and indeed the resulting mechanics associated with confidence interval estimation remain the same for the more realistic situations presented later in Section 4.

4   Single Sample: Estimating the Mean

The sampling distribution of $\bar{X}$ is centered at μ, and in most applications the variance is smaller than that of any other estimators of μ. Thus, the sample mean $\bar{x}$ will be used as a point estimate for the population mean μ. Recall that $\sigma_{\bar{X}}^2 = \sigma^2/n$, so a large sample will yield a value of $\bar{X}$ that comes from a sampling distribution with a small variance. Hence, $\bar{x}$ is likely to be a very accurate estimate of μ when n is large.

Let us now consider the interval estimate of μ. If our sample is selected from a normal population or, failing this, if n is sufficiently large, we can establish a confidence interval for μ by considering the sampling distribution of $\bar{X}$.

According to the Central Limit Theorem, we can expect the sampling distribution of $\bar{X}$ to be approximately normally distributed with mean $\mu_{\bar{X}} = \mu$ and standard deviation $\sigma_{\bar{X}} = \sigma/\sqrt{n}$. Writing $z_{\alpha/2}$ for the z-value above which we find an area of $\alpha/2$ under the normal curve, we can see from Figure 2 that

$$P(-z_{\alpha/2} < Z < z_{\alpha/2}) = 1 - \alpha,$$

where

$$Z = \frac{\bar{X} - \mu}{\sigma/\sqrt{n}}.$$

Hence,

$$P\left(-z_{\alpha/2} < \frac{\bar{X} - \mu}{\sigma/\sqrt{n}} < z_{\alpha/2}\right) = 1 - \alpha.$$

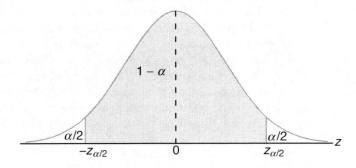

Figure 2: $P(-z_{\alpha/2} < Z < z_{\alpha/2}) = 1 - \alpha$.

Multiplying each term in the inequality by $\sigma/\sqrt{n}$ and then subtracting $\bar{X}$ from each term and multiplying by -1 (reversing the sense of the inequalities), we obtain

$$P\left(\bar{X} - z_{\alpha/2}\frac{\sigma}{\sqrt{n}} < \mu < \bar{X} + z_{\alpha/2}\frac{\sigma}{\sqrt{n}}\right) = 1 - \alpha.$$

A random sample of size n is selected from a population whose variance σ^2 is known, and the mean $\bar{x}$ is computed to give the $100(1 - \alpha)\%$ confidence interval below. It is important to emphasize that we have invoked the Central Limit Theorem above. As a result, it is important to note the conditions for applications that follow.

Confidence
Interval on μ, σ^2
Known

If $\bar{x}$ is the mean of a random sample of size n from a population with known variance σ^2, a $100(1 - \alpha)\%$ confidence interval for μ is given by

$$\bar{x} - z_{\alpha/2}\frac{\sigma}{\sqrt{n}} < \mu < \bar{x} + z_{\alpha/2}\frac{\sigma}{\sqrt{n}},$$

where $z_{\alpha/2}$ is the z-value leaving an area of $\alpha/2$ to the right.

For small samples selected from nonnormal populations, we cannot expect our degree of confidence to be accurate. However, for samples of size $n \geq 30$, with the shape of the distributions not too skewed, sampling theory guarantees good results.

Clearly, the values of the random variables $\hat{\Theta}_L$ and $\hat{\Theta}_U$, defined in Section 3, are the confidence limits

$$\hat{\theta}_L = \bar{x} - z_{\alpha/2}\frac{\sigma}{\sqrt{n}} \quad \text{and} \quad \hat{\theta}_U = \bar{x} + z_{\alpha/2}\frac{\sigma}{\sqrt{n}}.$$

Different samples will yield different values of $\bar{x}$ and therefore produce different interval estimates of the parameter μ, as shown in Figure 3. The dot at the center of each interval indicates the position of the point estimate $\bar{x}$ for that random sample. Note that all of these intervals are of the same width, since their widths depend only on the choice of $z_{\alpha/2}$ once $\bar{x}$ is determined. The larger the value we choose for $z_{\alpha/2}$, the wider we make all the intervals and the more confident we can be that the particular sample selected will produce an interval that contains the unknown parameter μ. In general, for a selection of $z_{\alpha/2}$, $100(1-\alpha)\%$ of the intervals will cover μ.

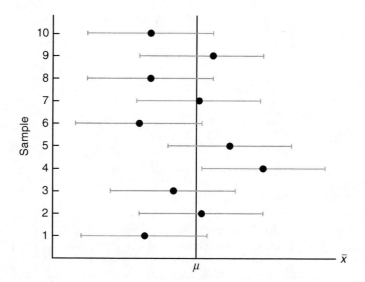

Figure 3: Interval estimates of μ for different samples.

Example 2: The average zinc concentration recovered from a sample of measurements taken in 36 different locations in a river is found to be 2.6 grams per milliliter. Find the 95% and 99% confidence intervals for the mean zinc concentration in the river. Assume that the population standard deviation is 0.3 gram per milliliter.

Solution: The point estimate of μ is $\bar{x} = 2.6$. The z-value leaving an area of 0.025 to the right, and therefore an area of 0.975 to the left, is $z_{0.025} = 1.96$ (Table Areas under the Normal Curve at the end of this chapter). Hence, the 95% confidence interval is

$$2.6 - (1.96)\left(\frac{0.3}{\sqrt{36}}\right) < \mu < 2.6 + (1.96)\left(\frac{0.3}{\sqrt{36}}\right),$$

which reduces to $2.50 < \mu < 2.70$. To find a 99% confidence interval, we find the z-value leaving an area of 0.005 to the right and 0.995 to the left. From Table Areas under the Normal Curve again, $z_{0.005} = 2.575$, and the 99% confidence interval is

$$2.6 - (2.575)\left(\frac{0.3}{\sqrt{36}}\right) < \mu < 2.6 + (2.575)\left(\frac{0.3}{\sqrt{36}}\right),$$

or simply

$$2.47 < \mu < 2.73.$$

We now see that a longer interval is required to estimate μ with a higher degree of confidence.

The $100(1-\alpha)\%$ confidence interval provides an estimate of the accuracy of our point estimate. If μ is actually the center value of the interval, then $\bar{x}$ estimates μ without error. Most of the time, however, $\bar{x}$ will not be exactly equal to μ and the point estimate will be in error. The size of this error will be the absolute value of the difference between μ and $\bar{x}$, and we can be $100(1-\alpha)\%$ confident that this difference will not exceed $z_{\alpha/2}\frac{\sigma}{\sqrt{n}}$. We can readily see this if we draw a diagram of a hypothetical confidence interval, as in Figure 4.

Figure 4: Error in estimating μ by $\bar{x}$.

Theorem 1: If $\bar{x}$ is used as an estimate of μ, we can be $100(1-\alpha)\%$ confident that the error will not exceed $z_{\alpha/2}\frac{\sigma}{\sqrt{n}}$.

In Example 2, we are 95% confident that the sample mean $\bar{x} = 2.6$ differs from the true mean μ by an amount less than $(1.96)(0.3)/\sqrt{36} = 0.1$ and 99% confident that the difference is less than $(2.575)(0.3)/\sqrt{36} = 0.13$.

Frequently, we wish to know how large a sample is necessary to ensure that the error in estimating μ will be less than a specified amount e. By Theorem 1, we must choose n such that $z_{\alpha/2}\frac{\sigma}{\sqrt{n}} = e$. Solving this equation gives the following formula for n.

Theorem 2: If $\bar{x}$ is used as an estimate of μ, we can be $100(1-\alpha)\%$ confident that the error will not exceed a specified amount e when the sample size is

$$n = \left(\frac{z_{\alpha/2}\sigma}{e}\right)^2.$$

When solving for the sample size, n, we round all fractional values up to the next whole number. By adhering to this principle, we can be sure that our degree of confidence never falls below $100(1-\alpha)\%$.

Strictly speaking, the formula in Theorem 2 is applicable only if we know the variance of the population from which we select our sample. Lacking this information, we could take a preliminary sample of size $n \geq 30$ to provide an estimate of σ. Then, using s as an approximation for σ in Theorem 2, we could determine approximately how many observations are needed to provide the desired degree of accuracy.

Example 3: How large a sample is required if we want to be 95% confident that our estimate of μ in Example 2 is off by less than 0.05?

Solution: The population standard deviation is $\sigma = 0.3$. Then, by Theorem 2,

$$n = \left[\frac{(1.96)(0.3)}{0.05} \right]^2 = 138.3.$$

Therefore, we can be 95% confident that a random sample of size 139 will provide an estimate $\bar{x}$ differing from μ by an amount less than 0.05.

One-Sided Confidence Bounds

The confidence intervals and resulting confidence bounds discussed thus far are *two-sided* (i.e., both upper and lower bounds are given). However, there are many applications in which only one bound is sought. For example, if the measurement of interest is tensile strength, the engineer receives better information from a lower bound only. This bound communicates the worst-case scenario. On the other hand, if the measurement is something for which a relatively large value of μ is not profitable or desirable, then an upper confidence bound is of interest. An example would be a case in which inferences need to be made concerning the mean mercury composition in a river. An upper bound is very informative in this case.

One-sided confidence bounds are developed in the same fashion as two-sided intervals. However, the source is a one-sided probability statement that makes use of the Central Limit Theorem:

$$P\left(\frac{\bar{X} - \mu}{\sigma/\sqrt{n}} < z_\alpha \right) = 1 - \alpha.$$

One can then manipulate the probability statement much as before and obtain

$$P(\mu > \bar{X} - z_\alpha \sigma/\sqrt{n}) = 1 - \alpha.$$

Similar manipulation of $P\left(\frac{\bar{X} - \mu}{\sigma/\sqrt{n}} > -z_\alpha \right) = 1 - \alpha$ gives

$$P(\mu < \bar{X} + z_\alpha \sigma/\sqrt{n}) = 1 - \alpha.$$

As a result, the upper and lower one-sided bounds follow.

One-Sided Confidence Bounds on μ, σ^2 Known

If $\bar{X}$ is the mean of a random sample of size n from a population with variance σ^2, the one-sided $100(1-\alpha)\%$ confidence bounds for μ are given by

upper one-sided bound:	$\bar{x} + z_\alpha \sigma/\sqrt{n}$;
lower one-sided bound:	$\bar{x} - z_\alpha \sigma/\sqrt{n}$.

Example 4: In a psychological testing experiment, 25 subjects are selected randomly and their reaction time, in seconds, to a particular stimulus is measured. Past experience suggests that the variance in reaction times to these types of stimuli is 4 sec^2 and that the distribution of reaction times is approximately normal. The average time for the subjects is 6.2 seconds. Give an upper 95% bound for the mean reaction time.

Solution: The upper 95% bound is given by

$$\bar{x} + z_\alpha \sigma / \sqrt{n} = 6.2 + (1.645)\sqrt{4/25} = 6.2 + 0.658$$
$$= 6.858 \text{ seconds.}$$

Hence, we are 95% confident that the mean reaction time is less than 6.858 seconds.

The Case of σ Unknown

Frequently, we must attempt to estimate the mean of a population when the variance is unknown. If we have a random sample from a *normal distribution*, then the random variable

$$T = \frac{\bar{X} - \mu}{S/\sqrt{n}}$$

has a Student t-distribution with $n - 1$ degrees of freedom. Here S is the sample standard deviation. In this situation, with σ unknown, T can be used to construct a confidence interval on μ. The procedure is the same as that with σ known except that σ is replaced by S and the standard normal distribution is replaced by the t-distribution. Referring to Figure 5, we can assert that

$$P(-t_{\alpha/2} < T < t_{\alpha/2}) = 1 - \alpha,$$

where $t_{\alpha/2}$ is the t-value with $n-1$ degrees of freedom, above which we find an area of $\alpha/2$. Because of symmetry, an equal area of $\alpha/2$ will fall to the left of $-t_{\alpha/2}$. Substituting for T, we write

$$P\left(-t_{\alpha/2} < \frac{\bar{X} - \mu}{S/\sqrt{n}} < t_{\alpha/2}\right) = 1 - \alpha.$$

Multiplying each term in the inequality by $S/\sqrt{n}$, and then subtracting $\bar{X}$ from each term and multiplying by -1, we obtain

$$P\left(\bar{X} - t_{\alpha/2}\frac{S}{\sqrt{n}} < \mu < \bar{X} + t_{\alpha/2}\frac{S}{\sqrt{n}}\right) = 1 - \alpha.$$

For a particular random sample of size n, the mean $\bar{x}$ and standard deviation s are computed and the following $100(1 - \alpha)$% confidence interval for μ is obtained.

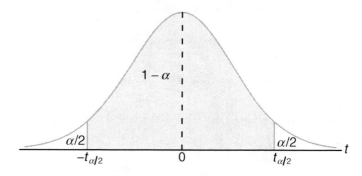

Figure 5: $P(-t_{\alpha/2} < T < t_{\alpha/2}) = 1 - \alpha$.

Confidence
Interval on μ, σ^2
Unknown
If $\bar{x}$ and s are the mean and standard deviation of a random sample from a normal population with unknown variance σ^2, a $100(1-\alpha)\%$ confidence interval for μ is

$$\bar{x} - t_{\alpha/2}\frac{s}{\sqrt{n}} < \mu < \bar{x} + t_{\alpha/2}\frac{s}{\sqrt{n}},$$

where $t_{\alpha/2}$ is the t-value with $v = n - 1$ degrees of freedom, leaving an area of $\alpha/2$ to the right.

We have made a distinction between the cases of σ known and σ unknown in computing confidence interval estimates. We should emphasize that for σ known we exploited the Central Limit Theorem, whereas for σ unknown we made use of the sampling distribution of the random variable T. However, the use of the t-distribution is based on the premise that the sampling is from a normal distribution. As long as the distribution is approximately bell shaped, confidence intervals can be computed when σ^2 is unknown by using the t-distribution and we may expect very good results.

Computed one-sided confidence bounds for μ with σ unknown are as the reader would expect, namely

$$\bar{x} + t_{\alpha}\frac{s}{\sqrt{n}} \qquad \text{and} \qquad \bar{x} - t_{\alpha}\frac{s}{\sqrt{n}}.$$

They are the upper and lower $100(1 - \alpha)\%$ bounds, respectively. Here t_{α} is the t-value having an area of α to the right.

Example 5:   The contents of seven similar containers of sulfuric acid are 9.8, 10.2, 10.4, 9.8, 10.0, 10.2, and 9.6 liters. Find a 95% confidence interval for the mean contents of all such containers, assuming an approximately normal distribution.

Solution: The sample mean and standard deviation for the given data are

$$\bar{x} = 10.0 \qquad \text{and} \qquad s = 0.283.$$

Using Table Critical Values of the t-Distribution at the end of this chapter, we find $t_{0.025} = 2.447$ for $v = 6$ degrees of freedom. Hence, the

95% confidence interval for μ is

$$10.0 - (2.447)\left(\frac{0.283}{\sqrt{7}}\right) < \mu < 10.0 + (2.447)\left(\frac{0.283}{\sqrt{7}}\right),$$

which reduces to $9.74 < \mu < 10.26$.

Concept of a Large-Sample Confidence Interval

Often statisticians recommend that even when normality cannot be assumed, σ is unknown, and $n \geq 30$, s can replace σ and the confidence interval

$$\bar{x} \pm z_{\alpha/2}\frac{s}{\sqrt{n}}$$

may be used. This is often referred to as a *large-sample confidence interval*. The justification lies only in the presumption that with a sample as large as 30 and the population distribution not too skewed, s will be very close to the true σ and thus the Central Limit Theorem prevails. It should be emphasized that this is only an approximation and the quality of the result becomes better as the sample size grows larger.

Example 6: Scholastic Aptitude Test (SAT) mathematics scores of a random sample of 500 high school seniors in the state of Texas are collected, and the sample mean and standard deviation are found to be 501 and 112, respectively. Find a 99% confidence interval on the mean SAT mathematics score for seniors in the state of Texas.

Solution: Since the sample size is large, it is reasonable to use the normal approximation. Using Table Areas under the Normal Curve, we find $z_{0.005} = 2.575$. Hence, a 99% confidence interval for μ is

$$501 \pm (2.575)\left(\frac{112}{\sqrt{500}}\right) = 501 \pm 12.9,$$

which yields $488.1 < \mu < 513.9$.

5   Standard Error of a Point Estimate

We have made a rather sharp distinction between the goal of a point estimate and that of a confidence interval estimate. The former supplies a single number extracted from a set of experimental data, and the latter provides an interval that is reasonable for the parameter, *given the experimental data*; that is, $100(1-\alpha)\%$ of such computed intervals "cover" the parameter.

These two approaches to estimation are related to each other. The common thread is the sampling distribution of the point estimator. Consider, for example, the estimator $\bar{X}$ of μ with σ known. We indicated earlier that a measure of the quality of an unbiased estimator is its variance. The variance of $\bar{X}$ is

$$\sigma_{\bar{X}}^2 = \frac{\sigma^2}{n}.$$

Thus, the standard deviation of $\bar{X}$, or *standard error* of $\bar{X}$, is $\sigma/\sqrt{n}$. Simply put, the standard error of an estimator is its standard deviation. For $\bar{X}$, the computed confidence limit

$$\bar{x} \pm z_{\alpha/2}\frac{\sigma}{\sqrt{n}} \text{ is written as } \bar{x} \pm z_{\alpha/2} \text{ s.e.}(\bar{x}),$$

where "s.e." is the "standard error." The important point is that the width of the confidence interval on μ is dependent on the quality of the point estimator through its standard error. In the case where σ is unknown and sampling is from a normal distribution, s replaces σ and the *estimated standard error $s/\sqrt{n}$* is involved. Thus, the confidence limits on μ are

Confidence Limits on μ, σ^2 Unknown

$$\bar{x} \pm t_{\alpha/2}\frac{s}{\sqrt{n}} = \bar{x} \pm t_{\alpha/2} \text{ s.e.}(\bar{x})$$

Again, the confidence interval is *no better* (in terms of width) *than the quality of the point estimate*, in this case through its estimated standard error. Computer packages often refer to estimated standard errors simply as "standard errors."

As we move to more complex confidence intervals, there is a prevailing notion that widths of confidence intervals become shorter as the quality of the corresponding point estimate becomes better, although it is not always quite as simple as we have illustrated here. It can be argued that a confidence interval is merely an augmentation of the point estimate to take into account the precision of the point estimate.

6   Prediction Intervals

The point and interval estimations of the mean in Sections 4 and 5 provide good information about the unknown parameter μ of a normal distribution or a nonnormal distribution from which a large sample is drawn. Sometimes, other than the population mean, the experimenter may also be interested in predicting the possible **value of a future observation**. For instance, in quality control, the experimenter may need to use the observed data to predict a new observation. A process that produces a metal part may be evaluated on the basis of whether the part meets specifications on tensile strength. On certain occasions, a customer may be interested in purchasing a **single part**. In this case, a confidence interval on the mean tensile strength does not capture the required information. The customer requires a statement regarding the uncertainty of a **single observation**. This type of requirement is nicely fulfilled by the construction of a **prediction interval**.

It is quite simple to obtain a prediction interval for the situations we have considered so far. Assume that the random sample comes from a normal population with unknown mean μ and known variance σ^2. A natural point estimator of a new observation is $\bar{X}$. It is known that the variance of $\bar{X}$ is σ^2/n. However, to predict a new observation, not only do we need to account for the variation due to estimating the mean, but also we should account for the **variation of a future observation**. From the assumption, we know that the variance of the random error in a new observation is σ^2. The development of a prediction interval is best illustrated by beginning with a normal random variable $x_0 - \bar{x}$, where x_0 is the new observation and $\bar{x}$ comes from the sample. Since x_0 and $\bar{x}$ are independent, we know that

$$z = \frac{x_0 - \bar{x}}{\sqrt{\sigma^2 + \sigma^2/n}} = \frac{x_0 - \bar{x}}{\sigma\sqrt{1 + 1/n}}$$

is $n(z; 0, 1)$. As a result, if we use the probability statement

$$P(-z_{\alpha/2} < Z < z_{\alpha/2}) = 1 - \alpha$$

with the z-statistic above and place x_0 in the center of the probability statement, we have the following event occurring with probability $1 - \alpha$:

$$\bar{x} - z_{\alpha/2}\sigma\sqrt{1 + 1/n} < x_0 < \bar{x} + z_{\alpha/2}\sigma\sqrt{1 + 1/n}.$$

As a result, computation of the prediction interval is formalized as follows.

Prediction Interval of a Future Observation, σ^2 Known

For a normal distribution of measurements with unknown mean μ and known variance σ^2, a $100(1 - \alpha)\%$ **prediction interval** of a future observation x_0 is

$$\bar{x} - z_{\alpha/2}\sigma\sqrt{1 + 1/n} < x_0 < \bar{x} + z_{\alpha/2}\sigma\sqrt{1 + 1/n},$$

where $z_{\alpha/2}$ is the z-value leaving an area of $\alpha/2$ to the right.

Example 7: Due to the decrease in interest rates, the First Citizens Bank received a lot of mortgage applications. A recent sample of 50 mortgage loans resulted in an average loan amount of \$257,300. Assume a population standard deviation of \$25,000. For the next customer who fills out a mortgage application, find a 95% prediction interval for the loan amount.

Solution: The point prediction of the next customer's loan amount is $\bar{x} = \$257,300$. The z-value here is $z_{0.025} = 1.96$. Hence, a 95% prediction interval for the future loan amount is

$$257,300 - (1.96)(25,000)\sqrt{1 + 1/50} < x_0 < 257,300 + (1.96)(25,000)\sqrt{1 + 1/50},$$

which gives the interval (\$207,812.43, \$306,787.57). ⌟

The prediction interval provides a good estimate of the location of a future observation, which is quite different from the estimate of the sample mean value. It should be noted that the variation of this prediction is the sum of the variation due to an estimation of the mean and the variation of a single observation. However, as in the past, we first consider the case with known variance. It is also important to deal with the prediction interval of a future observation in the situation where the variance is unknown. Indeed a Student t-distribution may be used in this case, as described in the following result. The normal distribution is merely replaced by the t-distribution.

Prediction Interval of a Future Observation, σ^2 Unknown	For a normal distribution of measurements with unknown mean μ and unknown variance σ^2, a $100(1-\alpha)\%$ **prediction interval** of a future observation x_0 is $$\bar{x} - t_{\alpha/2}s\sqrt{1 + 1/n} < x_0 < \bar{x} + t_{\alpha/2}s\sqrt{1 + 1/n},$$ where $t_{\alpha/2}$ is the t-value with $v = n - 1$ degrees of freedom, leaving an area of $\alpha/2$ to the right.

One-sided prediction intervals can also be constructed. Upper prediction bounds apply in cases where focus must be placed on future large observations. Concern over future small observations calls for the use of lower prediction bounds. The upper bound is given by

$$\bar{x} + t_{\alpha}s\sqrt{1 + 1/n}$$

and the lower bound by

$$\bar{x} - t_{\alpha}s\sqrt{1 + 1/n}.$$

Example 8: A meat inspector has randomly selected 30 packs of 95% lean beef. The sample resulted in a mean of 96.2% with a sample standard deviation of 0.8%. Find a 99% prediction interval for the leanness of a new pack. Assume normality.

Solution: For $v = 29$ degrees of freedom, $t_{0.005} = 2.756$. Hence, a 99% prediction interval for a new observation x_0 is

$$96.2 - (2.756)(0.8)\sqrt{1 + \frac{1}{30}} < x_0 < 96.2 + (2.756)(0.8)\sqrt{1 + \frac{1}{30}},$$

which reduces to $(93.96, 98.44)$.

Use of Prediction Limits for Outlier Detection

To this point very little attention has been paid to the concept of **outliers,** or aberrant observations. The majority of scientific investigators are keenly sensitive to the existence of outlying observations or so-called faulty or "bad data." This is certainly of interest here since there is an important relationship between outlier detection and prediction intervals.

It is convenient for our purposes to view an outlying observation as one that comes from a population with a mean that is different from the mean that governs the rest of the sample of size n being studied. The prediction interval produces a bound that "covers" a future single observation with probability $1 - \alpha$ if it comes from the population from which the sample was drawn. As a result, a methodology for outlier detection involves the rule that **an observation is an outlier if it falls outside the prediction interval computed without including the questionable observation in the sample.** As a result, for the prediction interval of Example 8, if a new pack of beef is measured and its leanness is outside the interval $(93.96, 98.44)$, that observation can be viewed as an outlier.

7   Tolerance Limits

As discussed in Section 6, the scientist or engineer may be less interested in estimating parameters than in gaining a notion about where an individual *observation* or measurement might fall. Such situations call for the use of prediction intervals. However, there is yet a third type of interval that is of interest in many applications. Once again, suppose that interest centers around the manufacturing of a component part and specifications exist on a dimension of that part. In addition, there is little concern about the mean of the dimension. But unlike in the scenario in Section 9.6, one may be less interested in a single observation and more interested in where the majority of the population falls. If process specifications are important, the manager of the process is concerned about long-range performance, **not the next observation**. One must attempt to determine bounds that, in some probabilistic sense, "cover" values in the population (i.e., the measured values of the dimension).

One method of establishing the desired bounds is to determine a confidence interval on a *fixed proportion* of the measurements. This is best motivated by visualizing a situation in which we are doing random sampling from a normal distribution with known mean μ and variance σ^2. Clearly, a bound that covers the middle 95% of the population of observations is

$$\mu \pm 1.96\sigma.$$

This is called a **tolerance interval**, and indeed its coverage of 95% of measured observations is exact. However, in practice, μ and σ are seldom known; thus, the user must apply

$$\bar{x} \pm ks.$$

Now, of course, the interval is a random variable, and hence the *coverage* of a proportion of the population by the interval is not exact. As a result, a $100(1-\gamma)\%$ confidence interval must be used since $\bar{x} \pm ks$ cannot be expected to cover any specified proportion all the time. As a result, we have the following definition.

Tolerance Limits	For a normal distribution of measurements with unknown mean μ and unknown standard deviation σ, **tolerance limits** are given by $\bar{x} \pm ks$, where k is determined such that one can assert with $100(1 - \gamma)\%$ confidence that the given limits contain at least the proportion $1 - \alpha$ of the measurements.

At the end of this chapter, Table Tolerance Factors for Normal Distribution gives values of k for $1 - \alpha = 0.90, 0.95, 0.99$; $\gamma = 0.05, 0.01$; and selected values of n from 2 to 300.

Example 9:   Consider Example 9.8. With the information given, find a tolerance interval that gives two-sided 95% bounds on 90% of the distribution of packages of 95% lean beef. Assume the data came from an approximately normal distribution.

Solution: Recall from Example 8 that $n = 30$, the sample means is 96.2%, and the sample standard deviation is 0.8%. From Table Tolerance Factors for Normal Distribution, $k = 2.14$. Using

$$\bar{x} \pm ks = 96.2 \pm (2.14)(0.8),$$

we find that the lower and upper bounds are 94.5 and 97.9.

We are 95% confident that the above range covers the central 90% of the distribution of 95% lean beef packages.

Distinction among Confidence Intervals, Prediction Intervals, and Tolerance Intervals

It is important to reemphasize the difference among the three types of intervals discussed and illustrated in the preceding sections. The computations are straightforward, but interpretation can be confusing. In real-life applications, these intervals are not interchangeable because their interpretations are quite distinct.

In the case of confidence intervals, one is attentive only to the **population mean**. For example, Exercise 13 deals with an engineering process that produces shearing pins. A specification will be set on Rockwell hardness, below which a customer will not accept any pins. Here, a population parameter must take a backseat. It is important that the engineer know where the *majority of the values of Rockwell hardness are going to be*. Thus, tolerance limits should be used. Surely, when tolerance limits on any process output are tighter than process specifications, that is good news for the process manager.

It is true that the tolerance limit interpretation is somewhat related to the confidence interval. The $100(1-\alpha)\%$ tolerance interval on, say, the proportion 0.95 can be viewed as a confidence interval **on the middle 95%** of the corresponding normal distribution. One-sided tolerance limits are also relevant. In the case of the Rockwell hardness problem, it is desirable to have a lower bound of the form $\bar{x} - ks$ such that there is 99% confidence that at least 99% of Rockwell hardness values will exceed the computed value.

Prediction intervals are applicable when it is important to determine a bound on a **single value**. The mean is not the issue here, nor is the location of the majority of the population. Rather, the location of a single new observation is required.

Case Study 1: **Machine Quality**: A machine produces metal pieces that are cylindrical in shape. A sample of these pieces is taken and the diameters are found to be 1.01, 0.97, 1.03, 1.04, 0.99, 0.98, 0.99, 1.01, and 1.03 centimeters. Use these data to calculate three interval types and draw interpretations that illustrate the distinction between them in the context of the system. For all computations, assume an approximately normal distribution. The sample mean and standard deviation for the given data are $\bar{x} = 1.0056$ and $s = 0.0246$.

(a) Find a 99% confidence interval on the mean diameter.

(b) Compute a 99% prediction interval on a measured diameter of a single metal piece taken from the machine.

(c) Find the 99% tolerance limits that will contain 95% of the metal pieces produced by this machine.

Solution: (a) The 99% confidence interval for the mean diameter is given by

$$\bar{x} \pm t_{0.005}s/\sqrt{n} = 1.0056 \pm (3.355)(0.0246/3) = 1.0056 \pm 0.0275.$$

Thus, the 99% confidence bounds are 0.9781 and 1.0331.

(b) The 99% prediction interval for a future observation is given by

$$\bar{x} \pm t_{0.005} s \sqrt{1 + 1/n} = 1.0056 \pm (3.355)(0.0246)\sqrt{1 + 1/9},$$

with the bounds being 0.9186 and 1.0926.

(c) From Table Tolerance Factors for Normal Distributions, for $n = 9$, $1 - \gamma = 0.99$, and $1 - \alpha = 0.95$, we find $k = 4.550$ for two-sided limits. Hence, the 99% tolerance limits are given by

$$\bar{x} + ks = 1.0056 \pm (4.550)(0.0246),$$

with the bounds being 0.8937 and 1.1175. We are 99% confident that the tolerance interval from 0.8937 to 1.1175 will contain the central 95% of the distribution of diameters produced.

This case study illustrates that the three types of limits can give appreciably different results even though they are all 99% bounds. In the case of the confidence interval on the mean, 99% of such intervals cover the population mean diameter. Thus, we say that we are 99% confident that the mean diameter produced by the process is between 0.9781 and 1.0331 centimeters. Emphasis is placed on the mean, with less concern about a single reading or the general nature of the distribution of diameters in the population. In the case of the prediction limits, the bounds 0.9186 and 1.0926 are based on the distribution of a single "new" metal piece taken from the process, and again 99% of such limits will cover the diameter of a new measured piece. On the other hand, the tolerance limits, as suggested in the previous section, give the engineer a sense of where the "majority," say the central 95%, of the diameters of measured pieces in the population reside. The 99% tolerance limits, 0.8937 and 1.1175, are numerically quite different from the other two bounds. If these bounds appear alarmingly wide to the engineer, it reflects negatively on process quality. On the other hand, if the bounds represent a desirable result, the engineer may conclude that a majority (95% in here) of the diameters are in a desirable range. Again, a confidence interval interpretation may be used: namely, 99% of such calculated bounds will cover the middle 95% of the population of diameters.

Exercises

1 A UCLA researcher claims that the life span of mice can be extended by as much as 25% when the calories in their diet are reduced by approximately 40% from the time they are weaned. The restricted diet is enriched to normal levels by vitamins and protein. Assuming that it is known from previous studies that $\sigma = 5.8$ months, how many mice should be included in our sample if we wish to be 99% confident that the mean life span of the sample will be within 2 months of the population mean for all mice subjected to this reduced diet?

2 An electrical firm manufactures light bulbs that have a length of life that is approximately normally distributed with a standard deviation of 40 hours. If a sample of 30 bulbs has an average life of 780 hours, find a 96% confidence interval for the population mean of all bulbs produced by this firm.

3 Many cardiac patients wear an implanted pacemaker to control their heartbeat. A plastic connector module mounts on the top of the pacemaker. Assuming a standard deviation of 0.0015 inch and an approximately normal distribution, find a 95% confidence interval for the mean of the depths of all connector modules made by a certain manufacturing company. A random sample of 75 modules has an average depth of 0.310 inch.

4   The heights of a random sample of 50 college students showed a mean of 174.5 centimeters and a standard deviation of 6.9 centimeters.

(a) Construct a 98% confidence interval for the mean height of all college students.

(b) What can we assert with 98% confidence about the possible size of our error if we estimate the mean height of all college students to be 174.5 centimeters?

5   A random sample of 100 automobile owners in the state of Virginia shows that an automobile is driven on average 23,500 kilometers per year with a standard deviation of 3900 kilometers. Assume the distribution of measurements to be approximately normal.

(a) Construct a 99% confidence interval for the average number of kilometers an automobile is driven annually in Virginia.

(b) What can we assert with 99% confidence about the possible size of our error if we estimate the average number of kilometers driven by car owners in Virginia to be 23,500 kilometers per year?

6   How large a sample is needed in Exercise 2 if we wish to be 96% confident that our sample mean will be within 10 hours of the true mean?

7   How large a sample is needed in Exercise 3 if we wish to be 95% confident that our sample mean will be within 0.0005 inch of the true mean?

8   An efficiency expert wishes to determine the average time that it takes to drill three holes in a certain metal clamp. How large a sample will she need to be 95% confident that her sample mean will be within 15 seconds of the true mean? Assume that it is known from previous studies that $\sigma = 40$ seconds.

9   Regular consumption of presweetened cereals contributes to tooth decay, heart disease, and other degenerative diseases, according to studies conducted by Dr. W. H. Bowen of the National Institute of Health and Dr. J. Yudben, Professor of Nutrition and Dietetics at the University of London. In a random sample consisting of 20 similar single servings of Alpha-Bits, the average sugar content was 11.3 grams with a standard deviation of 2.45 grams. Assuming that the sugar contents are normally distributed, construct a 95% confidence interval for the mean sugar content for single servings of Alpha-Bits.

10   A random sample of 12 graduates of a certain secretarial school typed an average of 79.3 words per minute with a standard deviation of 7.8 words per minute. Assuming a normal distribution for the number of words typed per minute, find a 95% confidence interval for the average number of words typed by all graduates of this school.

11   A machine produces metal pieces that are cylindrical in shape. A sample of pieces is taken, and the diameters are found to be 1.01, 0.97, 1.03, 1.04, 0.99, 0.98, 0.99, 1.01, and 1.03 centimeters. Find a 99% confidence interval for the mean diameter of pieces from this machine, assuming an approximately normal distribution.

12   A random sample of 10 chocolate energy bars of a certain brand has, on average, 230 calories per bar, with a standard deviation of 15 calories. Construct a 99% confidence interval for the true mean calorie content of this brand of energy bar. Assume that the distribution of the calorie content is approximately normal.

13   A random sample of 12 shearing pins is taken in a study of the Rockwell hardness of the pin head. Measurements on the Rockwell hardness are made for each of the 12, yielding an average value of 48.50 with a sample standard deviation of 1.5. Assuming the measurements to be normally distributed, construct a 90% confidence interval for the mean Rockwell hardness.

14   The following measurements were recorded for the drying time, in hours, of a certain brand of latex paint:

3.4	2.5	4.8	2.9	3.6
2.8	3.3	5.6	3.7	2.8
4.4	4.0	5.2	3.0	4.8

Assuming that the measurements represent a random sample from a normal population, find a 95% prediction interval for the drying time for the next trial of the paint.

15   Referring to Exercise 5, construct a 99% prediction interval for the kilometers traveled annually by an automobile owner in Virginia.

16   Consider Exercise 10. Compute the 95% prediction interval for the next observed number of words per minute typed by a graduate of the secretarial school.

17   Consider Exercise 9. Compute a 95% prediction interval for the sugar content of the next single serving of Alpha-Bits.

18   Referring to Exercise 13, construct a 95% tolerance interval containing 90% of the measurements.

19   A random sample of 25 tablets of buffered aspirin contains, on average, 325.05 mg of aspirin per tablet, with a standard deviation of 0.5 mg. Find the 95% tolerance limits that will contain 90% of the tablet contents for this brand of buffered aspirin. Assume that the aspirin content is normally distributed.

20   Consider the situation of Exercise 11. Estimation of the mean diameter, while important, is not nearly as important as trying to pin down the location of the majority of the distribution of diameters. Find the 95% tolerance limits that contain 95% of the diameters.

21   In a study conducted by the Department of Zoology at Virginia Tech, fifteen samples of water were collected from a certain station in the James River in order to gain some insight regarding the amount of orthophosphorus in the river. The concentration of the chemical is measured in milligrams per liter. Let us suppose that the mean at the station is not as important as the upper extreme of the distribution of the concentration of the chemical at the station. Concern centers around whether the concentration at the extreme is too large. Readings for the fifteen water samples gave a sample mean of 3.84 milligrams per liter and a sample standard deviation of 3.07 milligrams per liter. Assume that the readings are a random sample from a normal distribution. Calculate a prediction interval (upper 95% prediction limit) and a tolerance limit (95% upper tolerance limit that exceeds 95% of the population of values). Interpret both; that is, tell what each communicates about the upper extreme of the distribution of orthophosphorus at the sampling station.

22   A type of thread is being studied for its tensile strength properties. Fifty pieces were tested under similar conditions, and the results showed an average tensile strength of 78.3 kilograms and a standard deviation of 5.6 kilograms. Assuming a normal distribution of tensile strengths, give a lower 95% prediction limit on a single observed tensile strength value. In addition, give a lower 95% tolerance limit that is exceeded by 99% of the tensile strength values.

23   Refer to Exercise 22. Why are the quantities requested in the exercise likely to be more important to the manufacturer of the thread than, say, a confidence interval on the mean tensile strength?

24   Refer to Exercise 22 again. Suppose that specifications by a buyer of the thread are that the tensile strength of the material must be at least 62 kilograms. The manufacturer is satisfied if at most 5% of the manufactured pieces have tensile strength less than 62 kilograms. Is there cause for concern? Use a one-sided 99% tolerance limit that is exceeded by 95% of the tensile strength values.

25   Consider the drying time measurements in Exercise 14. Suppose the 15 observations in the data set are supplemented by a 16th value of 6.9 hours. In the context of the original 15 observations, is the 16th value an outlier? Show work.

26   Consider the data in Exercise 13. Suppose the manufacturer of the shearing pins insists that the Rockwell hardness of the product be less than or equal to 44.0 only 5% of the time. What is your reaction? Use a tolerance limit calculation as the basis for your judgment.

27   Consider the situation of Case Study 1 with a larger sample of metal pieces. The diameters are as follows: 1.01, 0.97, 1.03, 1.04, 0.99, 0.98, 1.01, 1.03, 0.99, 1.00, 1.00, 0.99, 0.98, 1.01, 1.02, 0.99 centimeters. Once again the normality assumption may be made. Do the following and compare your results to those of the case study. Discuss how they are different and why.

(a) Compute a 99% confidence interval on the mean diameter.

(b) Compute a 99% prediction interval on the next diameter to be measured.

(c) Compute a 99% tolerance interval for coverage of the central 95% of the distribution of diameters.

28   In Section 3, we emphasized the notion of "most efficient estimator" by comparing the variance of two unbiased estimators $\hat{\Theta}_1$ and $\hat{\Theta}_2$. However, this does not take into account bias in case one or both estimators are not unbiased. Consider the quantity

$$MSE = E(\hat{\Theta} - \theta),$$

where MSE denotes **mean squared error**. The MSE is often used to compare two estimators $\hat{\Theta}_1$ and $\hat{\Theta}_2$ of θ when either or both is unbiased because (i) it is intuitively reasonable and (ii) it accounts for bias. Show that MSE can be written

$$MSE = E[\hat{\Theta} - E(\hat{\Theta})]^2 + [E(\hat{\Theta} - \theta)]^2$$
$$= \text{Var}(\hat{\Theta}) + [\text{Bias}(\hat{\Theta})]^2.$$

29   Let us define $S'^2 = \sum_{i=1}^{n}(X_i - \bar{X})^2/n$. Show that

$$E(S'^2) = [(n-1)/n]\sigma^2,$$

and hence S'^2 is a biased estimator for σ^2.

30   Consider S'^2, the estimator of σ^2, from Exercise 29. Analysts often use S'^2 rather than dividing $\sum_{i=1}^{n}(X_i - \bar{X})^2$ by $n-1$, the degrees of freedom in the sample.

(a) What is the bias of S'^2?

(b) Show that the bias of S'^2 approaches zero as $n \to \infty$.

31 If X is a binomial random variable, show that

(a) $\widehat{P} = X/n$ is an unbiased estimator of p;

(b) $P' = \frac{X+\sqrt{n}/2}{n+\sqrt{n}}$ is a biased estimator of p.

32 Show that the estimator P' of Exercise 31(b) becomes unbiased as $n \to \infty$.

33 Compare S^2 and S'^2 (see Exercise 29), the

two estimators of σ^2, to determine which is more efficient. Assume these estimators are found using $X_1, X_2, \ldots, X_n$, independent random variables from $n(x; \mu, \sigma)$. Which estimator is more efficient considering only the variance of the estimators?

34 Consider Exercise 33. Use the MSE discussed in Exercise 28 to determine which estimator is more efficient. Write out

$$\frac{MSE(S^2)}{MSE(S'^2)}.$$

8 Two Samples: Estimating the Difference between Two Means

If we have two populations with means μ_1 and μ_2 and variances σ_1^2 and σ_2^2, respectively, a point estimator of the difference between μ_1 and μ_2 is given by the statistic $\bar{X}_1 - \bar{X}_2$. Therefore, to obtain a point estimate of $\mu_1 - \mu_2$, we shall select two independent random samples, one from each population, of sizes n_1 and n_2, and compute $\bar{x}_1 - \bar{x}_2$, the difference of the sample means. Clearly, we must consider the sampling distribution of $\bar{X}_1 - \bar{X}_2$.

Expect the sampling distribution of $\bar{X}_1 - \bar{X}_2$ to be approximately normally distributed with mean $\mu_{\bar{X}_1 - \bar{X}_2} = \mu_1 - \mu_2$ and standard deviation

$$\sigma_{\bar{X}_1 - \bar{X}_2} = \sqrt{\sigma_1^2/n_1 + \sigma_2^2/n_2}.$$

Therefore, we can assert with a probability of $1 - \alpha$ that the standard normal variable

$$Z = \frac{(\bar{X}_1 - \bar{X}_2) - (\mu_1 - \mu_2)}{\sqrt{\sigma_1^2/n_1 + \sigma_2^2/n_2}}$$

will fall between $-z_{\alpha/2}$ and $z_{\alpha/2}$. Referring once again to Figure 2, we write

$$P(-z_{\alpha/2} < Z < z_{\alpha/2}) = 1 - \alpha.$$

Substituting for Z, we state equivalently that

$$P\left(-z_{\alpha/2} < \frac{(\bar{X}_1 - \bar{X}_2) - (\mu_1 - \mu_2)}{\sqrt{\sigma_1^2/n_1 + \sigma_2^2/n_2}} < z_{\alpha/2}\right) = 1 - \alpha,$$

which leads to the following $100(1-\alpha)\%$ confidence interval for $\mu_1 - \mu_2$.

Confidence Interval for $\mu_1 - \mu_2$, σ_1^2 and σ_2^2 Known	If $\bar{x}_1$ and $\bar{x}_2$ are means of independent random samples of sizes n_1 and n_2 from populations with known variances σ_1^2 and σ_2^2, respectively, a $100(1-\alpha)\%$ confidence interval for $\mu_1 - \mu_2$ is given by

$$(\bar{x}_1 - \bar{x}_2) - z_{\alpha/2}\sqrt{\frac{\sigma_1^2}{n_1} + \frac{\sigma_2^2}{n_2}} < \mu_1 - \mu_2 < (\bar{x}_1 - \bar{x}_2) + z_{\alpha/2}\sqrt{\frac{\sigma_1^2}{n_1} + \frac{\sigma_2^2}{n_2}},$$

where $z_{\alpha/2}$ is the z-value leaving an area of $\alpha/2$ to the right.

The degree of confidence is exact when samples are selected from normal populations. For nonnormal populations, the Central Limit Theorem allows for a good approximation for reasonable size samples.

The Experimental Conditions and the Experimental Unit

For the case of confidence interval estimation on the difference between two means, we need to consider the experimental conditions in the data-taking process. It is assumed that we have two independent random samples from distributions with means μ_1 and μ_2, respectively. It is important that experimental conditions emulate this ideal described by these assumptions as closely as possible. Quite often, the experimenter should plan the strategy of the experiment accordingly. For almost any study of this type, there is a so-called *experimental unit*, which is that part of the experiment that produces experimental error and is responsible for the population variance we refer to as σ^2. In a drug study, the experimental unit is the patient or subject. In an agricultural experiment, it may be a plot of ground. In a chemical experiment, it may be a quantity of raw materials. It is important that differences between the experimental units have minimal impact on the results. The experimenter will have a degree of insurance that experimental units will not bias results if the conditions that define the two populations are *randomly assigned* to the experimental units. We shall again focus on randomization in future chapters that deal with hypothesis testing.

Example 10: A study was conducted in which two types of engines, A and B, were compared. Gas mileage, in miles per gallon, was measured. Fifty experiments were conducted using engine type A and 75 experiments were done with engine type B. The gasoline used and other conditions were held constant. The average gas mileage was 36 miles per gallon for engine A and 42 miles per gallon for engine B. Find a 96% confidence interval on $\mu_B - \mu_A$, where μ_A and μ_B are population mean gas mileages for engines A and B, respectively. Assume that the population standard deviations are 6 and 8 for engines A and B, respectively.

Solution: The point estimate of $\mu_B - \mu_A$ is $\bar{x}_B - \bar{x}_A = 42 - 36 = 6$. Using $\alpha = 0.04$, we find $z_{0.02} = 2.05$ from Table Areas under the Normal Curve. Hence, with substitution in the formula above, the 96% confidence interval is

$$6 - 2.05\sqrt{\frac{64}{75} + \frac{36}{50}} < \mu_B - \mu_A < 6 + 2.05\sqrt{\frac{64}{75} + \frac{36}{50}},$$

or simply $3.43 < \mu_B - \mu_A < 8.57$.

This procedure for estimating the difference between two means is applicable if σ_1^2 and σ_2^2 are known. If the variances are not known and the two distributions involved are approximately normal, the t-distribution becomes involved, as in the case of a single sample. If one is not willing to assume normality, large samples (say greater than 30) will allow the use of s_1 and s_2 in place of σ_1 and σ_2, respectively, with the rationale that $s_1 \approx \sigma_1$ and $s_2 \approx \sigma_2$. Again, of course, the confidence interval is an approximate one.

Variances Unknown but Equal

Consider the case where σ_1^2 and σ_2^2 are unknown. If $\sigma_1^2 = \sigma_2^2 = \sigma^2$, we obtain a standard normal variable of the form

$$Z = \frac{(\bar{X}_1 - \bar{X}_2) - (\mu_1 - \mu_2)}{\sqrt{\sigma^2[(1/n_1) + (1/n_2)]}}.$$

The two random variables

$$\frac{(n_1 - 1)S_1^2}{\sigma^2} \quad \text{and} \quad \frac{(n_2 - 1)S_2^2}{\sigma^2}$$

have chi-squared distributions with $n_1 - 1$ and $n_2 - 1$ degrees of freedom, respectively. Furthermore, they are independent chi-squared variables, since the random samples were selected independently. Consequently, their sum

$$V = \frac{(n_1 - 1)S_1^2}{\sigma^2} + \frac{(n_2 - 1)S_2^2}{\sigma^2} = \frac{(n_1 - 1)S_1^2 + (n_2 - 1)S_2^2}{\sigma^2}$$

has a chi-squared distribution with $v = n_1 + n_2 - 2$ degrees of freedom.

Since the preceding expressions for Z and V can be shown to be independent, it follows that the statistic

$$T = \frac{(\bar{X}_1 - \bar{X}_2) - (\mu_1 - \mu_2)}{\sqrt{\sigma^2[(1/n_1) + (1/n_2)]}} \bigg/ \sqrt{\frac{(n_1 - 1)S_1^2 + (n_2 - 1)S_2^2}{\sigma^2(n_1 + n_2 - 2)}}$$

has the t-distribution with $v = n_1 + n_2 - 2$ degrees of freedom.

A point estimate of the unknown common variance σ^2 can be obtained by pooling the sample variances. Denoting the pooled estimator by S_p^2, we have the following.

Pooled Estimate
of Variance

$$S_p^2 = \frac{(n_1 - 1)S_1^2 + (n_2 - 1)S_2^2}{n_1 + n_2 - 2}.$$

Substituting S_p^2 in the T statistic, we obtain the less cumbersome form

$$T = \frac{(\bar{X}_1 - \bar{X}_2) - (\mu_1 - \mu_2)}{S_p\sqrt{(1/n_1) + (1/n_2)}}.$$

Using the T statistic, we have

$$P(-t_{\alpha/2} < T < t_{\alpha/2}) = 1 - \alpha,$$

where $t_{\alpha/2}$ is the t-value with $n_1 + n_2 - 2$ degrees of freedom, above which we find an area of $\alpha/2$. Substituting for T in the inequality, we write

$$P\left[-t_{\alpha/2} < \frac{(\bar{X}_1 - \bar{X}_2) - (\mu_1 - \mu_2)}{S_p\sqrt{(1/n_1) + (1/n_2)}} < t_{\alpha/2}\right] = 1 - \alpha.$$

After the usual mathematical manipulations, the difference of the sample means $\bar{x}_1 - \bar{x}_2$ and the pooled variance are computed and then the following $100(1 - \alpha)\%$ confidence interval for $\mu_1 - \mu_2$ is obtained.

The value of s_p^2 is easily seen to be a weighted average of the two sample variances s_1^2 and s_2^2, where the weights are the degrees of freedom.

If $\bar{x}_1$ and $\bar{x}_2$ are the means of independent random samples of sizes n_1 and n_2, respectively, from approximately normal populations with unknown but equal variances, a $100(1 - \alpha)\%$ confidence interval for $\mu_1 - \mu_2$ is given by

$$(\bar{x}_1 - \bar{x}_2) - t_{\alpha/2}s_p\sqrt{\frac{1}{n_1} + \frac{1}{n_2}} < \mu_1 - \mu_2 < (\bar{x}_1 - \bar{x}_2) + t_{\alpha/2}s_p\sqrt{\frac{1}{n_1} + \frac{1}{n_2}},$$

where s_p is the pooled estimate of the population standard deviation and $t_{\alpha/2}$ is the t-value with $v = n_1 + n_2 - 2$ degrees of freedom, leaving an area of $\alpha/2$ to the right.

Example 11: The article "Macroinvertebrate Community Structure as an Indicator of Acid Mine Pollution," published in the *Journal of Environmental Pollution*, reports on an investigation undertaken in Cane Creek, Alabama, to determine the relationship between selected physiochemical parameters and different measures of macroinvertebrate community structure. One facet of the investigation was an evaluation of the effectiveness of a numerical species diversity index to indicate aquatic degradation due to acid mine drainage. Conceptually, a high index of macroinvertebrate species diversity should indicate an unstressed aquatic system, while a low diversity index should indicate a stressed aquatic system.

Two independent sampling stations were chosen for this study, one located downstream from the acid mine discharge point and the other located upstream. For 12 monthly samples collected at the downstream station, the species diversity index had a mean value $\bar{x}_1 = 3.11$ and a standard deviation $s_1 = 0.771$, while 10 monthly samples collected at the upstream station had a mean index value $\bar{x}_2 = 2.04$ and a standard deviation $s_2 = 0.448$. Find a 90% confidence interval for the difference between the population means for the two locations, assuming that the populations are approximately normally distributed with equal variances.

Solution: Let μ_1 and μ_2 represent the population means, respectively, for the species diversity indices at the downstream and upstream stations. We wish to find a 90% confidence interval for $\mu_1 - \mu_2$. Our point estimate of $\mu_1 - \mu_2$ is

$$\bar{x}_1 - \bar{x}_2 = 3.11 - 2.04 = 1.07.$$

The pooled estimate, s_p^2, of the common variance, σ^2, is

$$s_p^2 = \frac{(n_1 - 1)s_1^2 + (n_2 - 1)s_2^2}{n_1 + n_2 - 2} = \frac{(11)(0.771^2) + (9)(0.448^2)}{12 + 10 - 2} = 0.417.$$

Taking the square root, we obtain $s_p = 0.646$. Using $\alpha = 0.1$, we find in Table Critical Values of the t-Distribution that $t_{0.05} = 1.725$ for $v = n_1 + n_2 - 2 = 20$ degrees of freedom. Therefore, the 90% confidence interval for $\mu_1 - \mu_2$ is

$$1.07 - (1.725)(0.646)\sqrt{\frac{1}{12} + \frac{1}{10}} < \mu_1 - \mu_2 < 1.07 + (1.725)(0.646)\sqrt{\frac{1}{12} + \frac{1}{10}},$$

which simplifies to $0.593 < \mu_1 - \mu_2 < 1.547$.

Interpretation of the Confidence Interval

For the case of a single parameter, the confidence interval simply provides error bounds on the parameter. Values contained in the interval should be viewed as reasonable values given the experimental data. In the case of a difference between two means, the interpretation can be extended to one of comparing the two means. For example, if we have high confidence that a difference $\mu_1 - \mu_2$ is positive, we would certainly infer that $\mu_1 > \mu_2$ with little risk of being in error. For example, in Example 11, we are 90% confident that the interval from 0.593 to 1.547 contains the difference of the population means for values of the species diversity index at the two stations. The fact that both confidence limits are positive indicates that, on the average, the index for the station located downstream from the discharge point is greater than the index for the station located upstream.

Equal Sample Sizes

The procedure for constructing confidence intervals for $\mu_1 - \mu_2$ with $\sigma_1 = \sigma_2 = \sigma$ unknown requires the assumption that the populations are normal. Slight departures from either the equal variance or the normality assumption do not seriously alter the degree of confidence for our interval. If the population variances are considerably different, we still obtain reasonable results when the populations are normal, provided that $n_1 = n_2$. Therefore, in planning an experiment, one should make every effort to equalize the size of the samples.

Unknown and Unequal Variances

Let us now consider the problem of finding an interval estimate of $\mu_1 - \mu_2$ when the unknown population variances are not likely to be equal. The statistic most often used in this case is

$$T' = \frac{(\bar{X}_1 - \bar{X}_2) - (\mu_1 - \mu_2)}{\sqrt{(S_1^2/n_1) + (S_2^2/n_2)}},$$

which has approximately a t-distribution with v degrees of freedom, where

$$v = \frac{(s_1^2/n_1 + s_2^2/n_2)^2}{[(s_1^2/n_1)^2/(n_1 - 1)] + [(s_2^2/n_2)^2/(n_2 - 1)]}.$$

Since v is seldom an integer, we *round it down* to the nearest whole number. The above estimate of the degrees of freedom is called the Satterthwaite approximation (Satterthwaite, 1946).

Using the statistic T', we write

$$P(-t_{\alpha/2} < T' < t_{\alpha/2}) \approx 1 - \alpha,$$

where $t_{\alpha/2}$ is the value of the t-distribution with v degrees of freedom, above which we find an area of $\alpha/2$. Substituting for T' in the inequality and following the same steps as before, we state the final result.

Confidence
Interval for
$\mu_1 - \mu_2$, $\sigma_1^2 \neq \sigma_2^2$
and Both
Unknown

If $\bar{x}_1$ and s_1^2 and $\bar{x}_2$ and s_2^2 are the means and variances of independent random samples of sizes n_1 and n_2, respectively, from approximately normal populations with unknown and unequal variances, an approximate $100(1 - \alpha)\%$ confidence interval for $\mu_1 - \mu_2$ is given by

$$(\bar{x}_1 - \bar{x}_2) - t_{\alpha/2}\sqrt{\frac{s_1^2}{n_1} + \frac{s_2^2}{n_2}} < \mu_1 - \mu_2 < (\bar{x}_1 - \bar{x}_2) + t_{\alpha/2}\sqrt{\frac{s_1^2}{n_1} + \frac{s_2^2}{n_2}},$$

where $t_{\alpha/2}$ is the t-value with

$$v = \frac{(s_1^2/n_1 + s_2^2/n_2)^2}{[(s_1^2/n_1)^2/(n_1 - 1)] + [(s_2^2/n_2)^2/(n_2 - 1)]}$$

degrees of freedom, leaving an area of $\alpha/2$ to the right.

Note that the expression for v above involves random variables, and thus v is an *estimate* of the degrees of freedom. In applications, this estimate will not result in a whole number, and thus the analyst must round down to the nearest integer to achieve the desired confidence.

Before we illustrate the above confidence interval with an example, we should point out that all the confidence intervals on $\mu_1 - \mu_2$ are of the same general form as those on a single mean; namely, they can be written as

$$\text{point estimate} \pm t_{\alpha/2}\, \widehat{\text{s.e.}}(\text{point estimate})$$

or

$$\text{point estimate} \pm z_{\alpha/2}\, \text{s.e.}(\text{point estimate}).$$

For example, in the case where $\sigma_1 = \sigma_2 = \sigma$, the estimated standard error of $\bar{x}_1 - \bar{x}_2$ is $s_p\sqrt{1/n_1 + 1/n_2}$. For the case where $\sigma_1^2 \neq \sigma_2^2$,

$$\widehat{\text{s.e.}}(\bar{x}_1 - \bar{x}_2) = \sqrt{\frac{s_1^2}{n_1} + \frac{s_2^2}{n_2}}.$$

Example 12: A study was conducted by the Department of Zoology at the Virginia Tech to estimate the difference in the amounts of the chemical orthophosphorus measured at two different stations on the James River. Orthophosphorus was measured in milligrams per liter. Fifteen samples were collected from station 1, and 12 samples were obtained from station 2. The 15 samples from station 1 had an average orthophosphorus content of 3.84 milligrams per liter and a standard deviation of 3.07 milligrams per liter, while the 12 samples from station 2 had an average content of 1.49 milligrams per liter and a standard deviation of 0.80 milligram per liter. Find a 95% confidence interval for the difference in the true average orthophosphorus contents at these two stations, assuming that the observations came from normal populations with different variances.

Solution: For station 1, we have $\bar{x}_1 = 3.84$, $s_1 = 3.07$, and $n_1 = 15$. For station 2, $\bar{x}_2 = 1.49$, $s_2 = 0.80$, and $n_2 = 12$. We wish to find a 95% confidence interval for $\mu_1 - \mu_2$.

Since the population variances are assumed to be unequal, we can only find an approximate 95% confidence interval based on the t-distribution with v degrees of freedom, where

$$v = \frac{(3.07^2/15 + 0.80^2/12)^2}{[(3.07^2/15)^2/14] + [(0.80^2/12)^2/11]} = 16.3 \approx 16.$$

Our point estimate of $\mu_1 - \mu_2$ is

$$\bar{x}_1 - \bar{x}_2 = 3.84 - 1.49 = 2.35.$$

Using $\alpha = 0.05$, we find in Table Critical Values of the t-Distribution that $t_{0.025} = 2.120$ for $v = 16$ degrees of freedom. Therefore, the 95% confidence interval for $\mu_1 - \mu_2$ is

$$2.35 - 2.120\sqrt{\frac{3.07^2}{15} + \frac{0.80^2}{12}} < \mu_1 - \mu_2 < 2.35 + 2.120\sqrt{\frac{3.07^2}{15} + \frac{0.80^2}{12}},$$

which simplifies to $0.60 < \mu_1 - \mu_2 < 4.10$. Hence, we are 95% confident that the interval from 0.60 to 4.10 milligrams per liter contains the difference of the true average orthophosphorus contents for these two locations.

When two population variances are unknown, the assumption of equal variances or unequal variances may be precarious.

9   Paired Observations

At this point, we shall consider estimation procedures for the difference of two means when the samples are not independent and the variances of the two populations are not necessarily equal. The situation considered here deals with a very special experimental condition, namely that of *paired observations*. Unlike in the situation described earlier, the conditions of the two populations are not assigned randomly to experimental units. Rather, each homogeneous experimental unit receives both population conditions; as a result, each experimental unit has a pair of observations, one for each population. For example, if we run a test on a new diet using 15 individuals, the weights before and after going on the diet form the information for our two samples. The two populations are "before" and "after," and the experimental unit is the individual. Obviously, the observations in a pair have something in common. To determine if the diet is effective, we consider the differences $d_1, d_2, \ldots, d_n$ in the paired observations. These differences are the values of a random sample $D_1, D_2, \ldots, D_n$ from a population of differences that we shall assume to be normally distributed with mean $\mu_D = \mu_1 - \mu_2$ and variance σ_D^2. We estimate σ_D^2 by s_d^2, the variance of the differences that constitute our sample. The point estimator of μ_D is given by $\bar{D}$.

When Should Pairing Be Done?

Pairing observations in an experiment is a strategy that can be employed in many fields of application.

Selecting experimental units that are relatively homogeneous (within the units) and allowing each unit to experience both population conditions reduces the effective experimental error variance (in this case, σ_D^2). The reader may visualize the ith pair difference as

$$D_i = X_{1i} - X_{2i}.$$

Since the two observations are taken on the sample experimental unit, they are not independent and, in fact,

$$\mathrm{Var}(D_i) = \mathrm{Var}(X_{1i} - X_{2i}) = \sigma_1^2 + \sigma_2^2 - 2\,\mathrm{Cov}(X_{1i}, X_{2i}).$$

Now, intuitively, we expect that σ_D^2 should be reduced because of the similarity in nature of the "errors" of the two observations within a given experimental unit, and this comes through in the expression above. One certainly expects that if the unit is homogeneous, the covariance is positive. As a result, the gain in quality of the confidence interval over that obtained without pairing will be greatest when there is homogeneity within units and large differences as one goes from unit to unit. One should keep in mind that the performance of the confidence interval will depend on the standard error of $\bar{D}$, which is, of course, $\sigma_D/\sqrt{n}$, where n is the number of pairs. As we indicated earlier, the intent of pairing is to reduce σ_D.

Tradeoff between Reducing Variance and Losing Degrees of Freedom

Comparing the confidence intervals obtained with and without pairing makes apparent that there is a tradeoff involved. Although pairing should indeed reduce variance and hence reduce the standard error of the point estimate, the degrees of freedom are reduced by reducing the problem to a one-sample problem. As a result, the $t_{\alpha/2}$ point attached to the standard error is adjusted accordingly. Thus, pairing may be counterproductive. This would certainly be the case if one experienced only a modest reduction in variance (through σ_D^2) by pairing.

Another illustration of pairing involves choosing n pairs of subjects, with each pair having a similar characteristic such as IQ, age, or breed, and then selecting one member of each pair at random to yield a value of X_1, leaving the other member to provide the value of X_2. In this case, X_1 and X_2 might represent the grades obtained by two individuals of equal IQ when one of the individuals is assigned at random to a class using the conventional lecture approach while the other individual is assigned to a class using programmed materials.

A $100(1-\alpha)\%$ confidence interval for μ_D can be established by writing

$$P(-t_{\alpha/2} < T < t_{\alpha/2}) = 1 - \alpha,$$

where $T = \frac{\bar{D} - \mu_D}{S_d/\sqrt{n}}$ and $t_{\alpha/2}$, as before, is a value of the t-distribution with $n-1$ degrees of freedom.

It is now a routine procedure to replace T by its definition in the inequality above and carry out the mathematical steps that lead to the following $100(1-\alpha)\%$ confidence interval for $\mu_1 - \mu_2 = \mu_D$.

Confidence Interval for $\mu_D = \mu_1 - \mu_2$ for Paired Observations	If $\bar{d}$ and s_d are the mean and standard deviation, respectively, of the normally distributed differences of n random pairs of measurements, a $100(1-\alpha)\%$ confidence interval for $\mu_D = \mu_1 - \mu_2$ is

$$\bar{d} - t_{\alpha/2}\frac{s_d}{\sqrt{n}} < \mu_D < \bar{d} + t_{\alpha/2}\frac{s_d}{\sqrt{n}},$$

where $t_{\alpha/2}$ is the t-value with $v = n - 1$ degrees of freedom, leaving an area of $\alpha/2$ to the right.

Example 13: A study published in *Chemosphere* reported the levels of the dioxin TCDD of 20 Massachusetts Vietnam veterans who were possibly exposed to Agent Orange. The TCDD levels in plasma and in fat tissue are listed in Table 9.1.

Find a 95% confidence interval for $\mu_1 - \mu_2$, where μ_1 and μ_2 represent the true mean TCDD levels in plasma and in fat tissue, respectively. Assume the distribution of the differences to be approximately normal.

Table 1: Data for Example 13

Veteran	TCDD Levels in Plasma	TCDD Levels in Fat Tissue	d_i	Veteran	TCDD Levels in Plasma	TCDD Levels in Fat Tissue	d_i
1	2.5	4.9	−2.4	11	6.9	7.0	−0.1
2	3.1	5.9	−2.8	12	3.3	2.9	0.4
3	2.1	4.4	−2.3	13	4.6	4.6	0.0
4	3.5	6.9	−3.4	14	1.6	1.4	0.2
5	3.1	7.0	−3.9	15	7.2	7.7	−0.5
6	1.8	4.2	−2.4	16	1.8	1.1	0.7
7	6.0	10.0	−4.0	17	20.0	11.0	9.0
8	3.0	5.5	−2.5	18	2.0	2.5	−0.5
9	36.0	41.0	−5.0	19	2.5	2.3	0.2
10	4.7	4.4	0.3	20	4.1	2.5	1.6

Reprinted from *Chemosphere*, Vol. 20, Nos. 7-9 (Tables I and II), Schecter et al., "Partitioning 2,3,7,8-chlorinated dibenzo-p-dioxins and dibenzofurans between adipose tissue and plasma lipid of 20 Massachusetts Vietnam veterans," *pp.* 954–955, Copyright ©1990, with permission from Elsevier.

Solution: We wish to find a 95% confidence interval for $\mu_1 - \mu_2$. Since the observations are paired, $\mu_1 - \mu_2 = \mu_D$. The point estimate of μ_D is $\bar{d} = -0.87$. The standard deviation, s_d, of the sample differences is

$$s_d = \sqrt{\frac{1}{n-1}\sum_{i=1}^{n}(d_i - \bar{d})^2} = \sqrt{\frac{168.4220}{19}} = 2.9773.$$

Using $\alpha = 0.05$, we find in Table Critical Values of the t-Distribution that $t_{0.025} = 2.093$ for $v = n - 1 = 19$ degrees of freedom. Therefore, the 95% confidence interval is

$$-0.8700 - (2.093)\left(\frac{2.9773}{\sqrt{20}}\right) < \mu_D < -0.8700 + (2.093)\left(\frac{2.9773}{\sqrt{20}}\right),$$

or simply $-2.2634 < \mu_D < 0.5234$, from which we can conclude that there is no significant difference between the mean TCDD level in plasma and the mean TCDD level in fat tissue.

Exercises

35 A random sample of size $n_1 = 25$, taken from a normal population with a standard deviation $\sigma_1 = 5$, has a mean $\bar{x}_1 = 80$. A second random sample of size $n_2 = 36$, taken from a different normal population with a standard deviation $\sigma_2 = 3$, has a mean $\bar{x}_2 = 75$. Find a 94% confidence interval for $\mu_1 - \mu_2$.

36 Two kinds of thread are being compared for strength. Fifty pieces of each type of thread are tested under similar conditions. Brand A has an average tensile strength of 78.3 kilograms with a standard deviation of 5.6 kilograms, while brand B has an average tensile strength of 87.2 kilograms with a standard deviation of 6.3 kilograms. Construct a 95% confidence interval for the difference of the population means.

37 A study was conducted to determine if a certain treatment has any effect on the amount of metal removed in a pickling operation. A random sample of 100 pieces was immersed in a bath for 24 hours without the treatment, yielding an average of 12.2 millimeters of metal removed and a sample standard deviation of 1.1 millimeters. A second sample of 200 pieces was exposed to the treatment, followed by the 24-hour immersion in the bath, resulting in an average removal of 9.1 millimeters of metal with a sample standard deviation of 0.9 millimeter. Compute a 98% confidence interval estimate for the difference between the population means. Does the treatment appear to reduce the mean amount of metal removed?

38 Two catalysts in a batch chemical process, are being compared for their effect on the output of the process reaction. A sample of 12 batches was prepared using catalyst 1, and a sample of 10 batches was prepared using catalyst 2. The 12 batches for which catalyst 1 was used in the reaction gave an average yield of 85 with a sample standard deviation of 4, and the 10 batches for which catalyst 2 was used gave an average yield of 81 and a sample standard deviation of 5. Find a 90% confidence interval for the difference between the population means, assuming that the populations are approximately normally distributed with equal variances.

39 Students may choose between a 3-semester-hour physics course without labs and a 4-semester-hour course with labs. The final written examination is the same for each section. If 12 students in the section with labs made an average grade of 84 with a standard deviation of 4, and 18 students in the section without labs made an average grade of 77 with a standard deviation of 6, find a 99% confidence interval for the difference between the average grades for the two courses. Assume the populations to be approximately normally distributed with equal variances.

40 In a study conducted at Virginia Tech on the development of ectomycorrhizal, a symbiotic relationship between the roots of trees and a fungus, in which minerals are transferred from the fungus to the trees and sugars from the trees to the fungus, 20 northern red oak seedlings exposed to the fungus *Pisolithus tinctorus* were grown in a greenhouse. All seedlings were planted in the same type of soil and received the same amount of sunshine and water. Half received no nitrogen at planting time, to serve as a control, and the other half received 368 ppm of nitrogen in the form $NaNO_3$. The stem weights, in grams, at the end of 140 days were recorded as follows:

No Nitrogen	Nitrogen
0.32	0.26
0.53	0.43
0.28	0.47
0.37	0.49
0.47	0.52
0.43	0.75
0.36	0.79
0.42	0.86
0.38	0.62
0.43	0.46

Construct a 95% confidence interval for the difference in the mean stem weight between seedlings that receive no nitrogen and those that receive 368 ppm of nitrogen. Assume the populations to be normally distributed with equal variances.

41 The following data represent the length of time, in days, to recovery for patients randomly treated with one of two medications to clear up severe bladder infections:

Medication 1	Medication 2
$n_1 = 14$	$n_2 = 16$
$\bar{x}_1 = 17$	$\bar{x}_2 = 19$
$s_1^2 = 1.5$	$s_2^2 = 1.8$

Find a 99% confidence interval for the difference $\mu_2 - \mu_1$

in the mean recovery times for the two medications, assuming normal populations with equal variances.

42 An experiment reported in *Popular Science* compared fuel economies for two types of similarly equipped diesel mini-trucks. Let us suppose that 12 Volkswagen and 10 Toyota trucks were tested in 90-kilometer-per-hour steady-paced trials. If the 12 Volkswagen trucks averaged 16 kilometers per liter with a standard deviation of 1.0 kilometer per liter and the 10 Toyota trucks averaged 11 kilometers per liter with a standard deviation of 0.8 kilometer per liter, construct a 90% confidence interval for the difference between the average kilometers per liter for these two mini-trucks. Assume that the distances per liter for the truck models are approximately normally distributed with equal variances.

43 A taxi company is trying to decide whether to purchase brand A or brand B tires for its fleet of taxis. To estimate the difference in the two brands, an experiment is conducted using 12 of each brand. The tires are run until they wear out. The results are

Brand A: $\bar{x}_1 = 36,300$ kilometers,
            $s_1 = 5000$ kilometers.
Brand B: $\bar{x}_2 = 38,100$ kilometers,
            $s_2 = 6100$ kilometers.

Compute a 95% confidence interval for $\mu_A - \mu_B$ assuming the populations to be approximately normally distributed. You may not assume that the variances are equal.

44 Referring to Exercise 43, find a 99% confidence interval for $\mu_1 - \mu_2$ if tires of the two brands are assigned at random to the left and right rear wheels of 8 taxis and the following distances, in kilometers, are recorded:

Taxi	Brand A	Brand B
1	34,400	36,700
2	45,500	46,800
3	36,700	37,700
4	32,000	31,100
5	48,400	47,800
6	32,800	36,400
7	38,100	38,900
8	30,100	31,500

Assume that the differences of the distances are approximately normally distributed.

45 The federal government awarded grants to the agricultural departments of 9 universities to test the yield capabilities of two new varieties of wheat. Each variety was planted on a plot of equal area at each university, and the yields, in kilograms per plot, were recorded as follows:

Variety	University 1	2	3	4	5	6	7	8	9
1	38	23	35	41	44	29	37	31	38
2	45	25	31	38	50	33	36	40	43

Find a 95% confidence interval for the mean difference between the yields of the two varieties, assuming the differences of yields to be approximately normally distributed. Explain why pairing is necessary in this problem.

46 The following data represent the running times of films produced by two motion-picture companies.

Company	Time (minutes)
I	103 94 110 87 98
II	97 82 123 92 175 88 118

Compute a 90% confidence interval for the difference between the average running times of films produced by the two companies. Assume that the running-time differences are approximately normally distributed with unequal variances.

47 *Fortune* magazine (March 1997) reported the total returns to investors for the 10 years prior to 1996 and also for 1996 for 431 companies. The total returns for 10 of the companies are listed below. Find a 95% confidence interval for the mean change in percent return to investors.

Company	Total Return to Investors 1986–96	1996
Coca-Cola	29.8%	43.3%
Mirage Resorts	27.9%	25.4%
Merck	22.1%	24.0%
Microsoft	44.5%	88.3%
Johnson & Johnson	22.2%	18.1%
Intel	43.8%	131.2%
Pfizer	21.7%	34.0%
Procter & Gamble	21.9%	32.1%
Berkshire Hathaway	28.3%	6.2%
S&P 500	11.8%	20.3%

48 An automotive company is considering two types of batteries for its automobile. Sample information on battery life is collected for 20 batteries of type A and 20 batteries of type B. The summary statistics are $\bar{x}_A = 32.91$, $\bar{x}_B = 30.47$, $s_A = 1.57$, and $s_B = 1.74$. Assume the data on each battery are normally distributed and assume $\sigma_A = \sigma_B$.

(a) Find a 95% confidence interval on $\mu_A - \mu_B$.

(b) Draw a conclusion from (a) that provides insight into whether A or B should be adopted.

49 Two different brands of latex paint are being considered for use. Fifteen specimens of each type of paint were selected, and the drying times, in hours, were as follows:

Paint A					Paint B				
3.5	2.7	3.9	4.2	3.6	4.7	3.9	4.5	5.5	4.0
2.7	3.3	5.2	4.2	2.9	5.3	4.3	6.0	5.2	3.7
4.4	5.2	4.0	4.1	3.4	5.5	6.2	5.1	5.4	4.8

Assume the drying time is normally distributed with $\sigma_A = \sigma_B$. Find a 95% confidence interval on $\mu_B - \mu_A$, where μ_A and μ_B are the mean drying times.

50 Two levels (low and high) of insulin doses are given to two groups of diabetic rats to check the insulin-binding capacity, yielding the following data:

Low dose:	$n_1 = 8$	$\bar{x}_1 = 1.98$	$s_1 = 0.51$
High dose:	$n_2 = 13$	$\bar{x}_2 = 1.30$	$s_2 = 0.35$

Assume that the variances are equal. Give a 95% confidence interval for the difference in the true average insulin-binding capacity between the two samples.

10   Single Sample: Estimating a Proportion

A point estimator of the proportion p in a binomial experiment is given by the statistic $\widehat{P} = X/n$, where X represents the number of successes in n trials. Therefore, the sample proportion $\hat{p} = x/n$ will be used as the point estimate of the parameter p.

If the unknown proportion p is not expected to be too close to 0 or 1, we can establish a confidence interval for p by considering the sampling distribution of $\widehat{P}$. Designating a failure in each binomial trial by the value 0 and a success by the value 1, the number of successes, x, can be interpreted as the sum of n values consisting only of 0 and 1s, and $\hat{p}$ is just the sample mean of these n values. Hence, by the Central Limit Theorem, for n sufficiently large, $\widehat{P}$ is approximately normally distributed with mean

$$\mu_{\widehat{P}} = E(\widehat{P}) = E\left(\frac{X}{n}\right) = \frac{np}{n} = p$$

and variance

$$\sigma_{\widehat{P}}^2 = \sigma_{X/n}^2 = \frac{\sigma_X^2}{n^2} = \frac{npq}{n^2} = \frac{pq}{n}.$$

Therefore, we can assert that

$$P(-z_{\alpha/2} < Z < z_{\alpha/2}) = 1 - \alpha, \text{ with } Z = \frac{\widehat{P} - p}{\sqrt{pq/n}},$$

and $z_{\alpha/2}$ is the value above which we find an area of $\alpha/2$ under the standard normal curve. Substituting for Z, we write

$$P\left(-z_{\alpha/2} < \frac{\widehat{P} - p}{\sqrt{pq/n}} < z_{\alpha/2}\right) = 1 - \alpha.$$

When n is large, very little error is introduced by substituting the point estimate $\hat{p} = x/n$ for the p under the radical sign. Then we can write

$$P\left(\widehat{P} - z_{\alpha/2}\sqrt{\frac{\hat{p}\hat{q}}{n}} < p < \widehat{P} + z_{\alpha/2}\sqrt{\frac{\hat{p}\hat{q}}{n}}\right) \approx 1 - \alpha.$$

On the other hand, by solving for p in the quadratic inequality above,

$$-z_{\alpha/2} < \frac{\widehat{P} - p}{\sqrt{pq/n}} < z_{\alpha/2},$$

we obtain another form of the confidence interval for p with limits

$$\frac{\hat{p} + \frac{z_{\alpha/2}^2}{2n}}{1 + \frac{z_{\alpha/2}^2}{n}} \pm \frac{z_{\alpha/2}}{1 + \frac{z_{\alpha/2}^2}{n}} \sqrt{\frac{\hat{p}\hat{q}}{n} + \frac{z_{\alpha/2}^2}{4n^2}}.$$

For a random sample of size n, the sample proportion $\hat{p} = x/n$ is computed, and the following approximate $100(1 - \alpha)\%$ confidence intervals for p can be obtained.

Large-Sample Confidence Intervals for p

If $\hat{p}$ is the proportion of successes in a random sample of size n and $\hat{q} = 1 - \hat{p}$, an approximate $100(1 - \alpha)\%$ confidence interval, for the binomial parameter p is given by (method 1)

$$\hat{p} - z_{\alpha/2}\sqrt{\frac{\hat{p}\hat{q}}{n}} < p < \hat{p} + z_{\alpha/2}\sqrt{\frac{\hat{p}\hat{q}}{n}}$$

or by (method 2)

$$\frac{\hat{p} + \frac{z_{\alpha/2}^2}{2n}}{1 + \frac{z_{\alpha/2}^2}{n}} - \frac{z_{\alpha/2}}{1 + \frac{z_{\alpha/2}^2}{n}} \sqrt{\frac{\hat{p}\hat{q}}{n} + \frac{z_{\alpha/2}^2}{4n^2}} < p < \frac{\hat{p} + \frac{z_{\alpha/2}^2}{2n}}{1 + \frac{z_{\alpha/2}^2}{n}} + \frac{z_{\alpha/2}}{1 + \frac{z_{\alpha/2}^2}{n}} \sqrt{\frac{\hat{p}\hat{q}}{n} + \frac{z_{\alpha/2}^2}{4n^2}},$$

where $z_{\alpha/2}$ is the z-value leaving an area of $\alpha/2$ to the right.

When n is small and the unknown proportion p is believed to be close to 0 or to 1, the confidence-interval procedure established here is unreliable and, therefore, should not be used. To be on the safe side, one should require both $n\hat{p}$ and $n\hat{q}$ to be greater than or equal to 5. The methods for finding a confidence interval for the binomial parameter p are also applicable when the binomial distribution is being used to approximate the hypergeometric distribution, that is, when n is small relative to N, as illustrated by Example 14.

Note that although method 2 yields more accurate results, it is more complicated to calculate, and the gain in accuracy that it provides diminishes when the sample size is large enough. Hence, method 1 is commonly used in practice.

Example 14: In a random sample of $n = 500$ families owning television sets in the city of Hamilton, Canada, it is found that $x = 340$ subscribe to HBO. Find a 95% confidence interval for the actual proportion of families with television sets in this city that subscribe to HBO.

Solution: The point estimate of p is $\hat{p} = 340/500 = 0.68$. Using Table Areas under the Normal Curve, we find that $z_{0.025} = 1.96$. Therefore, using method 1, the 95% confidence interval for p is

$$0.68 - 1.96\sqrt{\frac{(0.68)(0.32)}{500}} < p < 0.68 + 1.96\sqrt{\frac{(0.68)(0.32)}{500}},$$

which simplifies to $0.6391 < p < 0.7209$.

If we use method 2, we can obtain

$$\frac{0.68 + \frac{1.96^2}{(2)(500)}}{1 + \frac{1.96^2}{500}} \pm \frac{1.96}{1 + \frac{1.96^2}{500}}\sqrt{\frac{(0.68)(0.32)}{500} + \frac{1.96^2}{(4)(500^2)}} = 0.6786 \pm 0.0408,$$

which simplifies to $0.6378 < p < 0.7194$. Apparently, when n is large (500 here), both methods yield very similar results.

If p is the center value of a $100(1-\alpha)\%$ confidence interval, then $\hat{p}$ estimates p without error. Most of the time, however, $\hat{p}$ will not be exactly equal to p and the point estimate will be in error. The size of this error will be the positive difference that separates p and $\hat{p}$, and we can be $100(1-\alpha)\%$ confident that this difference will not exceed $z_{\alpha/2}\sqrt{\hat{p}\hat{q}/n}$. We can readily see this if we draw a diagram of a typical confidence interval, as in Figure 9.6. Here we use method 1 to estimate the error.

Figure 6: Error in estimating p by $\hat{p}$.

Theorem 3: If $\hat{p}$ is used as an estimate of p, we can be $100(1-\alpha)\%$ confident that the error will not exceed $z_{\alpha/2}\sqrt{\hat{p}\hat{q}/n}$.

In Example 14, we are 95% confident that the sample proportion $\hat{p} = 0.68$ differs from the true proportion p by an amount not exceeding 0.04.

Choice of Sample Size

Let us now determine how large a sample is necessary to ensure that the error in estimating p will be less than a specified amount e. By Theorem 3, we must choose n such that $z_{\alpha/2}\sqrt{\hat{p}\hat{q}/n} = e$.

Theorem 4: If $\hat{p}$ is used as an estimate of p, we can be $100(1-\alpha)\%$ confident that the error will be less than a specified amount e when the sample size is approximately

$$n = \frac{z_{\alpha/2}^2 \hat{p}\hat{q}}{e^2}.$$

Theorem 4 is somewhat misleading in that we must use $\hat{p}$ to determine the sample size n, but $\hat{p}$ is computed from the sample. If a crude estimate of p can be made without taking a sample, this value can be used to determine n. Lacking such an estimate, we could take a preliminary sample of size $n \geq 30$ to provide an estimate of p. Using Theorem 4, we could determine approximately how many observations are needed to provide the desired degree of accuracy. Note that fractional values of n are rounded up to the next whole number.

Example 15: How large a sample is required if we want to be 95% confident that our estimate of p in Example 14 is within 0.02 of the true value?

Solution: Let us treat the 500 families as a preliminary sample, providing an estimate $\hat{p} = 0.68$. Then, by Theorem 4,

$$n = \frac{(1.96)^2(0.68)(0.32)}{(0.02)^2} = 2089.8 \approx 2090.$$

Therefore, if we base our estimate of p on a random sample of size 2090, we can be 95% confident that our sample proportion will not differ from the true proportion by more than 0.02.

Occasionally, it will be impractical to obtain an estimate of p to be used for determining the sample size for a specified degree of confidence. If this happens, an upper bound for n is established by noting that $\hat{p}\hat{q} = \hat{p}(1 - \hat{p})$, which must be at most $1/4$, since $\hat{p}$ must lie between 0 and 1. This fact may be verified by completing the square. Hence

$$\hat{p}(1 - \hat{p}) = -(\hat{p}^2 - \hat{p}) = \frac{1}{4} - \left(\hat{p}^2 - \hat{p} + \frac{1}{4}\right) = \frac{1}{4} - \left(\hat{p} - \frac{1}{2}\right)^2,$$

which is always less than $1/4$ except when $\hat{p} = 1/2$, and then $\hat{p}\hat{q} = 1/4$. Therefore, if we substitute $\hat{p} = 1/2$ into the formula for n in Theorem 4 when, in fact, p actually differs from $1/2$, n will turn out to be larger than necessary for the specified degree of confidence; as a result, our degree of confidence will increase.

Theorem 5: If $\hat{p}$ is used as an estimate of p, we can be **at least** $100(1 - \alpha)\%$ confident that the error will not exceed a specified amount e when the sample size is

$$n = \frac{z_{\alpha/2}^2}{4e^2}.$$

Example 16: How large a sample is required if we want to be at least 95% confident that our estimate of p in Example 14 is within 0.02 of the true value?

Solution: Unlike in Example 15, we shall now assume that no preliminary sample has been taken to provide an estimate of p. Consequently, we can be at least 95% confident that our sample proportion will not differ from the true proportion by more than 0.02 if we choose a sample of size

$$n = \frac{(1.96)^2}{(4)(0.02)^2} = 2401.$$

Comparing the results of Examples 15 and 16, we see that information concerning p, provided by a preliminary sample or from experience, enables us to choose a smaller sample while maintaining our required degree of accuracy.

11   Two Samples: Estimating the Difference between Two Proportions

Consider the problem where we wish to estimate the difference between two binomial parameters p_1 and p_2. For example, p_1 might be the proportion of smokers with lung cancer and p_2 the proportion of nonsmokers with lung cancer, and the problem is to estimate the difference between these two proportions. First, we select independent random samples of sizes n_1 and n_2 from the two binomial populations with means $n_1 p_1$ and $n_2 p_2$ and variances $n_1 p_1 q_1$ and $n_2 p_2 q_2$, respectively; then we determine the numbers x_1 and x_2 of people in each sample with lung cancer and form the proportions $\hat{p}_1 = x_1/n$ and $\hat{p}_2 = x_2/n$. A point estimator of the difference between the two proportions, $p_1 - p_2$, is given by the statistic $\widehat{P}_1 - \widehat{P}_2$. Therefore, the difference of the sample proportions, $\hat{p}_1 - \hat{p}_2$, will be used as the point estimate of $p_1 - p_2$.

A confidence interval for $p_1 - p_2$ can be established by considering the sampling distribution of $\widehat{P}_1 - \widehat{P}_2$. From Section 9.10 we know that $\widehat{P}_1$ and $\widehat{P}_2$ are each approximately normally distributed, with means p_1 and p_2 and variances $p_1 q_1/n_1$ and $p_2 q_2/n_2$, respectively. Choosing independent samples from the two populations ensures that the variables $\widehat{P}_1$ and $\widehat{P}_2$ will be independent, and then by the reproductive property of the normal distribution, we conclude that $\hat{P}_1 - \hat{P}_2$ is approximately normally distributed with mean

$$\mu_{\widehat{P}_1 - \widehat{P}_2} = p_1 - p_2$$

and variance

$$\sigma^2_{\widehat{P}_1 - \widehat{P}_2} = \frac{p_1 q_1}{n_1} + \frac{p_2 q_2}{n_2}.$$

Therefore, we can assert that

$$P(-z_{\alpha/2} < Z < z_{\alpha/2}) = 1 - \alpha,$$

where

$$Z = \frac{(\widehat{P}_1 - \widehat{P}_2) - (p_1 - p_2)}{\sqrt{p_1 q_1/n_1 + p_2 q_2/n_2}}$$

and $z_{\alpha/2}$ is the value above which we find an area of $\alpha/2$ under the standard normal curve. Substituting for Z, we write

$$P\left[-z_{\alpha/2} < \frac{(\widehat{P}_1 - \widehat{P}_2) - (p_1 - p_2)}{\sqrt{p_1 q_1/n_1 + p_2 q_2/n_2}} < z_{\alpha/2}\right] = 1 - \alpha.$$

After performing the usual mathematical manipulations, we replace p_1, p_2, q_1, and q_2 under the radical sign by their estimates $\hat{p}_1 = x_1/n_1$, $\hat{p}_2 = x_2/n_2$, $\hat{q}_1 = 1 - \hat{p}_1$, and $\hat{q}_2 = 1 - \hat{p}_2$, provided that $n_1\hat{p}_1$, $n_1\hat{q}_1$, $n_2\hat{p}_2$, and $n_2\hat{q}_2$ are all greater than or equal to 5, and the following approximate $100(1 - \alpha)\%$ confidence interval for $p_1 - p_2$ is obtained.

<table>
<tr><td>

Large-Sample
Confidence
Interval for
$p_1 - p_2$
</td><td>

If $\hat{p}_1$ and $\hat{p}_2$ are the proportions of successes in random samples of sizes n_1 and n_2, respectively, $\hat{q}_1 = 1 - \hat{p}_1$, and $\hat{q}_2 = 1 - \hat{p}_2$, an approximate $100(1 - \alpha)\%$ confidence interval for the difference of two binomial parameters, $p_1 - p_2$, is given by

$$(\hat{p}_1 - \hat{p}_2) - z_{\alpha/2}\sqrt{\frac{\hat{p}_1\hat{q}_1}{n_1} + \frac{\hat{p}_2\hat{q}_2}{n_2}} < p_1 - p_2 < (\hat{p}_1 - \hat{p}_2) + z_{\alpha/2}\sqrt{\frac{\hat{p}_1\hat{q}_1}{n_1} + \frac{\hat{p}_2\hat{q}_2}{n_2}},$$

where $z_{\alpha/2}$ is the z-value leaving an area of $\alpha/2$ to the right.
</td></tr>
</table>

Example 17: A certain change in a process for manufacturing component parts is being considered. Samples are taken under both the existing and the new process so as to determine if the new process results in an improvement. If 75 of 1500 items from the existing process are found to be defective and 80 of 2000 items from the new process are found to be defective, find a 90% confidence interval for the true difference in the proportion of defectives between the existing and the new process.

Solution: Let p_1 and p_2 be the true proportions of defectives for the existing and new processes, respectively. Hence, $\hat{p}_1 = 75/1500 = 0.05$ and $\hat{p}_2 = 80/2000 = 0.04$, and the point estimate of $p_1 - p_2$ is

$$\hat{p}_1 - \hat{p}_2 = 0.05 - 0.04 = 0.01.$$

Using Table Areas under the Normal Curve, we find that $z_{0.05} = 1.645$. Therefore, substituting into the formula, with

$$1.645\sqrt{\frac{(0.05)(0.95)}{1500} + \frac{(0.04)(0.96)}{2000}} = 0.0117,$$

we find the 90% confidence interval to be $-0.0017 < p_1 - p_2 < 0.0217$. Since the interval contains the value 0, there is no reason to believe that the new process produces a significant decrease in the proportion of defectives over the existing method.

Up to this point, all confidence intervals presented were of the form

$$\text{point estimate } \pm K \text{ s.e.(point estimate)},$$

where K is a constant (either t or normal percent point). This form is valid when the parameter is a mean, a difference between means, a proportion, or a difference between proportions, due to the symmetry of the t- and Z-distributions. However, it does not extend to variances and ratios of variances, which will be discussed in Sections 12 and 13.

Exercises

In this set of exercises, for estimation concerning one proportion, use only method 1 to obtain the confidence intervals, unless instructed otherwise.

51   In a random sample of 1000 homes in a certain city, it is found that 228 are heated by oil. Find 99% confidence intervals for the proportion of homes in this city that are heated by oil using both methods presented in Large-Sample Confidence intervals.

52   Compute 95% confidence intervals, using both methods in Large-Sample Confidence intervals for the proportion of defective items in a process when it is found that a sample of size 100 yields 8 defectives.

53   (a) A random sample of 200 voters in a town is selected, and 114 are found to support an annexation suit. Find the 96% confidence interval for the fraction of the voting population favoring the suit.

(b) What can we assert with 96% confidence about the possible size of our error if we estimate the fraction of voters favoring the annexation suit to be 0.57?

54   A manufacturer of MP3 players conducts a set of comprehensive tests on the electrical functions of its product. All MP3 players must pass all tests prior to being sold. Of a random sample of 500 MP3 players, 15 failed one or more tests. Find a 90% confidence interval for the proportion of MP3 players from the population that pass all tests.

55   A new rocket-launching system is being considered for deployment of small, short-range rockets. The existing system has $p = 0.8$ as the probability of a successful launch. A sample of 40 experimental launches is made with the new system, and 34 are successful.

(a) Construct a 95% confidence interval for p.

(b) Would you conclude that the new system is better?

56   A geneticist is interested in the proportion of African males who have a certain minor blood disorder. In a random sample of 100 African males, 24 are found to be afflicted.

(a) Compute a 99% confidence interval for the proportion of African males who have this blood disorder.

(b) What can we assert with 99% confidence about the possible size of our error if we estimate the proportion of African males with this blood disorder to be 0.24?

57   (a) According to a report in the *Roanoke Times & World-News*, approximately 2/3 of 1600 adults polled by telephone said they think the space shuttle program is a good investment for the country. Find a 95% confidence interval for the proportion of American adults who think the space shuttle program is a good investment for the country.

(b) What can we assert with 95% confidence about the possible size of our error if we estimate the proportion of American adults who think the space shuttle program is a good investment to be 2/3?

58   In the newspaper article referred to in Exercise 9.57, 32% of the 1600 adults polled said the U.S. space program should emphasize scientific exploration. How large a sample of adults is needed for the poll if one wishes to be 95% confident that the estimated percentage will be within 2% of the true percentage?

59   How large a sample is needed if we wish to be 96% confident that our sample proportion in Exercise 53 will be within 0.02 of the true fraction of the voting population?

60   How large a sample is needed if we wish to be 99% confident that our sample proportion in Exercise 51 will be within 0.05 of the true proportion of homes in the city that are heated by oil?

61   How large a sample is needed in Exercise 52 if we wish to be 98% confident that our sample proportion will be within 0.05 of the true proportion defective?

62   A conjecture by a faculty member in the microbiology department at Washington University School of Dental Medicine in St. Louis, Missouri, states that a couple of cups of either green or oolong tea each day will provide sufficient fluoride to protect your teeth from decay. How large a sample is needed to estimate the percentage of citizens in a certain town who favor having their water fluoridated if one wishes to be at least 99% confident that the estimate is within 1% of the true percentage?

63   A study is to be made to estimate the percentage of citizens in a town who favor having their water fluoridated. How large a sample is needed if one wishes to be at least 95% confident that the estimate is within 1% of the true percentage?

64   A study is to be made to estimate the proportion of residents of a certain city and its suburbs who favor the construction of a nuclear power plant near the city. How large a sample is needed if one wishes to be at least 95% confident that the estimate is within 0.04 of the true proportion of residents who favor the construction of the nuclear power plant?

65 A certain geneticist is interested in the proportion of males and females in the population who have a minor blood disorder. In a random sample of 1000 males, 250 are found to be afflicted, whereas 275 of 1000 females tested appear to have the disorder. Compute a 95% confidence interval for the difference between the proportions of males and females who have the blood disorder.

66 Ten engineering schools in the United States were surveyed. The sample contained 250 electrical engineers, 80 being women; 175 chemical engineers, 40 being women. Compute a 90% confidence interval for the difference between the proportions of women in these two fields of engineering. Is there a significant difference between the two proportions?

67 A clinical trial was conducted to determine if a certain type of inoculation has an effect on the incidence of a certain disease. A sample of 1000 rats was kept in a controlled environment for a period of 1 year, and 500 of the rats were given the inoculation. In the group not inoculated, there were 120 incidences of the disease, while 98 of the rats in the inoculated group contracted it. If p_1 is the probability of incidence of the disease in uninoculated rats and p_2 the probability of incidence in inoculated rats, compute a 90% confidence interval for $p_1 - p_2$.

68 In the study *Germination and Emergence of Broccoli*, conducted by the Department of Horticulture at Virginia Tech, a researcher found that at 5°C, 10 broccoli seeds out of 20 germinated, while at 15°C, 15 out of 20 germinated. Compute a 95% confidence interval for the difference between the proportions of germination at the two different temperatures and decide if there is a significant difference.

69 A survey of 1000 students found that 274 chose professional baseball team A as their favorite team. In a similar survey involving 760 students, 240 of them chose team A as their favorite. Compute a 95% confidence interval for the difference between the proportions of students favoring team A in the two surveys. Is there a significant difference?

70 According to *USA Today* (March 17, 1997), women made up 33.7% of the editorial staff at local TV stations in the United States in 1990 and 36.2% in 1994. Assume 20 new employees were hired as editorial staff.

(a) Estimate the number that would have been women in 1990 and 1994, respectively.

(b) Compute a 95% confidence interval to see if there is evidence that the proportion of women hired as editorial staff was higher in 1994 than in 1990.

12 Single Sample: Estimating the Variance

If a sample of size n is drawn from a normal population with variance σ^2 and the sample variance s^2 is computed, we obtain a value of the statistic S^2. This computed sample variance is used as a point estimate of σ^2. Hence, the statistic S^2 is called an estimator of σ^2.

An interval estimate of σ^2 can be established by using the statistic

$$X^2 = \frac{(n-1)S^2}{\sigma^2}.$$

The statistic X^2 has a chi-squared distribution with $n-1$ degrees of freedom when samples are chosen from a normal population. We may write (see Figure 7)

$$P(\chi^2_{1-\alpha/2} < X^2 < \chi^2_{\alpha/2}) = 1 - \alpha,$$

where $\chi^2_{1-\alpha/2}$ and $\chi^2_{\alpha/2}$ are values of the chi-squared distribution with $n-1$ degrees of freedom, leaving areas of $1-\alpha/2$ and $\alpha/2$, respectively, to the right. Substituting for X^2, we write

$$P\left[\chi^2_{1-\alpha/2} < \frac{(n-1)S^2}{\sigma^2} < \chi^2_{\alpha/2}\right] = 1 - \alpha.$$

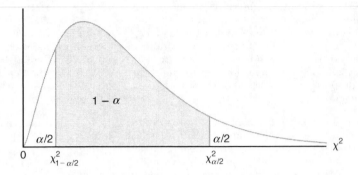

Figure 7: $P(\chi^2_{1-\alpha/2} < X^2 < \chi^2_{\alpha/2}) = 1 - \alpha$.

Dividing each term in the inequality by $(n-1)S^2$ and then inverting each term (thereby changing the sense of the inequalities), we obtain

$$P\left[\frac{(n-1)S^2}{\chi^2_{\alpha/2}} < \sigma^2 < \frac{(n-1)S^2}{\chi^2_{1-\alpha/2}}\right] = 1 - \alpha.$$

For a random sample of size n from a normal population, the sample variance s^2 is computed, and the following $100(1-\alpha)\%$ confidence interval for σ^2 is obtained.

Confidence   If s^2 is the variance of a random sample of size n from a normal population, a
Interval for σ^2 $100(1-\alpha)\%$ confidence interval for σ^2 is

$$\frac{(n-1)s^2}{\chi^2_{\alpha/2}} < \sigma^2 < \frac{(n-1)s^2}{\chi^2_{1-\alpha/2}},$$

where $\chi^2_{\alpha/2}$ and $\chi^2_{1-\alpha/2}$ are χ^2-values with $v = n-1$ degrees of freedom, leaving areas of $\alpha/2$ and $1 - \alpha/2$, respectively, to the right.

An approximate $100(1-\alpha)\%$ confidence interval for σ is obtained by taking the square root of each endpoint of the interval for σ^2.

Example 18:   The following are the weights, in decagrams, of 10 packages of grass seed distributed by a certain company: 46.4, 46.1, 45.8, 47.0, 46.1, 45.9, 45.8, 46.9, 45.2, and 46.0. Find a 95% confidence interval for the variance of the weights of all such packages of grass seed distributed by this company, assuming a normal population.

Solution: First we find

$$s^2 = \frac{n \sum_{i=1}^{n} x_i^2 - \left(\sum_{i=1}^{n} x_i\right)^2}{n(n-1)}$$

$$= \frac{(10)(21,273.12) - (461.2)^2}{(10)(9)} = 0.286.$$

To obtain a 95% confidence interval, we choose $\alpha = 0.05$. Then, using Table Critical Values of the Chi-Squared Distribution at the end of this chapter with $v = 9$ degrees of freedom, we find $\chi^2_{0.025} = 19.023$ and $\chi^2_{0.975} = 2.700$. Therefore, the 95% confidence interval for σ^2 is

$$\frac{(9)(0.286)}{19.023} < \sigma^2 < \frac{(9)(0.286)}{2.700},$$

or simply $0.135 < \sigma^2 < 0.953$.

13   Two Samples: Estimating the Ratio of Two Variances

A point estimate of the ratio of two population variances σ_1^2/σ_2^2 is given by the ratio s_1^2/s_2^2 of the sample variances. Hence, the statistic S_1^2/S_2^2 is called an estimator of σ_1^2/σ_2^2.

If σ_1^2 and σ_2^2 are the variances of normal populations, we can establish an interval estimate of σ_1^2/σ_2^2 by using the statistic

$$F = \frac{\sigma_2^2 S_1^2}{\sigma_1^2 S_2^2}.$$

The random variable F has an F-distribution with $v_1 = n_1 - 1$ and $v_2 = n_2 - 1$ degrees of freedom. Therefore, we may write (see Figure 8)

$$P[f_{1-\alpha/2}(v_1, v_2) < F < f_{\alpha/2}(v_1, v_2)] = 1 - \alpha,$$

where $f_{1-\alpha/2}(v_1, v_2)$ and $f_{\alpha/2}(v_1, v_2)$ are the values of the F-distribution with v_1 and v_2 degrees of freedom, leaving areas of $1 - \alpha/2$ and $\alpha/2$, respectively, to the right.

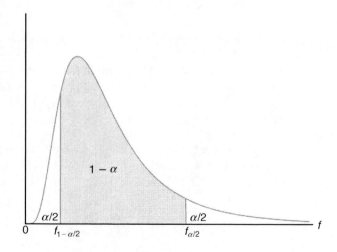

Figure 8: $P[f_{1-\alpha/2}(v_1, v_2) < F < f_{\alpha/2}(v_1, v_2)] = 1 - \alpha.$

Substituting for F, we write

$$P\left[f_{1-\alpha/2}(v_1, v_2) < \frac{\sigma_2^2 S_1^2}{\sigma_1^2 S_2^2} < f_{\alpha/2}(v_1, v_2)\right] = 1 - \alpha.$$

Multiplying each term in the inequality by S_2^2/S_1^2 and then inverting each term, we obtain

$$P\left[\frac{S_1^2}{S_2^2}\frac{1}{f_{\alpha/2}(v_1, v_2)} < \frac{\sigma_1^2}{\sigma_2^2} < \frac{S_1^2}{S_2^2}\frac{1}{f_{1-\alpha/2}(v_1, v_2)}\right] = 1 - \alpha.$$

The results enable us to replace the quantity $f_{1-\alpha/2}(v_1, v_2)$ by $1/f_{\alpha/2}(v_2, v_1)$. Therefore,

$$P\left[\frac{S_1^2}{S_2^2}\frac{1}{f_{\alpha/2}(v_1, v_2)} < \frac{\sigma_1^2}{\sigma_2^2} < \frac{S_1^2}{S_2^2}f_{\alpha/2}(v_2, v_1)\right] = 1 - \alpha.$$

For any two independent random samples of sizes n_1 and n_2 selected from two normal populations, the ratio of the sample variances s_1^2/s_2^2 is computed, and the following $100(1-\alpha)\%$ confidence interval for σ_1^2/σ_2^2 is obtained.

Confidence Interval for σ_1^2/σ_2^2

If s_1^2 and s_2^2 are the variances of independent samples of sizes n_1 and n_2, respectively, from normal populations, then a $100(1-\alpha)\%$ confidence interval for σ_1^2/σ_2^2 is

$$\frac{s_1^2}{s_2^2}\frac{1}{f_{\alpha/2}(v_1, v_2)} < \frac{\sigma_1^2}{\sigma_2^2} < \frac{s_1^2}{s_2^2}f_{\alpha/2}(v_2, v_1),$$

where $f_{\alpha/2}(v_1, v_2)$ is an f-value with $v_1 = n_1 - 1$ and $v_2 = n_2 - 1$ degrees of freedom, leaving an area of $\alpha/2$ to the right, and $f_{\alpha/2}(v_2, v_1)$ is a similar f-value with $v_2 = n_2 - 1$ and $v_1 = n_1 - 1$ degrees of freedom.

As in Section 12, an approximate $100(1-\alpha)\%$ confidence interval for σ_1/σ_2 is obtained by taking the square root of each endpoint of the interval for σ_1^2/σ_2^2.

Example 19: A confidence interval for the difference in the mean orthophosphorus contents, measured in milligrams per liter, at two stations on the James River was constructed in Example 12 by assuming the normal population variance to be unequal. Justify this assumption by constructing 98% confidence intervals for σ_1^2/σ_2^2 and for σ_1/σ_2, where σ_1^2 and σ_2^2 are the variances of the populations of orthophosphorus contents at station 1 and station 2, respectively.

Solution: From Example 12, we have $n_1 = 15$, $n_2 = 12$, $s_1 = 3.07$, and $s_2 = 0.80$. For a 98% confidence interval, $\alpha = 0.02$. Interpolating in Table A.6, we find $f_{0.01}(14, 11) \approx 4.30$ and $f_{0.01}(11, 14) \approx 3.87$. Therefore, the 98% confidence interval for σ_1^2/σ_2^2 is

$$\left(\frac{3.07^2}{0.80^2}\right)\left(\frac{1}{4.30}\right) < \frac{\sigma_1^2}{\sigma_2^2} < \left(\frac{3.07^2}{0.80^2}\right)(3.87),$$

which simplifies to $3.425 < \frac{\sigma_1^2}{\sigma_2^2} < 56.991$. Taking square roots of the confidence limits, we find that a 98% confidence interval for σ_1/σ_2 is

$$1.851 < \frac{\sigma_1}{\sigma_2} < 7.549.$$

Since this interval does not allow for the possibility of σ_1/σ_2 being equal to 1, we were correct in assuming that $\sigma_1 \neq \sigma_2$ or $\sigma_1^2 \neq \sigma_2^2$ in Example 12.

Exercises

71 A manufacturer of car batteries claims that the batteries will last, on average, 3 years with a variance of 1 year. If 5 of these batteries have lifetimes of 1.9, 2.4, 3.0, 3.5, and 4.2 years, construct a 95% confidence interval for σ^2 and decide if the manufacturer's claim that $\sigma^2 = 1$ is valid. Assume the population of battery lives to be approximately normally distributed.

72 A random sample of 20 students yielded a mean of $\bar{x} = 72$ and a variance of $s^2 = 16$ for scores on a college placement test in mathematics. Assuming the scores to be normally distributed, construct a 98% confidence interval for σ^2.

73 Construct a 95% confidence interval for σ^2 in Exercise 9.

74 Construct a 99% confidence interval for σ^2 in Exercise 11.

75 Construct a 99% confidence interval for σ in Exercise 12.

76 Construct a 90% confidence interval for σ in Exercise 13.

77 Construct a 98% confidence interval for σ_1/σ_2 in Exercise 42, where σ_1 and σ_1 are, respectively, the standard deviations for the distances traveled per liter of fuel by the Volkswagen and Toyota mini-trucks.

78 Construct a 90% confidence interval for σ_1^2/σ_2^2 in Exercise 43. Were we justified in assuming that $\sigma_1^2 \neq \sigma_2^2$ when we constructed the confidence interval for $\mu_1 - \mu_2$?

79 Construct a 90% confidence interval for σ_1^2/σ_2^2 in Exercise 46. Should we have assumed $\sigma_1^2 = \sigma_2^2$ in constructing our confidence interval for $\mu_1 - \mu_{11}$?

80 Construct a 95% confidence interval for σ_A^2/σ_B^2 in Exercise 49. Should the equal-variance assumption be used?

14   Maximum Likelihood Estimation (Optional)

Often the estimators of parameters have been those that appeal to intuition. The estimator $\bar{X}$ certainly seems reasonable as an estimator of a population mean μ. The virtue of S^2 as an estimator of σ^2 is underscored through the discussion of unbiasedness in Section 3. The estimator for a binomial parameter p is merely a sample proportion, which, of course, is an *average* and appeals to common sense. But there are many situations in which it is not at all obvious what the proper estimator should be. As a result, there is much to be learned by the student of statistics concerning different philosophies that produce different methods of estimation. In this section, we deal with the **method of maximum likelihood**.

Maximum likelihood estimation is one of the most important approaches to estimation in all of statistical inference. We will not give a thorough development of the method. Rather, we will attempt to communicate the philosophy of maximum likelihood and illustrate with examples that relate to other estimation problems discussed in this chapter.

The Likelihood Function

As the name implies, the method of maximum likelihood is that for which the *like-lihood function* is maximized. The likelihood function is best illustrated through the use of an example with a discrete distribution and a single parameter. Denote by $X_1, X_2, \ldots, X_n$ the independent random variables taken from a discrete probability distribution represented by $f(\mathbf{x}, \theta)$, where θ is a single parameter of the distribution. Now

$$L(x_1, x_2, \ldots, x_n; \theta) = f(x_1, x_2, \ldots, x_n; \theta)$$
$$= f(x_1, \theta) f(x_2, \theta) \cdots f(x_n, \theta)$$

is the *joint distribution of the random variables*, often referred to as the likelihood function. Note that the variable of the likelihood function is θ, not $\mathbf{x}$. Denote by $x_1, x_2, \ldots, x_n$ the observed values in a sample. In the case of a discrete random variable, the interpretation is very clear. The quantity $L(x_1, x_2, \ldots, x_n; \theta)$, *the likelihood of the sample*, is the following joint probability:

$$P(X_1 = x_1, X_2 = x_2, \ldots, X_n = x_n \mid \theta),$$

which is the probability of obtaining the sample values $x_1, x_2, \ldots, x_n$. For the discrete case, the maximum likelihood estimator is one that results in a maximum value for this joint probability or maximizes the likelihood of the sample.

Consider a fictitious example where three items from an assembly line are inspected. The items are ruled either defective or nondefective, and thus the Bernoulli process applies. Testing the three items results in two nondefective items followed by a defective item. It is of interest to estimate p, the proportion non-defective in the process. The likelihood of the sample for this illustration is given by

$$p \cdot p \cdot q = p^2 q = p^2 - p^3,$$

where $q = 1 - p$. Maximum likelihood estimation would give an estimate of p for which the likelihood is maximized. It is clear that if we differentiate the likelihood with respect to p, set the derivative to zero, and solve, we obtain the value

$$\hat{p} = \frac{2}{3}.$$

Now, of course, in this situation $\hat{p} = 2/3$ is the sample proportion defective and is thus a reasonable estimator of the probability of a defective. The reader should attempt to understand that the philosophy of maximum likelihood estimation evolves from the notion that the reasonable estimator of a parameter based on sample information *is that parameter value that produces the largest probability of obtaining the sample*. This is, indeed, the interpretation for the discrete case, since the likelihood is the probability of jointly observing the values in the sample.

Now, while the interpretation of the likelihood function as a joint probability is confined to the discrete case, the notion of maximum likelihood extends to the estimation of parameters of a continuous distribution. We now present a formal definition of maximum likelihood estimation.

One- and Two-Sample Estimation Problems

Definition 3:

> Given independent observations $x_1, x_2, \ldots, x_n$ from a probability density function (continuous case) or probability mass function (discrete case) $f(\mathbf{x}; \theta)$, the maximum likelihood estimator $\hat{\theta}$ is that which maximizes the likelihood function
>
> $$L(x_1, x_2, \ldots, x_n; \theta) = f(\mathbf{x}; \theta) = f(x_1, \theta) f(x_2, \theta) \cdots f(x_n, \theta).$$

Quite often it is convenient to work with the natural log of the likelihood function in finding the maximum of that function. Consider the following example dealing with the parameter μ of a Poisson distribution.

Example 20: Consider a Poisson distribution with probability mass function

$$f(x|\mu) = \frac{e^{-\mu}\mu^x}{x!}, \quad x = 0, 1, 2, \ldots.$$

Suppose that a random sample $x_1, x_2, \ldots, x_n$ is taken from the distribution. What is the maximum likelihood estimate of μ?

Solution: The likelihood function is

$$L(x_1, x_2, \ldots, x_n; \mu) = \prod_{i=1}^{n} f(x_i|\mu) = \frac{e^{-n\mu}\mu^{\sum_{i=1}^{n} x_i}}{\prod_{i=1}^{n} x_i!}.$$

Now consider

$$\ln L(x_1, x_2, \ldots, x_n; \mu) = -n\mu + \sum_{i=1}^{n} x_i \ln \mu - \ln \prod_{i=1}^{n} x_i!$$

$$\frac{\partial \ln L(x_1, x_2, \ldots, x_n; \mu)}{\partial \mu} = -n + \sum_{i=1}^{n} \frac{x_i}{\mu}.$$

Solving for $\hat{\mu}$, the maximum likelihood estimator, involves setting the derivative to zero and solving for the parameter. Thus,

$$\hat{\mu} = \sum_{i=1}^{n} \frac{x_i}{n} = \bar{x}.$$

The second derivative of the log-likelihood function is negative, which implies that the solution above indeed is a maximum. Since μ is the mean of the Poisson distribution, the sample average would certainly seem like a reasonable estimator.

The following example shows the use of the method of maximum likelihood for finding estimates of two parameters. We simply find the values of the parameters that maximize (jointly) the likelihood function.

Example 21: Consider a random sample $x_1, x_2, \ldots, x_n$ from a normal distribution $N(\mu, \sigma)$. Find the maximum likelihood estimators for μ and σ^2.

Solution: The likelihood function for the normal distribution is

$$L(x_1, x_2, \ldots, x_n; \mu, \sigma^2) = \frac{1}{(2\pi)^{n/2}(\sigma^2)^{n/2}} \exp\left[-\frac{1}{2}\sum_{i=1}^{n}\left(\frac{x_i - \mu}{\sigma}\right)^2\right].$$

Taking logarithms gives us

$$\ln L(x_1, x_2, \ldots, x_n; \mu, \sigma^2) = -\frac{n}{2}\ln(2\pi) - \frac{n}{2}\ln\sigma^2 - \frac{1}{2}\sum_{i=1}^{n}\left(\frac{x_i - \mu}{\sigma}\right)^2.$$

Hence,

$$\frac{\partial \ln L}{\partial \mu} = \sum_{i=1}^{n}\left(\frac{x_i - \mu}{\sigma^2}\right)$$

and

$$\frac{\partial \ln L}{\partial \sigma^2} = -\frac{n}{2\sigma^2} + \frac{1}{2(\sigma^2)^2}\sum_{i=1}^{n}(x_i - \mu)^2.$$

Setting both derivatives equal to 0, we obtain

$$\sum_{i=1}^{n} x_i - n\mu = 0 \quad \text{and} \quad n\sigma^2 = \sum_{i=1}^{n}(x_i - \mu)^2.$$

Thus, the maximum likelihood estimator of μ is given by

$$\hat{\mu} = \frac{1}{n}\sum_{i=1}^{n} x_i = \bar{x},$$

which is a pleasing result since $\bar{x}$ has played such an important role in this chapter as a point estimate of μ. On the other hand, the maximum likelihood estimator of σ^2 is

$$\hat{\sigma}^2 = \frac{1}{n}\sum_{i=1}^{n}(x_i - \bar{x})^2.$$

Checking the second-order partial derivative matrix confirms that the solution results in a maximum of the likelihood function.

It is interesting to note the distinction between the maximum likelihood estimator of σ^2 and the unbiased estimator S^2 developed earlier in this chapter. The numerators are identical, of course, and the denominator is the degrees of freedom $n-1$ for the unbiased estimator and n for the maximum likelihood estimator. Maximum likelihood estimators do not necessarily enjoy the property of unbiasedness. However, they do have very important asymptotic properties.

Example 22: Suppose 10 rats are used in a biomedical study where they are injected with cancer cells and then given a cancer drug that is designed to increase their survival rate. The survival times, in months, are 14, 17, 27, 18, 12, 8, 22, 13, 19, and 12. Assume that the exponential distribution applies. Give a maximum likelihood estimate of the mean survival time.

Solution: We know that the probability density function for the exponential random variable X is

$$f(x, \beta) = \begin{cases} \frac{1}{\beta} e^{-x/\beta}, & x > 0, \\ 0, & \text{elsewhere.} \end{cases}$$

Thus, the log-likelihood function for the data, given $n = 10$, is

$$\ln L(x_1, x_2, \ldots, x_{10}; \beta) = -10 \ln \beta - \frac{1}{\beta} \sum_{i=1}^{10} x_i.$$

Setting

$$\frac{\partial \ln L}{\partial \beta} = -\frac{10}{\beta} + \frac{1}{\beta^2} \sum_{i=1}^{10} x_i = 0$$

implies that

$$\hat{\beta} = \frac{1}{10} \sum_{i=1}^{10} x_i = \bar{x} = 16.2.$$

Evaluating the second derivative of the log-likelihood function at the value $\hat{\beta}$ above yields a negative value. As a result, the estimator of the parameter β, the population mean, is the sample average $\bar{x}$.

The following example shows the maximum likelihood estimator for a distribution that does not appear in previous chapters.

Example 23: It is known that a sample consisting of the values 12, 11.2, 13.5, 12.3, 13.8, and 11.9 comes from a population with the density function

$$f(x; \theta) = \begin{cases} \frac{\theta}{x^{\theta+1}}, & x > 1, \\ 0, & \text{elsewhere,} \end{cases}$$

where $\theta > 0$. Find the maximum likelihood estimate of θ.

Solution: The likelihood function of n observations from this population can be written as

$$L(x_1, x_2, \ldots, x_{10}; \theta) = \prod_{i=1}^{n} \frac{\theta}{x_i^{\theta+1}} = \frac{\theta^n}{(\prod_{i=1}^{n} x_i)^{\theta+1}},$$

which implies that

$$\ln L(x_1, x_2, \ldots, x_{10}; \theta) = n \ln(\theta) - (\theta + 1) \sum_{i=1}^{n} \ln(x_i).$$

Setting $0 = \frac{\partial \ln L}{\partial \theta} = \frac{n}{\theta} - \sum_{i=1}^{n} \ln(x_i)$ results in

$$\hat{\theta} = \frac{n}{\sum_{i=1}^{n} \ln(x_i)}$$

$$= \frac{6}{\ln(12) + \ln(11.2) + \ln(13.5) + \ln(12.3) + \ln(13.8) + \ln(11.9)} = 0.3970.$$

Since the second derivative of L is $-n/\theta^2$, which is always negative, the likelihood function does achieve its maximum value at $\hat{\theta}$.

Additional Comments Concerning Maximum Likelihood Estimation

A thorough discussion of the properties of maximum likelihood estimation is beyond the scope of this book and is usually a major topic of a course in the theory of statistical inference. The method of maximum likelihood allows the analyst to make use of knowledge of the distribution in determining an appropriate estimator. *The method of maximum likelihood cannot be applied without knowledge of the underlying distribution.* We learned in Example 21 that the maximum likelihood estimator is not necessarily unbiased. The maximum likelihood estimator is unbiased *asymptotically* or *in the limit*; that is, the amount of bias approaches zero as the sample size becomes large. Earlier in this chapter the notion of efficiency was discussed, efficiency being linked to the variance property of an estimator. Maximum likelihood estimators possess desirable variance properties in the limit. The reader should consult Lehmann and D'Abrera (1998) for details.

Exercises

81 Suppose that there are n trials $x_1, x_2, \ldots, x_n$ from a Bernoulli process with parameter p, the probability of a success. That is, the probability of r successes is given by $\binom{n}{r} p^r (1-p)^{n-r}$. Work out the maximum likelihood estimator for the parameter p.

82 Consider the lognormal distribution with the density function given in Chapter **Some Continuous Probability Distribution** Section 9. Suppose we have a random sample $x_1, x_2, \ldots, x_n$ from a lognormal distribution.
(a) Write out the likelihood function.
(b) Develop the maximum likelihood estimators of μ and σ^2.

83 Consider a random sample $x_1, \ldots, x_n$ coming from the gamma distribution discussed in Chapter **Some Continuous Probability Distribution** Section 6. Suppose the parameter α is known, say 5, and determine the maximum likelihood estimation for parameter β.

84 Consider a random sample of $x_1, x_2, \ldots, x_n$ observations from a Weibull distribution with parameters α and β and density function

$$f(x) = \begin{cases} \alpha\beta x^{\beta-1} e^{-\alpha x^\beta}, & x > 0, \\ 0, & \text{elsewhere,} \end{cases}$$

for $\alpha, \beta > 0$.
(a) Write out the likelihood function.
(b) Write out the equations that, when solved, give the maximum likelihood estimators of α and β.

85 Consider a random sample of $x_1, \ldots, x_n$ from a uniform distribution $U(0, \theta)$ with unknown parameter θ, where $\theta > 0$. Determine the maximum likelihood estimator of θ.

86 Consider the independent observations $x_1, x_2, \ldots, x_n$ from the gamma distribution discussed in Chapter **Some Continuous Probability Distribution** Section 6.

(a) Write out the likelihood function.

(b) Write out a set of equations that, when solved, give the maximum likelihood estimators of α and β.

87 Consider a hypothetical experiment where a man with a fungus uses an antifungal drug and is cured. Consider this, then, a sample of one from a Bernoulli distribution with probability function

$$f(x) = p^x q^{1-x}, \quad x = 0, 1,$$

where p is the probability of a success (cure) and $q = 1 - p$. Now, of course, the sample information gives $x = 1$. Write out a development that shows that $\hat{p} = 1.0$ is the maximum likelihood estimator of the probability of a cure.

88 Consider the observation X from the negative binomial distribution given in Chapter **Some Discrete Probability Distributions** Section 4. Find the maximum likelihood estimator for p, assuming k is known.

Review Exercises

89 Consider two estimators of σ^2 for a sample $x_1, x_2, \ldots, x_n$, which is drawn from a normal distribution with mean μ and variance σ^2. The estimators are the unbiased estimator $s^2 = \frac{1}{n-1} \sum_{i=1}^{n} (x_i - \bar{x})^2$ and the maximum likelihood estimator $\hat{\sigma}^2 = \frac{1}{n} \sum_{i=1}^{n} (x_i - \bar{x})^2$. Discuss the variance properties of these two estimators.

90 According to the *Roanoke Times*, McDonald's sold 42.1% of the market share of hamburgers. A random sample of 75 burgers sold resulted in 28 of them being from McDonald's. Use material in Section 10 to determine if this information supports the claim in the *Roanoke Times*.

91 It is claimed that a new diet will reduce a person's weight by 4.5 kilograms on average in a period of 2 weeks. The weights of 7 women who followed this diet were recorded before and after the 2-week period.

Woman	Weight Before	Weight After
1	58.5	60.0
2	60.3	54.9
3	61.7	58.1
4	69.0	62.1
5	64.0	58.5
6	62.6	59.9
7	56.7	54.4

Test the claim about the diet by computing a 95% confidence interval for the mean difference in weights. Assume the differences of weights to be approximately normally distributed.

92 A study was undertaken at Virginia Tech to determine if fire can be used as a viable management tool to increase the amount of forage available to deer during the critical months in late winter and early spring. Calcium is a required element for plants and animals. The amount taken up and stored in plants is closely correlated to the amount present in the soil. It was hypothesized that a fire may change the calcium levels present in the soil and thus affect the amount available to deer. A large tract of land in the Fishburn Forest was selected for a prescribed burn. Soil samples were taken from 12 plots of equal area just prior to the burn and analyzed for calcium. Postburn calcium levels were analyzed from the same plots. These values, in kilograms per plot, are presented in the following table:

Plot	Calcium Level (kg/plot) Preburn	Postburn
1	50	9
2	50	18
3	82	45
4	64	18
5	82	18
6	73	9
7	77	32
8	54	9
9	23	18
10	45	9
11	36	9
12	54	9

Construct a 95% confidence interval for the mean difference in calcium levels in the soil prior to and after the prescribed burn. Assume the distribution of differences in calcium levels to be approximately normal.

93 A health spa claims that a new exercise program will reduce a person's waist size by 2 centimeters on average over a 5-day period. The waist sizes, in centimeters, of 6 men who participated in this exercise program are recorded before and after the 5-day period in the following table:

Man	Waist Size Before	Waist Size After
1	90.4	91.7
2	95.5	93.9
3	98.7	97.4
4	115.9	112.8
5	104.0	101.3
6	85.6	84.0

By computing a 95% confidence interval for the mean reduction in waist size, determine whether the health spa's claim is valid. Assume the distribution of differences in waist sizes before and after the program to be approximately normal.

94 The Department of Civil Engineering at Virginia Tech compared a modified (M-5 hr) assay technique for recovering fecal coliforms in stormwater runoff from an urban area to a most probable number (MPN) technique. A total of 12 runoff samples were collected and analyzed by the two techniques. Fecal coliform counts per 100 milliliters are recorded in the following table.

Sample	MPN Count	M-5 hr Count
1	2300	2010
2	1200	930
3	450	400
4	210	436
5	270	4100
6	450	2090
7	154	219
8	179	169
9	192	194
10	230	174
11	340	274
12	194	183

Construct a 90% confidence interval for the difference in the mean fecal coliform counts between the M-5 hr and the MPN techniques. Assume that the count differences are approximately normally distributed.

95 An experiment was conducted to determine whether surface finish has an effect on the endurance limit of steel. There is a theory that polishing increases the average endurance limit (for reverse bending). From a practical point of view, polishing should not have any effect on the standard deviation of the endurance limit, which is known from numerous endurance limit experiments to be 4000 psi. An experiment was performed on 0.4% carbon steel using both unpolished and polished smooth-turned specimens. The data are as follows:

Endurance Limit (psi)	
Polished 0.4% Carbon	**Unpolished 0.4% Carbon**
85,500	82,600
91,900	82,400
89,400	81,700
84,000	79,500
89,900	79,400
78,700	69,800
87,500	79,900
83,100	83,400

Find a 95% confidence interval for the difference between the population means for the two methods, as-

suming that the populations are approximately normally distributed.

96 An anthropologist is interested in the proportion of individuals in two Indian tribes with double occipital hair whorls. Suppose that independent samples are taken from each of the two tribes, and it is found that 24 of 100 Indians from tribe A and 36 of 120 Indians from tribe B possess this characteristic. Construct a 95% confidence interval for the difference $p_B - p_A$ between the proportions of these two tribes with occipital hair whorls.

97 A manufacturer of electric irons produces these items in two plants. Both plants have the same suppliers of small parts. A saving can be made by purchasing thermostats for plant B from a local supplier. A single lot was purchased from the local supplier, and a test was conducted to see whether or not these new thermostats were as accurate as the old. The thermostats were tested on tile irons on the 550°F setting, and the actual temperatures were read to the nearest 0.1°F with a thermocouple. The data are as follows:

New Supplier (°F)					
530.3	559.3	549.4	544.0	551.7	566.3
549.9	556.9	536.7	558.8	538.8	543.3
559.1	555.0	538.6	551.1	565.4	554.9
550.0	554.9	554.7	536.1	569.1	

Old Supplier (°F)					
559.7	534.7	554.8	545.0	544.6	538.0
550.7	563.1	551.1	553.8	538.8	564.6
554.5	553.0	538.4	548.3	552.9	535.1
555.0	544.8	558.4	548.7	560.3	

Find 95% confidence intervals for σ_1^2/σ_2^2 and for σ_1/σ_2, where σ_1^2 and σ_2^2 are the population variances of the thermostat readings for the new and old suppliers, respectively.

98 It is argued that the resistance of wire A is greater than the resistance of wire B. An experiment on the wires shows the following results (in ohms):

Wire A	Wire B
0.140	0.135
0.138	0.140
0.143	0.136
0.142	0.142
0.144	0.138
0.137	0.140

Assuming equal variances, what conclusions do you draw? Justify your answer.

99 An alternative form of estimation is accomplished through the method of moments. This method involves equating the population mean and variance to the corresponding sample mean $\bar{x}$ and sample variance

s^2 and solving for the parameters, the results being the **moment estimators**. In the case of a single parameter, only the means are used. Give an argument that in the case of the Poisson distribution the maximum likelihood estimator and moment estimators are the same.

100 Specify the moment estimators for μ and σ^2 for the normal distribution.

101 Specify the moment estimators for μ and σ^2 for the lognormal distribution.

102 Specify the moment estimators for α and β for the gamma distribution.

103 A survey was done with the hope of comparing salaries of chemical plant managers employed in two areas of the country, the northern and west central regions. An independent random sample of 300 plant managers was selected from each of the two regions. These managers were asked their annual salaries. The results are as follows

North	West Central
$\bar{x}_1 = \$102,300$	$\bar{x}_2 = \$98,500$
$s_1 = \$5700$	$s_2 = \$3800$

(a) Construct a 99% confidence interval for $\mu_1 - \mu_2$, the difference in the mean salaries.

(b) What assumption did you make in (a) about the distribution of annual salaries for the two regions? Is the assumption of normality necessary? Why or why not?

(c) What assumption did you make about the two variances? Is the assumption of equality of variances reasonable? Explain!

104 Consider Review Exercise 103. Let us assume that the data have not been collected yet and that previous statistics suggest that $\sigma_1 = \sigma_2 = \$4000$. Are the sample sizes in Review Exercise 103 sufficient to produce a 95% confidence interval on $\mu_1 - \mu_2$ having a width of only $1000? Show all work.

105 A labor union is becoming defensive about gross absenteeism by its members. The union leaders had always claimed that, in a typical month, 95% of its members were absent less than 10 hours. The union decided to check this by monitoring a random sample of 300 of its members. The number of hours absent was recorded for each of the 300 members. The results were $\bar{x} = 6.5$ hours and $s = 2.5$ hours. Use the data to respond to this claim, using a one-sided tolerance limit and choosing the confidence level to be 99%. Be sure to interpret what you learn from the tolerance limit calculation.

106 A random sample of 30 firms dealing in wireless products was selected to determine the proportion of such firms that have implemented new software to improve productivity. It turned out that 8 of the 30 had implemented such software. Find a 95% confidence interval on p, the true proportion of such firms that have implemented new software.

107 Refer to Review Exercise 106. Suppose there is concern about whether the point estimate $\hat{p} = 8/30$ is accurate enough because the confidence interval around p is not sufficiently narrow. Using $\hat{p}$ as the estimate of p, how many companies would need to be sampled in order to have a 95% confidence interval with a width of only 0.05?

108 A manufacturer turns out a product item that is labeled either "defective" or "not defective." In order to estimate the proportion defective, a random sample of 100 items is taken from production, and 10 are found to be defective. Following implementation of a quality improvement program, the experiment is conducted again. A new sample of 100 is taken, and this time only 6 are found to be defective.

(a) Give a 95% confidence interval on $p_1 - p_2$, where p_1 is the population proportion defective before improvement and p_2 is the proportion defective after improvement.

(b) Is there information in the confidence interval found in (a) that would suggest that $p_1 > p_2$? Explain.

109 A machine is used to fill boxes with product in an assembly line operation. Much concern centers around the variability in the number of ounces of product in a box. The standard deviation in weight of product is known to be 0.3 ounce. An improvement is implemented, after which a random sample of 20 boxes is selected and the sample variance is found to be 0.045 ounce^2. Find a 95% confidence interval on the variance in the weight of the product. Does it appear from the range of the confidence interval that the improvement of the process enhanced quality as far as variability is concerned? Assume normality on the distribution of weights of product.

110 A consumer group is interested in comparing operating costs for two different types of automobile engines. The group is able to find 15 owners whose cars have engine type A and 15 whose cars have engine type B. All 30 owners bought their cars at roughly the same time, and all have kept good records for a certain 12-month period. In addition, these owners drove roughly the same number of miles. The cost statistics are $\bar{y}_A = \$87.00/1000$ miles, $\bar{y}_B = \$75.00/1000$ miles, $s_A = \$5.99$, and $s_B = \$4.85$. Compute a 95% confidence interval to estimate $\mu_A - \mu_B$, the difference in the mean operating costs. Assume normality and equal variances.

111 Consider the statistic S_p^2, the pooled estimate of σ^2 discussed in Section 9.8. It is used when one is willing to assume that $\sigma_1^2 = \sigma_2^2 = \sigma^2$. Show that the estimator is unbiased for σ^2 [i.e., show that $E(S_p^2) = \sigma^2$]. You may make use of results from any theorem or example in this chapter.

112 A group of human factor researchers are concerned about reaction to a stimulus by airplane pilots in a certain cockpit arrangement. An experiment was conducted in a simulation laboratory, and 15 pilots were used with average reaction time of 3.2 seconds with a sample standard deviation of 0.6 second. It is of interest to characterize the extreme (i.e., worst case scenario). To that end, do the following:

(a) Give a particular important one-sided 99% confidence bound on the mean reaction time. What assumption, if any, must you make on the distribution of reaction times?

(b) Give a 99% one-sided prediction interval and give an interpretation of what it means. Must you make

an assumption about the distribution of reaction times to compute this bound?

(c) Compute a one-sided tolerance bound with 99% confidence that involves 95% of reaction times. Again, give an interpretation and assumptions about the distribution, if any. (Note: The one-sided tolerance limit values are also included in Table Tolerance Factors for Normal Distributions.)

113 A certain supplier manufactures a type of rubber mat that is sold to automotive companies. The material used to produce the mats must have certain hardness characteristics. Defective mats are occasionally discovered and rejected. The supplier claims that the proportion defective is 0.05. A challenge was made by one of the clients who purchased the mats, so an experiment was conducted in which 400 mats are tested and 17 were found defective.

(a) Compute a 95% two-sided confidence interval on the proportion defective.

(b) Compute an appropriate 95% one-sided confidence interval on the proportion defective.

(c) Interpret both intervals from (a) and (b) and comment on the claim made by the supplier.

15   Potential Misconceptions and Hazards

The concept of a *large-sample confidence interval* on a population is often confusing to the beginning student. It is based on the notion that even when σ is unknown and one is not convinced that the distribution being sampled is normal, a confidence interval on μ can be computed from

$$\bar{x} \pm z_{\alpha/2} \frac{s}{\sqrt{n}}.$$

In practice, this formula is often used when the sample is too small. The genesis of this large sample interval is, of course, the Central Limit Theorem (CLT), under which normality is not necessary. Here the CLT requires a known σ, of which s is only an estimate. Thus, n must be at least as large as 30 and the underlying distribution must be close to symmetric, in which case the interval is still an approximation.

There are instances in which the appropriateness of the practical application of material in this chapter depends very much on the specific context. One very important illustration is the use of the t-distribution for the confidence interval on μ when σ is unknown. Strictly speaking, the use of the t-distribution requires that the distribution sampled from be normal. However, it is well known that any application of the t-distribution is reasonably insensitive (i.e., **robust**) to the normality assumption. This represents one of those fortunate situations which occur often in the field of statistics in which a basic assumption does not hold and yet "everything turns out all right!" However, one population from which the sample is drawn cannot deviate substantially from normal. Thus, the normal probability plots and the goodness-of-fit tests often need be called upon to ascertain some sense of "nearness to normality."

It is our experience that one of the most serious "misuses of statistics" in practice evolves from confusion about distinctions in the interpretation of the types of statistical intervals. Thus, the subsection in this chapter where differences among the three types of intervals are discussed is important. It is very likely that in practice the **confidence interval is heavily overused**. That is, it is used when there is really no interest in the mean; rather, the question is "Where is the next observation going to fall?" or often, more importantly, "Where is the large bulk of the distribution?" These are crucial questions that are not answered by computing an interval on the mean. The interpretation of a confidence interval is often misunderstood. It is tempting to conclude that the parameter falls inside the interval with probability 0.95. While this is a correct interpretation of a **Bayesian posterior interval**, it is not the proper frequency interpretation.

A confidence interval merely suggests that if the experiment is conducted and data are observed again and again, about 95% of such intervals will contain the true parameter. Any beginning student of practical statistics should be very clear on the difference among these statistical intervals.

Another potential serious misuse of statistics centers around the use of the χ^2-distribution for a confidence interval on a single variance. Again, normality of the distribution from which the sample is drawn is assumed. Unlike the use of the t-distribution, the use of the χ^2 test for this application is **not robust to the normality assumption** (i.e., the sampling distribution of $\frac{(n-1)S^2}{\sigma^2}$ deviates far from χ^2 if the underlying distribution is not normal). Thus, strict use of goodness-of-fit tests and/or normal probability plotting can be extremely important in such contexts.

Answers to Odd-Numbered Non-Review Exercises

1   56

3   $0.3097 < \mu < 0.3103$

5   (a) $22,496 < \mu < 24,504$; (b) error ≤ 1004

7   35

9   $10.15 < \mu < 12.45$

11   $0.978 < \mu < 1.033$

13   $47.722 < \mu < 49.278$

15   $(13,075, 33,925)$

17   $(6.05, 16.55)$

19   323.946 to 326.154

21   Upper prediction limit: 9.42;
     upper tolerance limit: 11.72

25   Yes, the value of 6.9 is outside of the prediction interval.

27   (a) $(0.9876, 1.0174)$;
     (b) $(0.9411, 1.0639)$;
     (c) $(0.9334, 1.0716)$

35   $2.9 < \mu_1 - \mu_2 < 7.1$

37   $2.80 < \mu_1 - \mu_2 < 3.40$

39   $1.5 < \mu_1 - \mu_2 < 12.5$

41   $0.70 < \mu_1 - \mu_2 < 3.30$

43   $-6536 < \mu_1 - \mu_2 < 2936$

45   $(-0.74, 6.30)$

47   $(-6.92, 36.70)$

49   $0.54652 < \mu_B - \mu_A < 1.69348$

51   Method 1: $0.194 < p < 0.262$; method 2: $0.1957 < p < 0.2639$

53   (a) $0.498 < p < 0.642$; (b) error ≤ 0.072

55   (a) $0.739 < p < 0.961$; (b) no

57   (a) $0.644 < p < 0.690$; (b) error ≤ 0.023

59   2576

61   160

63   9604

65   $-0.0136 < p_F - p_M < 0.0636$

67   $0.0011 < p_1 - p_2 < 0.0869$

69   $(-0.0849, 0.0013)$; not significantly different

71   $0.293 < \sigma^2 < 6.736$; valid claim

73   $3.472 < \sigma^2 < 12.804$

75   $9.27 < \sigma < 34.16$

77   $0.549 < \sigma_1/\sigma_2 < 2.690$

79   $0.016 < \sigma_1^2/\sigma_2^2 < 0.454$; no

81   $\frac{1}{n} \sum_{i=1}^{n} x_i$

83   $\hat{\beta} = \bar{x}/5$

85   $\hat{\theta} = \max\{x_1, \ldots, x_n\}$

87   $x \ln p + (1 - x) \ln(1 - p)$. Set the derivative with respect to $p = 0$; $\hat{p} = x = 1.0$

Table Areas under the Normal Curve

z	.00	.01	.02	.03	.04	.05	.06	.07	.08	.09
−3.4	0.0003	0.0003	0.0003	0.0003	0.0003	0.0003	0.0003	0.0003	0.0003	0.0002
−3.3	0.0005	0.0005	0.0005	0.0004	0.0004	0.0004	0.0004	0.0004	0.0004	0.0003
−3.2	0.0007	0.0007	0.0006	0.0006	0.0006	0.0006	0.0006	0.0005	0.0005	0.0005
−3.1	0.0010	0.0009	0.0009	0.0009	0.0008	0.0008	0.0008	0.0008	0.0007	0.0007
−3.0	0.0013	0.0013	0.0013	0.0012	0.0012	0.0011	0.0011	0.0011	0.0010	0.0010
−2.9	0.0019	0.0018	0.0018	0.0017	0.0016	0.0016	0.0015	0.0015	0.0014	0.0014
−2.8	0.0026	0.0025	0.0024	0.0023	0.0023	0.0022	0.0021	0.0021	0.0020	0.0019
−2.7	0.0035	0.0034	0.0033	0.0032	0.0031	0.0030	0.0029	0.0028	0.0027	0.0026
−2.6	0.0047	0.0045	0.0044	0.0043	0.0041	0.0040	0.0039	0.0038	0.0037	0.0036
−2.5	0.0062	0.0060	0.0059	0.0057	0.0055	0.0054	0.0052	0.0051	0.0049	0.0048
−2.4	0.0082	0.0080	0.0078	0.0075	0.0073	0.0071	0.0069	0.0068	0.0066	0.0064
−2.3	0.0107	0.0104	0.0102	0.0099	0.0096	0.0094	0.0091	0.0089	0.0087	0.0084
−2.2	0.0139	0.0136	0.0132	0.0129	0.0125	0.0122	0.0119	0.0116	0.0113	0.0110
−2.1	0.0179	0.0174	0.0170	0.0166	0.0162	0.0158	0.0154	0.0150	0.0146	0.0143
−2.0	0.0228	0.0222	0.0217	0.0212	0.0207	0.0202	0.0197	0.0192	0.0188	0.0183
−1.9	0.0287	0.0281	0.0274	0.0268	0.0262	0.0256	0.0250	0.0244	0.0239	0.0233
−1.8	0.0359	0.0351	0.0344	0.0336	0.0329	0.0322	0.0314	0.0307	0.0301	0.0294
−1.7	0.0446	0.0436	0.0427	0.0418	0.0409	0.0401	0.0392	0.0384	0.0375	0.0367
−1.6	0.0548	0.0537	0.0526	0.0516	0.0505	0.0495	0.0485	0.0475	0.0465	0.0455
−1.5	0.0668	0.0655	0.0643	0.0630	0.0618	0.0606	0.0594	0.0582	0.0571	0.0559
−1.4	0.0808	0.0793	0.0778	0.0764	0.0749	0.0735	0.0721	0.0708	0.0694	0.0681
−1.3	0.0968	0.0951	0.0934	0.0918	0.0901	0.0885	0.0869	0.0853	0.0838	0.0823
−1.2	0.1151	0.1131	0.1112	0.1093	0.1075	0.1056	0.1038	0.1020	0.1003	0.0985
−1.1	0.1357	0.1335	0.1314	0.1292	0.1271	0.1251	0.1230	0.1210	0.1190	0.1170
−1.0	0.1587	0.1562	0.1539	0.1515	0.1492	0.1469	0.1446	0.1423	0.1401	0.1379
−0.9	0.1841	0.1814	0.1788	0.1762	0.1736	0.1711	0.1685	0.1660	0.1635	0.1611
−0.8	0.2119	0.2090	0.2061	0.2033	0.2005	0.1977	0.1949	0.1922	0.1894	0.1867
−0.7	0.2420	0.2389	0.2358	0.2327	0.2296	0.2266	0.2236	0.2206	0.2177	0.2148
−0.6	0.2743	0.2709	0.2676	0.2643	0.2611	0.2578	0.2546	0.2514	0.2483	0.2451
−0.5	0.3085	0.3050	0.3015	0.2981	0.2946	0.2912	0.2877	0.2843	0.2810	0.2776
−0.4	0.3446	0.3409	0.3372	0.3336	0.3300	0.3264	0.3228	0.3192	0.3156	0.3121
−0.3	0.3821	0.3783	0.3745	0.3707	0.3669	0.3632	0.3594	0.3557	0.3520	0.3483
−0.2	0.4207	0.4168	0.4129	0.4090	0.4052	0.4013	0.3974	0.3936	0.3897	0.3859
−0.1	0.4602	0.4562	0.4522	0.4483	0.4443	0.4404	0.4364	0.4325	0.4286	0.4247
−0.0	0.5000	0.4960	0.4920	0.4880	0.4840	0.4801	0.4761	0.4721	0.4681	0.4641

Table (continued) Areas under the Normal Curve

z	.00	.01	.02	.03	.04	.05	.06	.07	.08	.09
0.0	0.5000	0.5040	0.5080	0.5120	0.5160	0.5199	0.5239	0.5279	0.5319	0.5359
0.1	0.5398	0.5438	0.5478	0.5517	0.5557	0.5596	0.5636	0.5675	0.5714	0.5753
0.2	0.5793	0.5832	0.5871	0.5910	0.5948	0.5987	0.6026	0.6064	0.6103	0.6141
0.3	0.6179	0.6217	0.6255	0.6293	0.6331	0.6368	0.6406	0.6443	0.6480	0.6517
0.4	0.6554	0.6591	0.6628	0.6664	0.6700	0.6736	0.6772	0.6808	0.6844	0.6879
0.5	0.6915	0.6950	0.6985	0.7019	0.7054	0.7088	0.7123	0.7157	0.7190	0.7224
0.6	0.7257	0.7291	0.7324	0.7357	0.7389	0.7422	0.7454	0.7486	0.7517	0.7549
0.7	0.7580	0.7611	0.7642	0.7673	0.7704	0.7734	0.7764	0.7794	0.7823	0.7852
0.8	0.7881	0.7910	0.7939	0.7967	0.7995	0.8023	0.8051	0.8078	0.8106	0.8133
0.9	0.8159	0.8186	0.8212	0.8238	0.8264	0.8289	0.8315	0.8340	0.8365	0.8389
1.0	0.8413	0.8438	0.8461	0.8485	0.8508	0.8531	0.8554	0.8577	0.8599	0.8621
1.1	0.8643	0.8665	0.8686	0.8708	0.8729	0.8749	0.8770	0.8790	0.8810	0.8830
1.2	0.8849	0.8869	0.8888	0.8907	0.8925	0.8944	0.8962	0.8980	0.8997	0.9015
1.3	0.9032	0.9049	0.9066	0.9082	0.9099	0.9115	0.9131	0.9147	0.9162	0.9177
1.4	0.9192	0.9207	0.9222	0.9236	0.9251	0.9265	0.9279	0.9292	0.9306	0.9319
1.5	0.9332	0.9345	0.9357	0.9370	0.9382	0.9394	0.9406	0.9418	0.9429	0.9441
1.6	0.9452	0.9463	0.9474	0.9484	0.9495	0.9505	0.9515	0.9525	0.9535	0.9545
1.7	0.9554	0.9564	0.9573	0.9582	0.9591	0.9599	0.9608	0.9616	0.9625	0.9633
1.8	0.9641	0.9649	0.9656	0.9664	0.9671	0.9678	0.9686	0.9693	0.9699	0.9706
1.9	0.9713	0.9719	0.9726	0.9732	0.9738	0.9744	0.9750	0.9756	0.9761	0.9767
2.0	0.9772	0.9778	0.9783	0.9788	0.9793	0.9798	0.9803	0.9808	0.9812	0.9817
2.1	0.9821	0.9826	0.9830	0.9834	0.9838	0.9842	0.9846	0.9850	0.9854	0.9857
2.2	0.9861	0.9864	0.9868	0.9871	0.9875	0.9878	0.9881	0.9884	0.9887	0.9890
2.3	0.9893	0.9896	0.9898	0.9901	0.9904	0.9906	0.9909	0.9911	0.9913	0.9916
2.4	0.9918	0.9920	0.9922	0.9925	0.9927	0.9929	0.9931	0.9932	0.9934	0.9936
2.5	0.9938	0.9940	0.9941	0.9943	0.9945	0.9946	0.9948	0.9949	0.9951	0.9952
2.6	0.9953	0.9955	0.9956	0.9957	0.9959	0.9960	0.9961	0.9962	0.9963	0.9964
2.7	0.9965	0.9966	0.9967	0.9968	0.9969	0.9970	0.9971	0.9972	0.9973	0.9974
2.8	0.9974	0.9975	0.9976	0.9977	0.9977	0.9978	0.9979	0.9979	0.9980	0.9981
2.9	0.9981	0.9982	0.9982	0.9983	0.9984	0.9984	0.9985	0.9985	0.9986	0.9986
3.0	0.9987	0.9987	0.9987	0.9988	0.9988	0.9989	0.9989	0.9989	0.9990	0.9990
3.1	0.9990	0.9991	0.9991	0.9991	0.9992	0.9992	0.9992	0.9992	0.9993	0.9993
3.2	0.9993	0.9993	0.9994	0.9994	0.9994	0.9994	0.9994	0.9995	0.9995	0.9995
3.3	0.9995	0.9995	0.9995	0.9996	0.9996	0.9996	0.9996	0.9996	0.9996	0.9997
3.4	0.9997	0.9997	0.9997	0.9997	0.9997	0.9997	0.9997	0.9997	0.9997	0.9998

Table Critical Values of the *t*-Distribution

	α						
v	0.40	0.30	0.20	0.15	0.10	0.05	0.025
1	0.325	0.727	1.376	1.963	3.078	6.314	12.706
2	0.289	0.617	1.061	1.386	1.886	2.920	4.303
3	0.277	0.584	0.978	1.250	1.638	2.353	3.182
4	0.271	0.569	0.941	1.190	1.533	2.132	2.776
5	0.267	0.559	0.920	1.156	1.476	2.015	2.571
6	0.265	0.553	0.906	1.134	1.440	1.943	2.447
7	0.263	0.549	0.896	1.119	1.415	1.895	2.365
8	0.262	0.546	0.889	1.108	1.397	1.860	2.306
9	0.261	0.543	0.883	1.100	1.383	1.833	2.262
10	0.260	0.542	0.879	1.093	1.372	1.812	2.228
11	0.260	0.540	0.876	1.088	1.363	1.796	2.201
12	0.259	0.539	0.873	1.083	1.356	1.782	2.179
13	0.259	0.538	0.870	1.079	1.350	1.771	2.160
14	0.258	0.537	0.868	1.076	1.345	1.761	2.145
15	0.258	0.536	0.866	1.074	1.341	1.753	2.131
16	0.258	0.535	0.865	1.071	1.337	1.746	2.120
17	0.257	0.534	0.863	1.069	1.333	1.740	2.110
18	0.257	0.534	0.862	1.067	1.330	1.734	2.101
19	0.257	0.533	0.861	1.066	1.328	1.729	2.093
20	0.257	0.533	0.860	1.064	1.325	1.725	2.086
21	0.257	0.532	0.859	1.063	1.323	1.721	2.080
22	0.256	0.532	0.858	1.061	1.321	1.717	2.074
23	0.256	0.532	0.858	1.060	1.319	1.714	2.069
24	0.256	0.531	0.857	1.059	1.318	1.711	2.064
25	0.256	0.531	0.856	1.058	1.316	1.708	2.060
26	0.256	0.531	0.856	1.058	1.315	1.706	2.056
27	0.256	0.531	0.855	1.057	1.314	1.703	2.052
28	0.256	0.530	0.855	1.056	1.313	1.701	2.048
29	0.256	0.530	0.854	1.055	1.311	1.699	2.045
30	0.256	0.530	0.854	1.055	1.310	1.697	2.042
40	0.255	0.529	0.851	1.050	1.303	1.684	2.021
60	0.254	0.527	0.848	1.045	1.296	1.671	2.000
120	0.254	0.526	0.845	1.041	1.289	1.658	1.980
∞	0.253	0.524	0.842	1.036	1.282	1.645	1.960

Table (continued) Critical Values of the *t*-Distribution

	α						
v	0.02	0.015	0.01	0.0075	0.005	0.0025	0.0005
1	15.894	21.205	31.821	42.433	63.656	127.321	636.578
2	4.849	5.643	6.965	8.073	9.925	14.089	31.600
3	3.482	3.896	4.541	5.047	5.841	7.453	12.924
4	2.999	3.298	3.747	4.088	4.604	5.598	8.610
5	2.757	3.003	3.365	3.634	4.032	4.773	6.869
6	2.612	2.829	3.143	3.372	3.707	4.317	5.959
7	2.517	2.715	2.998	3.203	3.499	4.029	5.408
8	2.449	2.634	2.896	3.085	3.355	3.833	5.041
9	2.398	2.574	2.821	2.998	3.250	3.690	4.781
10	2.359	2.527	2.764	2.932	3.169	3.581	4.587
11	2.328	2.491	2.718	2.879	3.106	3.497	4.437
12	2.303	2.461	2.681	2.836	3.055	3.428	4.318
13	2.282	2.436	2.650	2.801	3.012	3.372	4.221
14	2.264	2.415	2.624	2.771	2.977	3.326	4.140
15	2.249	2.397	2.602	2.746	2.947	3.286	4.073
16	2.235	2.382	2.583	2.724	2.921	3.252	4.015
17	2.224	2.368	2.567	2.706	2.898	3.222	3.965
18	2.214	2.356	2.552	2.689	2.878	3.197	3.922
19	2.205	2.346	2.539	2.674	2.861	3.174	3.883
20	2.197	2.336	2.528	2.661	2.845	3.153	3.850
21	2.189	2.328	2.518	2.649	2.831	3.135	3.819
22	2.183	2.320	2.508	2.639	2.819	3.119	3.792
23	2.177	2.313	2.500	2.629	2.807	3.104	3.768
24	2.172	2.307	2.492	2.620	2.797	3.091	3.745
25	2.167	2.301	2.485	2.612	2.787	3.078	3.725
26	2.162	2.296	2.479	2.605	2.779	3.067	3.707
27	2.158	2.291	2.473	2.598	2.771	3.057	3.689
28	2.154	2.286	2.467	2.592	2.763	3.047	3.674
29	2.150	2.282	2.462	2.586	2.756	3.038	3.660
30	2.147	2.278	2.457	2.581	2.750	3.030	3.646
40	2.123	2.250	2.423	2.542	2.704	2.971	3.551
60	2.099	2.223	2.390	2.504	2.660	2.915	3.460
120	2.076	2.196	2.358	2.468	2.617	2.860	3.373
∞	2.054	2.170	2.326	2.432	2.576	2.807	3.290

Table Tolerance Factors for Normal Distributions

	Two-Sided Intervals						One-Sided Intervals					
	γ = 0.05			γ = 0.01			γ = 0.05			γ = 0.01		
	1 − α			1 − α			1 − α			1 − α		
n	0.90	0.95	0.99	0.90	0.95	0.99	0.90	0.95	0.99	0.90	0.95	0.99
2	32.019	37.674	48.430	160.193	188.491	242.300	20.581	26.260	37.094	103.029	131.426	185.617
3	8.380	9.916	12.861	18.930	22.401	29.055	6.156	7.656	10.553	13.995	17.170	23.896
4	5.369	6.370	8.299	9.398	11.150	14.527	4.162	5.144	7.042	7.380	9.083	12.387
5	4.275	5.079	6.634	6.612	7.855	10.260	3.407	4.203	5.741	5.362	6.578	8.939
6	3.712	4.414	5.775	5.337	6.345	8.301	3.006	3.708	5.062	4.411	5.406	7.335
7	3.369	4.007	5.248	4.613	5.488	7.187	2.756	3.400	4.642	3.859	4.728	6.412
8	3.136	3.732	4.891	4.147	4.936	6.468	2.582	3.187	4.354	3.497	4.285	5.812
9	2.967	3.532	4.631	3.822	4.550	5.966	2.454	3.031	4.143	3.241	3.972	5.389
10	2.839	3.379	4.433	3.582	4.265	5.594	2.355	2.911	3.981	3.048	3.738	5.074
11	2.737	3.259	4.277	3.397	4.045	5.308	2.275	2.815	3.852	2.898	3.556	4.829
12	2.655	3.162	4.150	3.250	3.870	5.079	2.210	2.736	3.747	2.777	3.410	4.633
13	2.587	3.081	4.044	3.130	3.727	4.893	2.155	2.671	3.659	2.677	3.290	4.472
14	2.529	3.012	3.955	3.029	3.608	4.737	2.109	2.615	3.585	2.593	3.189	4.337
15	2.480	2.954	3.878	2.945	3.507	4.605	2.068	2.566	3.520	2.522	3.102	4.222
16	2.437	2.903	3.812	2.872	3.421	4.492	2.033	2.524	3.464	2.460	3.028	4.123
17	2.400	2.858	3.754	2.808	3.345	4.393	2.002	2.486	3.414	2.405	2.963	4.037
18	2.366	2.819	3.702	2.753	3.279	4.307	1.974	2.453	3.370	2.357	2.905	3.960
19	2.337	2.784	3.656	2.703	3.221	4.230	1.949	2.423	3.331	2.314	2.854	3.892
20	2.310	2.752	3.615	2.659	3.168	4.161	1.926	2.396	3.295	2.276	2.808	3.832
25	2.208	2.631	3.457	2.494	2.972	3.904	1.838	2.292	3.158	2.129	2.633	3.601
30	2.140	2.549	3.350	2.385	2.841	3.733	1.777	2.220	3.064	2.030	2.516	3.447
35	2.090	2.490	3.272	2.306	2.748	3.611	1.732	2.167	2.995	1.957	2.430	3.334
40	2.052	2.445	3.213	2.247	2.677	3.518	1.697	2.126	2.941	1.902	2.364	3.249
45	2.021	2.408	3.165	2.200	2.621	3.444	1.669	2.092	2.898	1.857	2.312	3.180
50	1.996	2.379	3.126	2.162	2.576	3.385	1.646	2.065	2.863	1.821	2.269	3.125
60	1.958	2.333	3.066	2.103	2.506	3.293	1.609	2.022	2.807	1.764	2.202	3.038
70	1.929	2.299	3.021	2.060	2.454	3.225	1.581	1.990	2.765	1.722	2.153	2.974
80	1.907	2.272	2.986	2.026	2.414	3.173	1.559	1.965	2.733	1.688	2.114	2.924
90	1.889	2.251	2.958	1.999	2.382	3.130	1.542	1.944	2.706	1.661	2.082	2.883
100	1.874	2.233	2.934	1.977	2.355	3.096	1.527	1.927	2.684	1.639	2.056	2.850
150	1.825	2.175	2.859	1.905	2.270	2.983	1.478	1.870	2.611	1.566	1.971	2.741
200	1.798	2.143	2.816	1.865	2.222	2.921	1.450	1.837	2.570	1.524	1.923	2.679
250	1.780	2.121	2.788	1.839	2.191	2.880	1.431	1.815	2.542	1.496	1.891	2.638
300	1.767	2.106	2.767	1.820	2.169	2.850	1.417	1.800	2.522	1.476	1.868	2.608
∞	1.645	1.960	2.576	1.645	1.960	2.576	1.282	1.645	2.326	1.282	1.645	2.326

Adapted from C. Eisenhart, M. W. Hastay, and W. A. Wallis, *Techniques of Statistical Analysis*, Chapter 2, McGraw-Hill Book Company, New York, 1947. Used with permission of McGraw-Hill Book Company.

Table Critical Values of the Chi-Squared Distribution

					α					
v	0.995	0.99	0.98	0.975	0.95	0.90	0.80	0.75	0.70	0.50
1	0.0^4393	0.0^3157	0.0^3628	0.0^3982	0.00393	0.0158	0.0642	0.102	0.148	0.455
2	0.0100	0.0201	0.0404	0.0506	0.103	0.211	0.446	0.575	0.713	1.386
3	0.0717	0.115	0.185	0.216	0.352	0.584	1.005	1.213	1.424	2.366
4	0.207	0.297	0.429	0.484	0.711	1.064	1.649	1.923	2.195	3.357
5	0.412	0.554	0.752	0.831	1.145	1.610	2.343	2.675	3.000	4.351
6	0.676	0.872	1.134	1.237	1.635	2.204	3.070	3.455	3.828	5.348
7	0.989	1.239	1.564	1.690	2.167	2.833	3.822	4.255	4.671	6.346
8	1.344	1.647	2.032	2.180	2.733	3.490	4.594	5.071	5.527	7.344
9	1.735	2.088	2.532	2.700	3.325	4.168	5.380	5.899	6.393	8.343
10	2.156	2.558	3.059	3.247	3.940	4.865	6.179	6.737	7.267	9.342
11	2.603	3.053	3.609	3.816	4.575	5.578	6.989	7.584	8.148	10.341
12	3.074	3.571	4.178	4.404	5.226	6.304	7.807	8.438	9.034	11.340
13	3.565	4.107	4.765	5.009	5.892	7.041	8.634	9.299	9.926	12.340
14	4.075	4.660	5.368	5.629	6.571	7.790	9.467	10.165	10.821	13.339
15	4.601	5.229	5.985	6.262	7.261	8.547	10.307	11.037	11.721	14.339
16	5.142	5.812	6.614	6.908	7.962	9.312	11.152	11.912	12.624	15.338
17	5.697	6.408	7.255	7.564	8.672	10.085	12.002	12.792	13.531	16.338
18	6.265	7.015	7.906	8.231	9.390	10.865	12.857	13.675	14.440	17.338
19	6.844	7.633	8.567	8.907	10.117	11.651	13.716	14.562	15.352	18.338
20	7.434	8.260	9.237	9.591	10.851	12.443	14.578	15.452	16.266	19.337
21	8.034	8.897	9.915	10.283	11.591	13.240	15.445	16.344	17.182	20.337
22	8.643	9.542	10.600	10.982	12.338	14.041	16.314	17.240	18.101	21.337
23	9.260	10.196	11.293	11.689	13.091	14.848	17.187	18.137	19.021	22.337
24	9.886	10.856	11.992	12.401	13.848	15.659	18.062	19.037	19.943	23.337
25	10.520	11.524	12.697	13.120	14.611	16.473	18.940	19.939	20.867	24.337
26	11.160	12.198	13.409	13.844	15.379	17.292	19.820	20.843	21.792	25.336
27	11.808	12.878	14.125	14.573	16.151	18.114	20.703	21.749	22.719	26.336
28	12.461	13.565	14.847	15.308	16.928	18.939	21.588	22.657	23.647	27.336
29	13.121	14.256	15.574	16.047	17.708	19.768	22.475	23.567	24.577	28.336
30	13.787	14.953	16.306	16.791	18.493	20.599	23.364	24.478	25.508	29.336
40	20.707	22.164	23.838	24.433	26.509	29.051	32.345	33.66	34.872	39.335
50	27.991	29.707	31.664	32.357	34.764	37.689	41.449	42.942	44.313	49.335
60	35.534	37.485	39.699	40.482	43.188	46.459	50.641	52.294	53.809	59.335

Table (continued) Critical Values of the Chi-Squared Distribution

					α					
v	0.30	0.25	0.20	0.10	0.05	0.025	0.02	0.01	0.005	0.001
1	1.074	1.323	1.642	2.706	3.841	5.024	5.412	6.635	7.879	10.827
2	2.408	2.773	3.219	4.605	5.991	7.378	7.824	9.210	10.597	13.815
3	3.665	4.108	4.642	6.251	7.815	9.348	9.837	11.345	12.838	16.266
4	4.878	5.385	5.989	7.779	9.488	11.143	11.668	13.277	14.860	18.466
5	6.064	6.626	7.289	9.236	11.070	12.832	13.388	15.086	16.750	20.515
6	7.231	7.841	8.558	10.645	12.592	14.449	15.033	16.812	18.548	22.457
7	8.383	9.037	9.803	12.017	14.067	16.013	16.622	18.475	20.278	24.321
8	9.524	10.219	11.030	13.362	15.507	17.535	18.168	20.090	21.955	26.124
9	10.656	11.389	12.242	14.684	16.919	19.023	19.679	21.666	23.589	27.877
10	11.781	12.549	13.442	15.987	18.307	20.483	21.161	23.209	25.188	29.588
11	12.899	13.701	14.631	17.275	19.675	21.920	22.618	24.725	26.757	31.264
12	14.011	14.845	15.812	18.549	21.026	23.337	24.054	26.217	28.300	32.909
13	15.119	15.984	16.985	19.812	22.362	24.736	25.471	27.688	29.819	34.527
14	16.222	17.117	18.151	21.064	23.685	26.119	26.873	29.141	31.319	36.124
15	17.322	18.245	19.311	22.307	24.996	27.488	28.259	30.578	32.801	37.698
16	18.418	19.369	20.465	23.542	26.296	28.845	29.633	32.000	34.267	39.252
17	19.511	20.489	21.615	24.769	27.587	30.191	30.995	33.409	35.718	40.791
18	20.601	21.605	22.760	25.989	28.869	31.526	32.346	34.805	37.156	42.312
19	21.689	22.718	23.900	27.204	30.144	32.852	33.687	36.191	38.582	43.819
20	22.775	23.828	25.038	28.412	31.410	34.170	35.020	37.566	39.997	45.314
21	23.858	24.935	26.171	29.615	32.671	35.479	36.343	38.932	41.401	46.796
22	24.939	26.039	27.301	30.813	33.924	36.781	37.659	40.289	42.796	48.268
23	26.018	27.141	28.429	32.007	35.172	38.076	38.968	41.638	44.181	49.728
24	27.096	28.241	29.553	33.196	36.415	39.364	40.270	42.980	45.558	51.179
25	28.172	29.339	30.675	34.382	37.652	40.646	41.566	44.314	46.928	52.619
26	29.246	30.435	31.795	35.563	38.885	41.923	42.856	45.642	48.290	54.051
27	30.319	31.528	32.912	36.741	40.113	43.195	44.140	46.963	49.645	55.475
28	31.391	32.620	34.027	37.916	41.337	44.461	45.419	48.278	50.994	56.892
29	32.461	33.711	35.139	39.087	42.557	45.722	46.693	49.588	52.335	58.301
30	33.530	34.800	36.250	40.256	43.773	46.979	47.962	50.892	53.672	59.702
40	44.165	45.616	47.269	51.805	55.758	59.342	60.436	63.691	66.766	73.403
50	54.723	56.334	58.164	63.167	67.505	71.420	72.613	76.154	79.490	86.660
60	65.226	66.981	68.972	74.397	79.082	83.298	84.58	88.379	91.952	99.608

One- and Two-Sample Tests of Hypotheses

1 Statistical Hypotheses: General Concepts

Often, the problem confronting the scientist or engineer is not so much the estimation of a population parameter, but rather the formation of a data-based decision procedure that can produce a conclusion about some scientific system. For example, a medical researcher may decide on the basis of experimental evidence whether coffee drinking increases the risk of cancer in humans; an engineer might have to decide on the basis of sample data whether there is a difference between the accuracy of two kinds of gauges; or a sociologist might wish to collect appropriate data to enable him or her to decide whether a person's blood type and eye color are independent variables. In each of these cases, the scientist or engineer *postulates* or *conjectures* something about a system. In addition, each must make use of experimental data and make a decision based on the data. In each case, the conjecture can be put in the form of a statistical hypothesis. Procedures that lead to the acceptance or rejection of statistical hypotheses such as these comprise a major area of statistical inference. First, let us define precisely what we mean by a **statistical hypothesis**.

Definition 1:

> A **statistical hypothesis** is an assertion or conjecture concerning one or more populations.

The truth or falsity of a statistical hypothesis is never known with absolute certainty unless we examine the entire population. This, of course, would be impractical in most situations. Instead, we take a random sample from the population of interest and use the data contained in this sample to provide evidence that either supports or does not support the hypothesis. Evidence from the sample that is inconsistent with the stated hypothesis leads to a rejection of the hypothesis.

From Chapter 10 of *Probability & Statistics for Engineers & Scientists*, Ninth Edition, Ronald E. Walpole, Raymond H. Myers, Sharon L. Myers, Keying Ye. Copyright © 2012 by Pearson Education, Inc. Published by Pearson Prentice Hall. All rights reserved.

The Role of Probability in Hypothesis Testing

It should be made clear to the reader that the decision procedure must include an awareness of the *probability of a wrong conclusion*. For example, suppose that the hypothesis postulated by the engineer is that the fraction defective p in a certain process is 0.10. The experiment is to observe a random sample of the product in question. Suppose that 100 items are tested and 12 items are found defective. It is reasonable to conclude that this evidence does not refute the condition that the binomial parameter $p = 0.10$, and thus it may lead one not to reject the hypothesis. However, it also does not refute $p = 0.12$ or perhaps even $p = 0.15$. As a result, the reader must be accustomed to understanding that **rejection of a hypothesis implies that the sample evidence refutes it**. Put another way, **rejection means that there is a small probability of obtaining the sample information observed when, in fact, the hypothesis is true**. For example, for our proportion-defective hypothesis, a sample of 100 revealing 20 defective items is certainly evidence for rejection. Why? If, indeed, $p = 0.10$, the probability of obtaining 20 or more defectives is approximately 0.002. With the resulting small risk of a wrong conclusion, it would seem safe to **reject the hypothesis** that $p = 0.10$. In other words, rejection of a hypothesis tends to all but "rule out" the hypothesis. On the other hand, it is very important to emphasize that acceptance or, rather, failure to reject does not rule out other possibilities. As a result, the *firm conclusion is established by the data analyst when a hypothesis is rejected*.

The formal statement of a hypothesis is often influenced by the structure of the probability of a wrong conclusion. If the scientist is interested in *strongly supporting* a contention, he or she hopes to arrive at the contention in the form of rejection of a hypothesis. If the medical researcher wishes to show strong evidence in favor of the contention that coffee drinking increases the risk of cancer, the hypothesis tested should be of the form "there is no increase in cancer risk produced by drinking coffee." As a result, the contention is reached via a rejection. Similarly, to support the claim that one kind of gauge is more accurate than another, the engineer tests the hypothesis that there is no difference in the accuracy of the two kinds of gauges.

The foregoing implies that when the data analyst formalizes experimental evidence on the basis of hypothesis testing, the formal **statement of the hypothesis** is very important.

The Null and Alternative Hypotheses

The structure of hypothesis testing will be formulated with the use of the term **null hypothesis**, which refers to any hypothesis we wish to test and is denoted by H_0. The rejection of H_0 leads to the acceptance of an **alternative hypothesis**, denoted by H_1. An understanding of the different roles played by the null hypothesis (H_0) and the alternative hypothesis (H_1) is crucial to one's understanding of the rudiments of hypothesis testing. The alternative hypothesis H_1 usually represents the *question to be answered or the theory to be tested,* and thus its specification is crucial. The null hypothesis H_0 *nullifies or opposes* H_1 and is often the logical complement to H_1. As the reader gains more understanding of hypothesis testing, he or she should note that the analyst arrives at one of the two following conclusions:

> ***reject*** H_0 in favor of H_1 because of sufficient evidence in the data or
>
> ***fail to reject*** H_0 because of insufficient evidence in the data.

Note that the *conclusions do not involve a formal and literal "accept H_0."* The statement of H_0 often represents the "status quo" in opposition to the new idea, conjecture, and so on, stated in H_1, while failure to reject H_0 represents the proper conclusion. In our binomial example, the practical issue may be a concern that the historical defective probability of 0.10 no longer is true. Indeed, the conjecture may be that p exceeds 0.10. We may then state

$$H_0:\ p = 0.10,$$
$$H_1:\ p > 0.10.$$

Now 12 defective items out of 100 does not refute $p = 0.10$, so the conclusion is "fail to reject H_0." However, if the data produce 20 out of 100 defective items, then the conclusion is "reject H_0" in favor of H_1: $p > 0.10$.

Though the applications of hypothesis testing are quite abundant in scientific and engineering work, perhaps the best illustration for a novice lies in the predicament encountered in a jury trial. The null and alternative hypotheses are

$$H_0: \text{defendant is innocent},$$
$$H_1: \text{defendant is guilty}.$$

The indictment comes because of suspicion of guilt. The hypothesis H_0 (the status quo) stands in opposition to H_1 and is maintained unless H_1 is supported by evidence "beyond a reasonable doubt." However, "failure to reject H_0" in this case does not imply innocence, but merely that the evidence was insufficient to convict. So the jury does not necessarily *accept H_0* but *fails to reject H_0*.

2 Testing a Statistical Hypothesis

To illustrate the concepts used in testing a statistical hypothesis about a population, we present the following example. A certain type of cold vaccine is known to be only 25% effective after a period of 2 years. To determine if a new and somewhat more expensive vaccine is superior in providing protection against the same virus for a longer period of time, suppose that 20 people are chosen at random and inoculated. (In an actual study of this type, the participants receiving the new vaccine might number several thousand. The number 20 is being used here only to demonstrate the basic steps in carrying out a statistical test.) If more than 8 of those receiving the new vaccine surpass the 2-year period without contracting the virus, the new vaccine will be considered superior to the one presently in use. The requirement that the number exceed 8 is somewhat arbitrary but appears reasonable in that it represents a modest gain over the 5 people who could be expected to receive protection if the 20 people had been inoculated with the vaccine already in use. We are essentially testing the null hypothesis that the new vaccine is equally effective after a period of 2 years as the one now commonly used. The alternative hypothesis is that the new vaccine is in fact superior. This is equivalent to testing the hypothesis that the binomial parameter for the probability of a success on a given trial is $p = 1/4$ against the alternative that $p > 1/4$. This is usually written as follows:

$$H_0: \ p = 0.25,$$
$$H_1: \ p > 0.25.$$

The Test Statistic

The **test statistic** on which we base our decision is X, the number of individuals in our test group who receive protection from the new vaccine for a period of at least 2 years. The possible values of X, from 0 to 20, are divided into two groups: those numbers less than or equal to 8 and those greater than 8. All possible scores greater than 8 constitute the **critical region**. The last number that we observe in passing into the critical region is called the **critical value**. In our illustration, the critical value is the number 8. Therefore, if $x > 8$, we reject H_0 in favor of the alternative hypothesis H_1. If $x \leq 8$, we fail to reject H_0. This decision criterion is illustrated in Figure 1.

Figure 1: Decision criterion for testing $p = 0.25$ versus $p > 0.25$.

The Probability of a Type I Error

The decision procedure just described could lead to either of two wrong conclusions. For instance, the new vaccine may be no better than the one now in use (H_0 true) and yet, in this particular randomly selected group of individuals, more than 8 surpass the 2-year period without contracting the virus. We would be committing an error by rejecting H_0 in favor of H_1 when, in fact, H_0 is true. Such an error is called a **type I error**.

Definition 2: | Rejection of the null hypothesis when it is true is called a **type I error**.

A second kind of error is committed if 8 or fewer of the group surpass the 2-year period successfully and we are unable to conclude that the vaccine is better when it actually is better (H_1 true). Thus, in this case, we fail to reject H_0 when in fact H_0 is false. This is called a **type II error**.

Definition 3: | Nonrejection of the null hypothesis when it is false is called a **type II error**.

In testing any statistical hypothesis, there are four possible situations that determine whether our decision is correct or in error. These four situations are summarized in Table 1.

Table 1: Possible Situations for Testing a Statistical Hypothesis

	H_0 **is true**	H_0 **is false**
Do not reject H_0	Correct decision	Type II error
Reject H_0	Type I error	Correct decision

The probability of committing a type I error, also called the **level of significance**, is denoted by the Greek letter α. In our illustration, a type I error will occur when more than 8 individuals inoculated with the new vaccine surpass the 2-year period without contracting the virus and researchers conclude that the new vaccine is better when it is actually equivalent to the one in use. Hence, if X is the number of individuals who remain free of the virus for at least 2 years,

$$\alpha = P(\text{type I error}) = P\left(X > 8 \text{ when } p = \frac{1}{4}\right) = \sum_{x=9}^{20} b\left(x; 20, \frac{1}{4}\right)$$

$$= 1 - \sum_{x=0}^{8} b\left(x; 20, \frac{1}{4}\right) = 1 - 0.9591 = 0.0409.$$

We say that the null hypothesis, $p = 1/4$, is being tested at the $\alpha = 0.0409$ level of significance. Sometimes the level of significance is called the **size of the test**. A critical region of size 0.0409 is very small, and therefore it is unlikely that a type I error will be committed. Consequently, it would be most unusual for more than 8 individuals to remain immune to a virus for a 2-year period using a new vaccine that is essentially equivalent to the one now on the market.

The Probability of a Type II Error

The probability of committing a type II error, denoted by β, is impossible to compute unless we have a specific alternative hypothesis. If we test the null hypothesis that $p = 1/4$ against the alternative hypothesis that $p = 1/2$, then we are able to compute the probability of not rejecting H_0 when it is false. We simply find the probability of obtaining 8 or fewer in the group that surpass the 2-year period when $p = 1/2$. In this case,

$$\beta = P(\text{type II error}) = P\left(X \leq 8 \text{ when } p = \frac{1}{2}\right)$$

$$= \sum_{x=0}^{8} b\left(x; 20, \frac{1}{2}\right) = 0.2517.$$

This is a rather high probability, indicating a test procedure in which it is quite likely that we shall reject the new vaccine when, in fact, it is superior to what is now in use. Ideally, we like to use a test procedure for which the type I and type II error probabilities are both small.

It is possible that the director of the testing program is willing to make a type II error if the more expensive vaccine is not significantly superior. In fact, the only time he wishes to guard against the type II error is when the true value of p is at least 0.7. If $p = 0.7$, this test procedure gives

$$\beta = P(\text{type II error}) = P(X \le 8 \text{ when } p = 0.7)$$

$$= \sum_{x=0}^{8} b(x; 20, 0.7) = 0.0051.$$

With such a small probability of committing a type II error, it is extremely unlikely that the new vaccine would be rejected when it was 70% effective after a period of 2 years. As the alternative hypothesis approaches unity, the value of β diminishes to zero.

The Role of α, β, and Sample Size

Let us assume that the director of the testing program is unwilling to commit a type II error when the alternative hypothesis $p = 1/2$ is true, even though we have found the probability of such an error to be $\beta = 0.2517$. It is always possible to reduce β by increasing the size of the critical region. For example, consider what happens to the values of α and β when we change our critical value to 7 so that all scores greater than 7 fall in the critical region and those less than or equal to 7 fall in the nonrejection region. Now, in testing $p = 1/4$ against the alternative hypothesis that $p = 1/2$, we find that

$$\alpha = \sum_{x=8}^{20} b\left(x; 20, \frac{1}{4}\right) = 1 - \sum_{x=0}^{7} b\left(x; 20, \frac{1}{4}\right) = 1 - 0.8982 = 0.1018$$

and

$$\beta = \sum_{x=0}^{7} b\left(x; 20, \frac{1}{2}\right) = 0.1316.$$

By adopting a new decision procedure, we have reduced the probability of committing a type II error at the expense of increasing the probability of committing a type I error. For a fixed sample size, a decrease in the probability of one error will usually result in an increase in the probability of the other error. Fortunately, **the probability of committing both types of error can be reduced by increasing the sample size.** Consider the same problem using a random sample of 100 individuals. If more than 36 of the group surpass the 2-year period, we reject the null hypothesis that $p = 1/4$ and accept the alternative hypothesis that $p > 1/4$. The critical value is now 36. All possible scores above 36 constitute the critical region, and all possible scores less than or equal to 36 fall in the acceptance region.

To determine the probability of committing a type I error, we shall use the normal curve approximation with

$$\mu = np = (100)\left(\frac{1}{4}\right) = 25 \quad \text{and} \quad \sigma = \sqrt{npq} = \sqrt{(100)(1/4)(3/4)} = 4.33.$$

Referring to Figure 2, we need the area under the normal curve to the right of $x = 36.5$. The corresponding z-value is

$$z = \frac{36.5 - 25}{4.33} = 2.66.$$

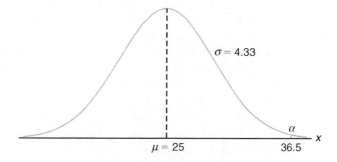

Figure 2: Probability of a type I error.

From Table Areas under the Normal Curve at the end of this chapter we find that
$$\alpha = P(\text{type I error}) = P\left(X > 36 \text{ when } p = \frac{1}{4} \right) \approx P(Z > 2.66)$$
$$= 1 - P(Z < 2.66) = 1 - 0.9961 = 0.0039.$$

If H_0 is false and the true value of H_1 is $p = 1/2$, we can determine the probability of a type II error using the normal curve approximation with
$$\mu = np = (100)(1/2) = 50 \quad \text{and} \quad \sigma = \sqrt{npq} = \sqrt{(100)(1/2)(1/2)} = 5.$$

The probability of a value falling in the nonrejection region when H_0 is true is given by the area of the shaded region to the left of $x = 36.5$ in Figure 3. The z-value corresponding to $x = 36.5$ is
$$z = \frac{36.5 - 50}{5} = -2.7.$$

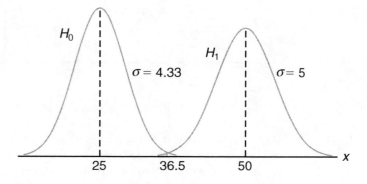

Figure 3: Probability of a type II error.

Therefore,

$$\beta = P(\text{type II error}) = P\left(X \le 36 \text{ when } p = \frac{1}{2} \right) \approx P(Z < -2.7) = 0.0035.$$

Obviously, the type I and type II errors will rarely occur if the experiment consists of 100 individuals.

The illustration above underscores the strategy of the scientist in hypothesis testing. After the null and alternative hypotheses are stated, it is important to consider the sensitivity of the test procedure. By this we mean that there should be a determination, for a fixed α, of a reasonable value for the probability of wrongly accepting H_0 (i.e., the value of β) when the true situation represents some *important deviation from H_0*. A value for the sample size can usually be determined for which there is a reasonable balance between the values of α and β computed in this fashion. The vaccine problem provides an illustration.

Illustration with a Continuous Random Variable

The concepts discussed here for a discrete population can be applied equally well to continuous random variables. Consider the null hypothesis that the average weight of male students in a certain college is 68 kilograms against the alternative hypothesis that it is unequal to 68. That is, we wish to test

$$H_0:\ \mu = 68,$$
$$H_1:\ \mu \neq 68.$$

The alternative hypothesis allows for the possibility that $\mu < 68$ or $\mu > 68$.

A sample mean that falls close to the hypothesized value of 68 would be considered evidence in favor of H_0. On the other hand, a sample mean that is considerably less than or more than 68 would be evidence inconsistent with H_0 and therefore favoring H_1. The sample mean is the test statistic in this case. A critical region for the test statistic might arbitrarily be chosen to be the two intervals $\bar{x} < 67$ and $\bar{x} > 69$. The nonrejection region will then be the interval $67 \leq \bar{x} \leq 69$. This decision criterion is illustrated in Figure 4.

Figure 4: Critical region (in blue).

Let us now use the decision criterion of Figure 4 to calculate the probabilities of committing type I and type II errors when testing the null hypothesis that $\mu = 68$ kilograms against the alternative that $\mu \neq 68$ kilograms.

Assume the standard deviation of the population of weights to be $\sigma = 3.6$. For large samples, we may substitute s for σ if no other estimate of σ is available. Our decision statistic, based on a random sample of size $n = 36$, will be $\bar{X}$, the most efficient estimator of μ. From the Central Limit Theorem, we know that the sampling distribution of $\bar{X}$ is approximately normal with standard deviation $\sigma_{\bar{X}} = \sigma/\sqrt{n} = 3.6/6 = 0.6$.

The probability of committing a type I error, or the level of significance of our test, is equal to the sum of the areas that have been shaded in each tail of the distribution in Figure 5. Therefore,

$$\alpha = P(\bar{X} < 67 \text{ when } \mu = 68) + P(\bar{X} > 69 \text{ when } \mu = 68).$$

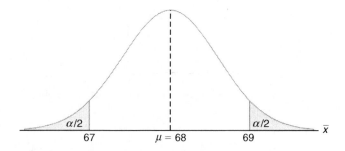

Figure 5: Critical region for testing $\mu = 68$ versus $\mu \neq 68$.

The z-values corresponding to $\bar{x}_1 = 67$ and $\bar{x}_2 = 69$ when H_0 is true are

$$z_1 = \frac{67 - 68}{0.6} = -1.67 \quad \text{and} \quad z_2 = \frac{69 - 68}{0.6} = 1.67.$$

Therefore,

$$\alpha = P(Z < -1.67) + P(Z > 1.67) = 2P(Z < -1.67) = 0.0950.$$

Thus, 9.5% of all samples of size 36 would lead us to reject $\mu = 68$ kilograms when, in fact, it is true. To reduce α, we have a choice of increasing the sample size or widening the fail-to-reject region. Suppose that we increase the sample size to $n = 64$. Then $\sigma_{\bar{X}} = 3.6/8 = 0.45$. Now

$$z_1 = \frac{67 - 68}{0.45} = -2.22 \quad \text{and} \quad z_2 = \frac{69 - 68}{0.45} = 2.22.$$

Hence,

$$\alpha = P(Z < -2.22) + P(Z > 2.22) = 2P(Z < -2.22) = 0.0264.$$

The reduction in α is not sufficient by itself to guarantee a good testing procedure. We must also evaluate β for various alternative hypotheses. If it is important to reject H_0 when the true mean is some value $\mu \geq 70$ or $\mu \leq 66$, then the probability of committing a type II error should be computed and examined for the alternatives $\mu = 66$ and $\mu = 70$. Because of symmetry, it is only necessary to consider the probability of not rejecting the null hypothesis that $\mu = 68$ when the alternative $\mu = 70$ is true. A type II error will result when the sample mean $\bar{x}$ falls between 67 and 69 when H_1 is true. Therefore, referring to Figure 6, we find that

$$\beta = P(67 \leq \bar{X} \leq 69 \text{ when } \mu = 70).$$

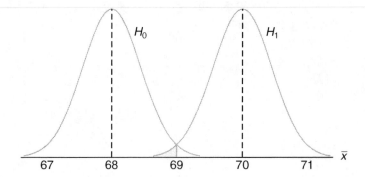

Figure 6: Probability of type II error for testing $\mu = 68$ versus $\mu = 70$.

The z-values corresponding to $\bar{x}_1 = 67$ and $\bar{x}_2 = 69$ when H_1 is true are

$$z_1 = \frac{67 - 70}{0.45} = -6.67 \quad \text{and} \quad z_2 = \frac{69 - 70}{0.45} = -2.22.$$

Therefore,

$$\beta = P(-6.67 < Z < -2.22) = P(Z < -2.22) - P(Z < -6.67)$$
$$= 0.0132 - 0.0000 = 0.0132.$$

If the true value of μ is the alternative $\mu = 66$, the value of β will again be 0.0132. For all possible values of $\mu < 66$ or $\mu > 70$, the value of β will be even smaller when $n = 64$, and consequently there would be little chance of not rejecting H_0 when it is false.

The probability of committing a type II error increases rapidly when the true value of μ approaches, but is not equal to, the hypothesized value. Of course, this is usually the situation where we do not mind making a type II error. For example, if the alternative hypothesis $\mu = 68.5$ is true, we do not mind committing a type II error by concluding that the true answer is $\mu = 68$. The probability of making such an error will be high when $n = 64$. Referring to Figure 7, we have

$$\beta = P(67 \le \bar{X} \le 69 \text{ when } \mu = 68.5).$$

The z-values corresponding to $\bar{x}_1 = 67$ and $\bar{x}_2 = 69$ when $\mu = 68.5$ are

$$z_1 = \frac{67 - 68.5}{0.45} = -3.33 \quad \text{and} \quad z_2 = \frac{69 - 68.5}{0.45} = 1.11.$$

Therefore,

$$\beta = P(-3.33 < Z < 1.11) = P(Z < 1.11) - P(Z < -3.33)$$
$$= 0.8665 - 0.0004 = 0.8661.$$

The preceding examples illustrate the following important properties:

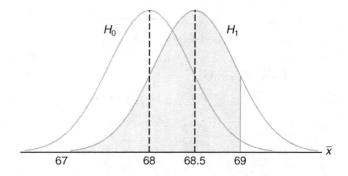

Figure 7: Type II error for testing $\mu = 68$ versus $\mu = 68.5$.

Important Properties of a Test of Hypothesis	
	1. The type I error and type II error are related. A decrease in the probability of one generally results in an increase in the probability of the other.
	2. The size of the critical region, and therefore the probability of committing a type I error, can always be reduced by adjusting the critical value(s).
	3. An increase in the sample size n will reduce α and β simultaneously.
	4. If the null hypothesis is false, β is a maximum when the true value of a parameter approaches the hypothesized value. The greater the distance between the true value and the hypothesized value, the smaller β will be.

One very important concept that relates to error probabilities is the notion of the **power** of a test.

Definition 4:

> The **power** of a test is the probability of rejecting H_0 given that a specific alternative is true.

The power of a test can be computed as $1 - \beta$. Often **different types of tests are compared by contrasting power properties**. Consider the previous illustration, in which we were testing $H_0 \colon \mu = 68$ and $H_1 \colon \mu \neq 68$. As before, suppose we are interested in assessing the sensitivity of the test. The test is governed by the rule that we do not reject H_0 if $67 \leq \bar{x} \leq 69$. We seek the capability of the test to properly reject H_0 when indeed $\mu = 68.5$. We have seen that the probability of a type II error is given by $\beta = 0.8661$. Thus, the **power** of the test is $1 - 0.8661 = 0.1339$. In a sense, the power is a more succinct measure of how sensitive the test is for detecting differences between a mean of 68 and a mean of 68.5. In this case, if μ is truly 68.5, the test as described will *properly reject H_0 only 13.39% of the time*. As a result, the test would not be a good one if it was important that the analyst have a reasonable chance of truly distinguishing between a mean of 68.0 (specified by H_0) and a mean of 68.5. From the foregoing, it is clear that to produce a desirable power (say, greater than 0.8), one must either increase α or increase the sample size.

So far in this chapter, much of the discussion of hypothesis testing has focused on foundations and definitions. In the sections that follow, we get more specific and put hypotheses in categories as well as discuss tests of hypotheses on various parameters of interest. We begin by drawing the distinction between a one-sided and a two-sided hypothesis.

One- and Two-Tailed Tests

A test of any statistical hypothesis where the alternative is **one sided**, such as

$$H_0: \theta = \theta_0,$$
$$H_1: \theta > \theta_0$$

or perhaps

$$H_0: \theta = \theta_0,$$
$$H_1: \theta < \theta_0,$$

is called a **one-tailed test**. Earlier in this section, we referred to the **test statistic** for a hypothesis. Generally, the critical region for the alternative hypothesis $\theta > \theta_0$ lies in the right tail of the distribution of the test statistic, while the critical region for the alternative hypothesis $\theta < \theta_0$ lies entirely in the left tail. (In a sense, the inequality symbol points in the direction of the critical region.) A one-tailed test was used in the vaccine experiment to test the hypothesis $p = 1/4$ against the one-sided alternative $p > 1/4$ for the binomial distribution. The one-tailed critical region is usually obvious; the reader should visualize the behavior of the test statistic and notice the obvious *signal* that would produce evidence supporting the alternative hypothesis.

A test of any statistical hypothesis where the alternative is **two sided**, such as

$$H_0: \theta = \theta_0,$$
$$H_1: \theta \neq \theta_0,$$

is called a **two-tailed test**, since the critical region is split into two parts, often having equal probabilities, in each tail of the distribution of the test statistic. The alternative hypothesis $\theta \neq \theta_0$ states that either $\theta < \theta_0$ or $\theta > \theta_0$. A two-tailed test was used to test the null hypothesis that $\mu = 68$ kilograms against the two-sided alternative $\mu \neq 68$ kilograms in the example of the continuous population of student weights.

How Are the Null and Alternative Hypotheses Chosen?

The null hypothesis H_0 will often be stated using the *equality sign*. With this approach, it is clear how the probability of type I error is controlled. However, there are situations in which "do not reject H_0" implies that the parameter θ might be any value defined by the natural complement to the alternative hypothesis. For example, in the vaccine example, where the alternative hypothesis is $H_1: p > 1/4$, it is quite possible that nonrejection of H_0 cannot rule out a value of p less than $1/4$. Clearly though, in the case of one-tailed tests, the statement of the alternative is the most important consideration.

Whether one sets up a one-tailed or a two-tailed test will depend on the conclusion to be drawn if H_0 is rejected. The location of the critical region can be determined only after H_1 has been stated. For example, in testing a new drug, one sets up the hypothesis that it is no better than similar drugs now on the market and tests this against the alternative hypothesis that the new drug is superior. Such an alternative hypothesis will result in a one-tailed test with the critical region in the right tail. However, if we wish to compare a new teaching technique with the conventional classroom procedure, the alternative hypothesis should allow for the new approach to be either inferior or superior to the conventional procedure. Hence, the test is two-tailed with the critical region divided equally so as to fall in the extreme left and right tails of the distribution of our statistic.

Example 1: A manufacturer of a certain brand of rice cereal claims that the average saturated fat content does not exceed 1.5 grams per serving. State the null and alternative hypotheses to be used in testing this claim and determine where the critical region is located.

Solution: The manufacturer's claim should be rejected only if μ is greater than 1.5 milligrams and should not be rejected if μ is less than or equal to 1.5 milligrams. We test

$$H_0: \ \mu = 1.5,$$
$$H_1: \ \mu > 1.5.$$

Nonrejection of H_0 does not rule out values less than 1.5 milligrams. Since we have a one-tailed test, the greater than symbol indicates that the critical region lies entirely in the right tail of the distribution of our test statistic $\bar{X}$.

Example 2: A real estate agent claims that 60% of all private residences being built today are 3-bedroom homes. To test this claim, a large sample of new residences is inspected; the proportion of these homes with 3 bedrooms is recorded and used as the test statistic. State the null and alternative hypotheses to be used in this test and determine the location of the critical region.

Solution: If the test statistic were substantially higher or lower than $p = 0.6$, we would reject the agent's claim. Hence, we should make the hypothesis

$$H_0: \ p = 0.6,$$
$$H_1: \ p \neq 0.6.$$

The alternative hypothesis implies a two-tailed test with the critical region divided equally in both tails of the distribution of $\widehat{P}$, our test statistic.

3 The Use of P-Values for Decision Making in Testing Hypotheses

In testing hypotheses in which the test statistic is discrete, the critical region may be chosen arbitrarily and its size determined. If α is too large, it can be reduced by making an adjustment in the critical value. It may be necessary to increase the sample size to offset the decrease that occurs automatically in the power of the test.

Over a number of generations of statistical analysis, it had become customary to choose an α of 0.05 or 0.01 and select the critical region accordingly. Then, of course, strict rejection or nonrejection of H_0 would depend on that critical region. For example, if the test is two tailed and α is set at the 0.05 level of significance and the test statistic involves, say, the standard normal distribution, then a z-value is observed from the data and the critical region is

$$z > 1.96 \qquad \text{or} \qquad z < -1.96,$$

where the value 1.96 is found as $z_{0.025}$ in Table Areas under the Normal Curve. A value of z in the critical region prompts the statement "The value of the test statistic is significant," which we can then translate into the user's language. For example, if the hypothesis is given by

$$H_0: \ \mu = 10,$$
$$H_1: \ \mu \neq 10,$$

one might say, "The mean differs significantly from the value 10."

Preselection of a Significance Level

This preselection of a significance level α has its roots in the philosophy that the maximum risk of making a type I error should be controlled. However, this approach does not account for values of test statistics that are "close" to the critical region. Suppose, for example, in the illustration with $H_0: \mu = 10$ versus $H_1: \mu \neq 10$, a value of $z = 1.87$ is observed; strictly speaking, with $\alpha = 0.05$, the value is not significant. But the risk of committing a type I error if one rejects H_0 in this case could hardly be considered severe. In fact, in a two-tailed scenario, one can quantify this risk as

$$P = 2P(Z > 1.87 \text{ when } \mu = 10) = 2(0.0307) = 0.0614.$$

As a result, 0.0614 is the probability of obtaining a value of z as large as or larger (in magnitude) than 1.87 when in fact $\mu = 10$. Although this evidence against H_0 is not as strong as that which would result from rejection at an $\alpha = 0.05$ level, it is important information to the user. Indeed, continued use of $\alpha = 0.05$ or 0.01 is only a result of what standards have been passed down through the generations. **The *P*-value approach has been adopted extensively by users of applied statistics.** The approach is designed to give the user an alternative (in terms of a probability) to a mere "reject" or "do not reject" conclusion. The P-value computation also gives the user important information when the z-value falls well *into the ordinary critical region.* For example, if z is 2.73, it is informative for the user to observe that

$$P = 2(0.0032) = 0.0064,$$

and thus the z-value is significant at a level considerably less than 0.05. It is important to know that under the condition of H_0, a value of $z = 2.73$ is an extremely rare event. That is, a value at least that large in magnitude would only occur 64 times in 10,000 experiments.

A Graphical Demonstration of a *P*-Value

One very simple way of explaining a *P*-value graphically is to consider two distinct samples. Suppose that two materials are being considered for coating a particular type of metal in order to inhibit corrosion. Specimens are obtained, and one collection is coated with material 1 and one collection coated with material 2. The sample sizes are $n_1 = n_2 = 10$, and corrosion is measured in percent of surface area affected. The hypothesis is that the samples came from common distributions with mean $\mu = 10$. Let us assume that the population variance is 1.0. Then we are testing

$$H_0: \ \mu_1 = \mu_2 = 10.$$

Let Figure 8 represent a point plot of the data; the data are placed on the distribution stated by the null hypothesis. Let us assume that the "×" data refer to material 1 and the "○" data refer to material 2. Now it seems clear that the data do refute the null hypothesis. But how can this be summarized in one number? **The *P*-value can be viewed as simply the probability of obtaining these data given that both samples come from the same distribution**. Clearly, this probability is quite small, say 0.00000001! Thus, the small *P*-value clearly refutes H_0, and the conclusion is that the population means are significantly different.

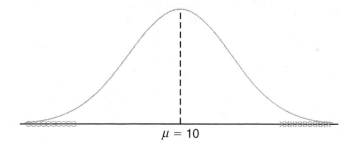

Figure 8: Data that are likely generated from populations having two different means.

Use of the *P*-value approach as an aid in decision-making is quite natural, and nearly all computer packages that provide hypothesis-testing computation print out *P*-values along with values of the appropriate test statistic. The following is a formal definition of a *P*-value.

Definition 5:

> A **P-value** is the lowest level (of significance) at which the observed value of the test statistic is significant.

How Does the Use of *P*-Values Differ from Classic Hypothesis Testing?

It is tempting at this point to summarize the procedures associated with testing, say, $H_0: \theta = \theta_0$. However, the student who is a novice in this area should understand that there are differences in approach and philosophy between the classic fixed α approach that is climaxed with either a "reject H_0" or a "do not reject H_0" conclusion and the P-value approach. In the latter, no fixed α is determined and conclusions are drawn on the basis of the size of the P-value in harmony with the subjective judgment of the engineer or scientist. While modern computer software will output P-values, nevertheless it is important that readers understand both approaches in order to appreciate the totality of the concepts. Thus, we offer a brief list of procedural steps for both the classical and the P-value approach.

Approach to Hypothesis Testing with Fixed Probability of Type I Error	**1.** State the null and alternative hypotheses. **2.** Choose a fixed significance level α. **3.** Choose an appropriate test statistic and establish the critical region based on α. **4.** Reject H_0 if the computed test statistic is in the critical region. Otherwise, do not reject. **5.** Draw scientific or engineering conclusions.

Significance Testing (P-Value Approach)	**1.** State null and alternative hypotheses. **2.** Choose an appropriate test statistic. **3.** Compute the P-value based on the computed value of the test statistic. **4.** Use judgment based on the P-value and knowledge of the scientific system.

In later sections of this chapter and chapters that follow, many examples and exercises emphasize the P-value approach to drawing scientific conclusions.

Exercises

1 Suppose that an allergist wishes to test the hypothesis that at least 30% of the public is allergic to some cheese products. Explain how the allergist could commit

(a) a type I error;

(b) a type II error.

2 A sociologist is concerned about the effectiveness of a training course designed to get more drivers to use seat belts in automobiles.

(a) What hypothesis is she testing if she commits a type I error by erroneously concluding that the training course is ineffective?

(b) What hypothesis is she testing if she commits a type II error by erroneously concluding that the training course is effective?

3 A large manufacturing firm is being charged with discrimination in its hiring practices.

(a) What hypothesis is being tested if a jury commits a type I error by finding the firm guilty?

(b) What hypothesis is being tested if a jury commits a type II error by finding the firm guilty?

4 A fabric manufacturer believes that the proportion of orders for raw material arriving late is $p = 0.6$. If a random sample of 10 orders shows that 3 or fewer arrived late, the hypothesis that $p = 0.6$ should be rejected in favor of the alternative $p < 0.6$. Use the binomial distribution.

(a) Find the probability of committing a type I error if the true proportion is $p = 0.6$.

(b) Find the probability of committing a type II error for the alternatives $p = 0.3$, $p = 0.4$, and $p = 0.5$.

5 Repeat Exercise 4 but assume that 50 orders are selected and the critical region is defined to be $x \leq 24$, where x is the number of orders in the sample that arrived late. Use the normal approximation.

6 The proportion of adults living in a small town who are college graduates is estimated to be $p = 0.6$. To test this hypothesis, a random sample of 15 adults is selected. If the number of college graduates in the sample is anywhere from 6 to 12, we shall not reject the null hypothesis that $p = 0.6$; otherwise, we shall conclude that $p \neq 0.6$.

(a) Evaluate α assuming that $p = 0.6$. Use the binomial distribution.

(b) Evaluate β for the alternatives $p = 0.5$ and $p = 0.7$.

(c) Is this a good test procedure?

7   Repeat Exercise 6 but assume that 200 adults are selected and the fail-to-reject region is defined to be $110 \leq x \leq 130$, where x is the number of college graduates in our sample. Use the normal approximation.

8   In *Relief from Arthritis* published by Thorsons Publishers, Ltd., John E. Croft claims that over 40% of those who suffer from osteoarthritis receive measurable relief from an ingredient produced by a particular species of mussel found off the coast of New Zealand. To test this claim, the mussel extract is to be given to a group of 7 osteoarthritic patients. If 3 or more of the patients receive relief, we shall not reject the null hypothesis that $p = 0.4$; otherwise, we conclude that $p < 0.4$.

(a) Evaluate α, assuming that $p = 0.4$.

(b) Evaluate β for the alternative $p = 0.3$.

9   A dry cleaning establishment claims that a new spot remover will remove more than 70% of the spots to which it is applied. To check this claim, the spot remover will be used on 12 spots chosen at random. If fewer than 11 of the spots are removed, we shall not reject the null hypothesis that $p = 0.7$; otherwise, we conclude that $p > 0.7$.

(a) Evaluate α, assuming that $p = 0.7$.

(b) Evaluate β for the alternative $p = 0.9$.

10   Repeat Exercise 9 but assume that 100 spots are treated and the critical region is defined to be $x > 82$, where x is the number of spots removed.

11   Repeat Exercise 8 but assume that 70 patients are given the mussel extract and the critical region is defined to be $x < 24$, where x is the number of osteoarthritic patients who receive relief.

12   A random sample of 400 voters in a certain city are asked if they favor an additional 4% gasoline sales tax to provide badly needed revenues for street repairs. If more than 220 but fewer than 260 favor the sales tax, we shall conclude that 60% of the voters are for it.

(a) Find the probability of committing a type I error if 60% of the voters favor the increased tax.

(b) What is the probability of committing a type II error using this test procedure if actually only 48% of the voters are in favor of the additional gasoline tax?

13   Suppose, in Exercise 12, we conclude that 60% of the voters favor the gasoline sales tax if more than 214 but fewer than 266 voters in our sample favor it. Show that this new critical region results in a smaller value for α at the expense of increasing β.

14   A manufacturer has developed a new fishing line, which the company claims has a mean breaking strength of 15 kilograms with a standard deviation of 0.5 kilogram. To test the hypothesis that $\mu = 15$ kilograms against the alternative that $\mu < 15$ kilograms, a random sample of 50 lines will be tested. The critical region is defined to be $\bar{x} < 14.9$.

(a) Find the probability of committing a type I error when H_0 is true.

(b) Evaluate β for the alternatives $\mu = 14.8$ and $\mu = 14.9$ kilograms.

15   A soft-drink machine at a steak house is regulated so that the amount of drink dispensed is approximately normally distributed with a mean of 200 milliliters and a standard deviation of 15 milliliters. The machine is checked periodically by taking a sample of 9 drinks and computing the average content. If $\bar{x}$ falls in the interval $191 < \bar{x} < 209$, the machine is thought to be operating satisfactorily; otherwise, we conclude that $\mu \neq 200$ milliliters.

(a) Find the probability of committing a type I error when $\mu = 200$ milliliters.

(b) Find the probability of committing a type II error when $\mu = 215$ milliliters.

16   Repeat Exercise 15 for samples of size $n = 25$. Use the same critical region.

17   A new curing process developed for a certain type of cement results in a mean compressive strength of 5000 kilograms per square centimeter with a standard deviation of 120 kilograms. To test the hypothesis that $\mu = 5000$ against the alternative that $\mu < 5000$, a random sample of 50 pieces of cement is tested. The critical region is defined to be $\bar{x} < 4970$.

(a) Find the probability of committing a type I error when H_0 is true.

(b) Evaluate β for the alternatives $\mu = 4970$ and $\mu = 4960$.

18   If we plot the probabilities of failing to reject H_0 corresponding to various alternatives for μ (including the value specified by H_0) and connect all the points by a smooth curve, we obtain the **operating characteristic curve** of the test criterion, or simply the OC curve. Note that the probability of failing to reject H_0 when it is true is simply $1 - \alpha$. Operating characteristic curves are widely used in industrial applications to provide a visual display of the merits of the test criterion. With reference to Exercise 10.15, find the probabilities of failing to reject H_0 for the following 9 values of μ and plot the OC curve: 184, 188, 192, 196, 200, 204, 208, 212, and 216.

4   Single Sample: Tests Concerning a Single Mean

In this section, we formally consider tests of hypotheses on a single population mean. Many of the illustrations from previous sections involved tests on the mean, so the reader should already have insight into some of the details that are outlined here.

Tests on a Single Mean (Variance Known)

We should first describe the assumptions on which the experiment is based. The model for the underlying situation centers around an experiment with $X_1, X_2, \ldots,$ X_n representing a random sample from a distribution with mean μ and variance $\sigma^2 > 0$. Consider first the hypothesis

$$H_0\colon \mu = \mu_0,$$
$$H_1\colon \mu \neq \mu_0.$$

The appropriate test statistic should be based on the random variable $\bar{X}$. The Central Limit Theorem, which essentially states that despite the distribution of X, the random variable $\bar{X}$ has approximately a normal distribution with mean μ and variance σ^2/n for reasonably large sample sizes. So, $\mu_{\bar{X}} = \mu$ and $\sigma_{\bar{X}}^2 = \sigma^2/n$. We can then determine a critical region based on the computed sample average, $\bar{x}$. It should be clear to the reader by now that there will be a two-tailed critical region for the test.

Standardization of $\bar{X}$

It is convenient to standardize $\bar{X}$ and formally involve the **standard normal** random variable Z, where

$$Z = \frac{\bar{X} - \mu}{\sigma/\sqrt{n}}.$$

We know that *under H_0*, that is, if $\mu = \mu_0$, $\sqrt{n}(\bar{X} - \mu_0)/\sigma$ follows an $n(x; 0, 1)$ distribution, and hence the expression

$$P\left(-z_{\alpha/2} < \frac{\bar{X} - \mu_0}{\sigma/\sqrt{n}} < z_{\alpha/2}\right) = 1 - \alpha$$

can be used to write an appropriate nonrejection region. The reader should keep in mind that, formally, the critical region is designed to control α, the probability of type I error. It should be obvious that a *two-tailed signal* of evidence is needed to support H_1. Thus, given a computed value $\bar{x}$, the formal test involves rejecting H_0 if the computed *test statistic* z falls in the critical region described next.

$$z = \frac{\bar{x} - \mu_0}{\sigma/\sqrt{n}} > z_{\alpha/2} \quad \text{or} \quad z = \frac{\bar{x} - \mu_0}{\sigma/\sqrt{n}} < -z_{\alpha/2}$$

If $-z_{\alpha/2} < z < z_{\alpha/2}$, do not reject H_0. Rejection of H_0, of course, implies acceptance of the alternative hypothesis $\mu \neq \mu_0$. With this definition of the critical region, it should be clear that there will be probability α of rejecting H_0 (falling into the critical region) when, indeed, $\mu = \mu_0$.

Although it is easier to understand the critical region written in terms of z, we can write the same critical region in terms of the computed average $\bar{x}$. The following can be written as an identical decision procedure:

reject H_0 if $\bar{x} < a$ or $\bar{x} > b$,

where

$$a = \mu_0 - z_{\alpha/2}\frac{\sigma}{\sqrt{n}}, \qquad b = \mu_0 + z_{\alpha/2}\frac{\sigma}{\sqrt{n}}.$$

Hence, for a significance level α, the critical values of the random variable z and $\bar{x}$ are both depicted in Figure 9.

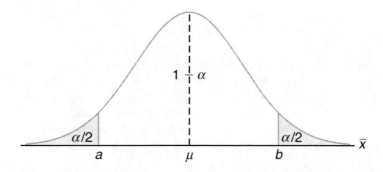

Figure 9: Critical region for the alternative hypothesis $\mu \neq \mu_0$.

Tests of one-sided hypotheses on the mean involve the same statistic described in the two-sided case. The difference, of course, is that the critical region is only in one tail of the standard normal distribution. For example, suppose that we seek to test

$$H_0: \ \mu = \mu_0,$$
$$H_1: \ \mu > \mu_0.$$

The signal that favors H_1 comes from *large values* of z. Thus, rejection of H_0 results when the computed $z > z_\alpha$. Obviously, if the alternative is $H_1: \mu < \mu_0$, the critical region is entirely in the lower tail and thus rejection results from $z < -z_\alpha$. Although in a one-sided testing case the null hypothesis can be written as $H_0: \mu \leq \mu_0$ or $H_0: \mu \geq \mu_0$, it is usually written as $H_0: \mu = \mu_0$.

The following two examples illustrate tests on means for the case in which σ is known.

Example 3:

A random sample of 100 recorded deaths in the United States during the past year showed an average life span of 71.8 years. Assuming a population standard deviation of 8.9 years, does this seem to indicate that the mean life span today is greater than 70 years? Use a 0.05 level of significance.

Solution:

1. H_0: $\mu = 70$ years.

2. H_1: $\mu > 70$ years.

3. $\alpha = 0.05$.

4. Critical region: $z > 1.645$, where $z = \frac{\bar{x} - \mu_0}{\sigma/\sqrt{n}}$.

5. Computations: $\bar{x} = 71.8$ years, $\sigma = 8.9$ years, and hence $z = \frac{71.8 - 70}{8.9/\sqrt{100}} = 2.02$.

6. Decision: Reject H_0 and conclude that the mean life span today is greater than 70 years.

The P-value corresponding to $z = 2.02$ is given by the area of the shaded region in Figure 10.

Using Table Areas under the Normal Curve, we have

$$P = P(Z > 2.02) = 0.0217.$$

As a result, the evidence in favor of H_1 is even stronger than that suggested by a 0.05 level of significance.

Example 4:

A manufacturer of sports equipment has developed a new synthetic fishing line that the company claims has a mean breaking strength of 8 kilograms with a standard deviation of 0.5 kilogram. Test the hypothesis that $\mu = 8$ kilograms against the alternative that $\mu \neq 8$ kilograms if a random sample of 50 lines is tested and found to have a mean breaking strength of 7.8 kilograms. Use a 0.01 level of significance.

Solution:

1. H_0: $\mu = 8$ kilograms.

2. H_1: $\mu \neq 8$ kilograms.

3. $\alpha = 0.01$.

4. Critical region: $z < -2.575$ and $z > 2.575$, where $z = \frac{\bar{x} - \mu_0}{\sigma/\sqrt{n}}$.

5. Computations: $\bar{x} = 7.8$ kilograms, $n = 50$, and hence $z = \frac{7.8 - 8}{0.5/\sqrt{50}} = -2.83$.

6. Decision: Reject H_0 and conclude that the average breaking strength is not equal to 8 but is, in fact, less than 8 kilograms.

Since the test in this example is two tailed, the desired P-value is twice the area of the shaded region in Figure 11 to the left of $z = -2.83$. Therefore, using Table Areas under the Normal Curve, we have

$$P = P(|Z| > 2.83) = 2P(Z < -2.83) = 0.0046,$$

which allows us to reject the null hypothesis that $\mu = 8$ kilograms at a level of significance smaller than 0.01.

Figure 10: *P*-value for Example 3.   Figure 11: *P*-value for Example 4.

Relationship to Confidence Interval Estimation

The reader should realize by now that the hypothesis-testing approach to statistical inference in this chapter is very closely related to the confidence interval approach. Confidence interval estimation involves computation of bounds within which it is "reasonable" for the parameter in question to lie. For the case of a single population mean μ with σ^2 known, the structure of both hypothesis testing and confidence interval estimation is based on the random variable

$$Z = \frac{\bar{X} - \mu}{\sigma/\sqrt{n}}.$$

It turns out that the testing of H_0: $\mu = \mu_0$ against H_1: $\mu \neq \mu_0$ at a significance level α *is equivalent to computing a* $100(1-\alpha)\%$ *confidence interval on* μ *and rejecting* H_0 *if* μ_0 *is outside the confidence interval.* If μ_0 is inside the confidence interval, the hypothesis is not rejected. The equivalence is very intuitive and quite simple to illustrate. Recall that with an observed value $\bar{x}$, failure to reject H_0 at significance level α implies that

$$-z_{\alpha/2} \leq \frac{\bar{x} - \mu_0}{\sigma/\sqrt{n}} \leq z_{\alpha/2},$$

which is equivalent to

$$\bar{x} - z_{\alpha/2}\frac{\sigma}{\sqrt{n}} \leq \mu_0 \leq \bar{x} + z_{\alpha/2}\frac{\sigma}{\sqrt{n}}.$$

The equivalence of confidence interval estimation to hypothesis testing extends to differences between two means, variances, ratios of variances, and so on. As a result, the student of statistics should not consider confidence interval estimation and hypothesis testing as separate forms of statistical inference. For example, consider Example 2. The 95% confidence interval on the mean is given by the bounds (2.50, 2.70). Thus, with the same sample information, a two-sided hypothesis on μ involving any hypothesized value between 2.50 and 2.70 will not be rejected. As we turn to different areas of hypothesis testing, the equivalence to the confidence interval estimation will continue to be exploited.

Tests on a Single Sample (Variance Unknown)

One would certainly suspect that tests on a population mean μ with σ^2 unknown, like confidence interval estimation, should involve the use of Student t-distribution. Strictly speaking, the application of Student t for both confidence intervals and hypothesis testing is developed under the following assumptions. The random variables $X_1, X_2, \ldots, X_n$ represent a random sample from a normal distribution with unknown μ and σ^2. Then the random variable $\sqrt{n}(\bar{X} - \mu)/S$ has a Student t-distribution with $n-1$ degrees of freedom. The structure of the test is identical to that for the case of σ known, with the exception that the value σ in the test statistic is replaced by the computed estimate S and the standard normal distribution is replaced by a t-distribution.

The t-Statistic for a Test on a Single Mean (Variance Unknown)

For the two-sided hypothesis

$$H_0: \ \mu = \mu_0,$$
$$H_1: \ \mu \neq \mu_0,$$

we reject H_0 at significance level α when the computed t-statistic

$$t = \frac{\bar{x} - \mu_0}{s/\sqrt{n}}$$

exceeds $t_{\alpha/2, n-1}$ or is less than $-t_{\alpha/2, n-1}$.

The t-distribution is symmetric around the value zero. Thus, this two-tailed critical region applies in a fashion similar to that for the case of known σ. For the two-sided hypothesis at significance level α, the two-tailed critical regions apply. For $H_1: \mu > \mu_0$, rejection results when $t > t_{\alpha, n-1}$. For $H_1: \mu < \mu_0$, the critical region is given by $t < -t_{\alpha, n=1}$.

Example 5:

The Edison Electric Institute has published figures on the number of kilowatt hours used annually by various home appliances. It is claimed that a vacuum cleaner uses an average of 46 kilowatt hours per year. If a random sample of 12 homes included in a planned study indicates that vacuum cleaners use an average of 42 kilowatt hours per year with a standard deviation of 11.9 kilowatt hours, does this suggest at the 0.05 level of significance that vacuum cleaners use, on average, less than 46 kilowatt hours annually? Assume the population of kilowatt hours to be normal.

Solution:
1. H_0: $\mu = 46$ kilowatt hours.
2. H_1: $\mu < 46$ kilowatt hours.
3. $\alpha = 0.05$.
4. Critical region: $t < -1.796$, where $t = \frac{\bar{x} - \mu_0}{s/\sqrt{n}}$ with 11 degrees of freedom.
5. Computations: $\bar{x} = 42$ kilowatt hours, $s = 11.9$ kilowatt hours, and $n = 12$. Hence,

$$t = \frac{42 - 46}{11.9/\sqrt{12}} = -1.16, \qquad P = P(T < -1.16) \approx 0.135.$$

6. Decision: Do not reject H_0 and conclude that the average number of kilowatt hours used annually by home vacuum cleaners is not significantly less than 46.

Comment on the Single-Sample *t*-Test

The reader has probably noticed that the equivalence of the two-tailed *t*-test for a single mean and the computation of a confidence interval on μ with σ replaced by s is maintained. Essentially, we can view that computation as one in which we have found all values of μ_0, the hypothesized mean volume of containers of sulfuric acid, for which the hypothesis H_0: $\mu = \mu_0$ *will not be rejected* at $\alpha = 0.05$. Again, this is consistent with the statement "Based on the sample information, values of the population mean volume between 9.74 and 10.26 liters are not unreasonable."

Comments regarding the normality assumption are worth emphasizing at this point. We have indicated that when σ is known, the Central Limit Theorem allows for the use of a test statistic or a confidence interval which is based on Z, the standard normal random variable. Strictly speaking, of course, the Central Limit Theorem, and thus the use of the standard normal distribution, does not apply unless σ is known. There we pointed out that normality on $X_1, X_2, \ldots X_n$ was an underlying assumption. Thus, *strictly speaking*, the Student's *t*-tables of percentage points for tests or confidence intervals should not be used unless it is known that the sample comes from a normal population. In practice, σ can rarely be assumed to be known. However, a very good estimate may be available from previous experiments. Many statistics textbooks suggest that one can safely replace σ by s in the test statistic

$$z = \frac{\bar{x} - \mu_0}{\sigma/\sqrt{n}}$$

when $n \geq 30$ with a bell-shaped population and still use the Z-tables for the appropriate critical region. The implication here is that the Central Limit Theorem is indeed being invoked and one is relying on the fact that $s \approx \sigma$. Obviously, when this is done, the results must be viewed as approximate. Thus, a computed P-value (from the Z-distribution) of 0.15 may be 0.12 or perhaps 0.17, or a computed confidence interval may be a 93% confidence interval rather than a 95% interval as desired. Now what about situations where $n \leq 30$? The user cannot rely on s being close to σ, and in order to take into account the inaccuracy of the estimate, the confidence interval should be wider or the critical value larger in magnitude. The *t*-distribution percentage points accomplish this but are correct only when the sample is from a normal distribution. Of course, normal probability plots can be used to ascertain some sense of the deviation of normality in a data set.

For small samples, it is often difficult to detect deviations from a normal distribution. (Goodness-of-fit tests are discussed in a later section of this chapter.) For bell-shaped distributions of the random variables $X_1, X_2, \ldots, X_n$, the use of the *t*-distribution for tests or confidence intervals is likely to produce quite good results. When in doubt, the user should resort to nonparametric procedures.

Annotated Computer Printout for Single-Sample *t*-Test

It should be of interest for the reader to see an annotated computer printout showing the result of a single-sample *t*-test. Suppose that an engineer is interested in testing the bias in a pH meter. Data are collected on a neutral substance (pH = 7.0). A sample of the measurements were taken with the data as follows:

$$7.07 \quad 7.00 \quad 7.10 \quad 6.97 \quad 7.00 \quad 7.03 \quad 7.01 \quad 7.01 \quad 6.98 \quad 7.08$$

It is, then, of interest to test

$$H_0: \mu = 7.0,$$
$$H_1: \mu \neq 7.0.$$

In this illustration, we use the computer package *MINITAB* to illustrate the analysis of the data set above. Notice the key components of the printout shown in Figure 12. Of course, the mean $\bar{y}$ is 7.0250, StDev is simply the sample standard deviation $s = 0.044$, and SE Mean is the estimated standard error of the mean and is computed as $s/\sqrt{n} = 0.0139$. The *t*-value is the ratio

$$(7.0250 - 7)/0.0139 = 1.80.$$

```
pH-meter
   7.07   7.00   7.10   6.97   7.00   7.03   7.01   7.01   6.98   7.08
MTB > Onet 'pH-meter'; SUBC>   Test 7.

One-Sample T: pH-meter Test of mu = 7 vs not = 7
Variable  N    Mean    StDev   SE Mean      95% CI        T     P
pH-meter 10 7.02500  0.04403  0.01392 (6.99350, 7.05650) 1.80 0.106
```

Figure 12: *MINITAB* printout for one sample *t*-test for pH meter.

The *P*-value of 0.106 suggests results that are inconclusive. There is no evidence suggesting a strong rejection of H_0 (based on an α of 0.05 or 0.10), **yet one certainly cannot truly conclude that the pH meter is unbiased**. Notice that the sample size of 10 is rather small. An increase in sample size (perhaps another experiment) may sort things out. A discussion regarding appropriate sample size appears in Section 6.

5 Two Samples: Tests on Two Means

The reader should now understand the relationship between tests and confidence intervals, and can only heavily rely on details supplied by the confidence interval material in Chapter **One- and Two-Sample Estimation Problems**. Tests concerning two means represent a set of very important analytical tools for the scientist or engineer. The experimental setting is very much like that described in Section 8 of **One- and Two-Sample Estimation Problems**. Two independent random samples of sizes

n_1 and n_2, respectively, are drawn from two populations with means μ_1 and μ_2 and variances σ_1^2 and σ_2^2. We know that the random variable

$$Z = \frac{(\bar{X}_1 - \bar{X}_2) - (\mu_1 - \mu_2)}{\sqrt{\sigma_1^2/n_1 + \sigma_2^2/n_2}}$$

has a standard normal distribution. Here we are assuming that n_1 and n_2 are sufficiently large that the Central Limit Theorem applies. Of course, if the two populations are normal, the statistic above has a standard normal distribution even for small n_1 and n_2. Obviously, if we can assume that $\sigma_1 = \sigma_2 = \sigma$, the statistic above reduces to

$$Z = \frac{(\bar{X}_1 - \bar{X}_2) - (\mu_1 - \mu_2)}{\sigma\sqrt{1/n_1 + 1/n_2}}.$$

The two statistics above serve as a basis for the development of the test procedures involving two means. The equivalence between tests and confidence intervals, along with the technical detail involving tests on one mean, allow a simple transition to tests on two means.

The two-sided hypothesis on two means can be written generally as

$$H_0\colon \mu_1 - \mu_2 = d_0.$$

Obviously, the alternative can be two sided or one sided. Again, the distribution used is the distribution of the test statistic under H_0. Values $\bar{x}_1$ and $\bar{x}_2$ are computed and, for σ_1 and σ_2 known, the test statistic is given by

$$z = \frac{(\bar{x}_1 - \bar{x}_2) - d_0}{\sqrt{\sigma_1^2/n_1 + \sigma_2^2/n_2}},$$

with a two-tailed critical region in the case of a two-sided alternative. That is, reject H_0 in favor of $H_1\colon \mu_1 - \mu_2 \neq d_0$ if $z > z_{\alpha/2}$ or $z < -z_{\alpha/2}$. One-tailed critical regions are used in the case of the one-sided alternatives. The reader should, as before, study the test statistic and be satisfied that for, say, $H_1\colon \mu_1 - \mu_2 > d_0$, the signal favoring H_1 comes from large values of z. Thus, the upper-tailed critical region applies.

Unknown But Equal Variances

The more prevalent situations involving tests on two means are those in which variances are unknown. If the scientist involved is willing to assume that both distributions are normal and that $\sigma_1 = \sigma_2 = \sigma$, the *pooled t-test* (often called the two-sample *t*-test) may be used. The test statistic is given by the following test procedure.

<table>
<tr><td>Two-Sample
Pooled *t*-Test</td><td>For the two-sided hypothesis</td></tr>
</table>

$$H_0: \ \mu_1 = \mu_2,$$
$$H_1: \ \mu_1 \neq \mu_2,$$

we reject H_0 at significance level α when the computed *t*-statistic

$$t = \frac{(\bar{x}_1 - \bar{x}_2) - d_0}{s_p\sqrt{1/n_1 + 1/n_2}},$$

where

$$s_p^2 = \frac{s_1^2(n_1 - 1) + s_2^2(n_2 - 1)}{n_1 + n_2 - 2}$$

exceeds $t_{\alpha/2, n_1+n_2-2}$ or is less than $-t_{\alpha/2, n_1+n_2-2}$.

Recall from Chapter **One- and Two-Sample Estimation Problems** that the degrees of freedom for the *t*-distribution are a result of pooling of information from the two samples to estimate σ^2. One-sided alternatives suggest one-sided critical regions, as one might expect. For example, for $H_1: \mu_1 - \mu_2 > d_0$, reject $H_1: \mu_1 - \mu_2 = d_0$ when $t > t_{\alpha, n_1 + n_2 - 2}$.

Example 6:	An experiment was performed to compare the abrasive wear of two different laminated materials. Twelve pieces of material 1 were tested by exposing each piece to a machine measuring wear. Ten pieces of material 2 were similarly tested. In each case, the depth of wear was observed. The samples of material 1 gave an average (coded) wear of 85 units with a sample standard deviation of 4, while the samples of material 2 gave an average of 81 with a sample standard deviation of 5. Can we conclude at the 0.05 level of significance that the abrasive wear of material 1 exceeds that of material 2 by more than 2 units? Assume the populations to be approximately normal with equal variances.

Solution: Let μ_1 and μ_2 represent the population means of the abrasive wear for material 1 and material 2, respectively.

1. $H_0: \mu_1 - \mu_2 = 2$.

2. $H_1: \mu_1 - \mu_2 > 2$.

3. $\alpha = 0.05$.

4. Critical region: $t > 1.725$, where $t = \frac{(\bar{x}_1 - \bar{x}_2) - d_0}{s_p\sqrt{1/n_1 + 1/n_2}}$ with $v = 20$ degrees of freedom.

5. Computations:

$$\bar{x}_1 = 85, \quad s_1 = 4, \quad n_1 = 12,$$
$$\bar{x}_2 = 81, \quad s_2 = 5, \quad n_2 = 10.$$

Hence

$$s_p = \sqrt{\frac{(11)(16) + (9)(25)}{12 + 10 - 2}} = 4.478,$$

$$t = \frac{(85 - 81) - 2}{4.478\sqrt{1/12 + 1/10}} = 1.04,$$

$$P = P(T > 1.04) \approx 0.16. \qquad \text{(See Table A.4.)}$$

6. Decision: Do not reject H_0. We are unable to conclude that the abrasive wear of material 1 exceeds that of material 2 by more than 2 units.

Unknown But Unequal Variances

There are situations where the analyst is **not** able to assume that $\sigma_1 = \sigma_2$. Recall from Section 8 of **One- and Two-Sample Estimation Problems** that, if the populations are normal, the statistic

$$T' = \frac{(\bar{X}_1 - \bar{X}_2) - d_0}{\sqrt{s_1^2/n_1 + s_2^2/n_2}}$$

has an approximate t-distribution with approximate degrees of freedom

$$v = \frac{(s_1^2/n_1 + s_2^2/n_2)^2}{(s_1^2/n_1)^2/(n_1 - 1) + (s_2^2/n_2)^2/(n_2 - 1)}.$$

As a result, the test procedure is to *not reject H_0* when

$$-t_{\alpha/2,v} < t' < t_{\alpha/2,v},$$

with v given as above. Again, as in the case of the pooled t-test, one-sided alternatives suggest one-sided critical regions.

Paired Observations

A study of the two-sample t-test or confidence interval on the difference between means should suggest the need for experimental design. Recall the discussion of experimental units in Chapter **One- and Two-Sample Estimation Problems,** where it was suggested that the conditions of the two populations (often referred to as the two treatments) should be assigned randomly to the experimental units. This is done to avoid biased results due to systematic differences between experimental units. In other words, in hypothesis-testing jargon, it is important that any significant difference found between means be due to the different conditions of the populations and not due to the experimental units in the study. For example, consider Chapter **One- and Two-Sample Estimation Problems** Exercise 40 in Section 9. The 20 seedlings play the role of the experimental units. Ten of them are to be treated with nitrogen and 10 with no nitrogen. It may be very important that this assignment to the "nitrogen" and "no-nitrogen" treatments be random to ensure that systematic differences between the seedlings do not interfere with a valid comparison between the means.

In Example 6, time of measurement is the most likely choice for the experimental unit. The 22 pieces of material should be measured in random order. We need to guard against the possibility that wear measurements made close together in time might tend to give similar results. **Systematic (nonrandom) differences in experimental units** *are not expected.* However, random assignments guard against the problem.

Testing of two means can be accomplished when data are in the form of paired observations, as discussed in Chapter **One- and Two-Sample Estimation Problems.** In this pairing structure, the conditions of the two populations (treatments) are assigned randomly within homogeneous units. Computation of the confidence interval for $\mu_1 - \mu_2$ in the situation with paired observations is based on the random variable

$$T = \frac{\bar{D} - \mu_D}{S_d/\sqrt{n}},$$

where $\bar{D}$ and S_d are random variables representing the sample mean and standard deviation of the differences of the observations in the experimental units. As in the case of the *pooled t-test*, the assumption is that the observations from each population are normal. This two-sample problem is essentially reduced to a one-sample problem by using the computed differences $d_1, d_2, \ldots, d_n$. Thus, the hypothesis reduces to

$$H_0: \ \mu_D = d_0.$$

The computed test statistic is then given by

$$t = \frac{\bar{d} - d_0}{s_d/\sqrt{n}}.$$

Critical regions are constructed using the t-distribution with $n - 1$ degrees of freedom.

Problem of Interaction in a Paired t-Test

Not only will the case study that follows illustrate the use of the paired t-test but the discussion will shed considerable light on the difficulties that arise when there is an interaction between the treatments and the experimental units in the paired t structure.

There are some types of statistical tests in which the existence of interaction results in difficulty. The paired t-test is one such example. In Chapter **One- and Two-Sample Estimation Problems** Section 9, the paired structure was used in the computation of a confidence interval on the difference between two means, and the advantage in pairing was revealed for situations in which the experimental units are homogeneous. The pairing results in a reduction in σ_D, the standard deviation of a difference $D_i = X_{1i} - X_{2i}$, as discussed in Chapter **One- and Two-Sample Estimation Problems** Section 9. If interaction exists between treatments and experimental units, the advantage gained in pairing may be substantially reduced. Thus, in Chapter **One- and Two-Sample Estimation Problems** Example 13, the no interaction assumption allowed the difference in mean TCDD levels (plasma vs. fat tissue) to be the same across veterans. A quick glance at the data would suggest that there is no significant violation of the assumption of no interaction.

In order to demonstrate how interaction influences Var(D) and hence the quality of the paired t-test, it is instructive to revisit the ith difference given by $D_i = X_{1i} - X_{2i} = (\mu_1 - \mu_2) + (\epsilon_1 - \epsilon_2)$, where X_{1i} and X_{2i} are taken on the ith experimental unit. If the pairing unit is homogeneous, the errors in X_{1i} and in X_{2i} should be similar and not independent. We noted in Chapter **One- and Two-Sample Estimation Problems** that the positive covariance between the errors results in a reduced Var(D). Thus, the size of the difference in the treatments and the relationship between the errors in X_{1i} and X_{2i} contributed by the experimental unit will tend to allow a significant difference to be detected.

What Conditions Result in Interaction?

Let us consider a situation in which the experimental units are not homogeneous. Rather, consider the ith experimental unit with random variables X_{1i} and X_{2i} that are not similar. Let ϵ_{1i} and ϵ_{2i} be random variables representing the errors in the values X_{1i} and X_{2i}, respectively, at the ith unit. Thus, we may write

$$X_{1i} = \mu_1 + \epsilon_{1i} \text{ and } X_{2i} = \mu_2 + \epsilon_{2i}.$$

The errors with expectation zero may tend to cause the response values X_{1i} and X_{2i} to move in opposite directions, resulting in a negative value for Cov($\epsilon_{1i}, \epsilon_{2i}$) and hence negative Cov(X_{1i}, X_{2i}). In fact, the model may be complicated even more by the fact that $\sigma_1^2 = \text{Var}(\epsilon_{1i}) \neq \sigma_2^2 = \text{Var}(\epsilon_{2i})$. The variance and covariance parameters may vary among the n experimental units. Thus, unlike in the homogeneous case, D_i will tend to be quite different across experimental units due to the heterogeneous nature of the difference in $\epsilon_1 - \epsilon_2$ among the units. This produces the interaction between treatments and units. In addition, for a specific experimental unit,

$$\sigma_D^2 = \text{Var}(D) = \text{Var}(\epsilon_1) + \text{Var}(\epsilon_2) - 2\,\text{Cov}(\epsilon_1, \epsilon_2)$$

is inflated by the negative covariance term, and thus the advantage gained in pairing in the homogeneous unit case is lost in the case described here. While the inflation in Var(D) will vary from case to case, there is a danger in some cases that the increase in variance may neutralize any difference that exists between μ_1 and μ_2. Of course, a large value of $\bar{d}$ in the t-statistic may reflect a treatment difference that overcomes the inflated variance estimate, s_d^2.

Case Study 1: **Blood Sample Data**: In a study conducted in the Forestry and Wildlife Department at Virginia Tech, J. A. Wesson examined the influence of the drug succinylcholine on the circulation levels of androgens in the blood. Blood samples were taken from wild, free-ranging deer immediately after they had received an intramuscular injection of succinylcholine administered using darts and a capture gun. A second blood sample was obtained from each deer 30 minutes after the first sample, after which the deer was released. The levels of androgens at time of capture and 30 minutes later, measured in nanograms per milliliter (ng/mL), for 15 deer are given in Table 2.

Assuming that the populations of androgen levels at time of injection and 30 minutes later are normally distributed, test at the 0.05 level of significance whether the androgen concentrations are altered after 30 minutes.

Table 2: Data for Case Study 1

Deer	Androgen (ng/mL) At Time of Injection	30 Minutes after Injection	d_i
1	2.76	7.02	4.26
2	5.18	3.10	−2.08
3	2.68	5.44	2.76
4	3.05	3.99	0.94
5	4.10	5.21	1.11
6	7.05	10.26	3.21
7	6.60	13.91	7.31
8	4.79	18.53	13.74
9	7.39	7.91	0.52
10	7.30	4.85	−2.45
11	11.78	11.10	−0.68
12	3.90	3.74	−0.16
13	26.00	94.03	68.03
14	67.48	94.03	26.55
15	17.04	41.70	24.66

Solution: Let μ_1 and μ_2 be the average androgen concentration at the time of injection and 30 minutes later, respectively. We proceed as follows:

1. H_0: $\mu_1 = \mu_2$ or $\mu_D = \mu_1 - \mu_2 = 0$.

2. H_1: $\mu_1 \neq \mu_2$ or $\mu_D = \mu_1 - \mu_2 \neq 0$.

3. $\alpha = 0.05$.

4. Critical region: $t < -2.145$ and $t > 2.145$, where $t = \frac{\bar{d} - d_0}{s_D/\sqrt{n}}$ with $v = 14$ degrees of freedom.

5. Computations: The sample mean and standard deviation for the d_i are

$$\bar{d} = 9.848 \qquad \text{and} \qquad s_d = 18.474.$$

Therefore,

$$t = \frac{9.848 - 0}{18.474/\sqrt{15}} = 2.06.$$

6. Though the t-statistic is not significant at the 0.05 level, from Table A.4,

$$P = P(|T| > 2.06) \approx 0.06.$$

As a result, there is some evidence that there is a difference in mean circulating levels of androgen.

The assumption of no interaction would imply that the effect on androgen levels of the deer is roughly the same in the data for both treatments, i.e., at the time of injection of succinylcholine and 30 minutes following injection. This can be expressed with the two factors switching roles; for example, the difference in treatments is roughly the same across the units (i.e., the deer). There certainly are some deer/treatment combinations for which the no interaction assumption seems to hold, but there is hardly any strong evidence that the experimental units are homogeneous. However, the nature of the interaction and the resulting increase in $\text{Var}(\bar{D})$ appear to be dominated by a substantial difference in the treatments. This is further demonstrated by the fact that 11 of the 15 deer exhibited positive signs for the computed d_i and the negative d_i (for deer 2, 10, 11, and 12) are small in magnitude compared to the 12 positive ones. Thus, it appears that the mean level of androgen is significantly higher 30 minutes following injection than at injection, and the conclusions may be stronger than $p = 0.06$ would suggest.

Annotated Computer Printout for Paired *t*-Test

Figure 13 displays a *SAS* computer printout for a paired *t*-test using the data of Case Study 1. Notice that the printout looks like that for a single sample *t*-test and, of course, that is exactly what is accomplished, since the test seeks to determine if $\bar{d}$ is significantly different from zero.

		Analysis Variable : Diff		
N	Mean	Std Error	t Value	Pr > |t|
15	9.8480000	4.7698699	2.06	0.0580

Figure 13: *SAS* printout of paired *t*-test for data of Case Study 1.

Summary of Test Procedures

As we complete the formal development of tests on population means, we offer Table 3, which summarizes the test procedure for the cases of a single mean and two means. Notice the approximate procedure when distributions are normal and variances are unknown but not assumed to be equal. This statistic was introduced in chapter **One- and Two-Sample Estimation Problems.**

6   Choice of Sample Size for Testing Means

In Section 2, we demonstrated how the analyst can exploit relationships among the sample size, the significance level α, and the power of the test to achieve a certain standard of quality. In most practical circumstances, the experiment should be planned, with a choice of sample size made prior to the data-taking process if possible. The sample size is usually determined to achieve good power for a fixed α and fixed specific alternative. This fixed alternative may be in the

Table 3: Tests Concerning Means

H_0	Value of Test Statistic	H_1	Critical Region
$\mu = \mu_0$	$z = \dfrac{\bar{x} - \mu_0}{\sigma/\sqrt{n}}$; σ known	$\mu < \mu_0$ $\mu > \mu_0$ $\mu \neq \mu_0$	$z < -z_\alpha$ $z > z_\alpha$ $z < -z_{\alpha/2}$ or $z > z_{\alpha/2}$
$\mu = \mu_0$	$t = \dfrac{\bar{x} - \mu_0}{s/\sqrt{n}}$; $v = n-1$, σ unknown	$\mu < \mu_0$ $\mu > \mu_0$ $\mu \neq \mu_0$	$t < -t_\alpha$ $t > t_\alpha$ $t < -t_{\alpha/2}$ or $t > t_{\alpha/2}$
$\mu_1 - \mu_2 = d_0$	$z = \dfrac{(\bar{x}_1 - \bar{x}_2) - d_0}{\sqrt{\sigma_1^2/n_1 + \sigma_2^2/n_2}}$; σ_1 and σ_2 known	$\mu_1 - \mu_2 < d_0$ $\mu_1 - \mu_2 > d_0$ $\mu_1 - \mu_2 \neq d_0$	$z < -z_\alpha$ $z > z_\alpha$ $z < -z_{\alpha/2}$ or $z > z_{\alpha/2}$
$\mu_1 - \mu_2 = d_0$	$t = \dfrac{(\bar{x}_1 - \bar{x}_2) - d_0}{s_p\sqrt{1/n_1 + 1/n_2}}$; $v = n_1 + n_2 - 2$, $\sigma_1 = \sigma_2$ but unknown, $s_p^2 = \dfrac{(n_1-1)s_1^2 + (n_2-1)s_2^2}{n_1 + n_2 - 2}$	$\mu_1 - \mu_2 < d_0$ $\mu_1 - \mu_2 > d_0$ $\mu_1 - \mu_2 \neq d_0$	$t < -t_\alpha$ $t > t_\alpha$ $t < -t_{\alpha/2}$ or $t > t_{\alpha/2}$
$\mu_1 - \mu_2 = d_0$	$t' = \dfrac{(\bar{x}_1 - \bar{x}_2) - d_0}{\sqrt{s_1^2/n_1 + s_2^2/n_2}}$; $v = \dfrac{(s_1^2/n_1 + s_2^2/n_2)^2}{\frac{(s_1^2/n_1)^2}{n_1-1} + \frac{(s_2^2/n_2)^2}{n_2-1}}$, $\sigma_1 \neq \sigma_2$ and unknown	$\mu_1 - \mu_2 < d_0$ $\mu_1 - \mu_2 > d_0$ $\mu_1 - \mu_2 \neq d_0$	$t' < -t_\alpha$ $t' > t_\alpha$ $t' < -t_{\alpha/2}$ or $t' > t_{\alpha/2}$
$\mu_D = d_0$ paired observations	$t = \dfrac{\bar{d} - d_0}{s_d/\sqrt{n}}$; $v = n-1$	$\mu_D < d_0$ $\mu_D > d_0$ $\mu_D \neq d_0$	$t < -t_\alpha$ $t > t_\alpha$ $t < -t_{\alpha/2}$ or $t > t_{\alpha/2}$

form of $\mu - \mu_0$ in the case of a hypothesis involving a single mean or $\mu_1 - \mu_2$ in the case of a problem involving two means. Specific cases will provide illustrations.

Suppose that we wish to test the hypothesis

$$H_0: \ \mu = \mu_0,$$
$$H_1: \ \mu > \mu_0,$$

with a significance level α, when the variance σ^2 is known. For a specific alternative, say $\mu = \mu_0 + \delta$, the power of our test is shown in Figure 14 to be

$$1 - \beta = P(\bar{X} > a \text{ when } \mu = \mu_0 + \delta).$$

Therefore,

$$\beta = P(\bar{X} < a \text{ when } \mu = \mu_0 + \delta)$$
$$= P\left[\frac{\bar{X} - (\mu_0 + \delta)}{\sigma/\sqrt{n}} < \frac{a - (\mu_0 + \delta)}{\sigma/\sqrt{n}} \text{ when } \mu = \mu_0 + \delta\right].$$

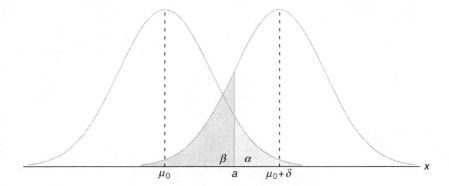

Figure 14: Testing $\mu = \mu_0$ versus $\mu = \mu_0 + \delta$.

Under the alternative hypothesis $\mu = \mu_0 + \delta$, the statistic

$$\frac{\bar{X} - (\mu_0 + \delta)}{\sigma/\sqrt{n}}$$

is the standard normal variable Z. So

$$\beta = P\left(Z < \frac{a - \mu_0}{\sigma/\sqrt{n}} - \frac{\delta}{\sigma/\sqrt{n}}\right) = P\left(Z < z_\alpha - \frac{\delta}{\sigma/\sqrt{n}}\right),$$

from which we conclude that

$$-z_\beta = z_\alpha - \frac{\delta\sqrt{n}}{\sigma},$$

and hence

Choice of sample size: $\quad n = \dfrac{(z_\alpha + z_\beta)^2\sigma^2}{\delta^2},$

a result that is also true when the alternative hypothesis is $\mu < \mu_0$.

In the case of a two-tailed test, we obtain the power $1 - \beta$ for a specified alternative when

$$n \approx \frac{(z_{\alpha/2} + z_\beta)^2\sigma^2}{\delta^2}.$$

Example 7: Suppose that we wish to test the hypothesis

$$H_0\!: \ \mu = 68 \text{ kilograms},$$
$$H_1\!: \ \mu > 68 \text{ kilograms}$$

for the weights of male students at a certain college, using an $\alpha = 0.05$ level of significance, when it is known that $\sigma = 5$. Find the sample size required if the power of our test is to be 0.95 when the true mean is 69 kilograms.

Solution: Since $\alpha = \beta = 0.05$, we have $z_\alpha = z_\beta = 1.645$. For the alternative $\beta = 69$, we take $\delta = 1$ and then

$$n = \frac{(1.645 + 1.645)^2(25)}{1} = 270.6.$$

Therefore, 271 observations are required if the test is to reject the null hypothesis 95% of the time when, in fact, μ is as large as 69 kilograms.

Two-Sample Case

A similar procedure can be used to determine the sample size $n = n_1 = n_2$ required for a specific power of the test in which two population means are being compared. For example, suppose that we wish to test the hypothesis

$$H_0: \ \mu_1 - \mu_2 = d_0,$$
$$H_1: \mu_1 - \mu_2 \neq d_0,$$

when σ_1 and σ_2 are known. For a specific alternative, say $\mu_1 - \mu_2 = d_0 + \delta$, the power of our test is shown in Figure 15 to be

$$1 - \beta = P(|\bar{X}_1 - \bar{X}_2| > a \text{ when } \mu_1 - \mu_2 = d_0 + \delta).$$

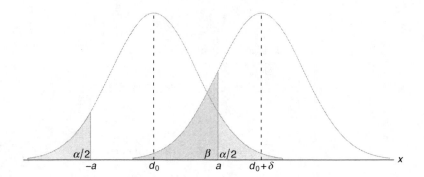

Figure 15: Testing $\mu_1 - \mu_2 = d_0$ versus $\mu_1 - \mu_2 = d_0 + \delta$.

Therefore,

$$\beta = P(-a < \bar{X}_1 - \bar{X}_2 < a \text{ when } \mu_1 - \mu_2 = d_0 + \delta)$$
$$= P\left[\frac{-a - (d_0 + \delta)}{\sqrt{(\sigma_1^2 + \sigma_2^2)/n}} < \frac{(\bar{X}_1 - \bar{X}_2) - (d_0 + \delta)}{\sqrt{(\sigma_1^2 + \sigma_2^2)/n}}\right.$$
$$\left. < \frac{a - (d_0 + \delta)}{\sqrt{(\sigma_1^2 + \sigma_2^2)/n}} \text{ when } \mu_1 - \mu_2 = d_0 + \delta\right].$$

Under the alternative hypothesis $\mu_1 - \mu_2 = d_0 + \delta$, the statistic

$$\frac{\bar{X}_1 - \bar{X}_2 - (d_0 + \delta)}{\sqrt{(\sigma_1^2 + \sigma_2^2)/n}}$$

is the standard normal variable Z. Now, writing

$$-z_{\alpha/2} = \frac{-a - d_0}{\sqrt{(\sigma_1^2 + \sigma_2^2)/n}} \quad \text{and} \quad z_{\alpha/2} = \frac{a - d_0}{\sqrt{(\sigma_1^2 + \sigma_2^2)/n}},$$

we have

$$\beta = P\left[-z_{\alpha/2} - \frac{\delta}{\sqrt{(\sigma_1^2 + \sigma_2^2)/n}} < Z < z_{\alpha/2} - \frac{\delta}{\sqrt{(\sigma_1^2 + \sigma_2^2)/n}}\right],$$

from which we conclude that

$$-z_{\beta} \approx z_{\alpha/2} - \frac{\delta}{\sqrt{(\sigma_1^2 + \sigma_2^2)/n}},$$

and hence

$$n \approx \frac{(z_{\alpha/2} + z_{\beta})^2(\sigma_1^2 + \sigma_2^2)}{\delta^2}.$$

For the one-tailed test, the expression for the required sample size when $n = n_1 = n_2$ is

$$\text{Choice of sample size:} \quad n = \frac{(z_\alpha + z_\beta)^2(\sigma_1^2 + \sigma_2^2)}{\delta^2}.$$

When the population variance (or variances, in the two-sample situation) is unknown, the choice of sample size is not straightforward. In testing the hypothesis $\mu = \mu_0$ when the true value is $\mu = \mu_0 + \delta$, the statistic

$$\frac{\bar{X} - (\mu_0 + \delta)}{S/\sqrt{n}}$$

does not follow the t-distribution, as one might expect, but instead follows the **noncentral t-distribution**. However, tables or charts based on the noncentral t-distribution do exist for determining the appropriate sample size if some estimate of σ is available or if δ is a multiple of σ. Table Sample Size for the t-Test of the Mean at the end of this chapter gives the sample sizes needed to control the values of α and β for various values of

$$\Delta = \frac{|\delta|}{\sigma} = \frac{|\mu - \mu_0|}{\sigma}$$

for both one- and two-tailed tests. In the case of the two-sample t-test in which the variances are unknown but assumed equal, we obtain the sample sizes $n = n_1 = n_2$ needed to control the values of α and β for various values of

$$\Delta = \frac{|\delta|}{\sigma} = \frac{|\mu_1 - \mu_2 - d_0|}{\sigma}$$

from Table Sample Size for the t-Test of the Difference between Two Means at the end of this chapter.

Example 8: In comparing the performance of two catalysts on the effect of a reaction yield, a two-sample t-test is to be conducted with $\alpha = 0.05$. The variances in the yields are considered to be the same for the two catalysts. How large a sample for each catalyst is needed to test the hypothesis

$$H_0: \ \mu_1 = \mu_2,$$
$$H_1: \ \mu_1 \neq \mu_2$$

if it is essential to detect a difference of 0.8σ between the catalysts with probability 0.9?

Solution: From Table Sample Size for the t-Test of the Difference Between Two Means, with $\alpha = 0.05$ for a two-tailed test, $\beta = 0.1$, and

$$\Delta = \frac{|0.8\sigma|}{\sigma} = 0.8,$$

we find the required sample size to be $n = 34$.

In practical situations, it might be difficult to force a scientist or engineer to make a commitment on information from which a value of Δ can be found. The reader is reminded that the Δ-value quantifies the kind of difference between the means that the scientist considers important, that is, a difference considered *significant* from a scientific, not a statistical, point of view. Example 10.8 illustrates how this choice is often made, namely, by selecting a fraction of σ. Obviously, if the sample size is based on a choice of $|\delta|$ that is a small fraction of σ, the resulting sample size may be quite large compared to what the study allows.

7 Graphical Methods for Comparing Means

Many computer software packages produce graphical displays. As we proceed to other forms of data analysis (e.g., regression analysis and analysis of variance), graphical methods become even more informative.

Graphical aids cannot be used as a replacement for the test procedure itself. Certainly, the value of the test statistic indicates the proper type of evidence in support of H_0 or H_1. However, a pictorial display provides a good illustration and is often a better communicator of evidence to the beneficiary of the analysis. Also, a picture will often clarify why a significant difference was found. Failure of an important assumption may be exposed by a summary type of graphical tool.

For the comparison of means, side-by-side box-and-whisker plots provide a telling display. The reader should recall that these plots display the 25th percentile, 75th percentile, and the median in a data set. In addition, the whiskers display the extremes in a data set. Consider Exercise 40 at the end of this section. Plasma ascorbic acid levels were measured in two groups of pregnant women, smokers and nonsmokers. Figure 16 shows the box-and-whisker plots for both groups of women. Two things are very apparent. Taking into account variability, there appears to be a negligible difference in the sample means. In addition, the variability in the two groups appears to be somewhat different. Of course, the analyst must keep in mind the rather sizable differences between the sample sizes in this case.

Figure 16: Two box-and-whisker plots of plasma ascorbic acid in smokers and nonsmokers.

Figure 17: Two box-and-whisker plots of seedling data.

Consider Chapter **One- and Two-Sample Estimation Problems** Exercise 40 in Section 9. Figure 17 shows the multiple box-and-whisker plot for the data on 10 seedlings, half given nitrogen and half given no nitrogen. The display reveals a smaller variability for the group containing no nitrogen. In addition, the lack of overlap of the box plots suggests a significant difference between the mean stem weights for the two groups. It would appear that the presence of nitrogen increases the stem weights and perhaps increases the variability in the weights.

There are no certain rules of thumb regarding when two box-and-whisker plots give evidence of significant difference between the means. However, a rough guideline is that if the 25th percentile line for one sample exceeds the median line for the other sample, there is strong evidence of a difference between means.

More emphasis is placed on graphical methods in a real-life case study presented later in this chapter.

Annotated Computer Printout for Two-Sample *t*-Test

Consider once again Chapter **One- and Two-Sample Estimation Problems** Exercise 40, where seedling data under conditions of nitrogen were collected. Test

$$H_0: \ \mu_{\text{NIT}} = \mu_{\text{NON}},$$
$$H_1: \ \mu_{\text{NIT}} > \mu_{\text{NON}},$$

where the population means indicate mean weights. Figure 18 is an annotated computer printout generated using the *SAS* package. Notice that sample standard deviation and standard error are shown for both samples. The *t*-statistics under the assumption of equal variance and unequal variance are both given. From the box-and-whisker plot of Figure 17 it would certainly appear that the equal variance assumption is violated. A *P*-value of 0.0229 suggests a conclusion of unequal means. This concurs with the diagnostic information given in Figure 18. Incidentally, notice that t and t' are equal in this case, since $n_1 = n_2$.

```
                    TTEST Procedure
Variable Weight
     Mineral      N    Mean   Std Dev Std Err
  No nitrogen    10   0.3990   0.0728  0.0230
    Nitrogen     10   0.5650   0.1867  0.0591


  Variances      DF    t Value    Pr > |t|
     Equal       18      2.62      0.0174
    Unequal     11.7     2.62      0.0229


        Test the Equality of Variances
 Variable   Num DF   Den DF   F Value   Pr > F
  Weight       9        9      6.58     0.0098
```

Figure 18: *SAS* printout for two-sample *t*-test.

Exercises

19 In a research report, Richard H. Weindruch of the UCLA Medical School claims that mice with an average life span of 32 months will live to be about 40 months old when 40% of the calories in their diet are replaced by vitamins and protein. Is there any reason to believe that $\mu < 40$ if 64 mice that are placed on this diet have an average life of 38 months with a standard deviation of 5.8 months? Use a *P*-value in your conclusion.

20 A random sample of 64 bags of white cheddar popcorn weighed, on average, 5.23 ounces with a standard deviation of 0.24 ounce. Test the hypothesis that $\mu = 5.5$ ounces against the alternative hypothesis, $\mu < 5.5$ ounces, at the 0.05 level of significance.

21 An electrical firm manufactures light bulbs that have a lifetime that is approximately normally distributed with a mean of 800 hours and a standard deviation of 40 hours. Test the hypothesis that $\mu = 800$ hours against the alternative, $\mu \neq 800$ hours, if a random sample of 30 bulbs has an average life of 788 hours. Use a *P*-value in your answer.

22 In the American Heart Association journal *Hypertension*, researchers report that individuals who practice Transcendental Meditation (TM) lower their blood pressure significantly. If a random sample of 225 male TM practitioners meditate for 8.5 hours per week with a standard deviation of 2.25 hours, does that suggest that, on average, men who use TM meditate more than 8 hours per week? Quote a *P*-value in your conclusion.

23 Test the hypothesis that the average content of containers of a particular lubricant is 10 liters if the contents of a random sample of 10 containers are 10.2, 9.7, 10.1, 10.3, 10.1, 9.8, 9.9, 10.4, 10.3, and 9.8 liters. Use a 0.01 level of significance and assume that the distribution of contents is normal.

24 The average height of females in the freshman class of a certain college has historically been 162.5 centimeters with a standard deviation of 6.9 centimeters. Is there reason to believe that there has been a change in the average height if a random sample of 50 females in the present freshman class has an average height of 165.2 centimeters? Use a *P*-value in your conclusion. Assume the standard deviation remains the same.

25 It is claimed that automobiles are driven on average more than 20,000 kilometers per year. To test this claim, 100 randomly selected automobile owners are asked to keep a record of the kilometers they travel. Would you agree with this claim if the random sample showed an average of 23,500 kilometers and a standard deviation of 3900 kilometers? Use a *P*-value in your conclusion.

26 According to a dietary study, high sodium intake may be related to ulcers, stomach cancer, and migraine headaches. The human requirement for salt is only 220 milligrams per day, which is surpassed in most single servings of ready-to-eat cereals. If a random sample of 20 similar servings of a certain cereal has a mean sodium content of 244 milligrams and a standard deviation of 24.5 milligrams, does this suggest at the 0.05 level of significance that the average sodium content for a single serving of such cereal is greater than 220 milligrams? Assume the distribution of sodium contents to be normal.

27 A study at the University of Colorado at Boulder shows that running increases the percent resting metabolic rate (RMR) in older women. The average RMR of 30 elderly women runners was 34.0% higher than the average RMR of 30 sedentary elderly women, and the standard deviations were reported to be 10.5 and 10.2%, respectively. Was there a significant increase in RMR of the women runners over the sedentary women? Assume the populations to be approximately normally distributed with equal variances. Use a P-value in your conclusions.

28 According to *Chemical Engineering*, an important property of fiber is its water absorbency. The average percent absorbency of 25 randomly selected pieces of cotton fiber was found to be 20 with a standard deviation of 1.5. A random sample of 25 pieces of acetate yielded an average percent of 12 with a standard deviation of 1.25. Is there strong evidence that the population mean percent absorbency is significantly higher for cotton fiber than for acetate? Assume that the percent absorbency is approximately normally distributed and that the population variances in percent absorbency for the two fibers are the same. Use a significance level of 0.05.

29 Past experience indicates that the time required for high school seniors to complete a standardized test is a normal random variable with a mean of 35 minutes. If a random sample of 20 high school seniors took an average of 33.1 minutes to complete this test with a standard deviation of 4.3 minutes, test the hypothesis, at the 0.05 level of significance, that $\mu = 35$ minutes against the alternative that $\mu < 35$ minutes.

30 A random sample of size $n_1 = 25$, taken from a normal population with a standard deviation $\sigma_1 = 5.2$, has a mean $\bar{x}_1 = 81$. A second random sample of size $n_2 = 36$, taken from a different normal population with a standard deviation $\sigma_2 = 3.4$, has a mean $\bar{x}_2 = 76$. Test the hypothesis that $\mu_1 = \mu_2$ against the alternative, $\mu_1 \neq \mu_2$. Quote a P-value in your conclusion.

31 A manufacturer claims that the average tensile strength of thread A exceeds the average tensile strength of thread B by at least 12 kilograms. To test this claim, 50 pieces of each type of thread were tested under similar conditions. Type A thread had an average tensile strength of 86.7 kilograms with a standard deviation of 6.28 kilograms, while type B thread had an average tensile strength of 77.8 kilograms with a standard deviation of 5.61 kilograms. Test the manufacturer's claim using a 0.05 level of significance.

32 *Amstat News* (December 2004) lists median salaries for associate professors of statistics at research institutions and at liberal arts and other institutions in the United States. Assume that a sample of 200 associate professors from research institutions has an average salary of $70,750 per year with a standard deviation of $6000. Assume also that a sample of 200 associate professors from other types of institutions has an average salary of $65,200 with a standard deviation of $5000. Test the hypothesis that the mean salary for associate professors in research institutions is $2000 higher than for those in other institutions. Use a 0.01 level of significance.

33 A study was conducted to see if increasing the substrate concentration has an appreciable effect on the velocity of a chemical reaction. With a substrate concentration of 1.5 moles per liter, the reaction was run 15 times, with an average velocity of 7.5 micromoles per 30 minutes and a standard deviation of 1.5. With a substrate concentration of 2.0 moles per liter, 12 runs were made, yielding an average velocity of 8.8 micromoles per 30 minutes and a sample standard deviation of 1.2. Is there any reason to believe that this increase in substrate concentration causes an increase in the mean velocity of the reaction of more than 0.5 micromole per 30 minutes? Use a 0.01 level of significance and assume the populations to be approximately normally distributed with equal variances.

34 A study was made to determine if the subject matter in a physics course is better understood when a lab constitutes part of the course. Students were randomly selected to participate in either a 3-semester-hour course without labs or a 4-semester-hour course with labs. In the section with labs, 11 students made an average grade of 85 with a standard deviation of 4.7, and in the section without labs, 17 students made an average grade of 79 with a standard deviation of 6.1. Would you say that the laboratory course increases the average grade by as much as 8 points? Use a P-value in your conclusion and assume the populations to be approximately normally distributed with equal variances.

35 To find out whether a new serum will arrest leukemia, 9 mice, all with an advanced stage of the disease, are selected. Five mice receive the treatment and 4 do not. Survival times, in years, from the time the experiment commenced are as follows:

Treatment	2.1	5.3	1.4	4.6	0.9
No Treatment	1.9	0.5	2.8	3.1	

At the 0.05 level of significance, can the serum be said to be effective? Assume the two populations to be normally distributed with equal variances.

36 Engineers at a large automobile manufacturing company are trying to decide whether to purchase brand A or brand B tires for the company's new models. To help them arrive at a decision, an experiment is conducted using 12 of each brand. The tires are run until they wear out. The results are as follows:

$$\text{Brand } A: \quad \bar{x}_1 = 37,900 \text{ kilometers,}$$
$$s_1 = 5100 \text{ kilometers.}$$
$$\text{Brand } B: \quad \bar{x}_1 = 39,800 \text{ kilometers,}$$
$$s_2 = 5900 \text{ kilometers.}$$

Test the hypothesis that there is no difference in the average wear of the two brands of tires. Assume the populations to be approximately normally distributed with equal variances. Use a P-value.

37 In Chapter **One- and Two-Sample Estimation Problems** Exercise 42, test the hypothesis that the fuel economy of Volkswagen mini-trucks, on average, exceeds that of similarly equipped Toyota mini-trucks by 4 kilometers per liter. Use a 0.10 level of significance.

38 A UCLA researcher claims that the average life span of mice can be extended by as much as 8 months when the calories in their diet are reduced by approximately 40% from the time they are weaned. The restricted diets are enriched to normal levels by vitamins and protein. Suppose that a random sample of 10 mice is fed a normal diet and has an average life span of 32.1 months with a standard deviation of 3.2 months, while a random sample of 15 mice is fed the restricted diet and has an average life span of 37.6 months with a standard deviation of 2.8 months. Test the hypothesis, at the 0.05 level of significance, that the average life span of mice on this restricted diet is increased by 8 months against the alternative that the increase is less than 8 months. Assume the distributions of life spans for the regular and restricted diets are approximately normal with equal variances.

39 The following data represent the running times of films produced by two motion-picture companies:

Company	Time (minutes)						
1	102	86	98	109	92		
2	81	165	97	134	92	87	114

Test the hypothesis that the average running time of films produced by company 2 exceeds the average running time of films produced by company 1 by 10 minutes against the one-sided alternative that the difference is less than 10 minutes. Use a 0.1 level of significance and assume the distributions of times to be approximately normal with unequal variances.

40 In a study conducted at Virginia Tech, the plasma ascorbic acid levels of pregnant women were compared for smokers versus nonsmokers. Thirty-two women in the last three months of pregnancy, free of major health disorders and ranging in age from 15 to 32 years, were selected for the study. Prior to the collection of 20 ml of blood, the participants were told to avoid breakfast, forgo their vitamin supplements, and avoid foods high in ascorbic acid content. From the blood samples, the following plasma ascorbic acid values were determined, in milligrams per 100 milliliters:

Plasma Ascorbic Acid Values

Nonsmokers		Smokers
0.97	1.16	0.48
0.72	0.86	0.71
1.00	0.85	0.98
0.81	0.58	0.68
0.62	0.57	1.18
1.32	0.64	1.36
1.24	0.98	0.78
0.99	1.09	1.64
0.90	0.92	
0.74	0.78	
0.88	1.24	
0.94	1.18	

Is there sufficient evidence to conclude that there is a difference between plasma ascorbic acid levels of smokers and nonsmokers? Assume that the two sets of data came from normal populations with unequal variances. Use a P-value.

41 A study was conducted by the Department of Zoology at Virginia Tech to determine if there is a significant difference in the density of organisms at two different stations located on Cedar Run, a secondary stream in the Roanoke River drainage basin. Sewage from a sewage treatment plant and overflow from the Federal Mogul Corporation settling pond enter the stream near its headwaters. The following data give the density measurements, in number of organisms per square meter, at the two collecting stations:

Number of Organisms per Square Meter

Station 1		Station 2	
5030	4980	2800	2810
13,700	11,910	4670	1330
10,730	8130	6890	3320
11,400	26,850	7720	1230
860	17,660	7030	2130
2200	22,800	7330	2190
4250	1130		
15,040	1690		

Can we conclude, at the 0.05 level of significance, that the average densities at the two stations are equal? Assume that the observations come from normal populations with different variances.

42 Five samples of a ferrous-type substance were used to determine if there is a difference between a laboratory chemical analysis and an X-ray fluorescence analysis of the iron content. Each sample was split into two subsamples and the two types of analysis were applied. Following are the coded data showing the iron content analysis:

Analysis	Sample				
	1	2	3	4	5
X-ray	2.0	2.0	2.3	2.1	2.4
Chemical	2.2	1.9	2.5	2.3	2.4

Assuming that the populations are normal, test at the 0.05 level of significance whether the two methods of analysis give, on the average, the same result.

43 According to published reports, practice under fatigued conditions distorts mechanisms that govern performance. An experiment was conducted using 15 college males, who were trained to make a continuous horizontal right-to-left arm movement from a microswitch to a barrier, knocking over the barrier coincident with the arrival of a clock sweephand to the 6 o'clock position. The absolute value of the difference between the time, in milliseconds, that it took to knock over the barrier and the time for the sweephand to reach the 6 o'clock position (500 msec) was recorded. Each participant performed the task five times under prefatigue and postfatigue conditions, and the sums of the absolute differences for the five performances were recorded.

Absolute Time Differences

Subject	Prefatigue	Postfatigue
1	158	91
2	92	59
3	65	215
4	98	226
5	33	223
6	89	91
7	148	92
8	58	177
9	142	134
10	117	116
11	74	153
12	66	219
13	109	143
14	57	164
15	85	100

An increase in the mean absolute time difference when the task is performed under postfatigue conditions would support the claim that practice under fatigued conditions distorts mechanisms that govern performance. Assuming the populations to be normally distributed, test this claim.

44 In a study conducted by the Department of Human Nutrition and Foods at Virginia Tech, the following data were recorded on sorbic acid residuals, in parts per million, in ham immediately after dipping in a sorbate solution and after 60 days of storage:

Sorbic Acid Residuals in Ham

Slice	Before Storage	After Storage
1	224	116
2	270	96
3	400	239
4	444	329
5	590	437
6	660	597
7	1400	689
8	680	576

Assuming the populations to be normally distributed, is there sufficient evidence, at the 0.05 level of significance, to say that the length of storage influences sorbic acid residual concentrations?

45 A taxi company manager is trying to decide whether the use of radial tires instead of regular belted tires improves fuel economy. Twelve cars were equipped with radial tires and driven over a prescribed test course. Without changing drivers, the same cars were then equipped with regular belted tires and driven once again over the test course. The gasoline consumption, in kilometers per liter, was recorded as follows:

Kilometers per Liter

Car	Radial Tires	Belted Tires
1	4.2	4.1
2	4.7	4.9
3	6.6	6.2
4	7.0	6.9
5	6.7	6.8
6	4.5	4.4
7	5.7	5.7
8	6.0	5.8
9	7.4	6.9
10	4.9	4.7
11	6.1	6.0
12	5.2	4.9

Can we conclude that cars equipped with radial tires give better fuel economy than those equipped with belted tires? Assume the populations to be normally distributed. Use a P-value in your conclusion.

46 In Chapter **One- and Two-Sample Estimation Problems** Review Exercise 91, use the t-distribution to test the hypothesis that the diet reduces a woman's weight by 4.5 kilograms on average against the alternative hypothesis that the mean difference in weight is less than 4.5 kilograms. Use a P-value.

47 How large a sample is required in Exercise 20 if the power of the test is to be 0.90 when the true mean is 5.20? Assume that $\sigma = 0.24$.

48 If the distribution of life spans in Exercise 19 is approximately normal, how large a sample is required in order that the probability of committing a type II error be 0.1 when the true mean is 35.9 months? Assume that $\sigma = 5.8$ months.

49 How large a sample is required in Exercise 24 if the power of the test is to be 0.95 when the true average height differs from 162.5 by 3.1 centimeters? Use $\alpha = 0.02$.

50 How large should the samples be in Exercise 31 if the power of the test is to be 0.95 when the true difference between thread types A and B is 8 kilograms?

51 How large a sample is required in Exercise 22 if the power of the test is to be 0.8 when the true mean meditation time exceeds the hypothesized value by 1.2σ? Use $\alpha = 0.05$.

52 For testing

$$H_0: \ \mu = 14,$$
$$H_1: \ \mu \neq 14,$$

an $\alpha = 0.05$ level t-test is being considered. What sample size is necessary in order for the probability to be 0.1 of falsely failing to reject H_0 when the true population mean differs from 14 by 0.5? From a preliminary sample we estimate σ to be 1.25.

53 A study was conducted at the Department of Veterinary Medicine at Virginia Tech to determine if the "strength" of a wound from surgical incision is affected by the temperature of the knife. Eight dogs were used in the experiment. "Hot" and "cold" incisions were made on the abdomen of each dog, and the strength was measured. The resulting data appear below.

Dog	Knife	Strength
1	Hot	5120
1	Cold	8200
2	Hot	10,000
2	Cold	8600
3	Hot	10,000
3	Cold	9200
4	Hot	10,000
4	Cold	6200

Dog	Knife	Strength
5	Hot	10,000
5	Cold	10,000
6	Hot	7900
6	Cold	5200
7	Hot	510
7	Cold	885
8	Hot	1020
8	Cold	460

(a) Write an appropriate hypothesis to determine if there is a significant difference in strength between the hot and cold incisions.

(b) Test the hypothesis using a paired t-test. Use a P-value in your conclusion.

54 Nine subjects were used in an experiment to determine if exposure to carbon monoxide has an impact on breathing capability. The data were collected by personnel in the Health and Physical Education Department at Virginia Tech and were analyzed in the Statistics Consulting Center at Hokie Land. The subjects were exposed to breathing chambers, one of which contained a high concentration of CO. Breathing frequency measures were made for each subject for each chamber. The subjects were exposed to the breathing chambers in random sequence. The data give the breathing frequency, in number of breaths taken per minute. Make a one-sided test of the hypothesis that mean breathing frequency is the same for the two environments. Use $\alpha = 0.05$. Assume that breathing frequency is approximately normal.

Subject	With CO	Without CO
1	30	30
2	45	40
3	26	25
4	25	23
5	34	30
6	51	49
7	46	41
8	32	35
9	30	28

8   One Sample: Test on a Single Proportion

Tests of hypotheses concerning proportions are required in many areas. Politicians are certainly interested in knowing what fraction of the voters will favor them in the next election. All manufacturing firms are concerned about the proportion of defective items when a shipment is made. Gamblers depend on a knowledge of the proportion of outcomes that they consider favorable.

We shall consider the problem of testing the hypothesis that the proportion of successes in a binomial experiment equals some specified value. That is, we are testing the null hypothesis H_0 that $p = p_0$, where p is the parameter of the binomial distribution. The alternative hypothesis may be one of the usual one-sided or two-sided alternatives:

$$p < p_0, \quad p > p_0, \quad \text{or} \quad p \neq p_0.$$

The appropriate random variable on which we base our decision criterion is the binomial random variable X, although we could just as well use the statistic $\hat{p} = X/n$. Values of X that are far from the mean $\mu = np_0$ will lead to the rejection of the null hypothesis. Because X is a discrete binomial variable, it is unlikely that a critical region can be established whose size is *exactly* equal to a prespecified value of α. For this reason it is preferable, in dealing with small samples, to base our decisions on P-values. To test the hypothesis

$$H_0: \ p = p_0,$$
$$H_1: \ p < p_0,$$

we use the binomial distribution to compute the P-value

$$P = P(X \leq x \text{ when } p = p_0).$$

The value x is the number of successes in our sample of size n. If this P-value is less than or equal to α, our test is significant at the α level and we reject H_0 in favor of H_1. Similarly, to test the hypothesis

$$H_0: \ p = p_0,$$
$$H_1: \ p > p_0,$$

at the α-level of significance, we compute

$$P = P(X \geq x \text{ when } p = p_0)$$

and reject H_0 in favor of H_1 if this P-value is less than or equal to α. Finally, to test the hypothesis

$$H_0: \ p = p_0,$$
$$H_1: \ p \neq p_0,$$

at the α-level of significance, we compute

$$P = 2P(X \leq x \text{ when } p = p_0) \qquad \text{if } x < np_0$$

or

$$P = 2P(X \geq x \text{ when } p = p_0) \qquad \text{if } x > np_0$$

and reject H_0 in favor of H_1 if the computed P-value is less than or equal to α.

The steps for testing a null hypothesis about a proportion against various alternatives using the binomial probabilities of Table Binomial Probability Sums at the end of this chapter are as follows:

Testing a Proportion (Small Samples)
1. $H_0: \ p = p_0$.
2. One of the alternatives $H_1: \ p < p_0, \ p > p_0,$ or $p \neq p_0$.
3. Choose a level of significance equal to α.
4. Test statistic: Binomial variable X with $p = p_0$.
5. Computations: Find x, the number of successes, and compute the appropriate P-value.
6. Decision: Draw appropriate conclusions based on the P-value.

Example 9: A builder claims that heat pumps are installed in 70% of all homes being constructed today in the city of Richmond, Virginia. Would you agree with this claim if a random survey of new homes in this city showed that 8 out of 15 had heat pumps installed? Use a 0.10 level of significance.

Solution:
1. H_0: $p = 0.7$.

2. H_1: $p \neq 0.7$.

3. $\alpha = 0.10$.

4. Test statistic: Binomial variable X with $p = 0.7$ and $n = 15$.

5. Computations: $x = 8$ and $np_0 = (15)(0.7) = 10.5$. Therefore, from Table A.1, the computed P-value is

$$P = 2P(X \leq 8 \text{ when } p = 0.7) = 2\sum_{x=0}^{8} b(x; 15, 0.7) = 0.2622 > 0.10.$$

6. Decision: Do not reject H_0. Conclude that there is insufficient reason to doubt the builder's claim.

Binomial probabilities can be obtained from the actual binomial formula or from Table Binomial Probability Sums when n is small. For large n, approximation procedures are required. When the hypothesized value p_0 is very close to 0 or 1, the Poisson distribution, with parameter $\mu = np_0$, may be used. However, the normal curve approximation, with parameters $\mu = np_0$ and $\sigma^2 = np_0q_0$, is usually preferred for large n and is very accurate as long as p_0 is not extremely close to 0 or to 1. If we use the normal approximation, the **z-value for testing $p = p_0$** is given by

$$z = \frac{x - np_0}{\sqrt{np_0q_0}} = \frac{\hat{p} - p_0}{\sqrt{p_0q_0/n}},$$

which is a value of the standard normal variable Z. Hence, for a two-tailed test at the α-level of significance, the critical region is $z < -z_{\alpha/2}$ or $z > z_{\alpha/2}$. For the one-sided alternative $p < p_0$, the critical region is $z < -z_\alpha$, and for the alternative $p > p_0$, the critical region is $z > z_\alpha$.

Example 10: A commonly prescribed drug for relieving nervous tension is believed to be only 60% effective. Experimental results with a new drug administered to a random sample of 100 adults who were suffering from nervous tension show that 70 received relief. Is this sufficient evidence to conclude that the new drug is superior to the one commonly prescribed? Use a 0.05 level of significance.

Solution:
1. H_0: $p = 0.6$.

2. H_1: $p > 0.6$.

3. $\alpha = 0.05$.

4. Critical region: $z > 1.645$.

5. Computations: $x = 70$, $n = 100$, $\hat{p} = 70/100 = 0.7$, and

$$z = \frac{0.7 - 0.6}{\sqrt{(0.6)(0.4)/100}} = 2.04, \quad P = P(Z > 2.04) < 0.0207.$$

6. Decision: Reject H_0 and conclude that the new drug is superior.

9 Two Samples: Tests on Two Proportions

Situations often arise where we wish to test the hypothesis that two proportions are equal. For example, we might want to show evidence that the proportion of doctors who are pediatricians in one state is equal to the proportion in another state. A person may decide to give up smoking only if he or she is convinced that the proportion of smokers with lung cancer exceeds the proportion of nonsmokers with lung cancer.

In general, we wish to test the null hypothesis that two proportions, or binomial parameters, are equal. That is, we are testing $p_1 = p_2$ against one of the alternatives $p_1 < p_2$, $p_1 > p_2$, or $p_1 \neq p_2$. Of course, this is equivalent to testing the null hypothesis that $p_1 - p_2 = 0$ against one of the alternatives $p_1 - p_2 < 0$, $p_1 - p_2 > 0$, or $p_1 - p_2 \neq 0$. The statistic on which we base our decision is the random variable $\hat{P}_1 - \hat{P}_2$. Independent samples of sizes n_1 and n_2 are selected at random from two binomial populations and the proportions of successes $\hat{P}_1$ and $\hat{P}_2$ for the two samples are computed.

In our construction of confidence intervals for p_1 and p_2 we noted, for n_1 and n_2 sufficiently large, that the point estimator $\hat{P}_1$ minus $\hat{P}_2$ was approximately normally distributed with mean

$$\mu_{\hat{P}_1 - \hat{P}_2} = p_1 - p_2$$

and variance

$$\sigma^2_{\hat{P}_1 - \hat{P}_2} = \frac{p_1 q_1}{n_1} + \frac{p_2 q_2}{n_2}.$$

Therefore, our critical region(s) can be established by using the standard normal variable

$$Z = \frac{(\hat{P}_1 - \hat{P}_2) - (p_1 - p_2)}{\sqrt{p_1 q_1/n_1 + p_2 q_2/n_2}}.$$

When H_0 is true, we can substitute $p_1 = p_2 = p$ and $q_1 = q_2 = q$ (where p and q are the common values) in the preceding formula for Z to give the form

$$Z = \frac{\hat{P}_1 - \hat{P}_2}{\sqrt{pq(1/n_1 + 1/n_2)}}.$$

To compute a value of Z, however, we must estimate the parameters p and q that appear in the radical. Upon pooling the data from both samples, the **pooled estimate of the proportion p** is

$$\hat{p} = \frac{x_1 + x_2}{n_1 + n_2},$$

where x_1 and x_2 are the numbers of successes in each of the two samples. Substituting $\hat{p}$ for p and $\hat{q} = 1 - \hat{p}$ for q, the **z-value for testing $p_1 = p_2$** is determined from the formula

$$z = \frac{\hat{p}_1 - \hat{p}_2}{\sqrt{\hat{p}\hat{q}(1/n_1 + 1/n_2)}}.$$

The critical regions for the appropriate alternative hypotheses are set up as before, using critical points of the standard normal curve. Hence, for the alternative $p_1 \neq p_2$ at the α-level of significance, the critical region is $z < -z_{\alpha/2}$ or $z > z_{\alpha/2}$. For a test where the alternative is $p_1 < p_2$, the critical region is $z < -z_\alpha$, and when the alternative is $p_1 > p_2$, the critical region is $z > z_\alpha$.

Example 11: A vote is to be taken among the residents of a town and the surrounding county to determine whether a proposed chemical plant should be constructed. The construction site is within the town limits, and for this reason many voters in the county believe that the proposal will pass because of the large proportion of town voters who favor the construction. To determine if there is a significant difference in the proportions of town voters and county voters favoring the proposal, a poll is taken. If 120 of 200 town voters favor the proposal and 240 of 500 county residents favor it, would you agree that the proportion of town voters favoring the proposal is higher than the proportion of county voters? Use an $\alpha = 0.05$ level of significance.

Solution: Let p_1 and p_2 be the true proportions of voters in the town and county, respectively, favoring the proposal.

1. H_0: $p_1 = p_2$.

2. H_1: $p_1 > p_2$.

3. $\alpha = 0.05$.

4. Critical region: $z > 1.645$.

5. Computations:

$$\hat{p}_1 = \frac{x_1}{n_1} = \frac{120}{200} = 0.60, \quad \hat{p}_2 = \frac{x_2}{n_2} = \frac{240}{500} = 0.48, \quad \text{and}$$

$$\hat{p} = \frac{x_1 + x_2}{n_1 + n_2} = \frac{120 + 240}{200 + 500} = 0.51.$$

Therefore,

$$z = \frac{0.60 - 0.48}{\sqrt{(0.51)(0.49)(1/200 + 1/500)}} = 2.9,$$
$$P = P(Z > 2.9) = 0.0019.$$

6. Decision: Reject H_0 and agree that the proportion of town voters favoring the proposal is higher than the proportion of county voters.

Exercises

55 A marketing expert for a pasta-making company believes that 40% of pasta lovers prefer lasagna. If 9 out of 20 pasta lovers choose lasagna over other pastas, what can be concluded about the expert's claim? Use a 0.05 level of significance.

56 Suppose that, in the past, 40% of all adults favored capital punishment. Do we have reason to believe that the proportion of adults favoring capital punishment has increased if, in a random sample of 15 adults, 8 favor capital punishment? Use a 0.05 level of significance.

57 A new radar device is being considered for a certain missile defense system. The system is checked by experimenting with aircraft in which a kill or a no kill is simulated. If, in 300 trials, 250 kills occur, accept or reject, at the 0.04 level of significance, the claim that the probability of a kill with the new system does not exceed the 0.8 probability of the existing device.

58 It is believed that at least 60% of the residents in a certain area favor an annexation suit by a neighboring city. What conclusion would you draw if only 110 in a sample of 200 voters favored the suit? Use a 0.05 level of significance.

59 A fuel oil company claims that one-fifth of the homes in a certain city are heated by oil. Do we have reason to believe that fewer than one-fifth are heated by oil if, in a random sample of 1000 homes in this city, 136 are heated by oil? Use a P-value in your conclusion.

60 At a certain college, it is estimated that at most 25% of the students ride bicycles to class. Does this seem to be a valid estimate if, in a random sample of 90 college students, 28 are found to ride bicycles to class? Use a 0.05 level of significance.

61 In a winter of an epidemic flu, the parents of 2000 babies were surveyed by researchers at a well-known pharmaceutical company to determine if the company's new medicine was effective after two days. Among 120 babies who had the flu and were given the medicine, 29 were cured within two days. Among 280 babies who had the flu but were not given the medicine, 56 recovered within two days. Is there any significant indication that supports the company's claim of the effectiveness of the medicine?

62 In a controlled laboratory experiment, scientists at the University of Minnesota discovered that 25% of a certain strain of rats subjected to a 20% coffee bean diet and then force-fed a powerful cancer-causing chemical later developed cancerous tumors. Would we have reason to believe that the proportion of rats developing tumors when subjected to this diet has increased if the experiment were repeated and 16 of 48 rats developed tumors? Use a 0.05 level of significance.

63 In a study to estimate the proportion of residents in a certain city and its suburbs who favor the construction of a nuclear power plant, it is found that 63 of 100 urban residents favor the construction while only 59 of 125 suburban residents are in favor. Is there a significant difference between the proportions of urban and suburban residents who favor construction of the nuclear plant? Make use of a P-value.

64 In a study on the fertility of married women conducted by Martin O'Connell and Carolyn C. Rogers for the Census Bureau in 1979, two groups of childless wives aged 25 to 29 were selected at random, and each was asked if she eventually planned to have a child. One group was selected from among wives married less than two years and the other from among wives married five years. Suppose that 240 of the 300 wives married less than two years planned to have children some day compared to 288 of the 400 wives married five years. Can we conclude that the proportion of wives married less than two years who planned to have children is significantly higher than the proportion of wives married five years? Make use of a P-value.

65 An urban community would like to show that the incidence of breast cancer is higher in their area than in a nearby rural area. (PCB levels were found to be higher in the soil of the urban community.) If it is found that 20 of 200 adult women in the urban community have breast cancer and 10 of 150 adult women in the rural community have breast cancer, can we conclude at the 0.05 level of significance that breast cancer is more prevalent in the urban community?

66 **Group Project**: The class should be divided into pairs of students for this project. Suppose it is conjectured that at least 25% of students at your university exercise for more than two hours a week. Collect data from a random sample of 50 students. Ask each student if he or she works out for at least two hours per week. Then do the computations that allow either rejection or nonrejection of the above conjecture. Show all work and quote a P-value in your conclusion.

10   One- and Two-Sample Tests Concerning Variances

In this section, we are concerned with testing hypotheses concerning population variances or standard deviations. Applications of one- and two-sample tests on variances are certainly not difficult to motivate. Engineers and scientists are confronted with studies in which they are required to demonstrate that measurements involving products or processes adhere to specifications set by consumers. The specifications are often met if the process variance is sufficiently small. Attention is also focused on comparative experiments between methods or processes, where inherent reproducibility or variability must formally be compared. In addition, to determine if the equal variance assumption is violated, a test comparing two variances is often applied prior to conducting a t-test on two means.

Let us first consider the problem of testing the null hypothesis H_0 that the population variance σ^2 equals a specified value σ_0^2 against one of the usual alternatives $\sigma^2 < \sigma_0^2$, $\sigma^2 > \sigma_0^2$, or $\sigma^2 \neq \sigma_0^2$. The appropriate statistic on which to base our decision is the chi-squared statistic, which was used in Chapter **One- and Two-Sample Estimation Problems** to construct a confidence interval for σ^2. Therefore, if we assume that the distribution of the population being sampled is normal, the chi-squared value for testing $\sigma^2 = \sigma_0^2$ is given by

$$\chi^2 = \frac{(n-1)s^2}{\sigma_0^2},$$

where n is the sample size, s^2 is the sample variance, and σ_0^2 is the value of σ^2 given by the null hypothesis. If H_0 is true, χ^2 is a value of the chi-squared distribution with $v = n - 1$ degrees of freedom. Hence, for a two-tailed test at the α-level of significance, the critical region is $\chi^2 < \chi_{1-\alpha/2}^2$ or $\chi^2 > \chi_{\alpha/2}^2$. For the one-sided alternative $\sigma^2 < \sigma_0^2$, the critical region is $\chi^2 < \chi_{1-\alpha}^2$, and for the one-sided alternative $\sigma^2 > \sigma_0^2$, the critical region is $\chi^2 > \chi_\alpha^2$.

Robustness of χ^2-Test to Assumption of Normality

The reader may have discerned that various tests depend, at least theoretically, on the assumption of normality. In general, many procedures in applied statistics have theoretical underpinnings that depend on the normal distribution. These procedures vary in the degree of their dependency on the assumption of normality. A procedure that is reasonably insensitive to the assumption is called a **robust procedure** (i.e., robust to normality). The χ^2-test on a single variance is very nonrobust to normality (i.e., the practical success of the procedure depends on normality). As a result, the P-value computed may be appreciably different from the actual P-value if the population sampled is not normal. Indeed, it is quite feasible that a statistically significant P-value may not truly signal H_1: $\sigma \neq \sigma_0$; rather, a significant value may be a result of the violation of the normality assumptions. Therefore, the analyst should approach the use of this particular χ^2-test with caution.

Example 12: A manufacturer of car batteries claims that the life of the company's batteries is approximately normally distributed with a standard deviation equal to 0.9 year.

If a random sample of 10 of these batteries has a standard deviation of 1.2 years, do you think that $\sigma > 0.9$ year? Use a 0.05 level of significance.

Solution: 1. H_0: $\sigma^2 = 0.81$.

2. H_1: $\sigma^2 > 0.81$.

3. $\alpha = 0.05$.

4. Critical region: From Figure 19 we see that the null hypothesis is rejected when $\chi^2 > 16.919$, where $\chi^2 = \frac{(n-1)s^2}{\sigma_0^2}$, with $v = 9$ degrees of freedom.

Figure 19: Critical region for the alternative hypothesis $\sigma > 0.9$.

5. Computations: $s^2 = 1.44$, $n = 10$, and

$$\chi^2 = \frac{(9)(1.44)}{0.81} = 16.0, \qquad P \approx 0.07.$$

6. Decision: The χ^2-statistic is not significant at the 0.05 level. However, based on the P-value 0.07, there is evidence that $\sigma > 0.9$.

Now let us consider the problem of testing the equality of the variances σ_1^2 and σ_2^2 of two populations. That is, we shall test the null hypothesis H_0 that $\sigma_1^2 = \sigma_2^2$ against one of the usual alternatives

$$\sigma_1^2 < \sigma_2^2, \quad \sigma_1^2 > \sigma_2^2, \quad \text{or} \quad \sigma_1^2 \neq \sigma_2^2.$$

For independent random samples of sizes n_1 and n_2, respectively, from the two populations, the ***f*-value for testing $\sigma_1^2 = \sigma_2^2$** is the ratio

$$f = \frac{s_1^2}{s_2^2},$$

where s_1^2 and s_2^2 are the variances computed from the two samples. If the two populations are approximately normally distributed and the null hypothesis is true, according to Theorem 8.8 the ratio $f = s_1^2/s_2^2$ is a value of the F-distribution with $v_1 = n_1 - 1$ and $v_2 = n_2 - 1$ degrees of freedom. Therefore, the critical regions of size α corresponding to the one-sided alternatives $\sigma_1^2 < \sigma_2^2$ and $\sigma_1^2 > \sigma_2^2$ are, respectively, $f < f_{1-\alpha}(v_1, v_2)$ and $f > f_\alpha(v_1, v_2)$. For the two-sided alternative $\sigma_1^2 \neq \sigma_2^2$, the critical region is $f < f_{1-\alpha/2}(v_1, v_2)$ or $f > f_{\alpha/2}(v_1, v_2)$.

Example 13: In testing for the difference in the abrasive wear of the two materials in Example 10.6, we assumed that the two unknown population variances were equal. Were we justified in making this assumption? Use a 0.10 level of significance.

Solution: Let σ_1^2 and σ_2^2 be the population variances for the abrasive wear of material 1 and material 2, respectively.

1. H_0: $\sigma_1^2 = \sigma_2^2$.

2. H_1: $\sigma_1^2 \neq \sigma_2^2$.

3. $\alpha = 0.10$.

4. Critical region: From Figure 20, we see that $f_{0.05}(11, 9) = 3.11$, and we find

$$f_{0.95}(11, 9) = \frac{1}{f_{0.05}(9, 11)} = 0.34.$$

Therefore, the null hypothesis is rejected when $f < 0.34$ or $f > 3.11$, where $f = s_1^2/s_2^2$ with $v_1 = 11$ and $v_2 = 9$ degrees of freedom.

5. Computations: $s_1^2 = 16$, $s_2^2 = 25$, and hence $f = \frac{16}{25} = 0.64$.

6. Decision: Do not reject H_0. Conclude that there is insufficient evidence that the variances differ.

Figure 20: Critical region for the alternative hypothesis $\sigma_1^2 \neq \sigma_2^2$.

F-Test for Testing Variances in *SAS*

Figure 18 displays the printout of a two-sample t-test where two means from the seedling data in Chapter **One- and Two-Sample Estimation Problems** Exercise 40 were compared. Box-and-whisker plots in Figure 17 suggest that variances are not homogeneous, and thus the t'-statistic and its corresponding P-value are relevant.

Note also that the printout displays the F-statistic for H_0: $\sigma_1 = \sigma_2$ with a P-value of 0.0098, additional evidence that more variability is to be expected when nitrogen is used than under the no-nitrogen condition.

Exercises

67 The content of containers of a particular lubricant is known to be normally distributed with a variance of 0.03 liter. Test the hypothesis that $\sigma^2 = 0.03$ against the alternative that $\sigma^2 \neq 0.03$ for the random sample of 10 containers in Exercise 23.
Use a P-value in your conclusion.

68 Past experience indicates that the time required for high school seniors to complete a standardized test is a normal random variable with a standard deviation of 6 minutes. Test the hypothesis that $\sigma = 6$ against the alternative that $\sigma < 6$ if a random sample of the test times of 20 high school seniors has a standard deviation $s = 4.51$. Use a 0.05 level of significance.

69 Aflotoxins produced by mold on peanut crops in Virginia must be monitored. A sample of 64 batches of peanuts reveals levels of 24.17 ppm, on average, with a variance of 4.25 ppm. Test the hypothesis that $\sigma^2 = 4.2$ ppm against the alternative that $\sigma^2 \neq 4.2$ ppm. Use a P-value in your conclusion.

70 Past data indicate that the amount of money contributed by the working residents of a large city to a volunteer rescue squad is a normal random variable with a standard deviation of $1.40. It has been suggested that the contributions to the rescue squad from just the employees of the sanitation department are much more variable. If the contributions of a random sample of 12 employees from the sanitation department have a standard deviation of $1.75, can we conclude at the 0.01 level of significance that the standard deviation of the contributions of all sanitation workers is greater than that of all workers living in the city?

71 A soft-drink dispensing machine is said to be out of control if the variance of the contents exceeds 1.15 deciliters. If a random sample of 25 drinks from this machine has a variance of 2.03 deciliters, does this indicate at the 0.05 level of significance that the machine is out of control? Assume that the contents are approximately normally distributed.

72 **Large-Sample Test of $\sigma^2 = \sigma_0^2$:** When $n \geq 30$, we can test the null hypothesis that $\sigma^2 = \sigma_0^2$, or $\sigma = \sigma_0$, by computing

$$z = \frac{s - \sigma_0}{\sigma_0 / \sqrt{2n}},$$

which is a value of a random variable whose sampling distribution is approximately the standard normal distribution.

(a) With reference to Example 4, test at the 0.05 level of significance whether $\sigma = 10.0$ years against the alternative that $\sigma \neq 10.0$ years.

(b) It is suspected that the variance of the distribution of distances in kilometers traveled on 5 liters of fuel by a new automobile model equipped with a diesel engine is less than the variance of the distribution of distances traveled by the same model equipped with a six-cylinder gasoline engine, which is known to be $\sigma^2 = 6.25$. If 72 test runs of the diesel model have a variance of 4.41, can we conclude at the 0.05 level of significance that the variance of the distances traveled by the diesel model is less than that of the gasoline model?

73 A study is conducted to compare the lengths of time required by men and women to assemble a certain product. Past experience indicates that the distribution of times for both men and women is approximately normal but the variance of the times for women is less than that for men. A random sample of times for 11 men and 14 women produced the following data:

Men	Women
$n_1 = 11$	$n_2 = 14$
$s_1 = 6.1$	$s_2 = 5.3$

Test the hypothesis that $\sigma_1^2 = \sigma_2^2$ against the alternative that $\sigma_1^2 > \sigma_2^2$. Use a P-value in your conclusion.

74 For Exercise 41, test the hypothesis at the 0.05 level of significance that $\sigma_1^2 = \sigma_2^2$ against the alternative that $\sigma_1^2 \neq \sigma_2^2$, where σ_1^2 and σ_2^2 are the variances of the number of organisms per square meter of water at the two different locations on Cedar Run.

75 With reference to Exercise 39, test the hypothesis that $\sigma_1^2 = \sigma_2^2$ against the alternative that $\sigma_1^2 \neq \sigma_2^2$, where σ_1^2 and σ_2^2 are the variances for the running times of films produced by company 1 and company 2, respectively. Use a P-value.

76 Two types of instruments for measuring the amount of sulfur monoxide in the atmosphere are being compared in an air-pollution experiment. Researchers wish to determine whether the two types of instruments yield measurements having the same variability. The readings in the following table were recorded for the two instruments.

Sulfur Monoxide

Instrument *A*	Instrument *B*
0.86	0.87
0.82	0.74
0.75	0.63
0.61	0.55
0.89	0.76
0.64	0.70
0.81	0.69
0.68	0.57
0.65	0.53

Assuming the populations of measurements to be approximately normally distributed, test the hypothesis that $\sigma_A = \sigma_B$ against the alternative that $\sigma_A \neq \sigma_B$. Use a P-value.

77 An experiment was conducted to compare the alcohol content of soy sauce on two different production lines. Production was monitored eight times a day. The data are shown here.

```
Production line 1:
```

```
    0.48 0.39 0.42 0.52 0.40 0.48 0.52 0.52
Production line 2:
    0.38 0.37 0.39 0.41 0.38 0.39 0.40 0.39
```

Assume both populations are normal. It is suspected that production line 1 is not producing as consistently as production line 2 in terms of alcohol content. Test the hypothesis that $\sigma_1 = \sigma_2$ against the alternative that $\sigma_1 \neq \sigma_2$. Use a P-value.

78 Hydrocarbon emissions from cars are known to have decreased dramatically during the 1980s. A study was conducted to compare the hydrocarbon emissions at idling speed, in parts per million (ppm), for automobiles from 1980 and 1990. Twenty cars of each model year were randomly selected, and their hydrocarbon emission levels were recorded. The data are as follows:

```
1980 models:
141 359 247 940 882 494 306 210 105 880
200 223 188 940 241 190 300 435 241 380
1990 models:
140 160  20 20 223  60  20  95 360 70
220 400 217 58 235 380 200 175  85 65
```

Test the hypothesis that $\sigma_1 = \sigma_2$ against the alternative that $\sigma_1 \neq \sigma_2$. Assume both populations are normal. Use a P-value.

11 Goodness-of-Fit Test

Throughout this chapter, we have been concerned with the testing of statistical hypotheses about single population parameters such as μ, σ^2, and p. Now we shall consider a test to determine if a population has a specified theoretical distribution. The test is based on how good a fit we have between the frequency of occurrence of observations in an observed sample and the expected frequencies obtained from the hypothesized distribution.

To illustrate, we consider the tossing of a die. We hypothesize that the die is honest, which is equivalent to testing the hypothesis that the distribution of outcomes is the discrete uniform distribution

$$f(x) = \frac{1}{6}, \quad x = 1, 2, \ldots, 6.$$

Suppose that the die is tossed 120 times and each outcome is recorded. Theoretically, if the die is balanced, we would expect each face to occur 20 times. The results are given in Table 4.

Table 4: Observed and Expected Frequencies of 120 Tosses of a Die

Face:	1	2	3	4	5	6
Observed	20	22	17	18	19	24
Expected	20	20	20	20	20	20

By comparing the observed frequencies with the corresponding expected frequencies, we must decide whether these discrepancies are likely to occur as a result of sampling fluctuations and the die is balanced or whether the die is not honest and the distribution of outcomes is not uniform. It is common practice to refer to each possible outcome of an experiment as a cell. In our illustration, we have 6 cells. The appropriate statistic on which we base our decision criterion for an experiment involving k cells is defined by the following.

A **goodness-of-fit test** between observed and expected frequencies is based on the quantity

Goodness-of-Fit
Test

$$\chi^2 = \sum_{i=1}^{k} \frac{(o_i - e_i)^2}{e_i},$$

where χ^2 is a value of a random variable whose sampling distribution is approximated very closely by the chi-squared distribution with $v = k - 1$ degrees of freedom. The symbols o_i and e_i represent the observed and expected frequencies, respectively, for the ith cell.

The number of degrees of freedom associated with the chi-squared distribution used here is equal to $k - 1$, since there are only $k - 1$ freely determined cell frequencies. That is, once $k - 1$ cell frequencies are determined, so is the frequency for the kth cell.

If the observed frequencies are close to the corresponding expected frequencies, the χ^2-value will be small, indicating a good fit. If the observed frequencies differ considerably from the expected frequencies, the χ^2-value will be large and the fit is poor. A good fit leads to the acceptance of H_0, whereas a poor fit leads to its rejection. The critical region will, therefore, fall in the right tail of the chi-squared distribution. For a level of significance equal to α, we find the critical value χ_α^2 from Table Critical Values of the Chi-Squared Distribution at the end of this chapter, and then $\chi^2 > \chi_\alpha^2$ constitutes the critical region. **The decision criterion described here should not be used unless each of the expected frequencies is at least equal to 5.** This restriction may require the combining of adjacent cells, resulting in a reduction in the number of degrees of freedom.

From Table 10.4, we find the χ^2-value to be

$$\chi^2 = \frac{(20 - 20)^2}{20} + \frac{(22 - 20)^2}{20} + \frac{(17 - 20)^2}{20}$$
$$+ \frac{(18 - 20)^2}{20} + \frac{(19 - 20)^2}{20} + \frac{(24 - 20)^2}{20} = 1.7.$$

Using Table Critical Values of the Chi-Squared Distribution, we find $\chi_{0.05}^2 = 11.070$ for $v = 5$ degrees of freedom. Since 1.7 is less than the critical value, we fail to reject H_0. We conclude that there is insufficient evidence that the die is not balanced.

As a second illustration, let us test the hypothesis that the frequency distribution of battery lives may be approximated by a normal distribution with mean $\mu = 3.5$ and standard deviation $\sigma = 0.7$. The expected frequencies for the 7 classes (cells), listed in Table 5, are obtained by computing the areas under the hypothesized normal curve that fall between the various class boundaries.

Table 5: Observed and Expected Frequencies of Battery Lives, Assuming Normality

Class Boundaries	o_i		e_i	
1.45–1.95	2		0.5	
1.95–2.45	1	7	2.1	8.5
2.45–2.95	4		5.9	
2.95–3.45	15		10.3	
3.45–3.95	10		10.7	
3.95–4.45	5	8	7.0	10.5
4.45–4.95	3		3.5	

For example, the z-values corresponding to the boundaries of the fourth class are

$$z_1 = \frac{2.95 - 3.5}{0.7} = -0.79 \quad \text{and} \quad z_2 = \frac{3.45 - 3.5}{0.7} = -0.07.$$

From Table A.3 we find the area between $z_1 = -0.79$ and $z_2 = -0.07$ to be

$$\text{area} = P(-0.79 < Z < -0.07) = P(Z < -0.07) - P(Z < -0.79)$$
$$= 0.4721 - 0.2148 = 0.2573.$$

Hence, the expected frequency for the fourth class is

$$e_4 = (0.2573)(40) = 10.3.$$

It is customary to round these frequencies to one decimal.

The expected frequency for the first class interval is obtained by using the total area under the normal curve to the left of the boundary 1.95. For the last class interval, we use the total area to the right of the boundary 4.45. All other expected frequencies are determined by the method described for the fourth class. Note that we have combined adjacent classes in Table 5 where the expected frequencies are less than 5 (a rule of thumb in the goodness-of-fit test). Consequently, the total number of intervals is reduced from 7 to 4, resulting in $v = 3$ degrees of freedom. The χ^2-value is then given by

$$\chi^2 = \frac{(7 - 8.5)^2}{8.5} + \frac{(15 - 10.3)^2}{10.3} + \frac{(10 - 10.7)^2}{10.7} + \frac{(8 - 10.5)^2}{10.5} = 3.05.$$

Since the computed χ^2-value is less than $\chi^2_{0.05} = 7.815$ for 3 degrees of freedom, we have no reason to reject the null hypothesis and conclude that the normal distribution with $\mu = 3.5$ and $\sigma = 0.7$ provides a good fit for the distribution of battery lives.

The chi-squared goodness-of-fit test is an important resource, particularly since so many statistical procedures in practice depend, in a theoretical sense, on the assumption that the data gathered come from a specific type of distribution. As we have already seen, the normality assumption is often made. We shall continue to make normality assumptions in order to provide a theoretical basis for certain tests and confidence intervals.

There are tests in the literature that are more powerful than the chi-squared test for testing normality. One such test is called **Geary's test**. This test is based on a very simple statistic which is a ratio of two estimators of the population standard deviation σ. Suppose that a random sample $X_1, X_2, \ldots, X_n$ is taken from a normal distribution, $N(\mu, \sigma)$. Consider the ratio

$$U = \frac{\sqrt{\pi/2} \sum\limits_{i=1}^{n} |X_i - \bar{X}|/n}{\sqrt{\sum\limits_{i=1}^{n} (X_i - \bar{X})^2/n}}.$$

The reader should recognize that the denominator is a reasonable estimator of σ whether the distribution is normal or not. The numerator is a good estimator of σ if the distribution is normal but may overestimate or underestimate σ when there are departures from normality. Thus, values of U differing considerably from 1.0 represent the signal that the hypothesis of normality should be rejected.

For large samples, a reasonable test is based on approximate normality of U. The test statistic is then a standardization of U, given by

$$Z = \frac{U - 1}{0.2661/\sqrt{n}}.$$

Of course, the test procedure involves the two-sided critical region. We compute a value of z from the data and do not reject the hypothesis of normality when

$$-z_{\alpha/2} < Z < z_{\alpha/2}.$$

A paper dealing with Geary's test is cited in the Bibliography (Geary, 1947).

12 Test for Independence (Categorical Data)

The chi-squared test procedure discussed in Section 11 can also be used to test the hypothesis of independence of two variables of classification. Suppose that we wish to determine whether the opinions of the voting residents of the state of Illinois concerning a new tax reform are independent of their levels of income. Members of a random sample of 1000 registered voters from the state of Illinois are classified as to whether they are in a low, medium, or high income bracket and whether or not they favor the tax reform. The observed frequencies are presented in Table 10.6, which is known as a **contingency table**.

Table 6: 2 × 3 Contingency Table

Tax Reform	Income Level			Total
	Low	**Medium**	**High**	
For	182	213	203	598
Against	154	138	110	402
Total	336	351	313	1000

A contingency table with r rows and c columns is referred to as an $r \times c$ table ("$r \times c$" is read "r by c"). The row and column totals in Table 6 are called **marginal frequencies**. Our decision to accept or reject the null hypothesis, H_0, of independence between a voter's opinion concerning the tax reform and his or her level of income is based upon how good a fit we have between the observed frequencies in each of the 6 cells of Table 6 and the frequencies that we would expect for each cell under the assumption that H_0 is true. To find these expected frequencies, let us define the following events:

> L: A person selected is in the low-income level.
>
> M: A person selected is in the medium-income level.
>
> H: A person selected is in the high-income level.
>
> F: A person selected is for the tax reform.
>
> A: A person selected is against the tax reform.

By using the marginal frequencies, we can list the following probability estimates:

$$P(L) = \frac{336}{1000}, \quad P(M) = \frac{351}{1000}, \quad P(H) = \frac{313}{1000},$$
$$P(F) = \frac{598}{1000}, \quad P(A) = \frac{402}{1000}.$$

Now, if H_0 is true and the two variables are independent, we should have

$$P(L \cap F) = P(L)P(F) = \left(\frac{336}{1000}\right)\left(\frac{598}{1000}\right),$$
$$P(L \cap A) = P(L)P(A) = \left(\frac{336}{1000}\right)\left(\frac{402}{1000}\right),$$

$$P(M \cap F) = P(M)P(F) = \left(\frac{351}{1000}\right)\left(\frac{598}{1000}\right),$$
$$P(M \cap A) = P(M)P(A) = \left(\frac{351}{1000}\right)\left(\frac{402}{1000}\right),$$
$$P(H \cap F) = P(H)P(F) = \left(\frac{313}{1000}\right)\left(\frac{598}{1000}\right),$$
$$P(H \cap A) = P(H)P(A) = \left(\frac{313}{1000}\right)\left(\frac{402}{1000}\right).$$

The expected frequencies are obtained by multiplying each cell probability by the total number of observations. As before, we round these frequencies to one decimal. Thus, the expected number of low-income voters in our sample who favor the tax reform is estimated to be

$$\left(\frac{336}{1000}\right)\left(\frac{598}{1000}\right)(1000) = \frac{(336)(598)}{1000} = 200.9$$

when H_0 is true. The general rule for obtaining the expected frequency of any cell is given by the following formula:

$$\text{expected frequency} = \frac{(\text{column total}) \times (\text{row total})}{\text{grand total}}.$$

The expected frequency for each cell is recorded in parentheses beside the actual observed value in Table 7. Note that the expected frequencies in any row or column add up to the appropriate marginal total. In our example, we need to compute only two expected frequencies in the top row of Table 7 and then find the others by subtraction. The number of degrees of freedom associated with the chi-squared test used here is equal to the number of cell frequencies that may be filled in freely when we are given the marginal totals and the grand total, and in this illustration that number is 2. A simple formula providing the correct number of degrees of freedom is

$$v = (r-1)(c-1).$$

Table 7: Observed and Expected Frequencies

Tax Reform	Income Level			Total
	Low	**Medium**	**High**	
For	182 (200.9)	213 (209.9)	203 (187.2)	598
Against	154 (135.1)	138 (141.1)	110 (125.8)	402
Total	336	351	313	1000

Hence, for our example, $v = (2-1)(3-1) = 2$ degrees of freedom. To test the null hypothesis of independence, we use the following decision criterion.

Calculate

$$\chi^2 = \sum_i \frac{(o_i - e_i)^2}{e_i},$$

where the summation extends over all rc cells in the $r \times c$ contingency table. If $\chi^2 > \chi_\alpha^2$ with $v = (r-1)(c-1)$ degrees of freedom, reject the null hypothesis of independence at the α-level of significance; otherwise, fail to reject the null hypothesis.

Applying this criterion to our example, we find that

$$\chi^2 = \frac{(182-200.9)^2}{200.9} + \frac{(213-209.9)^2}{209.9} + \frac{(203-187.2)^2}{187.2}$$
$$+ \frac{(154-135.1)^2}{135.1} + \frac{(138-141.1)^2}{141.1} + \frac{(110-125.8)^2}{125.8} = 7.85,$$
$$P \approx 0.02.$$

From Table Critical Values of the Chi-Squared Distribution, we find that $x_{0.05}^2 = 5.991$ for $v = (2-1)(3-1) = 2$ degrees of freedom. The null hypothesis is rejected and we conclude that the voter's opinion concerning the tax reform and his or her level of income are not independent.

It is important to remember that the statistic on which we base our decision has a distribution that is only approximated by the chi-squared distribution. The computed χ^2-values depend on the cell frequencies and consequently are discrete. The continuous chi-squared distribution seems to approximate the discrete sampling distribution of χ^2 very well, provided that the number of degrees of freedom is greater than 1. In a 2×2 contingency table, where we have only 1 degree of freedom, a correction called **Yates' correction for continuity** is applied. The corrected formula then becomes

$$\chi^2(\text{corrected}) = \sum_i \frac{(|o_i - e_i| - 0.5)^2}{e_i}.$$

If the expected cell frequencies are large, the corrected and uncorrected results are almost the same. When the expected frequencies are between 5 and 10, Yates' correction should be applied. For expected frequencies less than 5, the Fisher-Irwin exact test should be used. A discussion of this test may be found in *Basic Concepts of Probability and Statistics* by Hodges and Lehmann (2005). The Fisher-Irwin test may be avoided, however, by choosing a larger sample.

13   Test for Homogeneity

When we tested for independence in Section 12, a random sample of 1000 voters was selected and the row and column totals for our contingency table were determined by chance. Another type of problem for which the method of Section 12 applies is one in which either the row or column totals are predetermined. Suppose, for example, that we decide in advance to select 200 Democrats, 150 Republicans, and 150 Independents from the voters of the state of North Carolina and record whether they are for a proposed abortion law, against it, or undecided. The observed responses are given in Table 8.

Table 8: Observed Frequencies

Abortion Law	Political Affiliation			Total
	Democrat	**Republican**	**Independent**	
For	82	70	62	214
Against	93	62	67	222
Undecided	25	18	21	64
Total	200	150	150	500

Now, rather than test for independence, we test the hypothesis that the population proportions within each row are the same. That is, we test the hypothesis that the proportions of Democrats, Republicans, and Independents favoring the abortion law are the same; the proportions of each political affiliation against the law are the same; and the proportions of each political affiliation that are undecided are the same. We are basically interested in determining whether the three categories of voters are **homogeneous** with respect to their opinions concerning the proposed abortion law. Such a test is called a test for homogeneity.

Assuming homogeneity, we again find the expected cell frequencies by multiplying the corresponding row and column totals and then dividing by the grand total. The analysis then proceeds using the same chi-squared statistic as before. We illustrate this process for the data of Table 8 in the following example.

Example 14: Referring to the data of Table 8, test the hypothesis that opinions concerning the proposed abortion law are the same within each political affiliation. Use a 0.05 level of significance.

Solution: 1. H_0: For each opinion, the proportions of Democrats, Republicans, and Independents are the same.

2. H_1: For at least one opinion, the proportions of Democrats, Republicans, and Independents are not the same.

3. $\alpha = 0.05$.

4. Critical region: $\chi^2 > 9.488$ with $v = 4$ degrees of freedom.

5. Computations: Using the expected cell frequency formula, we need to compute 4 cell frequencies. All other frequencies are found by subtraction. The observed and expected cell frequencies are displayed in Table 9.

Table 9: Observed and Expected Frequencies

Abortion Law	Political Affiliation			Total
	Democrat	**Republican**	**Independent**	
For	82 (85.6)	70 (64.2)	62 (64.2)	214
Against	93 (88.8)	62 (66.6)	67 (66.6)	222
Undecided	25 (25.6)	18 (19.2)	21 (19.2)	64
Total	200	150	150	500

Now,

$$\chi^2 = \frac{(82 - 85.6)^2}{85.6} + \frac{(70 - 64.2)^2}{64.2} + \frac{(62 - 64.2)^2}{64.2}$$
$$+ \frac{(93 - 88.8)^2}{88.8} + \frac{(62 - 66.6)^2}{66.6} + \frac{(67 - 66.6)^2}{66.6}$$
$$+ \frac{(25 - 25.6)^2}{25.6} + \frac{(18 - 19.2)^2}{19.2} + \frac{(21 - 19.2)^2}{19.2}$$
$$= 1.53.$$

6. Decision: Do not reject H_0. There is insufficient evidence to conclude that the proportions of Democrats, Republicans, and Independents differ for each stated opinion.

Testing for Several Proportions

The chi-squared statistic for testing for homogeneity is also applicable when testing the hypothesis that k binomial parameters have the same value. This is, therefore, an extension of the test presented in Section 9 for determining differences between two proportions to a test for determining differences among k proportions. Hence, we are interested in testing the null hypothesis

$$H_0 : \ p_1 = p_2 = \cdots = p_k$$

against the alternative hypothesis, H_1, that the population proportions are *not all equal*. To perform this test, we first observe independent random samples of size $n_1, n_2, \ldots, n_k$ from the k populations and arrange the data in a $2 \times k$ contingency table, Table 10.

Table 10: k Independent Binomial Samples

Sample:	1	2	$\cdots$	k
Successes	x_1	x_2	$\cdots$	x_k
Failures	$n_1 - x_1$	$n_2 - x_2$	$\cdots$	$n_k - x_k$

Depending on whether the sizes of the random samples were predetermined or occurred at random, the test procedure is identical to the test for homogeneity or the test for independence. Therefore, the expected cell frequencies are calculated as before and substituted, together with the observed frequencies, into the chi-squared statistic

$$\chi^2 = \sum_i \frac{(o_i - e_i)^2}{e_i},$$

with

$$v = (2 - 1)(k - 1) = k - 1$$

degrees of freedom.

By selecting the appropriate upper-tail critical region of the form $\chi^2 > \chi_\alpha^2$, we can now reach a decision concerning H_0.

Example 15: In a shop study, a set of data was collected to determine whether or not the proportion of defectives produced was the same for workers on the day, evening, and night shifts. The data collected are shown in Table 11.

Table 11: Data for Example 15

Shift:	Day	Evening	Night
Defectives	45	55	70
Nondefectives	905	890	870

Use a 0.025 level of significance to determine if the proportion of defectives is the same for all three shifts.

Solution: Let p_1, p_2, and p_3 represent the true proportions of defectives for the day, evening, and night shifts, respectively.

1. H_0: $p_1 = p_2 = p_3$.

2. H_1: p_1, p_2, and p_3 are not all equal.

3. $\alpha = 0.025$.

4. Critical region: $\chi^2 > 7.378$ for $v = 2$ degrees of freedom.

5. Computations: Corresponding to the observed frequencies $o_1 = 45$ and $o_2 = 55$, we find

$$e_1 = \frac{(950)(170)}{2835} = 57.0 \quad \text{and} \quad e_2 = \frac{(945)(170)}{2835} = 56.7.$$

All other expected frequencies are found by subtraction and are displayed in Table 12.

Table 12: Observed and Expected Frequencies

Shift:	Day	Evening	Night	Total
Defectives	45 (57.0)	55 (56.7)	70 (56.3)	170
Nondefectives	905 (893.0)	890 (888.3)	870 (883.7)	2665
Total	950	945	940	2835

Now

$$\chi^2 = \frac{(45-57.0)^2}{57.0} + \frac{(55-56.7)^2}{56.7} + \frac{(70-56.3)^2}{56.3}$$
$$+ \frac{(905-893.0)^2}{893.0} + \frac{(890-888.3)^2}{888.3} + \frac{(870-883.7)^2}{883.7} = 6.29,$$
$$P \approx 0.04.$$

6. Decision: We do not reject H_0 at $\alpha = 0.025$. Nevertheless, with the above P-value computed, it would certainly be dangerous to conclude that the proportion of defectives produced is the same for all shifts.

Often a complete study involving the use of statistical methods in hypothesis testing can be illustrated for the scientist or engineer using both test statistics, complete with P-values and statistical graphics. The graphics supplement the numerical diagnostics with pictures that show intuitively why the P-values appear as they do, as well as how reasonable (or not) the operative assumptions are.

14   Two-Sample Case Study

In this section, we consider a study involving a thorough graphical and formal analysis, along with annotated computer printout and conclusions. In a data analysis study conducted by personnel at the Statistics Consulting Center at Virginia Tech, two different materials, alloy A and alloy B, were compared in terms of breaking strength. Alloy B is more expensive, but it should certainly be adopted if it can be shown to be stronger than alloy A. The consistency of performance of the two alloys should also be taken into account.

Random samples of beams made from each alloy were selected, and strength was measured in units of 0.001-inch deflection as a fixed force was applied at both ends of the beam. Twenty specimens were used for each of the two alloys. The data are given in Table 13.

It is important that the engineer compare the two alloys. Of concern is average strength and reproducibility. It is of interest to determine if there is a severe

Table 13: Data for Two-Sample Case Study

Alloy A			Alloy B		
88	82	87	75	81	80
79	85	90	77	78	81
84	88	83	86	78	77
89	80	81	84	82	78
81	85		80	80	
83	87		78	76	
82	80		83	85	
79	78		76	79	

violation of the normality assumption required of both the t- and F-tests. Figures 21 and 22 are normal quantile-quantile plots of the samples of the two alloys.

There does not appear to be any serious violation of the normality assumption. In addition, Figure 23 shows two box-and-whisker plots on the same graph. The box-and-whisker plots suggest that there is no appreciable difference in the variability of deflection for the two alloys. However, it seems that the mean deflection for alloy B is significantly smaller, suggesting, at least graphically, that alloy B is stronger. The sample means and standard deviations are

$$\bar{y}_A = 83.55, \quad s_A = 3.663; \qquad \bar{y}_B = 79.70, \quad s_B = 3.097.$$

The *SAS* printout for the PROC TTEST is shown in Figure 24. The F-test suggests no significant difference in variances ($P = 0.4709$), and the two-sample t-statistic for testing

$$H_0\colon \ \mu_A = \mu_B,$$
$$H_1\colon \ \mu_A > \mu_B$$

($t = 3.59$, $P = 0.0009$) rejects H_0 in favor of H_1 and thus confirms what the graphical information suggests. Here we use the t-test that pools the two-sample variances together in light of the results of the F-test. On the basis of this analysis, the adoption of alloy B would seem to be in order.

Statistical Significance and Engineering or Scientific Significance

While the statistician may feel quite comfortable with the results of the comparison between the two alloys in the case study above, a dilemma remains for the engineer. The analysis demonstrated a statistically significant improvement with the use of alloy B. However, is the difference found really worth pursuing, since alloy B is more expensive? This illustration highlights a very important issue often overlooked by statisticians and data analysts—*the distinction between statistical significance and engineering or scientific significance*. Here the average difference in deflection is $\bar{y}_A - \bar{y}_B = 0.00385$ inch. In a complete analysis, the engineer must determine if the difference is sufficient to justify the extra cost in the long run. This is an economic and engineering issue. The reader should understand that a statistically significant difference merely implies that the difference in the sample

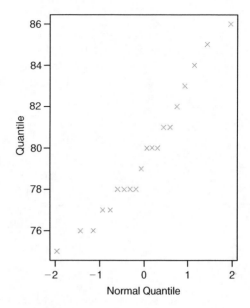

Figure 21: Normal quantile-quantile plot of data for alloy *A*.

Figure 22: Normal quantile-quantile plot of data for alloy *B*.

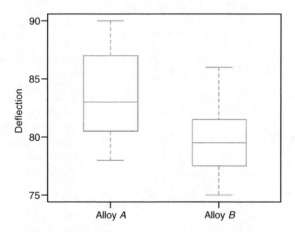

Figure 23: Box-and-whisker plots for both alloys.

means found in the data could hardly have occurred by chance. It does not imply that the difference in the population means is profound or particularly significant in the context of the problem. For example, in Section 4, an annotated computer printout was used to show evidence that a pH meter was, in fact, biased. That is, it does not demonstrate a mean pH of 7.00 for the material on which it was tested. But the variability among the observations in the sample is very small. The engineer may decide that the small deviations from 7.0 render the pH meter adequate.

	The TTEST Procedure			
Alloy	N	Mean	Std Dev	Std Err
Alloy A	20	83.55	3.6631	0.8191
Alloy B	20	79.7	3.0967	0.6924

Variances	DF	t Value	Pr > |t|
Equal	38	3.59	0.0009
Unequal	37	3.59	0.0010

Equality of Variances			
Num DF	Den DF	F Value	Pr > F
19	19	1.40	0.4709

Figure 24: Annotated *SAS* printout for alloy data.

Exercises

79 A machine is supposed to mix peanuts, hazelnuts, cashews, and pecans in the ratio 5:2:2:1. A can containing 500 of these mixed nuts was found to have 269 peanuts, 112 hazelnuts, 74 cashews, and 45 pecans. At the 0.05 level of significance, test the hypothesis that the machine is mixing the nuts in the ratio 5:2:2:1.

80 The grades in a statistics course for a particular semester were as follows:

Grade	A	B	C	D	F
f	14	18	32	20	16

Test the hypothesis, at the 0.05 level of significance, that the distribution of grades is uniform.

81 A die is tossed 180 times with the following results:

x	1	2	3	4	5	6
f	28	36	36	30	27	23

Is this a balanced die? Use a 0.01 level of significance.

82 Three marbles are selected from an urn containing 5 red marbles and 3 green marbles. After the number X of red marbles is recorded, the marbles are replaced in the urn and the experiment repeated 112 times. The results obtained are as follows:

x	0	1	2	3
f	1	31	55	25

Test the hypothesis, at the 0.05 level of significance, that the recorded data may be fitted by the hypergeometric distribution $h(x; 8, 3, 5)$, $x = 0, 1, 2, 3$.

83 A coin is thrown until a head occurs and the number X of tosses recorded. After repeating the experiment 256 times, we obtained the following results:

x	1	2	3	4	5	6	7	8
f	136	60	34	12	9	1	3	1

Test the hypothesis, at the 0.05 level of significance, that the observed distribution of X may be fitted by the geometric distribution $g(x; 1/2)$, $x = 1, 2, 3, \ldots$.

84 For chapter **Introduction to Statistics and Data Analysis** Exercise 18, test the goodness of fit between the observed class frequencies and the corresponding expected frequencies of a normal distribution with $\mu = 65$ and $\sigma = 21$, using a 0.01 level of significance.

85 For chapter **Introduction to Statistics and Data Analysis** Exercise 19, test the goodness of fit between the observed class frequencies and the corresponding expected frequencies of a normal distribution with $\mu = 1.8$ and $\sigma = 0.4$, using a 0.05 level of significance.

86 In an experiment to study the dependence of hypertension on smoking habits, the following data were taken on 180 individuals:

	Non-smokers	Moderate Smokers	Heavy Smokers
Hypertension	21	36	30
No hypertension	48	26	19

Test the hypothesis that the presence or absence of hypertension is independent of smoking habits. Use a 0.05 level of significance.

87 A random sample of 90 adults is classified according to gender and the number of hours of television watched during a week:

	Gender	
	Male	**Female**
Over 25 hours	15	29
Under 25 hours	27	19

Use a 0.01 level of significance and test the hypothesis that the time spent watching television is independent of whether the viewer is male or female.

88 A random sample of 200 married men, all retired, was classified according to education and number of children:

	Number of Children		
Education	**0–1**	**2–3**	**Over 3**
Elementary	14	37	32
Secondary	19	42	17
College	12	17	10

Test the hypothesis, at the 0.05 level of significance, that the size of a family is independent of the level of education attained by the father.

89 A criminologist conducted a survey to determine whether the incidence of certain types of crime varied from one part of a large city to another. The particular crimes of interest were assault, burglary, larceny, and homicide. The following table shows the numbers of crimes committed in four areas of the city during the past year.

	Type of Crime			
District	**Assault**	**Burglary**	**Larceny**	**Homicide**
1	162	118	451	18
2	310	196	996	25
3	258	193	458	10
4	280	175	390	19

Can we conclude from these data at the 0.01 level of significance that the occurrence of these types of crime is dependent on the city district?

90 According to a Johns Hopkins University study published in the *American Journal of Public Health*, widows live longer than widowers. Consider the following survival data collected on 100 widows and 100 widowers following the death of a spouse:

Years Lived	**Widow**	**Widower**
Less than 5	25	39
5 to 10	42	40
More than 10	33	21

Can we conclude at the 0.05 level of significance that the proportions of widows and widowers are equal with respect to the different time periods that a spouse survives after the death of his or her mate?

91 The following responses concerning the standard of living at the time of an independent opinion poll of 1000 households versus one year earlier seem to be in agreement with the results of a study published in *Across the Board* (June 1981):

	Standard of Living			
Period	**Somewhat Better**	**Same**	**Not as Good**	**Total**
1980: Jan.	72	144	84	300
May	63	135	102	300
Sept.	47	100	53	200
1981: Jan.	40	105	55	200

Test the hypothesis that the proportions of households within each standard of living category are the same for each of the four time periods. Use a *P*-value.

92 A college infirmary conducted an experiment to determine the degree of relief provided by three cough remedies. Each cough remedy was tried on 50 students and the following data recorded:

	Cough Remedy		
	NyQuil	**Robitussin**	**Triaminic**
No relief	11	13	9
Some relief	32	28	27
Total relief	7	9	14

Test the hypothesis that the three cough remedies are equally effective. Use a *P*-value in your conclusion.

93 To determine current attitudes about prayer in public schools, a survey was conducted in four Virginia counties. The following table gives the attitudes of 200 parents from Craig County, 150 parents from Giles County, 100 parents from Franklin County, and 100 parents from Montgomery County:

	County			
Attitude	**Craig**	**Giles**	**Franklin**	**Mont.**
Favor	65	66	40	34
Oppose	42	30	33	42
No opinion	93	54	27	24

Test for homogeneity of attitudes among the four counties concerning prayer in the public schools. Use a *P*-value in your conclusion.

94 A survey was conducted in Indiana, Kentucky, and Ohio to determine the attitude of voters concerning school busing. A poll of 200 voters from each of these states yielded the following results:

	Voter Attitude		
State	**Support**	**Do Not Support**	**Undecided**
Indiana	82	97	21
Kentucky	107	66	27
Ohio	93	74	33

At the 0.05 level of significance, test the null hypothesis that the proportions of voters within each attitude category are the same for each of the three states.

95 A survey was conducted in two Virginia cities to determine voter sentiment about two gubernatorial candidates in an upcoming election. Five hundred voters were randomly selected from each city and the following data were recorded:

Voter Sentiment	City	
	Richmond	Norfolk
Favor A	204	225
Favor B	211	198
Undecided	85	77

At the 0.05 level of significance, test the null hypothesis that proportions of voters favoring candidate A, favoring candidate B, and undecided are the same for each city.

96 In a study to estimate the proportion of wives who regularly watch soap operas, it is found that 52 of 200 wives in Denver, 31 of 150 wives in Phoenix, and 37 of 150 wives in Rochester watch at least one soap opera. Use a 0.05 level of significance to test the hypothesis that there is no difference among the true proportions of wives who watch soap operas in these three cities.

Review Exercises

97 State the null and alternative hypotheses to be used in testing the following claims and determine generally where the critical region is located:

(a) The mean snowfall at Lake George during the month of February is 21.8 centimeters.

(b) No more than 20% of the faculty at the local university contributed to the annual giving fund.

(c) On the average, children attend schools within 6.2 kilometers of their homes in suburban St. Louis.

(d) At least 70% of next year's new cars will be in the compact and subcompact category.

(e) The proportion of voters favoring the incumbent in the upcoming election is 0.58.

(f) The average rib-eye steak at the Longhorn Steak house weighs at least 340 grams.

98 A geneticist is interested in the proportions of males and females in a population who have a certain minor blood disorder. In a random sample of 100 males, 31 are found to be afflicted, whereas only 24 of 100 females tested have the disorder. Can we conclude at the 0.01 level of significance that the proportion of men in the population afflicted with this blood disorder is significantly greater than the proportion of women afflicted?

99 A study was made to determine whether more Italians than Americans prefer white champagne to pink champagne at weddings. Of the 300 Italians selected at random, 72 preferred white champagne, and of the 400 Americans selected, 70 preferred white champagne. Can we conclude that a higher proportion of Italians than Americans prefer white champagne at weddings? Use a 0.05 level of significance.

100 Consider the situation of Exercise 54. Oxygen consumption in mL/kg/min, was also measured.

Subject	With CO	Without CO
1	26.46	25.41
2	17.46	22.53
3	16.32	16.32
4	20.19	27.48
5	19.84	24.97
6	20.65	21.77
7	28.21	28.17
8	33.94	32.02
9	29.32	28.96

It is conjectured that oxygen consumption should be higher in an environment relatively free of CO. Do a significance test and discuss the conjecture.

101 In a study analyzed by the Statistics Consulting Center at Virginia Tech, a group of subjects was asked to complete a certain task on the computer. The response measured was the time to completion. The purpose of the experiment was to test a set of facilitation tools developed by the Department of Computer Science at the university. There were 10 subjects involved. With a random assignment, five were given a standard procedure using Fortran language for completion of the task. The other five were asked to do the task with the use of the facilitation tools. The data on the completion times for the task are given here.

Group 1 (Standard Procedure)	Group 2 (Facilitation Tool)
161	132
169	162
174	134
158	138
163	133

Assuming that the population distributions are normal and variances are the same for the two groups, support or refute the conjecture that the facilitation tools increase the speed with which the task can be accomplished.

102 State the null and alternative hypotheses to be used in testing the following claims, and determine generally where the critical region is located:

(a) At most, 20% of next year's wheat crop will be exported to the Soviet Union.

(b) On the average, American homemakers drink 3 cups of coffee per day.

(c) The proportion of college graduates in Virginia this year who majored in the social sciences is at least 0.15.

(d) The average donation to the American Lung Association is no more than $10.

(e) Residents in suburban Richmond commute, on the average, 15 kilometers to their place of employment.

103 If one can containing 500 nuts is selected at random from each of three different distributors of mixed nuts and there are, respectively, 345, 313, and 359 peanuts in each of the cans, can we conclude at the 0.01 level of significance that the mixed nuts of the three distributors contain equal proportions of peanuts?

104 A study was made to determine whether there is a difference between the proportions of parents in the states of Maryland (MD), Virginia (VA), Georgia (GA), and Alabama (AL) who favor placing Bibles in the elementary schools. The responses of 100 parents selected at random in each of these states are recorded in the following table:

	State			
Preference	MD	VA	GA	AL
Yes	65	71	78	82
No	35	29	22	18

Can we conclude that the proportions of parents who favor placing Bibles in the schools are the same for these four states? Use a 0.01 level of significance.

105 A study was conducted at the Virginia-Maryland Regional College of Veterinary Medicine Equine Center to determine if the performance of a certain type of surgery on young horses had any effect on certain kinds of blood cell types in the animal. Fluid samples were taken from each of six foals before and after surgery. The samples were analyzed for the number of postoperative white blood cell (WBC) leukocytes. A preoperative measure of WBC leukocytes was also measured. The data are given as follows:

Foal	Presurgery*	Postsurgery*
1	10.80	10.60
2	12.90	16.60
3	9.59	17.20
4	8.81	14.00
5	12.00	10.60
6	6.07	8.60

*All values $\times 10^{-3}$.

Use a paired sample t-test to determine if there is a sig-

nificant change in WBC leukocytes with the surgery.

106 A study was conducted at the Department of Health and Physical Education at Virginia Tech to determine if 8 weeks of training truly reduces the cholesterol levels of the participants. A treatment group consisting of 15 people was given lectures twice a week on how to reduce cholesterol level. Another group of 18 people of similar age was randomly selected as a control group. All participants' cholesterol levels were recorded at the end of the 8-week program and are listed below.

```
Treatment:
    129 131 154 172 115 126 175 191
    122 238 159 156 176 175 126
Control:
    151 132 196 195 188 198 187 168 115
    165 137 208 133 217 191 193 140 146
```

Can we conclude, at the 5% level of significance, that the average cholesterol level has been reduced due to the program? Make the appropriate test on means.

107 In a study conducted by the Department of Mechanical Engineering and analyzed by the Statistics Consulting Center at Virginia Tech, steel rods supplied by two different companies were compared. Ten sample springs were made out of the steel rods supplied by each company, and the "bounciness" was studied. The data are as follows:

```
Company A:
 9.3 8.8 6.8  8.7  8.5 6.7  8.0  6.5  9.2 7.0
Company B:
11.0 9.8 9.9 10.2 10.1 9.7 11.0 11.1 10.2 9.6
```

Can you conclude that there is virtually no difference in means between the steel rods supplied by the two companies? Use a P-value to reach your conclusion. Should variances be pooled here?

108 In a study conducted by the Water Resources Center and analyzed by the Statistics Consulting Center at Virginia Tech, two different wastewater treatment plants are compared. Plant A is located where the median household income is below $22,000 a year, and plant B is located where the median household income is above $60,000 a year. The amount of wastewater treated at each plant (thousands of gallons/day) was randomly sampled for 10 days. The data are as follows:

```
Plant A:
21 19 20 23 22 28 32 19 13 18

Plant B:
20 39 24 33 30 28 30 22 33 24
```

Can we conclude, at the 5% level of significance, that

the average amount of wastewater treated at the plant in the high-income neighborhood is more than that treated at the plant in the low-income area? Assume normality.

109 The following data show the numbers of defects in 100,000 lines of code in a particular type of software program developed in the United States and Japan. Is there enough evidence to claim that there is a significant difference between the programs developed in the two countries? Test on means. Should variances be pooled?

U.S.	48	39	42	52	40	48	52	52
	54	48	52	55	43	46	48	52
Japan	50	48	42	40	43	48	50	46
	38	38	36	40	40	48	48	45

110 Studies show that the concentration of PCBs is much higher in malignant breast tissue than in normal breast tissue. If a study of 50 women with breast cancer reveals an average PCB concentration of 22.8×10^{-4} gram, with a standard deviation of 4.8×10^{-4} gram, is the mean concentration of PCBs less than 24×10^{-4} gram?

111 **z-Value for Testing $p_1 - p_2 = d_0$:** To test the null hypothesis H_0 that $p_1 - p_2 = d_0$, where $d_0 \neq 0$, we base our decision on

$$z = \frac{\hat{p}_1 - \hat{p}_2 - d_0}{\sqrt{\hat{p}_1 \hat{q}_1/n_1 + \hat{p}_2 \hat{q}_2/n_2}},$$

which is a value of a random variable whose distribution approximates the standard normal distribution as long as n_1 and n_2 are both large. With reference to Example 11, test the hypothesis that the percentage of town voters favoring the construction of the chemical plant will not exceed the percentage of county voters by more than 3%. Use a P-value in your conclusion.

15   Potential Misconceptions and Hazards

One of the easiest ways to misuse statistics relates to the final scientific conclusion drawn when the analyst does not reject the null hypothesis H_0. We have attempted to make clear what the null hypothesis means and what the alternative means, and to stress that, in a large sense, the alternative hypothesis is much more important. Put in the form of an example, if an engineer is attempting to compare two gauges using a two-sample t-test, and H_0 is "the gauges are equivalent" while H_1 is "the gauges are not equivalent," not rejecting H_0 does not lead to the conclusion of equivalent gauges. In fact, a case can be made for never writing or saying "accept H_0"! Not rejecting H_0 merely implies insufficient evidence. Depending on the nature of the hypothesis, a lot of possibilities are still not ruled out.

In chapter **One- and Two-Sample Estimation Problems,** we considered the case of the large-sample confidence interval using

$$z = \frac{\bar{x} - \mu}{s/\sqrt{n}}.$$

In hypothesis testing, replacing σ by s for $n < 30$ is risky. If $n \geq 30$ and the distribution is not normal but somehow close to normal, the Central Limit Theorem is being called upon and one is relying on the fact that with $n \geq 30$, $s \approx \sigma$. Of course, any t-test is accompanied by the concomitant assumption of normality. As in the case of confidence intervals, the t-test is relatively robust to normality. However, one should still use normal probability plotting, goodness-of-fit tests, or other graphical procedures when the sample is not too small.

The topics of estimation and hypothesis testing are both used in a major way in nearly all of the techniques that fall under the umbrella of "statistical methods." As far as material in this chapter is concerned, the framework of hypothesis testing, *P*-values, power of tests, and choice of sample size will collectively play a major role. Since initial model formulation quite often must be supplemented by model editing before the analyst is sufficiently comfortable to use the model for either process understanding or prediction.

Answers to Odd-Numbered Non-Review Exercises

1 (a) Conclude that less than 30% of the public is allergic to some cheese products when, in fact, 30% or more is allergic.

   (b) Conclude that at least 30% of the public is allergic to some cheese products when, in fact, less than 30% is allergic.

3 (a) The firm is not guilty;

   (b) the firm is guilty.

5 (a) 0.0559;

   (b) $\beta = 0.0017$; $\beta = 0.00968$; $\beta = 0.5557$

7 (a) 0.1286;

   (b) $\beta = 0.0901$; $\beta = 0.0708$.

   (c) The probability of a type I error is somewhat large.

9 (a) $\alpha = 0.0850$; (b) $\beta = 0.3410$

11 (a) $\alpha = 0.1357$; (b) $\beta = 0.2578$

13 $\alpha = 0.0094$; $\beta = 0.0122$

15 (a) $\alpha = 0.0718$; (b) $\beta = 0.1151$

17 (a) $\alpha = 0.0384$; (b) $\beta = 0.5$; $\beta = 0.2776$

19 $z = -2.76$; yes, $\mu < 40$ months; P-value $= 0.0029$

21 $z = -1.64$; P-value $= 0.10$

23 $t = 0.77$; fail to reject H_0.

25 $z = 8.97$; yes, $\mu > 20,000$ kilometers; P-value < 0.001

27 $t = 12.72$; P-value < 0.0005; reject H_0.

29 $t = -1.98$; P-value $= 0.0312$; reject H_0

31 $z = -2.60$; conclude $\mu_A - \mu_B \le 12$ kilograms.

33 $t = 1.50$; there is not sufficient evidence to conclude that the increase in substrate concentration would cause an increase in the mean velocity of more than 0.5 micromole per 30 minutes.

35 $t = 0.70$; there is not sufficient evidence to support the conclusion that the serum is effective.

37 $t = 2.55$; reject H_0: $\mu_1 - \mu_2 > 4$ kilometers.

39 $t' = 0.22$; fail to reject H_0.

41 $t' = 2.76$; reject H_0.

43 $t = -2.53$; reject H_0; the claim is valid.

45 $t = 2.48$; P-value < 0.02; reject H_0.

47 $n = 6$

49 $78.28 \approx 79$

51 5

53 (a) H_0: $M_{\text{hot}} - M_{\text{cold}} = 0$,
        H_1: $M_{\text{hot}} - M_{\text{cold}} \ne 0$;

   (b) paired t, $t = 0.99$; P-value > 0.30; fail to reject H_0.

55   P-value $= 0.4044$ (with a one-tailed test); the claim is not refuted.

57    $z = 1.44$; fail to reject H_0.

59    $z = -5.06$ with P-value ≈ 0; conclude that fewer than one-fifth of the homes are heated by oil.

61    $z = 0.93$ with P-value $= P(Z > 0.93) = 0.1762$; there is not sufficient evidence to conclude that the new medicine is effective.

63    $z = 2.36$ with P-value $= 0.0182$; yes, the difference is significant.

65    $z = 1.10$ with P-value $= 0.1357$; we do not have sufficient evidence to conclude that breast cancer is more prevalent in the urban community.

67    $\chi^2 = 18.13$ with P-value $= 0.0676$ (from computer output); do not reject H_0: $\sigma^2 = 0.03$.

69    $\chi^2 = 63.75$ with P-value $= 0.8998$ (from computer output); do not reject H_0.

71    $\chi^2 = 42.37$ with P-value $= 0.0117$ (from computer output); machine is out of control.

73    $f = 1.33$ with P-value $= 0.3095$ (from computer output); fail to reject H_0: $\sigma_1 = \sigma_2$.

75    $f = 0.086$ with P-value $= 0.0328$ (from computer output); reject H_0: $\sigma_1 = \sigma_2$ at level greater than 0.0328.

77    $f = 19.67$ with P-value $= 0.0008$ (from computer output); reject H_0: $\sigma_1 = \sigma_2$.

79    $\chi^2 = 10.14$; reject H_0, the ratio is not 5:2:2:1.

81    $\chi^2 = 4.47$; there is not sufficient evidence to claim that the die is unbalanced.

83    $\chi^2 = 3.125$; do not reject H_0: geometric distribution.

85    $\chi^2 = 5.19$; do not reject H_0: normal distribution.

87    $\chi^2 = 5.47$; do not reject H_0.

89    $\chi^2 = 124.59$; yes, occurrence of these types of crime is dependent on the city district.

91    $\chi^2 = 5.92$ with P-value $= 0.4332$; do not reject H_0.

93    $\chi^2 = 31.17$ with P-value < 0.0001; attitudes are not homogeneous.

95    $\chi^2 = 1.84$; do not reject H_0.

Table Areas under the Normal Curve

z	.00	.01	.02	.03	.04	.05	.06	.07	.08	.09
−3.4	0.0003	0.0003	0.0003	0.0003	0.0003	0.0003	0.0003	0.0003	0.0003	0.0002
−3.3	0.0005	0.0005	0.0005	0.0004	0.0004	0.0004	0.0004	0.0004	0.0004	0.0003
−3.2	0.0007	0.0007	0.0006	0.0006	0.0006	0.0006	0.0006	0.0005	0.0005	0.0005
−3.1	0.0010	0.0009	0.0009	0.0009	0.0008	0.0008	0.0008	0.0008	0.0007	0.0007
−3.0	0.0013	0.0013	0.0013	0.0012	0.0012	0.0011	0.0011	0.0011	0.0010	0.0010
−2.9	0.0019	0.0018	0.0018	0.0017	0.0016	0.0016	0.0015	0.0015	0.0014	0.0014
−2.8	0.0026	0.0025	0.0024	0.0023	0.0023	0.0022	0.0021	0.0021	0.0020	0.0019
−2.7	0.0035	0.0034	0.0033	0.0032	0.0031	0.0030	0.0029	0.0028	0.0027	0.0026
−2.6	0.0047	0.0045	0.0044	0.0043	0.0041	0.0040	0.0039	0.0038	0.0037	0.0036
−2.5	0.0062	0.0060	0.0059	0.0057	0.0055	0.0054	0.0052	0.0051	0.0049	0.0048
−2.4	0.0082	0.0080	0.0078	0.0075	0.0073	0.0071	0.0069	0.0068	0.0066	0.0064
−2.3	0.0107	0.0104	0.0102	0.0099	0.0096	0.0094	0.0091	0.0089	0.0087	0.0084
−2.2	0.0139	0.0136	0.0132	0.0129	0.0125	0.0122	0.0119	0.0116	0.0113	0.0110
−2.1	0.0179	0.0174	0.0170	0.0166	0.0162	0.0158	0.0154	0.0150	0.0146	0.0143
−2.0	0.0228	0.0222	0.0217	0.0212	0.0207	0.0202	0.0197	0.0192	0.0188	0.0183
−1.9	0.0287	0.0281	0.0274	0.0268	0.0262	0.0256	0.0250	0.0244	0.0239	0.0233
−1.8	0.0359	0.0351	0.0344	0.0336	0.0329	0.0322	0.0314	0.0307	0.0301	0.0294
−1.7	0.0446	0.0436	0.0427	0.0418	0.0409	0.0401	0.0392	0.0384	0.0375	0.0367
−1.6	0.0548	0.0537	0.0526	0.0516	0.0505	0.0495	0.0485	0.0475	0.0465	0.0455
−1.5	0.0668	0.0655	0.0643	0.0630	0.0618	0.0606	0.0594	0.0582	0.0571	0.0559
−1.4	0.0808	0.0793	0.0778	0.0764	0.0749	0.0735	0.0721	0.0708	0.0694	0.0681
−1.3	0.0968	0.0951	0.0934	0.0918	0.0901	0.0885	0.0869	0.0853	0.0838	0.0823
−1.2	0.1151	0.1131	0.1112	0.1093	0.1075	0.1056	0.1038	0.1020	0.1003	0.0985
−1.1	0.1357	0.1335	0.1314	0.1292	0.1271	0.1251	0.1230	0.1210	0.1190	0.1170
−1.0	0.1587	0.1562	0.1539	0.1515	0.1492	0.1469	0.1446	0.1423	0.1401	0.1379
−0.9	0.1841	0.1814	0.1788	0.1762	0.1736	0.1711	0.1685	0.1660	0.1635	0.1611
−0.8	0.2119	0.2090	0.2061	0.2033	0.2005	0.1977	0.1949	0.1922	0.1894	0.1867
−0.7	0.2420	0.2389	0.2358	0.2327	0.2296	0.2266	0.2236	0.2206	0.2177	0.2148
−0.6	0.2743	0.2709	0.2676	0.2643	0.2611	0.2578	0.2546	0.2514	0.2483	0.2451
−0.5	0.3085	0.3050	0.3015	0.2981	0.2946	0.2912	0.2877	0.2843	0.2810	0.2776
−0.4	0.3446	0.3409	0.3372	0.3336	0.3300	0.3264	0.3228	0.3192	0.3156	0.3121
−0.3	0.3821	0.3783	0.3745	0.3707	0.3669	0.3632	0.3594	0.3557	0.3520	0.3483
−0.2	0.4207	0.4168	0.4129	0.4090	0.4052	0.4013	0.3974	0.3936	0.3897	0.3859
−0.1	0.4602	0.4562	0.4522	0.4483	0.4443	0.4404	0.4364	0.4325	0.4286	0.4247
−0.0	0.5000	0.4960	0.4920	0.4880	0.4840	0.4801	0.4761	0.4721	0.4681	0.4641

Table (continued) Areas under the Normal Curve

z	.00	.01	.02	.03	.04	.05	.06	.07	.08	.09
0.0	0.5000	0.5040	0.5080	0.5120	0.5160	0.5199	0.5239	0.5279	0.5319	0.5359
0.1	0.5398	0.5438	0.5478	0.5517	0.5557	0.5596	0.5636	0.5675	0.5714	0.5753
0.2	0.5793	0.5832	0.5871	0.5910	0.5948	0.5987	0.6026	0.6064	0.6103	0.6141
0.3	0.6179	0.6217	0.6255	0.6293	0.6331	0.6368	0.6406	0.6443	0.6480	0.6517
0.4	0.6554	0.6591	0.6628	0.6664	0.6700	0.6736	0.6772	0.6808	0.6844	0.6879
0.5	0.6915	0.6950	0.6985	0.7019	0.7054	0.7088	0.7123	0.7157	0.7190	0.7224
0.6	0.7257	0.7291	0.7324	0.7357	0.7389	0.7422	0.7454	0.7486	0.7517	0.7549
0.7	0.7580	0.7611	0.7642	0.7673	0.7704	0.7734	0.7764	0.7794	0.7823	0.7852
0.8	0.7881	0.7910	0.7939	0.7967	0.7995	0.8023	0.8051	0.8078	0.8106	0.8133
0.9	0.8159	0.8186	0.8212	0.8238	0.8264	0.8289	0.8315	0.8340	0.8365	0.8389
1.0	0.8413	0.8438	0.8461	0.8485	0.8508	0.8531	0.8554	0.8577	0.8599	0.8621
1.1	0.8643	0.8665	0.8686	0.8708	0.8729	0.8749	0.8770	0.8790	0.8810	0.8830
1.2	0.8849	0.8869	0.8888	0.8907	0.8925	0.8944	0.8962	0.8980	0.8997	0.9015
1.3	0.9032	0.9049	0.9066	0.9082	0.9099	0.9115	0.9131	0.9147	0.9162	0.9177
1.4	0.9192	0.9207	0.9222	0.9236	0.9251	0.9265	0.9279	0.9292	0.9306	0.9319
1.5	0.9332	0.9345	0.9357	0.9370	0.9382	0.9394	0.9406	0.9418	0.9429	0.9441
1.6	0.9452	0.9463	0.9474	0.9484	0.9495	0.9505	0.9515	0.9525	0.9535	0.9545
1.7	0.9554	0.9564	0.9573	0.9582	0.9591	0.9599	0.9608	0.9616	0.9625	0.9633
1.8	0.9641	0.9649	0.9656	0.9664	0.9671	0.9678	0.9686	0.9693	0.9699	0.9706
1.9	0.9713	0.9719	0.9726	0.9732	0.9738	0.9744	0.9750	0.9756	0.9761	0.9767
2.0	0.9772	0.9778	0.9783	0.9788	0.9793	0.9798	0.9803	0.9808	0.9812	0.9817
2.1	0.9821	0.9826	0.9830	0.9834	0.9838	0.9842	0.9846	0.9850	0.9854	0.9857
2.2	0.9861	0.9864	0.9868	0.9871	0.9875	0.9878	0.9881	0.9884	0.9887	0.9890
2.3	0.9893	0.9896	0.9898	0.9901	0.9904	0.9906	0.9909	0.9911	0.9913	0.9916
2.4	0.9918	0.9920	0.9922	0.9925	0.9927	0.9929	0.9931	0.9932	0.9934	0.9936
2.5	0.9938	0.9940	0.9941	0.9943	0.9945	0.9946	0.9948	0.9949	0.9951	0.9952
2.6	0.9953	0.9955	0.9956	0.9957	0.9959	0.9960	0.9961	0.9962	0.9963	0.9964
2.7	0.9965	0.9966	0.9967	0.9968	0.9969	0.9970	0.9971	0.9972	0.9973	0.9974
2.8	0.9974	0.9975	0.9976	0.9977	0.9977	0.9978	0.9979	0.9979	0.9980	0.9981
2.9	0.9981	0.9982	0.9982	0.9983	0.9984	0.9984	0.9985	0.9985	0.9986	0.9986
3.0	0.9987	0.9987	0.9987	0.9988	0.9988	0.9989	0.9989	0.9989	0.9990	0.9990
3.1	0.9990	0.9991	0.9991	0.9991	0.9992	0.9992	0.9992	0.9992	0.9993	0.9993
3.2	0.9993	0.9993	0.9994	0.9994	0.9994	0.9994	0.9994	0.9995	0.9995	0.9995
3.3	0.9995	0.9995	0.9995	0.9996	0.9996	0.9996	0.9996	0.9996	0.9996	0.9997
3.4	0.9997	0.9997	0.9997	0.9997	0.9997	0.9997	0.9997	0.9997	0.9997	0.9998

Table Sample Size for the t-Test of the Mean

Level of t-Test

Value of $\Delta = \lvert\delta\rvert/\sigma$	Single-Sided $\alpha = 0.005$ / Double-Sided $\alpha = 0.01$					Single $\alpha = 0.01$ / Double $\alpha = 0.02$					Single $\alpha = 0.025$ / Double $\alpha = 0.05$					Single $\alpha = 0.05$ / Double $\alpha = 0.1$				
$\beta = 0.1$	.01	.05	.1	.2	.5	.01	.05	.1	.2	.5	.01	.05	.1	.2	.5	.01	.05	.1	.2	.5
0.05																				
0.10																				
0.15																				122
0.20										139					99					70
0.25					110					90				128	64			139	101	45
0.30				134	78				115	63			119	90	45		122	97	71	32
0.35			125	99	58			109	85	47		109	88	67	34		90	72	52	24
0.40		115	97	77	45		101	85	66	37	117	84	68	51	26	101	70	55	40	19
0.45		92	77	62	37	110	81	68	53	30	93	67	54	41	21	80	55	44	33	15
0.50	100	75	63	51	30	90	66	55	43	25	76	54	44	34	18	65	45	36	27	13
0.55	83	63	53	42	26	75	55	46	36	21	63	45	37	28	15	54	38	30	22	11
0.60	71	53	45	36	22	63	47	39	31	18	53	38	32	24	13	46	32	26	19	9
0.65	61	46	39	31	20	55	41	34	27	16	46	33	27	21	12	39	28	22	17	8
0.70	53	40	34	28	17	47	35	30	24	14	40	29	24	19	10	34	24	19	15	8
0.75	47	36	30	25	16	42	31	27	21	13	35	26	21	16	9	30	21	17	13	7
0.80	41	32	27	22	14	37	28	24	19	12	31	22	19	15	9	27	19	15	12	6
0.85	37	29	24	20	13	33	25	21	17	11	28	21	17	13	8	24	17	14	11	6
0.90	34	26	22	18	12	29	23	19	16	10	25	19	16	12	7	21	15	13	10	5
0.95	31	24	20	17	11	27	21	18	14	9	23	17	14	11	7	19	14	11	9	5
1.00	28	22	19	16	10	25	19	16	13	9	21	16	13	10	6	18	13	11	8	5
1.1	24	19	16	14	9	21	16	14	12	8	18	13	11	9	6	15	11	9	7	
1.2	21	16	14	12	8	18	14	12	10	7	15	12	10	8	5	13	10	8	6	
1.3	18	15	13	11	8	16	13	11	9	6	14	10	9	7		11	8	7	6	
1.4	16	13	12	10	7	14	11	10	9	6	12	9	8	7		10	8	7	5	
1.5	15	12	11	9	7	13	10	9	8	6	11	8	7	6		9	7	6		
1.6	13	11	10	8	6	12	10	9	7	5	10	8	7	6		8	6	6		
1.7	12	10	9	8	6	11	9	8	7		9	7	6	5		8	6	5		
1.8	12	10	9	8	6	10	8	7	7		8	7	6			7	6			
1.9	11	9	8	7	6	10	8	7	6		8	6	6			7	5			
2.0	10	8	8	7	5	9	7	7	6		7	6	5			6				
2.1	10	8	7	7		8	7	6	6		7	6				6				
2.2	9	8	7	6		8	7	6	5		7	6				6				
2.3	9	7	7	6		8	6	6			6	5				5				
2.4	8	7	7	6		7	6	6			6									
2.5	8	7	6	6		7	6	6			6									
3.0	7	6	6	5		6	5	5			5									
3.5	6	5	5			5														
4.0	6																			

Reproduced with permission from O. L. Davies, ed., *Design and Analysis of Industrial Experiments*, Oliver & Boyd, Edinburgh, 1956.

Table Sample Size for the *t*-Test of the Difference between Two Means

	Level of *t*-Test																			
Single-Sided Test	$\alpha=0.005$					$\alpha=0.01$					$\alpha=0.025$					$\alpha=0.05$				
Double-Sided Test	$\alpha=0.01$					$\alpha=0.02$					$\alpha=0.05$					$\alpha=0.1$				
$\beta=0.1$	.01	.05	.1	.2	.5	.01	.05	.1	.2	.5	.01	.05	.1	.2	.5	.01	.05	.1	.2	.5
0.05																				
0.10																				
0.15																				
0.20																				137
0.25															124					88
0.30										123					87					61
0.35			110							90					64				102	45
0.40			85							70				100	50			108	78	35
0.45				118	68				101	55			105	79	39		108	86	62	28
0.50				96	55			106	82	45		106	86	64	32		88	70	51	23
0.55			101	79	46		106	88	68	38		87	71	53	27	112	73	58	42	19
0.60		101	85	67	39		90	74	58	32	104	74	60	45	23	89	61	49	36	16
0.65		87	73	57	34	104	77	64	49	27	88	63	51	39	20	76	52	42	30	14
0.70	100	75	63	50	29	90	66	55	43	24	76	55	44	34	17	66	45	36	26	12
0.75	88	66	55	44	26	79	58	48	38	21	67	48	39	29	15	57	40	32	23	11
0.80	77	58	49	39	23	70	51	43	33	19	59	42	34	26	14	50	35	28	21	10
0.85	69	51	43	35	21	62	46	38	30	17	52	37	31	23	12	45	31	25	18	9
0.90	62	46	39	31	19	55	41	34	27	15	47	34	27	21	11	40	28	22	16	8
0.95	55	42	35	28	17	50	37	31	24	14	42	30	25	19	10	36	25	20	15	7
1.00	50	38	32	26	15	45	33	28	22	13	38	27	23	17	9	33	23	18	14	7
1.1	42	32	27	22	13	38	28	23	19	11	32	23	19	14	8	27	19	15	12	6
1.2	36	27	23	18	11	32	24	20	16	9	27	20	16	12	7	23	16	13	10	5
1.3	31	23	20	16	10	28	21	17	14	8	23	17	14	11	6	20	14	11	9	5
1.4	27	20	17	14	9	24	18	15	12	8	20	15	12	10	6	17	12	10	8	4
1.5	24	18	15	13	8	21	16	14	11	7	18	13	11	9	5	15	11	9	7	4
1.6	21	16	14	11	7	19	14	12	10	6	16	12	10	8	5	14	10	8	6	4
1.7	19	15	13	10	7	17	13	11	9	6	14	11	9	7	4	12	9	7	6	3
1.8	17	13	71	10	6	15	12	10	8	5	13	10	8	6	4	11	8	7	5	
1.9	16	12	11	9	6	14	11	9	8	5	12	9	7	6	4	10	7	6	5	
2.0	14	11	10	8	6	13	10	9	7	5	11	8	7	6	4	9	7	6	4	
2.1	13	10	9	8	5	12	9	8	7	5	10	8	6	5	3	8	6	5	4	
2.2	12	10	8	7	5	11	9	7	6	4	9	7	6	5		8	6	5	4	
2.3	11	9	8	7	5	10	8	7	6	4	9	7	6	5		7	5	5	4	
2.4	11	9	8	6	5	10	8	7	6	4	8	6	5	4		7	5	4	4	
2.5	10	8	7	6	4	9	7	6	5	4	8	6	5	4		6	5	4	3	
3.0	8	6	6	5	4	7	6	5	4	3	6	5	4	4		5	4	3		
3.5	6	5	5	4	3	6	5	4	4		5	4	4	3	3	4	3			
4.0	6	5	4	4		5	4	4	3		4	4	3			4				

Value of $\Delta = |\delta|/\sigma$

Reproduced with permission from O. L. Davies, ed., *Design and Analysis of Industrial Experiments*, Oliver & Boyd, Edinburgh, 1956.

Table Binomial Probability Sums $\sum_{x=0}^{r} b(x; n, p)$

						p					
n	r	**0.10**	**0.20**	**0.25**	**0.30**	**0.40**	**0.50**	**0.60**	**0.70**	**0.80**	**0.90**
1	0	0.9000	0.8000	0.7500	0.7000	0.6000	0.5000	0.4000	0.3000	0.2000	0.1000
	1	1.0000	1.0000	1.0000	1.0000	1.0000	1.0000	1.0000	1.0000	1.0000	1.0000
2	0	0.8100	0.6400	0.5625	0.4900	0.3600	0.2500	0.1600	0.0900	0.0400	0.0100
	1	0.9900	0.9600	0.9375	0.9100	0.8400	0.7500	0.6400	0.5100	0.3600	0.1900
	2	1.0000	1.0000	1.0000	1.0000	1.0000	1.0000	1.0000	1.0000	1.0000	1.0000
3	0	0.7290	0.5120	0.4219	0.3430	0.2160	0.1250	0.0640	0.0270	0.0080	0.0010
	1	0.9720	0.8960	0.8438	0.7840	0.6480	0.5000	0.3520	0.2160	0.1040	0.0280
	2	0.9990	0.9920	0.9844	0.9730	0.9360	0.8750	0.7840	0.6570	0.4880	0.2710
	3	1.0000	1.0000	1.0000	1.0000	1.0000	1.0000	1.0000	1.0000	1.0000	1.0000
4	0	0.6561	0.4096	0.3164	0.2401	0.1296	0.0625	0.0256	0.0081	0.0016	0.0001
	1	0.9477	0.8192	0.7383	0.6517	0.4752	0.3125	0.1792	0.0837	0.0272	0.0037
	2	0.9963	0.9728	0.9492	0.9163	0.8208	0.6875	0.5248	0.3483	0.1808	0.0523
	3	0.9999	0.9984	0.9961	0.9919	0.9744	0.9375	0.8704	0.7599	0.5904	0.3439
	4	1.0000	1.0000	1.0000	1.0000	1.0000	1.0000	1.0000	1.0000	1.0000	1.0000
5	0	0.5905	0.3277	0.2373	0.1681	0.0778	0.0313	0.0102	0.0024	0.0003	0.0000
	1	0.9185	0.7373	0.6328	0.5282	0.3370	0.1875	0.0870	0.0308	0.0067	0.0005
	2	0.9914	0.9421	0.8965	0.8369	0.6826	0.5000	0.3174	0.1631	0.0579	0.0086
	3	0.9995	0.9933	0.9844	0.9692	0.9130	0.8125	0.6630	0.4718	0.2627	0.0815
	4	1.0000	0.9997	0.9990	0.9976	0.9898	0.9688	0.9222	0.8319	0.6723	0.4095
	5	1.0000	1.0000	1.0000	1.0000	1.0000	1.0000	1.0000	1.0000	1.0000	1.0000
6	0	0.5314	0.2621	0.1780	0.1176	0.0467	0.0156	0.0041	0.0007	0.0001	0.0000
	1	0.8857	0.6554	0.5339	0.4202	0.2333	0.1094	0.0410	0.0109	0.0016	0.0001
	2	0.9842	0.9011	0.8306	0.7443	0.5443	0.3438	0.1792	0.0705	0.0170	0.0013
	3	0.9987	0.9830	0.9624	0.9295	0.8208	0.6563	0.4557	0.2557	0.0989	0.0159
	4	0.9999	0.9984	0.9954	0.9891	0.9590	0.8906	0.7667	0.5798	0.3446	0.1143
	5	1.0000	0.9999	0.9998	0.9993	0.9959	0.9844	0.9533	0.8824	0.7379	0.4686
	6	1.0000	1.0000	1.0000	1.0000	1.0000	1.0000	1.0000	1.0000	1.0000	1.0000
7	0	0.4783	0.2097	0.1335	0.0824	0.0280	0.0078	0.0016	0.0002	0.0000	
	1	0.8503	0.5767	0.4449	0.3294	0.1586	0.0625	0.0188	0.0038	0.0004	0.0000
	2	0.9743	0.8520	0.7564	0.6471	0.4199	0.2266	0.0963	0.0288	0.0047	0.0002
	3	0.9973	0.9667	0.9294	0.8740	0.7102	0.5000	0.2898	0.1260	0.0333	0.0027
	4	0.9998	0.9953	0.9871	0.9712	0.9037	0.7734	0.5801	0.3529	0.1480	0.0257
	5	1.0000	0.9996	0.9987	0.9962	0.9812	0.9375	0.8414	0.6706	0.4233	0.1497
	6		1.0000	0.9999	0.9998	0.9984	0.9922	0.9720	0.9176	0.7903	0.5217
	7			1.0000	1.0000	1.0000	1.0000	1.0000	1.0000	1.0000	1.0000

Table (continued) Binomial Probability Sums $\sum_{x=0}^{r} b(x; n, p)$

						p					
n	r	0.10	0.20	0.25	0.30	0.40	0.50	0.60	0.70	0.80	0.90
8	0	0.4305	0.1678	0.1001	0.0576	0.0168	0.0039	0.0007	0.0001	0.0000	
	1	0.8131	0.5033	0.3671	0.2553	0.1064	0.0352	0.0085	0.0013	0.0001	
	2	0.9619	0.7969	0.6785	0.5518	0.3154	0.1445	0.0498	0.0113	0.0012	0.0000
	3	0.9950	0.9437	0.8862	0.8059	0.5941	0.3633	0.1737	0.0580	0.0104	0.0004
	4	0.9996	0.9896	0.9727	0.9420	0.8263	0.6367	0.4059	0.1941	0.0563	0.0050
	5	1.0000	0.9988	0.9958	0.9887	0.9502	0.8555	0.6846	0.4482	0.2031	0.0381
	6		0.9999	0.9996	0.9987	0.9915	0.9648	0.8936	0.7447	0.4967	0.1869
	7		1.0000	1.0000	0.9999	0.9993	0.9961	0.9832	0.9424	0.8322	0.5695
	8				1.0000	1.0000	1.0000	1.0000	1.0000	1.0000	1.0000
9	0	0.3874	0.1342	0.0751	0.0404	0.0101	0.0020	0.0003	0.0000		
	1	0.7748	0.4362	0.3003	0.1960	0.0705	0.0195	0.0038	0.0004	0.0000	
	2	0.9470	0.7382	0.6007	0.4628	0.2318	0.0898	0.0250	0.0043	0.0003	0.0000
	3	0.9917	0.9144	0.8343	0.7297	0.4826	0.2539	0.0994	0.0253	0.0031	0.0001
	4	0.9991	0.9804	0.9511	0.9012	0.7334	0.5000	0.2666	0.0988	0.0196	0.0009
	5	0.9999	0.9969	0.9900	0.9747	0.9006	0.7461	0.5174	0.2703	0.0856	0.0083
	6	1.0000	0.9997	0.9987	0.9957	0.9750	0.9102	0.7682	0.5372	0.2618	0.0530
	7		1.0000	0.9999	0.9996	0.9962	0.9805	0.9295	0.8040	0.5638	0.2252
	8			1.0000	1.0000	0.9997	0.9980	0.9899	0.9596	0.8658	0.6126
	9					1.0000	1.0000	1.0000	1.0000	1.0000	1.0000
10	0	0.3487	0.1074	0.0563	0.0282	0.0060	0.0010	0.0001	0.0000		
	1	0.7361	0.3758	0.2440	0.1493	0.0464	0.0107	0.0017	0.0001	0.0000	
	2	0.9298	0.6778	0.5256	0.3828	0.1673	0.0547	0.0123	0.0016	0.0001	
	3	0.9872	0.8791	0.7759	0.6496	0.3823	0.1719	0.0548	0.0106	0.0009	0.0000
	4	0.9984	0.9672	0.9219	0.8497	0.6331	0.3770	0.1662	0.0473	0.0064	0.0001
	5	0.9999	0.9936	0.9803	0.9527	0.8338	0.6230	0.3669	0.1503	0.0328	0.0016
	6	1.0000	0.9991	0.9965	0.9894	0.9452	0.8281	0.6177	0.3504	0.1209	0.0128
	7		0.9999	0.9996	0.9984	0.9877	0.9453	0.8327	0.6172	0.3222	0.0702
	8		1.0000	1.0000	0.9999	0.9983	0.9893	0.9536	0.8507	0.6242	0.2639
	9				1.0000	0.9999	0.9990	0.9940	0.9718	0.8926	0.6513
	10					1.0000	1.0000	1.0000	1.0000	1.0000	1.0000
11	0	0.3138	0.0859	0.0422	0.0198	0.0036	0.0005	0.0000			
	1	0.6974	0.3221	0.1971	0.1130	0.0302	0.0059	0.0007	0.0000		
	2	0.9104	0.6174	0.4552	0.3127	0.1189	0.0327	0.0059	0.0006	0.0000	
	3	0.9815	0.8389	0.7133	0.5696	0.2963	0.1133	0.0293	0.0043	0.0002	
	4	0.9972	0.9496	0.8854	0.7897	0.5328	0.2744	0.0994	0.0216	0.0020	0.0000
	5	0.9997	0.9883	0.9657	0.9218	0.7535	0.5000	0.2465	0.0782	0.0117	0.0003
	6	1.0000	0.9980	0.9924	0.9784	0.9006	0.7256	0.4672	0.2103	0.0504	0.0028
	7		0.9998	0.9988	0.9957	0.9707	0.8867	0.7037	0.4304	0.1611	0.0185
	8		1.0000	0.9999	0.9994	0.9941	0.9673	0.8811	0.6873	0.3826	0.0896
	9			1.0000	1.0000	0.9993	0.9941	0.9698	0.8870	0.6779	0.3026
	10					1.0000	0.9995	0.9964	0.9802	0.9141	0.6862
	11						1.0000	1.0000	1.0000	1.0000	1.0000

Table (continued) Binomial Probability Sums $\sum_{x=0}^{r} b(x; n, p)$

						p					
n	r	0.10	0.20	0.25	0.30	0.40	0.50	0.60	0.70	0.80	0.90
12	0	0.2824	0.0687	0.0317	0.0138	0.0022	0.0002	0.0000			
	1	0.6590	0.2749	0.1584	0.0850	0.0196	0.0032	0.0003	0.0000		
	2	0.8891	0.5583	0.3907	0.2528	0.0834	0.0193	0.0028	0.0002	0.0000	
	3	0.9744	0.7946	0.6488	0.4925	0.2253	0.0730	0.0153	0.0017	0.0001	
	4	0.9957	0.9274	0.8424	0.7237	0.4382	0.1938	0.0573	0.0095	0.0006	0.0000
	5	0.9995	0.9806	0.9456	0.8822	0.6652	0.3872	0.1582	0.0386	0.0039	0.0001
	6	0.9999	0.9961	0.9857	0.9614	0.8418	0.6128	0.3348	0.1178	0.0194	0.0005
	7	1.0000	0.9994	0.9972	0.9905	0.9427	0.8062	0.5618	0.2763	0.0726	0.0043
	8		0.9999	0.9996	0.9983	0.9847	0.9270	0.7747	0.5075	0.2054	0.0256
	9		1.0000	1.0000	0.9998	0.9972	0.9807	0.9166	0.7472	0.4417	0.1109
	10				1.0000	0.9997	0.9968	0.9804	0.9150	0.7251	0.3410
	11					1.0000	0.9998	0.9978	0.9862	0.9313	0.7176
	12						1.0000	1.0000	1.0000	1.0000	1.0000
13	0	0.2542	0.0550	0.0238	0.0097	0.0013	0.0001	0.0000			
	1	0.6213	0.2336	0.1267	0.0637	0.0126	0.0017	0.0001	0.0000		
	2	0.8661	0.5017	0.3326	0.2025	0.0579	0.0112	0.0013	0.0001		
	3	0.9658	0.7473	0.5843	0.4206	0.1686	0.0461	0.0078	0.0007	0.0000	
	4	0.9935	0.9009	0.7940	0.6543	0.3530	0.1334	0.0321	0.0040	0.0002	
	5	0.9991	0.9700	0.9198	0.8346	0.5744	0.2905	0.0977	0.0182	0.0012	0.0000
	6	0.9999	0.9930	0.9757	0.9376	0.7712	0.5000	0.2288	0.0624	0.0070	0.0001
	7	1.0000	0.9988	0.9944	0.9818	0.9023	0.7095	0.4256	0.1654	0.0300	0.0009
	8		0.9998	0.9990	0.9960	0.9679	0.8666	0.6470	0.3457	0.0991	0.0065
	9		1.0000	0.9999	0.9993	0.9922	0.9539	0.8314	0.5794	0.2527	0.0342
	10			1.0000	0.9999	0.9987	0.9888	0.9421	0.7975	0.4983	0.1339
	11				1.0000	0.9999	0.9983	0.9874	0.9363	0.7664	0.3787
	12					1.0000	0.9999	0.9987	0.9903	0.9450	0.7458
	13						1.0000	1.0000	1.0000	1.0000	1.0000
14	0	0.2288	0.0440	0.0178	0.0068	0.0008	0.0001	0.0000			
	1	0.5846	0.1979	0.1010	0.0475	0.0081	0.0009	0.0001			
	2	0.8416	0.4481	0.2811	0.1608	0.0398	0.0065	0.0006	0.0000		
	3	0.9559	0.6982	0.5213	0.3552	0.1243	0.0287	0.0039	0.0002		
	4	0.9908	0.8702	0.7415	0.5842	0.2793	0.0898	0.0175	0.0017	0.0000	
	5	0.9985	0.9561	0.8883	0.7805	0.4859	0.2120	0.0583	0.0083	0.0004	
	6	0.9998	0.9884	0.9617	0.9067	0.6925	0.3953	0.1501	0.0315	0.0024	0.0000
	7	1.0000	0.9976	0.9897	0.9685	0.8499	0.6047	0.3075	0.0933	0.0116	0.0002
	8		0.9996	0.9978	0.9917	0.9417	0.7880	0.5141	0.2195	0.0439	0.0015
	9		1.0000	0.9997	0.9983	0.9825	0.9102	0.7207	0.4158	0.1298	0.0092
	10			1.0000	0.9998	0.9961	0.9713	0.8757	0.6448	0.3018	0.0441
	11				1.0000	0.9994	0.9935	0.9602	0.8392	0.5519	0.1584
	12					0.9999	0.9991	0.9919	0.9525	0.8021	0.4154
	13					1.0000	0.9999	0.9992	0.9932	0.9560	0.7712
	14						1.0000	1.0000	1.0000	1.0000	1.0000

Table (continued) Binomial Probability Sums $\sum_{x=0}^{r} b(x; n, p)$

		p									
n	r	0.10	0.20	0.25	0.30	0.40	0.50	0.60	0.70	0.80	0.90
15	0	0.2059	0.0352	0.0134	0.0047	0.0005	0.0000				
	1	0.5490	0.1671	0.0802	0.0353	0.0052	0.0005	0.0000			
	2	0.8159	0.3980	0.2361	0.1268	0.0271	0.0037	0.0003	0.0000		
	3	0.9444	0.6482	0.4613	0.2969	0.0905	0.0176	0.0019	0.0001		
	4	0.9873	0.8358	0.6865	0.5155	0.2173	0.0592	0.0093	0.0007	0.0000	
	5	0.9978	0.9389	0.8516	0.7216	0.4032	0.1509	0.0338	0.0037	0.0001	
	6	0.9997	0.9819	0.9434	0.8689	0.6098	0.3036	0.0950	0.0152	0.0008	
	7	1.0000	0.9958	0.9827	0.9500	0.7869	0.5000	0.2131	0.0500	0.0042	0.0000
	8		0.9992	0.9958	0.9848	0.9050	0.6964	0.3902	0.1311	0.0181	0.0003
	9		0.9999	0.9992	0.9963	0.9662	0.8491	0.5968	0.2784	0.0611	0.0022
	10		1.0000	0.9999	0.9993	0.9907	0.9408	0.7827	0.4845	0.1642	0.0127
	11			1.0000	0.9999	0.9981	0.9824	0.9095	0.7031	0.3518	0.0556
	12				1.0000	0.9997	0.9963	0.9729	0.8732	0.6020	0.1841
	13					1.0000	0.9995	0.9948	0.9647	0.8329	0.4510
	14						1.0000	0.9995	0.9953	0.9648	0.7941
	15							1.0000	1.0000	1.0000	1.0000
16	0	0.1853	0.0281	0.0100	0.0033	0.0003	0.0000				
	1	0.5147	0.1407	0.0635	0.0261	0.0033	0.0003	0.0000			
	2	0.7892	0.3518	0.1971	0.0994	0.0183	0.0021	0.0001			
	3	0.9316	0.5981	0.4050	0.2459	0.0651	0.0106	0.0009	0.0000		
	4	0.9830	0.7982	0.6302	0.4499	0.1666	0.0384	0.0049	0.0003		
	5	0.9967	0.9183	0.8103	0.6598	0.3288	0.1051	0.0191	0.0016	0.0000	
	6	0.9995	0.9733	0.9204	0.8247	0.5272	0.2272	0.0583	0.0071	0.0002	
	7	0.9999	0.9930	0.9729	0.9256	0.7161	0.4018	0.1423	0.0257	0.0015	0.0000
	8	1.0000	0.9985	0.9925	0.9743	0.8577	0.5982	0.2839	0.0744	0.0070	0.0001
	9		0.9998	0.9984	0.9929	0.9417	0.7728	0.4728	0.1753	0.0267	0.0005
	10		1.0000	0.9997	0.9984	0.9809	0.8949	0.6712	0.3402	0.0817	0.0033
	11			1.0000	0.9997	0.9951	0.9616	0.8334	0.5501	0.2018	0.0170
	12				1.0000	0.9991	0.9894	0.9349	0.7541	0.4019	0.0684
	13					0.9999	0.9979	0.9817	0.9006	0.6482	0.2108
	14					1.0000	0.9997	0.9967	0.9739	0.8593	0.4853
	15						1.0000	0.9997	0.9967	0.9719	0.8147
	16							1.0000	1.0000	1.0000	1.0000

Table (continued) Binomial Probability Sums $\sum_{x=0}^{r} b(x; n, p)$

						p					
n	r	0.10	0.20	0.25	0.30	0.40	0.50	0.60	0.70	0.80	0.90
17	0	0.1668	0.0225	0.0075	0.0023	0.0002	0.0000				
	1	0.4818	0.1182	0.0501	0.0193	0.0021	0.0001	0.0000			
	2	0.7618	0.3096	0.1637	0.0774	0.0123	0.0012	0.0001			
	3	0.9174	0.5489	0.3530	0.2019	0.0464	0.0064	0.0005	0.0000		
	4	0.9779	0.7582	0.5739	0.3887	0.1260	0.0245	0.0025	0.0001		
	5	0.9953	0.8943	0.7653	0.5968	0.2639	0.0717	0.0106	0.0007	0.0000	
	6	0.9992	0.9623	0.8929	0.7752	0.4478	0.1662	0.0348	0.0032	0.0001	
	7	0.9999	0.9891	0.9598	0.8954	0.6405	0.3145	0.0919	0.0127	0.0005	
	8	1.0000	0.9974	0.9876	0.9597	0.8011	0.5000	0.1989	0.0403	0.0026	0.0000
	9		0.9995	0.9969	0.9873	0.9081	0.6855	0.3595	0.1046	0.0109	0.0001
	10		0.9999	0.9994	0.9968	0.9652	0.8338	0.5522	0.2248	0.0377	0.0008
	11		1.0000	0.9999	0.9993	0.9894	0.9283	0.7361	0.4032	0.1057	0.0047
	12			1.0000	0.9999	0.9975	0.9755	0.8740	0.6113	0.2418	0.0221
	13				1.0000	0.9995	0.9936	0.9536	0.7981	0.4511	0.0826
	14					0.9999	0.9988	0.9877	0.9226	0.6904	0.2382
	15					1.0000	0.9999	0.9979	0.9807	0.8818	0.5182
	16						1.0000	0.9998	0.9977	0.9775	0.8332
	17							1.0000	1.0000	1.0000	1.0000
18	0	0.1501	0.0180	0.0056	0.0016	0.0001	0.0000				
	1	0.4503	0.0991	0.0395	0.0142	0.0013	0.0001				
	2	0.7338	0.2713	0.1353	0.0600	0.0082	0.0007	0.0000			
	3	0.9018	0.5010	0.3057	0.1646	0.0328	0.0038	0.0002			
	4	0.9718	0.7164	0.5187	0.3327	0.0942	0.0154	0.0013	0.0000		
	5	0.9936	0.8671	0.7175	0.5344	0.2088	0.0481	0.0058	0.0003		
	6	0.9988	0.9487	0.8610	0.7217	0.3743	0.1189	0.0203	0.0014	0.0000	
	7	0.9998	0.9837	0.9431	0.8593	0.5634	0.2403	0.0576	0.0061	0.0002	
	8	1.0000	0.9957	0.9807	0.9404	0.7368	0.4073	0.1347	0.0210	0.0009	
	9		0.9991	0.9946	0.9790	0.8653	0.5927	0.2632	0.0596	0.0043	0.0000
	10		0.9998	0.9988	0.9939	0.9424	0.7597	0.4366	0.1407	0.0163	0.0002
	11		1.0000	0.9998	0.9986	0.9797	0.8811	0.6257	0.2783	0.0513	0.0012
	12			1.0000	0.9997	0.9942	0.9519	0.7912	0.4656	0.1329	0.0064
	13				1.0000	0.9987	0.9846	0.9058	0.6673	0.2836	0.0282
	14					0.9998	0.9962	0.9672	0.8354	0.4990	0.0982
	15					1.0000	0.9993	0.9918	0.9400	0.7287	0.2662
	16						0.9999	0.9987	0.9858	0.9009	0.5497
	17						1.0000	0.9999	0.9984	0.9820	0.8499
	18							1.0000	1.0000	1.0000	1.0000

Table (continued) Binomial Probability Sums $\sum_{x=0}^{r} b(x; n, p)$

n	r	0.10	0.20	0.25	0.30	0.40	0.50	0.60	0.70	0.80	0.90
19	0	0.1351	0.0144	0.0042	0.0011	0.0001					
	1	0.4203	0.0829	0.0310	0.0104	0.0008	0.0000				
	2	0.7054	0.2369	0.1113	0.0462	0.0055	0.0004	0.0000			
	3	0.8850	0.4551	0.2631	0.1332	0.0230	0.0022	0.0001			
	4	0.9648	0.6733	0.4654	0.2822	0.0696	0.0096	0.0006	0.0000		
	5	0.9914	0.8369	0.6678	0.4739	0.1629	0.0318	0.0031	0.0001		
	6	0.9983	0.9324	0.8251	0.6655	0.3081	0.0835	0.0116	0.0006		
	7	0.9997	0.9767	0.9225	0.8180	0.4878	0.1796	0.0352	0.0028	0.0000	
	8	1.0000	0.9933	0.9713	0.9161	0.6675	0.3238	0.0885	0.0105	0.0003	
	9		0.9984	0.9911	0.9674	0.8139	0.5000	0.1861	0.0326	0.0016	
	10		0.9997	0.9977	0.9895	0.9115	0.6762	0.3325	0.0839	0.0067	0.0000
	11		1.0000	0.9995	0.9972	0.9648	0.8204	0.5122	0.1820	0.0233	0.0003
	12			0.9999	0.9994	0.9884	0.9165	0.6919	0.3345	0.0676	0.0017
	13			1.0000	0.9999	0.9969	0.9682	0.8371	0.5261	0.1631	0.0086
	14				1.0000	0.9994	0.9904	0.9304	0.7178	0.3267	0.0352
	15					0.9999	0.9978	0.9770	0.8668	0.5449	0.1150
	16					1.0000	0.9996	0.9945	0.9538	0.7631	0.2946
	17						1.0000	0.9992	0.9896	0.9171	0.5797
	18							0.9999	0.9989	0.9856	0.8649
	19							1.0000	1.0000	1.0000	1.0000
20	0	0.1216	0.0115	0.0032	0.0008	0.0000					
	1	0.3917	0.0692	0.0243	0.0076	0.0005	0.0000				
	2	0.6769	0.2061	0.0913	0.0355	0.0036	0.0002				
	3	0.8670	0.4114	0.2252	0.1071	0.0160	0.0013	0.0000			
	4	0.9568	0.6296	0.4148	0.2375	0.0510	0.0059	0.0003			
	5	0.9887	0.8042	0.6172	0.4164	0.1256	0.0207	0.0016	0.0000		
	6	0.9976	0.9133	0.7858	0.6080	0.2500	0.0577	0.0065	0.0003		
	7	0.9996	0.9679	0.8982	0.7723	0.4159	0.1316	0.0210	0.0013	0.0000	
	8	0.9999	0.9900	0.9591	0.8867	0.5956	0.2517	0.0565	0.0051	0.0001	
	9	1.0000	0.9974	0.9861	0.9520	0.7553	0.4119	0.1275	0.0171	0.0006	
	10		0.9994	0.9961	0.9829	0.8725	0.5881	0.2447	0.0480	0.0026	0.0000
	11		0.9999	0.9991	0.9949	0.9435	0.7483	0.4044	0.1133	0.0100	0.0001
	12		1.0000	0.9998	0.9987	0.9790	0.8684	0.5841	0.2277	0.0321	0.0004
	13			1.0000	0.9997	0.9935	0.9423	0.7500	0.3920	0.0867	0.0024
	14				1.0000	0.9984	0.9793	0.8744	0.5836	0.1958	0.0113
	15					0.9997	0.9941	0.9490	0.7625	0.3704	0.0432
	16					1.0000	0.9987	0.9840	0.8929	0.5886	0.1330
	17						0.9998	0.9964	0.9645	0.7939	0.3231
	18						1.0000	0.9995	0.9924	0.9308	0.6083
	19							1.0000	0.9992	0.9885	0.8784
	20								1.0000	1.0000	1.0000

Table Critical Values of the Chi-Squared Distribution

	α									
v	**0.995**	**0.99**	**0.98**	**0.975**	**0.95**	**0.90**	**0.80**	**0.75**	**0.70**	**0.50**
1	0.0^4393	0.0^3157	0.0^3628	0.0^3982	0.00393	0.0158	0.0642	0.102	0.148	0.455
2	0.0100	0.0201	0.0404	0.0506	0.103	0.211	0.446	0.575	0.713	1.386
3	0.0717	0.115	0.185	0.216	0.352	0.584	1.005	1.213	1.424	2.366
4	0.207	0.297	0.429	0.484	0.711	1.064	1.649	1.923	2.195	3.357
5	0.412	0.554	0.752	0.831	1.145	1.610	2.343	2.675	3.000	4.351
6	0.676	0.872	1.134	1.237	1.635	2.204	3.070	3.455	3.828	5.348
7	0.989	1.239	1.564	1.690	2.167	2.833	3.822	4.255	4.671	6.346
8	1.344	1.647	2.032	2.180	2.733	3.490	4.594	5.071	5.527	7.344
9	1.735	2.088	2.532	2.700	3.325	4.168	5.380	5.899	6.393	8.343
10	2.156	2.558	3.059	3.247	3.940	4.865	6.179	6.737	7.267	9.342
11	2.603	3.053	3.609	3.816	4.575	5.578	6.989	7.584	8.148	10.341
12	3.074	3.571	4.178	4.404	5.226	6.304	7.807	8.438	9.034	11.340
13	3.565	4.107	4.765	5.009	5.892	7.041	8.634	9.299	9.926	12.340
14	4.075	4.660	5.368	5.629	6.571	7.790	9.467	10.165	10.821	13.339
15	4.601	5.229	5.985	6.262	7.261	8.547	10.307	11.037	11.721	14.339
16	5.142	5.812	6.614	6.908	7.962	9.312	11.152	11.912	12.624	15.338
17	5.697	6.408	7.255	7.564	8.672	10.085	12.002	12.792	13.531	16.338
18	6.265	7.015	7.906	8.231	9.390	10.865	12.857	13.675	14.440	17.338
19	6.844	7.633	8.567	8.907	10.117	11.651	13.716	14.562	15.352	18.338
20	7.434	8.260	9.237	9.591	10.851	12.443	14.578	15.452	16.266	19.337
21	8.034	8.897	9.915	10.283	11.591	13.240	15.445	16.344	17.182	20.337
22	8.643	9.542	10.600	10.982	12.338	14.041	16.314	17.240	18.101	21.337
23	9.260	10.196	11.293	11.689	13.091	14.848	17.187	18.137	19.021	22.337
24	9.886	10.856	11.992	12.401	13.848	15.659	18.062	19.037	19.943	23.337
25	10.520	11.524	12.697	13.120	14.611	16.473	18.940	19.939	20.867	24.337
26	11.160	12.198	13.409	13.844	15.379	17.292	19.820	20.843	21.792	25.336
27	11.808	12.878	14.125	14.573	16.151	18.114	20.703	21.749	22.719	26.336
28	12.461	13.565	14.847	15.308	16.928	18.939	21.588	22.657	23.647	27.336
29	13.121	14.256	15.574	16.047	17.708	19.768	22.475	23.567	24.577	28.336
30	13.787	14.953	16.306	16.791	18.493	20.599	23.364	24.478	25.508	29.336
40	20.707	22.164	23.838	24.433	26.509	29.051	32.345	33.66	34.872	39.335
50	27.991	29.707	31.664	32.357	34.764	37.689	41.449	42.942	44.313	49.335
60	35.534	37.485	39.699	40.482	43.188	46.459	50.641	52.294	53.809	59.335

Table (continued) Critical Values of the Chi-Squared Distribution

					α					
v	0.30	0.25	0.20	0.10	0.05	0.025	0.02	0.01	0.005	0.001
1	1.074	1.323	1.642	2.706	3.841	5.024	5.412	6.635	7.879	10.827
2	2.408	2.773	3.219	4.605	5.991	7.378	7.824	9.210	10.597	13.815
3	3.665	4.108	4.642	6.251	7.815	9.348	9.837	11.345	12.838	16.266
4	4.878	5.385	5.989	7.779	9.488	11.143	11.668	13.277	14.860	18.466
5	6.064	6.626	7.289	9.236	11.070	12.832	13.388	15.086	16.750	20.515
6	7.231	7.841	8.558	10.645	12.592	14.449	15.033	16.812	18.548	22.457
7	8.383	9.037	9.803	12.017	14.067	16.013	16.622	18.475	20.278	24.321
8	9.524	10.219	11.030	13.362	15.507	17.535	18.168	20.090	21.955	26.124
9	10.656	11.389	12.242	14.684	16.919	19.023	19.679	21.666	23.589	27.877
10	11.781	12.549	13.442	15.987	18.307	20.483	21.161	23.209	25.188	29.588
11	12.899	13.701	14.631	17.275	19.675	21.920	22.618	24.725	26.757	31.264
12	14.011	14.845	15.812	18.549	21.026	23.337	24.054	26.217	28.300	32.909
13	15.119	15.984	16.985	19.812	22.362	24.736	25.471	27.688	29.819	34.527
14	16.222	17.117	18.151	21.064	23.685	26.119	26.873	29.141	31.319	36.124
15	17.322	18.245	19.311	22.307	24.996	27.488	28.259	30.578	32.801	37.698
16	18.418	19.369	20.465	23.542	26.296	28.845	29.633	32.000	34.267	39.252
17	19.511	20.489	21.615	24.769	27.587	30.191	30.995	33.409	35.718	40.791
18	20.601	21.605	22.760	25.989	28.869	31.526	32.346	34.805	37.156	42.312
19	21.689	22.718	23.900	27.204	30.144	32.852	33.687	36.191	38.582	43.819
20	22.775	23.828	25.038	28.412	31.410	34.170	35.020	37.566	39.997	45.314
21	23.858	24.935	26.171	29.615	32.671	35.479	36.343	38.932	41.401	46.796
22	24.939	26.039	27.301	30.813	33.924	36.781	37.659	40.289	42.796	48.268
23	26.018	27.141	28.429	32.007	35.172	38.076	38.968	41.638	44.181	49.728
24	27.096	28.241	29.553	33.196	36.415	39.364	40.270	42.980	45.558	51.179
25	28.172	29.339	30.675	34.382	37.652	40.646	41.566	44.314	46.928	52.619
26	29.246	30.435	31.795	35.563	38.885	41.923	42.856	45.642	48.290	54.051
27	30.319	31.528	32.912	36.741	40.113	43.195	44.140	46.963	49.645	55.475
28	31.391	32.620	34.027	37.916	41.337	44.461	45.419	48.278	50.994	56.892
29	32.461	33.711	35.139	39.087	42.557	45.722	46.693	49.588	52.335	58.301
30	33.530	34.800	36.250	40.256	43.773	46.979	47.962	50.892	53.672	59.702
40	44.165	45.616	47.269	51.805	55.758	59.342	60.436	63.691	66.766	73.403
50	54.723	56.334	58.164	63.167	67.505	71.420	72.613	76.154	79.490	86.660
60	65.226	66.981	68.972	74.397	79.082	83.298	84.58	88.379	91.952	99.608

Appendix:
Statistical Tables and Proofs

Table Binomial Probability Sums $\sum_{r=0}^{r} b(x; n, p)$

						p					
n	r	0.10	0.20	0.25	0.30	0.40	0.50	0.60	0.70	0.80	0.90
1	0	0.9000	0.8000	0.7500	0.7000	0.6000	0.5000	0.4000	0.3000	0.2000	0.1000
	1	1.0000	1.0000	1.0000	1.0000	1.0000	1.0000	1.0000	1.0000	1.0000	1.0000
2	0	0.8100	0.6400	0.5625	0.4900	0.3600	0.2500	0.1600	0.0900	0.0400	0.0100
	1	0.9900	0.9600	0.9375	0.9100	0.8400	0.7500	0.6400	0.5100	0.3600	0.1900
	2	1.0000	1.0000	1.0000	1.0000	1.0000	1.0000	1.0000	1.0000	1.0000	1.0000
3	0	0.7290	0.5120	0.4219	0.3430	0.2160	0.1250	0.0640	0.0270	0.0080	0.0010
	1	0.9720	0.8960	0.8438	0.7840	0.6480	0.5000	0.3520	0.2160	0.1040	0.0280
	2	0.9990	0.9920	0.9844	0.9730	0.9360	0.8750	0.7840	0.6570	0.4880	0.2710
	3	1.0000	1.0000	1.0000	1.0000	1.0000	1.0000	1.0000	1.0000	1.0000	1.0000
4	0	0.6561	0.4096	0.3164	0.2401	0.1296	0.0625	0.0256	0.0081	0.0016	0.0001
	1	0.9477	0.8192	0.7383	0.6517	0.4752	0.3125	0.1792	0.0837	0.0272	0.0037
	2	0.9963	0.9728	0.9492	0.9163	0.8208	0.6875	0.5248	0.3483	0.1808	0.0523
	3	0.9999	0.9984	0.9961	0.9919	0.9744	0.9375	0.8704	0.7599	0.5904	0.3439
	4	1.0000	1.0000	1.0000	1.0000	1.0000	1.0000	1.0000	1.0000	1.0000	1.0000
5	0	0.5905	0.3277	0.2373	0.1681	0.0778	0.0313	0.0102	0.0024	0.0003	0.0000
	1	0.9185	0.7373	0.6328	0.5282	0.3370	0.1875	0.0870	0.0308	0.0067	0.0005
	2	0.9914	0.9421	0.8965	0.8369	0.6826	0.5000	0.3174	0.1631	0.0579	0.0086
	3	0.9995	0.9933	0.9844	0.9692	0.9130	0.8125	0.6630	0.4718	0.2627	0.0815
	4	1.0000	0.9997	0.9990	0.9976	0.9898	0.9688	0.9222	0.8319	0.6723	0.4095
	5	1.0000	1.0000	1.0000	1.0000	1.0000	1.0000	1.0000	1.0000	1.0000	1.0000
6	0	0.5314	0.2621	0.1780	0.1176	0.0467	0.0156	0.0041	0.0007	0.0001	0.0000
	1	0.8857	0.6554	0.5339	0.4202	0.2333	0.1094	0.0410	0.0109	0.0016	0.0001
	2	0.9842	0.9011	0.8306	0.7443	0.5443	0.3438	0.1792	0.0705	0.0170	0.0013
	3	0.9987	0.9830	0.9624	0.9295	0.8208	0.6563	0.4557	0.2557	0.0989	0.0159
	4	0.9999	0.9984	0.9954	0.9891	0.9590	0.8906	0.7667	0.5798	0.3446	0.1143
	5	1.0000	0.9999	0.9998	0.9993	0.9959	0.9844	0.9533	0.8824	0.7379	0.4686
	6	1.0000	1.0000	1.0000	1.0000	1.0000	1.0000	1.0000	1.0000	1.0000	1.0000
7	0	0.4783	0.2097	0.1335	0.0824	0.0280	0.0078	0.0016	0.0002	0.0000	
	1	0.8503	0.5767	0.4449	0.3294	0.1586	0.0625	0.0188	0.0038	0.0004	0.0000
	2	0.9743	0.8520	0.7564	0.6471	0.4199	0.2266	0.0963	0.0288	0.0047	0.0002
	3	0.9973	0.9667	0.9294	0.8740	0.7102	0.5000	0.2898	0.1260	0.0333	0.0027
	4	0.9998	0.9953	0.9871	0.9712	0.9037	0.7734	0.5801	0.3529	0.1480	0.0257
	5	1.0000	0.9996	0.9987	0.9962	0.9812	0.9375	0.8414	0.6706	0.4233	0.1497
	6		1.0000	0.9999	0.9998	0.9984	0.9922	0.9720	0.9176	0.7903	0.5217
	7			1.0000	1.0000	1.0000	1.0000	1.0000	1.0000	1.0000	1.0000

Table (continued) Binomial Probability Sums $\sum_{x=0}^{r} b(x; n, p)$

						p					
n	r	0.10	0.20	0.25	0.30	0.40	0.50	0.60	0.70	0.80	0.90
8	0	0.4305	0.1678	0.1001	0.0576	0.0168	0.0039	0.0007	0.0001	0.0000	
	1	0.8131	0.5033	0.3671	0.2553	0.1064	0.0352	0.0085	0.0013	0.0001	
	2	0.9619	0.7969	0.6785	0.5518	0.3154	0.1445	0.0498	0.0113	0.0012	0.0000
	3	0.9950	0.9437	0.8862	0.8059	0.5941	0.3633	0.1737	0.0580	0.0104	0.0004
	4	0.9996	0.9896	0.9727	0.9420	0.8263	0.6367	0.4059	0.1941	0.0563	0.0050
	5	1.0000	0.9988	0.9958	0.9887	0.9502	0.8555	0.6846	0.4482	0.2031	0.0381
	6		0.9999	0.9996	0.9987	0.9915	0.9648	0.8936	0.7447	0.4967	0.1869
	7		1.0000	1.0000	0.9999	0.9993	0.9961	0.9832	0.9424	0.8322	0.5695
	8				1.0000	1.0000	1.0000	1.0000	1.0000	1.0000	1.0000
9	0	0.3874	0.1342	0.0751	0.0404	0.0101	0.0020	0.0003	0.0000		
	1	0.7748	0.4362	0.3003	0.1960	0.0705	0.0195	0.0038	0.0004	0.0000	
	2	0.9470	0.7382	0.6007	0.4628	0.2318	0.0898	0.0250	0.0043	0.0003	0.0000
	3	0.9917	0.9144	0.8343	0.7297	0.4826	0.2539	0.0994	0.0253	0.0031	0.0001
	4	0.9991	0.9804	0.9511	0.9012	0.7334	0.5000	0.2666	0.0988	0.0196	0.0009
	5	0.9999	0.9969	0.9900	0.9747	0.9006	0.7461	0.5174	0.2703	0.0856	0.0083
	6	1.0000	0.9997	0.9987	0.9957	0.9750	0.9102	0.7682	0.5372	0.2618	0.0530
	7		1.0000	0.9999	0.9996	0.9962	0.9805	0.9295	0.8040	0.5638	0.2252
	8			1.0000	1.0000	0.9997	0.9980	0.9899	0.9596	0.8658	0.6126
	9					1.0000	1.0000	1.0000	1.0000	1.0000	1.0000
10	0	0.3487	0.1074	0.0563	0.0282	0.0060	0.0010	0.0001	0.0000		
	1	0.7361	0.3758	0.2440	0.1493	0.0464	0.0107	0.0017	0.0001	0.0000	
	2	0.9298	0.6778	0.5256	0.3828	0.1673	0.0547	0.0123	0.0016	0.0001	
	3	0.9872	0.8791	0.7759	0.6496	0.3823	0.1719	0.0548	0.0106	0.0009	0.0000
	4	0.9984	0.9672	0.9219	0.8497	0.6331	0.3770	0.1662	0.0473	0.0064	0.0001
	5	0.9999	0.9936	0.9803	0.9527	0.8338	0.6230	0.3669	0.1503	0.0328	0.0016
	6	1.0000	0.9991	0.9965	0.9894	0.9452	0.8281	0.6177	0.3504	0.1209	0.0128
	7		0.9999	0.9996	0.9984	0.9877	0.9453	0.8327	0.6172	0.3222	0.0702
	8		1.0000	1.0000	0.9999	0.9983	0.9893	0.9536	0.8507	0.6242	0.2639
	9				1.0000	0.9999	0.9990	0.9940	0.9718	0.8926	0.6513
	10					1.0000	1.0000	1.0000	1.0000	1.0000	1.0000
11	0	0.3138	0.0859	0.0422	0.0198	0.0036	0.0005	0.0000			
	1	0.6974	0.3221	0.1971	0.1130	0.0302	0.0059	0.0007	0.0000		
	2	0.9104	0.6174	0.4552	0.3127	0.1189	0.0327	0.0059	0.0006	0.0000	
	3	0.9815	0.8389	0.7133	0.5696	0.2963	0.1133	0.0293	0.0043	0.0002	
	4	0.9972	0.9496	0.8854	0.7897	0.5328	0.2744	0.0994	0.0216	0.0020	0.0000
	5	0.9997	0.9883	0.9657	0.9218	0.7535	0.5000	0.2465	0.0782	0.0117	0.0003
	6	1.0000	0.9980	0.9924	0.9784	0.9006	0.7256	0.4672	0.2103	0.0504	0.0028
	7		0.9998	0.9988	0.9957	0.9707	0.8867	0.7037	0.4304	0.1611	0.0185
	8		1.0000	0.9999	0.9994	0.9941	0.9673	0.8811	0.6873	0.3826	0.0896
	9			1.0000	1.0000	0.9993	0.9941	0.9698	0.8870	0.6779	0.3026
	10					1.0000	0.9995	0.9964	0.9802	0.9141	0.6862
	11						1.0000	1.0000	1.0000	1.0000	1.0000

Table (continued) Binomial Probability Sums $\sum_{r=0}^{r} b(x; n, p)$

						p					
n	*r*	0.10	0.20	0.25	0.30	0.40	0.50	0.60	0.70	0.80	0.90
12	0	0.2824	0.0687	0.0317	0.0138	0.0022	0.0002	0.0000			
	1	0.6590	0.2749	0.1584	0.0850	0.0196	0.0032	0.0003	0.0000		
	2	0.8891	0.5583	0.3907	0.2528	0.0834	0.0193	0.0028	0.0002	0.0000	
	3	0.9744	0.7946	0.6488	0.4925	0.2253	0.0730	0.0153	0.0017	0.0001	
	4	0.9957	0.9274	0.8424	0.7237	0.4382	0.1938	0.0573	0.0095	0.0006	0.0000
	5	0.9995	0.9806	0.9456	0.8822	0.6652	0.3872	0.1582	0.0386	0.0039	0.0001
	6	0.9999	0.9961	0.9857	0.9614	0.8418	0.6128	0.3348	0.1178	0.0194	0.0005
	7	1.0000	0.9994	0.9972	0.9905	0.9427	0.8062	0.5618	0.2763	0.0726	0.0043
	8		0.9999	0.9996	0.9983	0.9847	0.9270	0.7747	0.5075	0.2054	0.0256
	9		1.0000	1.0000	0.9998	0.9972	0.9807	0.9166	0.7472	0.4417	0.1109
	10				1.0000	0.9997	0.9968	0.9804	0.9150	0.7251	0.3410
	11					1.0000	0.9998	0.9978	0.9862	0.9313	0.7176
	12						1.0000	1.0000	1.0000	1.0000	1.0000
13	0	0.2542	0.0550	0.0238	0.0097	0.0013	0.0001	0.0000			
	1	0.6213	0.2336	0.1267	0.0637	0.0126	0.0017	0.0001	0.0000		
	2	0.8661	0.5017	0.3326	0.2025	0.0579	0.0112	0.0013	0.0001		
	3	0.9658	0.7473	0.5843	0.4206	0.1686	0.0461	0.0078	0.0007	0.0000	
	4	0.9935	0.9009	0.7940	0.6543	0.3530	0.1334	0.0321	0.0040	0.0002	
	5	0.9991	0.9700	0.9198	0.8346	0.5744	0.2905	0.0977	0.0182	0.0012	0.0000
	6	0.9999	0.9930	0.9757	0.9376	0.7712	0.5000	0.2288	0.0624	0.0070	0.0001
	7	1.0000	0.9988	0.9944	0.9818	0.9023	0.7095	0.4256	0.1654	0.0300	0.0009
	8		0.9998	0.9990	0.9960	0.9679	0.8666	0.6470	0.3457	0.0991	0.0065
	9		1.0000	0.9999	0.9993	0.9922	0.9539	0.8314	0.5794	0.2527	0.0342
	10			1.0000	0.9999	0.9987	0.9888	0.9421	0.7975	0.4983	0.1339
	11				1.0000	0.9999	0.9983	0.9874	0.9363	0.7664	0.3787
	12					1.0000	0.9999	0.9987	0.9903	0.9450	0.7458
	13						1.0000	1.0000	1.0000	1.0000	1.0000
14	0	0.2288	0.0440	0.0178	0.0068	0.0008	0.0001	0.0000			
	1	0.5846	0.1979	0.1010	0.0475	0.0081	0.0009	0.0001			
	2	0.8416	0.4481	0.2811	0.1608	0.0398	0.0065	0.0006	0.0000		
	3	0.9559	0.6982	0.5213	0.3552	0.1243	0.0287	0.0039	0.0002		
	4	0.9908	0.8702	0.7415	0.5842	0.2793	0.0898	0.0175	0.0017	0.0000	
	5	0.9985	0.9561	0.8883	0.7805	0.4859	0.2120	0.0583	0.0083	0.0004	
	6	0.9998	0.9884	0.9617	0.9067	0.6925	0.3953	0.1501	0.0315	0.0024	0.0000
	7	1.0000	0.9976	0.9897	0.9685	0.8499	0.6047	0.3075	0.0933	0.0116	0.0002
	8		0.9996	0.9978	0.9917	0.9417	0.7880	0.5141	0.2195	0.0439	0.0015
	9		1.0000	0.9997	0.9983	0.9825	0.9102	0.7207	0.4158	0.1298	0.0092
	10			1.0000	0.9998	0.9961	0.9713	0.8757	0.6448	0.3018	0.0441
	11				1.0000	0.9994	0.9935	0.9602	0.8392	0.5519	0.1584
	12					0.9999	0.9991	0.9919	0.9525	0.8021	0.4154
	13					1.0000	0.9999	0.9992	0.9932	0.9560	0.7712
	14						1.0000	1.0000	1.0000	1.0000	1.0000

Table (continued) Binomial Probability Sums $\sum_{x=0}^{r} b(x; n, p)$

		\multicolumn{10}{c	}{p}
n	r	0.10	0.20	0.25	0.30	0.40	0.50	0.60	0.70	0.80	0.90
15	0	0.2059	0.0352	0.0134	0.0047	0.0005	0.0000				
	1	0.5490	0.1671	0.0802	0.0353	0.0052	0.0005	0.0000			
	2	0.8159	0.3980	0.2361	0.1268	0.0271	0.0037	0.0003	0.0000		
	3	0.9444	0.6482	0.4613	0.2969	0.0905	0.0176	0.0019	0.0001		
	4	0.9873	0.8358	0.6865	0.5155	0.2173	0.0592	0.0093	0.0007	0.0000	
	5	0.9978	0.9389	0.8516	0.7216	0.4032	0.1509	0.0338	0.0037	0.0001	
	6	0.9997	0.9819	0.9434	0.8689	0.6098	0.3036	0.0950	0.0152	0.0008	
	7	1.0000	0.9958	0.9827	0.9500	0.7869	0.5000	0.2131	0.0500	0.0042	0.0000
	8		0.9992	0.9958	0.9848	0.9050	0.6964	0.3902	0.1311	0.0181	0.0003
	9		0.9999	0.9992	0.9963	0.9662	0.8491	0.5968	0.2784	0.0611	0.0022
	10		1.0000	0.9999	0.9993	0.9907	0.9408	0.7827	0.4845	0.1642	0.0127
	11			1.0000	0.9999	0.9981	0.9824	0.9095	0.7031	0.3518	0.0556
	12				1.0000	0.9997	0.9963	0.9729	0.8732	0.6020	0.1841
	13					1.0000	0.9995	0.9948	0.9647	0.8329	0.4510
	14						1.0000	0.9995	0.9953	0.9648	0.7941
	15							1.0000	1.0000	1.0000	1.0000
16	0	0.1853	0.0281	0.0100	0.0033	0.0003	0.0000				
	1	0.5147	0.1407	0.0635	0.0261	0.0033	0.0003	0.0000			
	2	0.7892	0.3518	0.1971	0.0994	0.0183	0.0021	0.0001			
	3	0.9316	0.5981	0.4050	0.2459	0.0651	0.0106	0.0009	0.0000		
	4	0.9830	0.7982	0.6302	0.4499	0.1666	0.0384	0.0049	0.0003		
	5	0.9967	0.9183	0.8103	0.6598	0.3288	0.1051	0.0191	0.0016	0.0000	
	6	0.9995	0.9733	0.9204	0.8247	0.5272	0.2272	0.0583	0.0071	0.0002	
	7	0.9999	0.9930	0.9729	0.9256	0.7161	0.4018	0.1423	0.0257	0.0015	0.0000
	8	1.0000	0.9985	0.9925	0.9743	0.8577	0.5982	0.2839	0.0744	0.0070	0.0001
	9		0.9998	0.9984	0.9929	0.9417	0.7728	0.4728	0.1753	0.0267	0.0005
	10		1.0000	0.9997	0.9984	0.9809	0.8949	0.6712	0.3402	0.0817	0.0033
	11			1.0000	0.9997	0.9951	0.9616	0.8334	0.5501	0.2018	0.0170
	12				1.0000	0.9991	0.9894	0.9349	0.7541	0.4019	0.0684
	13					0.9999	0.9979	0.9817	0.9006	0.6482	0.2108
	14					1.0000	0.9997	0.9967	0.9739	0.8593	0.4853
	15						1.0000	0.9997	0.9967	0.9719	0.8147
	16							1.0000	1.0000	1.0000	1.0000

Table (continued) Binomial Probability Sums $\sum_{x=0}^{r} b(x; n, p)$

						p					
n	r	0.10	0.20	0.25	0.30	0.40	0.50	0.60	0.70	0.80	0.90
17	0	0.1668	0.0225	0.0075	0.0023	0.0002	0.0000				
	1	0.4818	0.1182	0.0501	0.0193	0.0021	0.0001	0.0000			
	2	0.7618	0.3096	0.1637	0.0774	0.0123	0.0012	0.0001			
	3	0.9174	0.5489	0.3530	0.2019	0.0464	0.0064	0.0005	0.0000		
	4	0.9779	0.7582	0.5739	0.3887	0.1260	0.0245	0.0025	0.0001		
	5	0.9953	0.8943	0.7653	0.5968	0.2639	0.0717	0.0106	0.0007	0.0000	
	6	0.9992	0.9623	0.8929	0.7752	0.4478	0.1662	0.0348	0.0032	0.0001	
	7	0.9999	0.9891	0.9598	0.8954	0.6405	0.3145	0.0919	0.0127	0.0005	
	8	1.0000	0.9974	0.9876	0.9597	0.8011	0.5000	0.1989	0.0403	0.0026	0.0000
	9		0.9995	0.9969	0.9873	0.9081	0.6855	0.3595	0.1046	0.0109	0.0001
	10		0.9999	0.9994	0.9968	0.9652	0.8338	0.5522	0.2248	0.0377	0.0008
	11		1.0000	0.9999	0.9993	0.9894	0.9283	0.7361	0.4032	0.1057	0.0047
	12			1.0000	0.9999	0.9975	0.9755	0.8740	0.6113	0.2418	0.0221
	13				1.0000	0.9995	0.9936	0.9536	0.7981	0.4511	0.0826
	14					0.9999	0.9988	0.9877	0.9226	0.6904	0.2382
	15					1.0000	0.9999	0.9979	0.9807	0.8818	0.5182
	16						1.0000	0.9998	0.9977	0.9775	0.8332
	17							1.0000	1.0000	1.0000	1.0000
18	0	0.1501	0.0180	0.0056	0.0016	0.0001	0.0000				
	1	0.4503	0.0991	0.0395	0.0142	0.0013	0.0001				
	2	0.7338	0.2713	0.1353	0.0600	0.0082	0.0007	0.0000			
	3	0.9018	0.5010	0.3057	0.1646	0.0328	0.0038	0.0002			
	4	0.9718	0.7164	0.5187	0.3327	0.0942	0.0154	0.0013	0.0000		
	5	0.9936	0.8671	0.7175	0.5344	0.2088	0.0481	0.0058	0.0003		
	6	0.9988	0.9487	0.8610	0.7217	0.3743	0.1189	0.0203	0.0014	0.0000	
	7	0.9998	0.9837	0.9431	0.8593	0.5634	0.2403	0.0576	0.0061	0.0002	
	8	1.0000	0.9957	0.9807	0.9404	0.7368	0.4073	0.1347	0.0210	0.0009	
	9		0.9991	0.9946	0.9790	0.8653	0.5927	0.2632	0.0596	0.0043	0.0000
	10		0.9998	0.9988	0.9939	0.9424	0.7597	0.4366	0.1407	0.0163	0.0002
	11		1.0000	0.9998	0.9986	0.9797	0.8811	0.6257	0.2783	0.0513	0.0012
	12			1.0000	0.9997	0.9942	0.9519	0.7912	0.4656	0.1329	0.0064
	13				1.0000	0.9987	0.9846	0.9058	0.6673	0.2836	0.0282
	14					0.9998	0.9962	0.9672	0.8354	0.4990	0.0982
	15					1.0000	0.9993	0.9918	0.9400	0.7287	0.2662
	16						0.9999	0.9987	0.9858	0.9009	0.5497
	17						1.0000	0.9999	0.9984	0.9820	0.8499
	18							1.0000	1.0000	1.0000	1.0000

Table (continued) Binomial Probability Sums $\sum_{x=0}^{r} b(x; n, p)$

						p					
n	r	0.10	0.20	0.25	0.30	0.40	0.50	0.60	0.70	0.80	0.90
19	0	0.1351	0.0144	0.0042	0.0011	0.0001					
	1	0.4203	0.0829	0.0310	0.0104	0.0008	0.0000				
	2	0.7054	0.2369	0.1113	0.0462	0.0055	0.0004	0.0000			
	3	0.8850	0.4551	0.2631	0.1332	0.0230	0.0022	0.0001			
	4	0.9648	0.6733	0.4654	0.2822	0.0696	0.0096	0.0006	0.0000		
	5	0.9914	0.8369	0.6678	0.4739	0.1629	0.0318	0.0031	0.0001		
	6	0.9983	0.9324	0.8251	0.6655	0.3081	0.0835	0.0116	0.0006		
	7	0.9997	0.9767	0.9225	0.8180	0.4878	0.1796	0.0352	0.0028	0.0000	
	8	1.0000	0.9933	0.9713	0.9161	0.6675	0.3238	0.0885	0.0105	0.0003	
	9		0.9984	0.9911	0.9674	0.8139	0.5000	0.1861	0.0326	0.0016	
	10		0.9997	0.9977	0.9895	0.9115	0.6762	0.3325	0.0839	0.0067	0.0000
	11		1.0000	0.9995	0.9972	0.9648	0.8204	0.5122	0.1820	0.0233	0.0003
	12			0.9999	0.9994	0.9884	0.9165	0.6919	0.3345	0.0676	0.0017
	13			1.0000	0.9999	0.9969	0.9682	0.8371	0.5261	0.1631	0.0086
	14				1.0000	0.9994	0.9904	0.9304	0.7178	0.3267	0.0352
	15					0.9999	0.9978	0.9770	0.8668	0.5449	0.1150
	16					1.0000	0.9996	0.9945	0.9538	0.7631	0.2946
	17						1.0000	0.9992	0.9896	0.9171	0.5797
	18							0.9999	0.9989	0.9856	0.8649
	19							1.0000	1.0000	1.0000	1.0000
20	0	0.1216	0.0115	0.0032	0.0008	0.0000					
	1	0.3917	0.0692	0.0243	0.0076	0.0005	0.0000				
	2	0.6769	0.2061	0.0913	0.0355	0.0036	0.0002				
	3	0.8670	0.4114	0.2252	0.1071	0.0160	0.0013	0.0000			
	4	0.9568	0.6296	0.4148	0.2375	0.0510	0.0059	0.0003			
	5	0.9887	0.8042	0.6172	0.4164	0.1256	0.0207	0.0016	0.0000		
	6	0.9976	0.9133	0.7858	0.6080	0.2500	0.0577	0.0065	0.0003		
	7	0.9996	0.9679	0.8982	0.7723	0.4159	0.1316	0.0210	0.0013	0.0000	
	8	0.9999	0.9900	0.9591	0.8867	0.5956	0.2517	0.0565	0.0051	0.0001	
	9	1.0000	0.9974	0.9861	0.9520	0.7553	0.4119	0.1275	0.0171	0.0006	
	10		0.9994	0.9961	0.9829	0.8725	0.5881	0.2447	0.0480	0.0026	0.0000
	11		0.9999	0.9991	0.9949	0.9435	0.7483	0.4044	0.1133	0.0100	0.0001
	12		1.0000	0.9998	0.9987	0.9790	0.8684	0.5841	0.2277	0.0321	0.0004
	13			1.0000	0.9997	0.9935	0.9423	0.7500	0.3920	0.0867	0.0024
	14				1.0000	0.9984	0.9793	0.8744	0.5836	0.1958	0.0113
	15					0.9997	0.9941	0.9490	0.7625	0.3704	0.0432
	16					1.0000	0.9987	0.9840	0.8929	0.5886	0.1330
	17						0.9998	0.9964	0.9645	0.7939	0.3231
	18						1.0000	0.9995	0.9924	0.9308	0.6083
	19							1.0000	0.9992	0.9885	0.8784
	20								1.0000	1.0000	1.0000

Table Poisson Probability Sums $\sum_{x=0}^{r} p(x; \mu)$

	μ								
r	0.1	0.2	0.3	0.4	0.5	0.6	0.7	0.8	0.9
0	0.9048	0.8187	0.7408	0.6703	0.6065	0.5488	0.4966	0.4493	0.4066
1	0.9953	0.9825	0.9631	0.9384	0.9098	0.8781	0.8442	0.8088	0.7725
2	0.9998	0.9989	0.9964	0.9921	0.9856	0.9769	0.9659	0.9526	0.9371
3	1.0000	0.9999	0.9997	0.9992	0.9982	0.9966	0.9942	0.9909	0.9865
4		1.0000	1.0000	0.9999	0.9998	0.9996	0.9992	0.9986	0.9977
5				1.0000	1.0000	1.0000	0.9999	0.9998	0.9997
6							1.0000	1.0000	1.0000

	μ								
r	1.0	1.5	2.0	2.5	3.0	3.5	4.0	4.5	5.0
0	0.3679	0.2231	0.1353	0.0821	0.0498	0.0302	0.0183	0.0111	0.0067
1	0.7358	0.5578	0.4060	0.2873	0.1991	0.1359	0.0916	0.0611	0.0404
2	0.9197	0.8088	0.6767	0.5438	0.4232	0.3208	0.2381	0.1736	0.1247
3	0.9810	0.9344	0.8571	0.7576	0.6472	0.5366	0.4335	0.3423	0.2650
4	0.9963	0.9814	0.9473	0.8912	0.8153	0.7254	0.6288	0.5321	0.4405
5	0.9994	0.9955	0.9834	0.9580	0.9161	0.8576	0.7851	0.7029	0.6160
6	0.9999	0.9991	0.9955	0.9858	0.9665	0.9347	0.8893	0.8311	0.7622
7	1.0000	0.9998	0.9989	0.9958	0.9881	0.9733	0.9489	0.9134	0.8666
8		1.0000	0.9998	0.9989	0.9962	0.9901	0.9786	0.9597	0.9319
9			1.0000	0.9997	0.9989	0.9967	0.9919	0.9829	0.9682
10				0.9999	0.9997	0.9990	0.9972	0.9933	0.9863
11				1.0000	0.9999	0.9997	0.9991	0.9976	0.9945
12					1.0000	0.9999	0.9997	0.9992	0.9980
13						1.0000	0.9999	0.9997	0.9993
14							1.0000	0.9999	0.9998
15								1.0000	0.9999
16									1.0000

Table (continued) Poisson Probability Sums $\sum_{x=0}^{r} p(x; \mu)$

					μ				
r	5.5	6.0	6.5	7.0	7.5	8.0	8.5	9.0	9.5
0	0.0041	0.0025	0.0015	0.0009	0.0006	0.0003	0.0002	0.0001	0.0001
1	0.0266	0.0174	0.0113	0.0073	0.0047	0.0030	0.0019	0.0012	0.0008
2	0.0884	0.0620	0.0430	0.0296	0.0203	0.0138	0.0093	0.0062	0.0042
3	0.2017	0.1512	0.1118	0.0818	0.0591	0.0424	0.0301	0.0212	0.0149
4	0.3575	0.2851	0.2237	0.1730	0.1321	0.0996	0.0744	0.0550	0.0403
5	0.5289	0.4457	0.3690	0.3007	0.2414	0.1912	0.1496	0.1157	0.0885
6	0.6860	0.6063	0.5265	0.4497	0.3782	0.3134	0.2562	0.2068	0.1649
7	0.8095	0.7440	0.6728	0.5987	0.5246	0.4530	0.3856	0.3239	0.2687
8	0.8944	0.8472	0.7916	0.7291	0.6620	0.5925	0.5231	0.4557	0.3918
9	0.9462	0.9161	0.8774	0.8305	0.7764	0.7166	0.6530	0.5874	0.5218
10	0.9747	0.9574	0.9332	0.9015	0.8622	0.8159	0.7634	0.7060	0.6453
11	0.9890	0.9799	0.9661	0.9467	0.9208	0.8881	0.8487	0.8030	0.7520
12	0.9955	0.9912	0.9840	0.9730	0.9573	0.9362	0.9091	0.8758	0.8364
13	0.9983	0.9964	0.9929	0.9872	0.9784	0.9658	0.9486	0.9261	0.8981
14	0.9994	0.9986	0.9970	0.9943	0.9897	0.9827	0.9726	0.9585	0.9400
15	0.9998	0.9995	0.9988	0.9976	0.9954	0.9918	0.9862	0.9780	0.9665
16	0.9999	0.9998	0.9996	0.9990	0.9980	0.9963	0.9934	0.9889	0.9823
17	1.0000	0.9999	0.9998	0.9996	0.9992	0.9984	0.9970	0.9947	0.9911
18		1.0000	0.9999	0.9999	0.9997	0.9993	0.9987	0.9976	0.9957
19			1.0000	1.0000	0.9999	0.9997	0.9995	0.9989	0.9980
20						0.9999	0.9998	0.9996	0.9991
21						1.0000	0.9999	0.9998	0.9996
22							1.0000	0.9999	0.9999
23								1.0000	0.9999
24									1.0000

Table (continued) Poisson Probability Sums $\sum_{x=0}^{r} p(x;\mu)$

					μ				
r	10.0	11.0	12.0	13.0	14.0	15.0	16.0	17.0	18.0
0	0.0000	0.0000	0.0000						
1	0.0005	0.0002	0.0001	0.0000	0.0000				
2	0.0028	0.0012	0.0005	0.0002	0.0001	0.0000	0.0000		
3	0.0103	0.0049	0.0023	0.0011	0.0005	0.0002	0.0001	0.0000	0.0000
4	0.0293	0.0151	0.0076	0.0037	0.0018	0.0009	0.0004	0.0002	0.0001
5	0.0671	0.0375	0.0203	0.0107	0.0055	0.0028	0.0014	0.0007	0.0003
6	0.1301	0.0786	0.0458	0.0259	0.0142	0.0076	0.0040	0.0021	0.0010
7	0.2202	0.1432	0.0895	0.0540	0.0316	0.0180	0.0100	0.0054	0.0029
8	0.3328	0.2320	0.1550	0.0998	0.0621	0.0374	0.0220	0.0126	0.0071
9	0.4579	0.3405	0.2424	0.1658	0.1094	0.0699	0.0433	0.0261	0.0154
10	0.5830	0.4599	0.3472	0.2517	0.1757	0.1185	0.0774	0.0491	0.0304
11	0.6968	0.5793	0.4616	0.3532	0.2600	0.1848	0.1270	0.0847	0.0549
12	0.7916	0.6887	0.5760	0.4631	0.3585	0.2676	0.1931	0.1350	0.0917
13	0.8645	0.7813	0.6815	0.5730	0.4644	0.3632	0.2745	0.2009	0.1426
14	0.9165	0.8540	0.7720	0.6751	0.5704	0.4657	0.3675	0.2808	0.2081
15	0.9513	0.9074	0.8444	0.7636	0.6694	0.5681	0.4667	0.3715	0.2867
16	0.9730	0.9441	0.8987	0.8355	0.7559	0.6641	0.5660	0.4677	0.3751
17	0.9857	0.9678	0.9370	0.8905	0.8272	0.7489	0.6593	0.5640	0.4686
18	0.9928	0.9823	0.9626	0.9302	0.8826	0.8195	0.7423	0.6550	0.5622
19	0.9965	0.9907	0.9787	0.9573	0.9235	0.8752	0.8122	0.7363	0.6509
20	0.9984	0.9953	0.9884	0.9750	0.9521	0.9170	0.8682	0.8055	0.7307
21	0.9993	0.9977	0.9939	0.9859	0.9712	0.9469	0.9108	0.8615	0.7991
22	0.9997	0.9990	0.9970	0.9924	0.9833	0.9673	0.9418	0.9047	0.8551
23	0.9999	0.9995	0.9985	0.9960	0.9907	0.9805	0.9633	0.9367	0.8989
24	1.0000	0.9998	0.9993	0.9980	0.9950	0.9888	0.9777	0.9594	0.9317
25		0.9999	0.9997	0.9990	0.9974	0.9938	0.9869	0.9748	0.9554
26		1.0000	0.9999	0.9995	0.9987	0.9967	0.9925	0.9848	0.9718
27			0.9999	0.9998	0.9994	0.9983	0.9959	0.9912	0.9827
28			1.0000	0.9999	0.9997	0.9991	0.9978	0.9950	0.9897
29				1.0000	0.9999	0.9996	0.9989	0.9973	0.9941
30					0.9999	0.9998	0.9994	0.9986	0.9967
31					1.0000	0.9999	0.9997	0.9993	0.9982
32						1.0000	0.9999	0.9996	0.9990
33							0.9999	0.9998	0.9995
34							1.0000	0.9999	0.9998
35								1.0000	0.9999
36									0.9999
37									1.0000

Table Areas under the Normal Curve

z	.00	.01	.02	.03	.04	.05	.06	.07	.08	.09
−3.4	0.0003	0.0003	0.0003	0.0003	0.0003	0.0003	0.0003	0.0003	0.0003	0.0002
−3.3	0.0005	0.0005	0.0005	0.0004	0.0004	0.0004	0.0004	0.0004	0.0004	0.0003
−3.2	0.0007	0.0007	0.0006	0.0006	0.0006	0.0006	0.0006	0.0005	0.0005	0.0005
−3.1	0.0010	0.0009	0.0009	0.0009	0.0008	0.0008	0.0008	0.0008	0.0007	0.0007
−3.0	0.0013	0.0013	0.0013	0.0012	0.0012	0.0011	0.0011	0.0011	0.0010	0.0010
−2.9	0.0019	0.0018	0.0018	0.0017	0.0016	0.0016	0.0015	0.0015	0.0014	0.0014
−2.8	0.0026	0.0025	0.0024	0.0023	0.0023	0.0022	0.0021	0.0021	0.0020	0.0019
−2.7	0.0035	0.0034	0.0033	0.0032	0.0031	0.0030	0.0029	0.0028	0.0027	0.0026
−2.6	0.0047	0.0045	0.0044	0.0043	0.0041	0.0040	0.0039	0.0038	0.0037	0.0036
−2.5	0.0062	0.0060	0.0059	0.0057	0.0055	0.0054	0.0052	0.0051	0.0049	0.0048
−2.4	0.0082	0.0080	0.0078	0.0075	0.0073	0.0071	0.0069	0.0068	0.0066	0.0064
−2.3	0.0107	0.0104	0.0102	0.0099	0.0096	0.0094	0.0091	0.0089	0.0087	0.0084
−2.2	0.0139	0.0136	0.0132	0.0129	0.0125	0.0122	0.0119	0.0116	0.0113	0.0110
−2.1	0.0179	0.0174	0.0170	0.0166	0.0162	0.0158	0.0154	0.0150	0.0146	0.0143
−2.0	0.0228	0.0222	0.0217	0.0212	0.0207	0.0202	0.0197	0.0192	0.0188	0.0183
−1.9	0.0287	0.0281	0.0274	0.0268	0.0262	0.0256	0.0250	0.0244	0.0239	0.0233
−1.8	0.0359	0.0351	0.0344	0.0336	0.0329	0.0322	0.0314	0.0307	0.0301	0.0294
−1.7	0.0446	0.0436	0.0427	0.0418	0.0409	0.0401	0.0392	0.0384	0.0375	0.0367
−1.6	0.0548	0.0537	0.0526	0.0516	0.0505	0.0495	0.0485	0.0475	0.0465	0.0455
−1.5	0.0668	0.0655	0.0643	0.0630	0.0618	0.0606	0.0594	0.0582	0.0571	0.0559
−1.4	0.0808	0.0793	0.0778	0.0764	0.0749	0.0735	0.0721	0.0708	0.0694	0.0681
−1.3	0.0968	0.0951	0.0934	0.0918	0.0901	0.0885	0.0869	0.0853	0.0838	0.0823
−1.2	0.1151	0.1131	0.1112	0.1093	0.1075	0.1056	0.1038	0.1020	0.1003	0.0985
−1.1	0.1357	0.1335	0.1314	0.1292	0.1271	0.1251	0.1230	0.1210	0.1190	0.1170
−1.0	0.1587	0.1562	0.1539	0.1515	0.1492	0.1469	0.1446	0.1423	0.1401	0.1379
−0.9	0.1841	0.1814	0.1788	0.1762	0.1736	0.1711	0.1685	0.1660	0.1635	0.1611
−0.8	0.2119	0.2090	0.2061	0.2033	0.2005	0.1977	0.1949	0.1922	0.1894	0.1867
−0.7	0.2420	0.2389	0.2358	0.2327	0.2296	0.2266	0.2236	0.2206	0.2177	0.2148
−0.6	0.2743	0.2709	0.2676	0.2643	0.2611	0.2578	0.2546	0.2514	0.2483	0.2451
−0.5	0.3085	0.3050	0.3015	0.2981	0.2946	0.2912	0.2877	0.2843	0.2810	0.2776
−0.4	0.3446	0.3409	0.3372	0.3336	0.3300	0.3264	0.3228	0.3192	0.3156	0.3121
−0.3	0.3821	0.3783	0.3745	0.3707	0.3669	0.3632	0.3594	0.3557	0.3520	0.3483
−0.2	0.4207	0.4168	0.4129	0.4090	0.4052	0.4013	0.3974	0.3936	0.3897	0.3859
−0.1	0.4602	0.4562	0.4522	0.4483	0.4443	0.4404	0.4364	0.4325	0.4286	0.4247
−0.0	0.5000	0.4960	0.4920	0.4880	0.4840	0.4801	0.4761	0.4721	0.4681	0.4641

Table (continued) Areas under the Normal Curve

z	.00	.01	.02	.03	.04	.05	.06	.07	.08	.09
0.0	0.5000	0.5040	0.5080	0.5120	0.5160	0.5199	0.5239	0.5279	0.5319	0.5359
0.1	0.5398	0.5438	0.5478	0.5517	0.5557	0.5596	0.5636	0.5675	0.5714	0.5753
0.2	0.5793	0.5832	0.5871	0.5910	0.5948	0.5987	0.6026	0.6064	0.6103	0.6141
0.3	0.6179	0.6217	0.6255	0.6293	0.6331	0.6368	0.6406	0.6443	0.6480	0.6517
0.4	0.6554	0.6591	0.6628	0.6664	0.6700	0.6736	0.6772	0.6808	0.6844	0.6879
0.5	0.6915	0.6950	0.6985	0.7019	0.7054	0.7088	0.7123	0.7157	0.7190	0.7224
0.6	0.7257	0.7291	0.7324	0.7357	0.7389	0.7422	0.7454	0.7486	0.7517	0.7549
0.7	0.7580	0.7611	0.7642	0.7673	0.7704	0.7734	0.7764	0.7794	0.7823	0.7852
0.8	0.7881	0.7910	0.7939	0.7967	0.7995	0.8023	0.8051	0.8078	0.8106	0.8133
0.9	0.8159	0.8186	0.8212	0.8238	0.8264	0.8289	0.8315	0.8340	0.8365	0.8389
1.0	0.8413	0.8438	0.8461	0.8485	0.8508	0.8531	0.8554	0.8577	0.8599	0.8621
1.1	0.8643	0.8665	0.8686	0.8708	0.8729	0.8749	0.8770	0.8790	0.8810	0.8830
1.2	0.8849	0.8869	0.8888	0.8907	0.8925	0.8944	0.8962	0.8980	0.8997	0.9015
1.3	0.9032	0.9049	0.9066	0.9082	0.9099	0.9115	0.9131	0.9147	0.9162	0.9177
1.4	0.9192	0.9207	0.9222	0.9236	0.9251	0.9265	0.9279	0.9292	0.9306	0.9319
1.5	0.9332	0.9345	0.9357	0.9370	0.9382	0.9394	0.9406	0.9418	0.9429	0.9441
1.6	0.9452	0.9463	0.9474	0.9484	0.9495	0.9505	0.9515	0.9525	0.9535	0.9545
1.7	0.9554	0.9564	0.9573	0.9582	0.9591	0.9599	0.9608	0.9616	0.9625	0.9633
1.8	0.9641	0.9649	0.9656	0.9664	0.9671	0.9678	0.9686	0.9693	0.9699	0.9706
1.9	0.9713	0.9719	0.9726	0.9732	0.9738	0.9744	0.9750	0.9756	0.9761	0.9767
2.0	0.9772	0.9778	0.9783	0.9788	0.9793	0.9798	0.9803	0.9808	0.9812	0.9817
2.1	0.9821	0.9826	0.9830	0.9834	0.9838	0.9842	0.9846	0.9850	0.9854	0.9857
2.2	0.9861	0.9864	0.9868	0.9871	0.9875	0.9878	0.9881	0.9884	0.9887	0.9890
2.3	0.9893	0.9896	0.9898	0.9901	0.9904	0.9906	0.9909	0.9911	0.9913	0.9916
2.4	0.9918	0.9920	0.9922	0.9925	0.9927	0.9929	0.9931	0.9932	0.9934	0.9936
2.5	0.9938	0.9940	0.9941	0.9943	0.9945	0.9946	0.9948	0.9949	0.9951	0.9952
2.6	0.9953	0.9955	0.9956	0.9957	0.9959	0.9960	0.9961	0.9962	0.9963	0.9964
2.7	0.9965	0.9966	0.9967	0.9968	0.9969	0.9970	0.9971	0.9972	0.9973	0.9974
2.8	0.9974	0.9975	0.9976	0.9977	0.9977	0.9978	0.9979	0.9979	0.9980	0.9981
2.9	0.9981	0.9982	0.9982	0.9983	0.9984	0.9984	0.9985	0.9985	0.9986	0.9986
3.0	0.9987	0.9987	0.9987	0.9988	0.9988	0.9989	0.9989	0.9989	0.9990	0.9990
3.1	0.9990	0.9991	0.9991	0.9991	0.9992	0.9992	0.9992	0.9992	0.9993	0.9993
3.2	0.9993	0.9993	0.9994	0.9994	0.9994	0.9994	0.9994	0.9995	0.9995	0.9995
3.3	0.9995	0.9995	0.9995	0.9996	0.9996	0.9996	0.9996	0.9996	0.9996	0.9997
3.4	0.9997	0.9997	0.9997	0.9997	0.9997	0.9997	0.9997	0.9997	0.9997	0.9998

Table Critical Values of the *t*-Distribution

				α			
v	**0.40**	**0.30**	**0.20**	**0.15**	**0.10**	**0.05**	**0.025**
1	0.325	0.727	1.376	1.963	3.078	6.314	12.706
2	0.289	0.617	1.061	1.386	1.886	2.920	4.303
3	0.277	0.584	0.978	1.250	1.638	2.353	3.182
4	0.271	0.569	0.941	1.190	1.533	2.132	2.776
5	0.267	0.559	0.920	1.156	1.476	2.015	2.571
6	0.265	0.553	0.906	1.134	1.440	1.943	2.447
7	0.263	0.549	0.896	1.119	1.415	1.895	2.365
8	0.262	0.546	0.889	1.108	1.397	1.860	2.306
9	0.261	0.543	0.883	1.100	1.383	1.833	2.262
10	0.260	0.542	0.879	1.093	1.372	1.812	2.228
11	0.260	0.540	0.876	1.088	1.363	1.796	2.201
12	0.259	0.539	0.873	1.083	1.356	1.782	2.179
13	0.259	0.538	0.870	1.079	1.350	1.771	2.160
14	0.258	0.537	0.868	1.076	1.345	1.761	2.145
15	0.258	0.536	0.866	1.074	1.341	1.753	2.131
16	0.258	0.535	0.865	1.071	1.337	1.746	2.120
17	0.257	0.534	0.863	1.069	1.333	1.740	2.110
18	0.257	0.534	0.862	1.067	1.330	1.734	2.101
19	0.257	0.533	0.861	1.066	1.328	1.729	2.093
20	0.257	0.533	0.860	1.064	1.325	1.725	2.086
21	0.257	0.532	0.859	1.063	1.323	1.721	2.080
22	0.256	0.532	0.858	1.061	1.321	1.717	2.074
23	0.256	0.532	0.858	1.060	1.319	1.714	2.069
24	0.256	0.531	0.857	1.059	1.318	1.711	2.064
25	0.256	0.531	0.856	1.058	1.316	1.708	2.060
26	0.256	0.531	0.856	1.058	1.315	1.706	2.056
27	0.256	0.531	0.855	1.057	1.314	1.703	2.052
28	0.256	0.530	0.855	1.056	1.313	1.701	2.048
29	0.256	0.530	0.854	1.055	1.311	1.699	2.045
30	0.256	0.530	0.854	1.055	1.310	1.697	2.042
40	0.255	0.529	0.851	1.050	1.303	1.684	2.021
60	0.254	0.527	0.848	1.045	1.296	1.671	2.000
120	0.254	0.526	0.845	1.041	1.289	1.658	1.980
∞	0.253	0.524	0.842	1.036	1.282	1.645	1.960

Table (continued) Critical Values of the *t*-Distribution

	α						
v	0.02	0.015	0.01	0.0075	0.005	0.0025	0.0005
1	15.894	21.205	31.821	42.433	63.656	127.321	636.578
2	4.849	5.643	6.965	8.073	9.925	14.089	31.600
3	3.482	3.896	4.541	5.047	5.841	7.453	12.924
4	2.999	3.298	3.747	4.088	4.604	5.598	8.610
5	2.757	3.003	3.365	3.634	4.032	4.773	6.869
6	2.612	2.829	3.143	3.372	3.707	4.317	5.959
7	2.517	2.715	2.998	3.203	3.499	4.029	5.408
8	2.449	2.634	2.896	3.085	3.355	3.833	5.041
9	2.398	2.574	2.821	2.998	3.250	3.690	4.781
10	2.359	2.527	2.764	2.932	3.169	3.581	4.587
11	2.328	2.491	2.718	2.879	3.106	3.497	4.437
12	2.303	2.461	2.681	2.836	3.055	3.428	4.318
13	2.282	2.436	2.650	2.801	3.012	3.372	4.221
14	2.264	2.415	2.624	2.771	2.977	3.326	4.140
15	2.249	2.397	2.602	2.746	2.947	3.286	4.073
16	2.235	2.382	2.583	2.724	2.921	3.252	4.015
17	2.224	2.368	2.567	2.706	2.898	3.222	3.965
18	2.214	2.356	2.552	2.689	2.878	3.197	3.922
19	2.205	2.346	2.539	2.674	2.861	3.174	3.883
20	2.197	2.336	2.528	2.661	2.845	3.153	3.850
21	2.189	2.328	2.518	2.649	2.831	3.135	3.819
22	2.183	2.320	2.508	2.639	2.819	3.119	3.792
23	2.177	2.313	2.500	2.629	2.807	3.104	3.768
24	2.172	2.307	2.492	2.620	2.797	3.091	3.745
25	2.167	2.301	2.485	2.612	2.787	3.078	3.725
26	2.162	2.296	2.479	2.605	2.779	3.067	3.707
27	2.158	2.291	2.473	2.598	2.771	3.057	3.689
28	2.154	2.286	2.467	2.592	2.763	3.047	3.674
29	2.150	2.282	2.462	2.586	2.756	3.038	3.660
30	2.147	2.278	2.457	2.581	2.750	3.030	3.646
40	2.123	2.250	2.423	2.542	2.704	2.971	3.551
60	2.099	2.223	2.390	2.504	2.660	2.915	3.460
120	2.076	2.196	2.358	2.468	2.617	2.860	3.373
∞	2.054	2.170	2.326	2.432	2.576	2.807	3.290

Table Critical Values of the Chi-Squared Distribution

					α					
v	0.995	0.99	0.98	0.975	0.95	0.90	0.80	0.75	0.70	0.50
1	0.0^4393	0.0^3157	0.0^3628	0.0^3982	0.00393	0.0158	0.0642	0.102	0.148	0.455
2	0.0100	0.0201	0.0404	0.0506	0.103	0.211	0.446	0.575	0.713	1.386
3	0.0717	0.115	0.185	0.216	0.352	0.584	1.005	1.213	1.424	2.366
4	0.207	0.297	0.429	0.484	0.711	1.064	1.649	1.923	2.195	3.357
5	0.412	0.554	0.752	0.831	1.145	1.610	2.343	2.675	3.000	4.351
6	0.676	0.872	1.134	1.237	1.635	2.204	3.070	3.455	3.828	5.348
7	0.989	1.239	1.564	1.690	2.167	2.833	3.822	4.255	4.671	6.346
8	1.344	1.647	2.032	2.180	2.733	3.490	4.594	5.071	5.527	7.344
9	1.735	2.088	2.532	2.700	3.325	4.168	5.380	5.899	6.393	8.343
10	2.156	2.558	3.059	3.247	3.940	4.865	6.179	6.737	7.267	9.342
11	2.603	3.053	3.609	3.816	4.575	5.578	6.989	7.584	8.148	10.341
12	3.074	3.571	4.178	4.404	5.226	6.304	7.807	8.438	9.034	11.340
13	3.565	4.107	4.765	5.009	5.892	7.041	8.634	9.299	9.926	12.340
14	4.075	4.660	5.368	5.629	6.571	7.790	9.467	10.165	10.821	13.339
15	4.601	5.229	5.985	6.262	7.261	8.547	10.307	11.037	11.721	14.339
16	5.142	5.812	6.614	6.908	7.962	9.312	11.152	11.912	12.624	15.338
17	5.697	6.408	7.255	7.564	8.672	10.085	12.002	12.792	13.531	16.338
18	6.265	7.015	7.906	8.231	9.390	10.865	12.857	13.675	14.440	17.338
19	6.844	7.633	8.567	8.907	10.117	11.651	13.716	14.562	15.352	18.338
20	7.434	8.260	9.237	9.591	10.851	12.443	14.578	15.452	16.266	19.337
21	8.034	8.897	9.915	10.283	11.591	13.240	15.445	16.344	17.182	20.337
22	8.643	9.542	10.600	10.982	12.338	14.041	16.314	17.240	18.101	21.337
23	9.260	10.196	11.293	11.689	13.091	14.848	17.187	18.137	19.021	22.337
24	9.886	10.856	11.992	12.401	13.848	15.659	18.062	19.037	19.943	23.337
25	10.520	11.524	12.697	13.120	14.611	16.473	18.940	19.939	20.867	24.337
26	11.160	12.198	13.409	13.844	15.379	17.292	19.820	20.843	21.792	25.336
27	11.808	12.878	14.125	14.573	16.151	18.114	20.703	21.749	22.719	26.336
28	12.461	13.565	14.847	15.308	16.928	18.939	21.588	22.657	23.647	27.336
29	13.121	14.256	15.574	16.047	17.708	19.768	22.475	23.567	24.577	28.336
30	13.787	14.953	16.306	16.791	18.493	20.599	23.364	24.478	25.508	29.336
40	20.707	22.164	23.838	24.433	26.509	29.051	32.345	33.66	34.872	39.335
50	27.991	29.707	31.664	32.357	34.764	37.689	41.449	42.942	44.313	49.335
60	35.534	37.485	39.699	40.482	43.188	46.459	50.641	52.294	53.809	59.335

Table (continued) Critical Values of the Chi-Squared Distribution

v	0.30	0.25	0.20	0.10	0.05	0.025	0.02	0.01	0.005	0.001
					α					
1	1.074	1.323	1.642	2.706	3.841	5.024	5.412	6.635	7.879	10.827
2	2.408	2.773	3.219	4.605	5.991	7.378	7.824	9.210	10.597	13.815
3	3.665	4.108	4.642	6.251	7.815	9.348	9.837	11.345	12.838	16.266
4	4.878	5.385	5.989	7.779	9.488	11.143	11.668	13.277	14.860	18.466
5	6.064	6.626	7.289	9.236	11.070	12.832	13.388	15.086	16.750	20.515
6	7.231	7.841	8.558	10.645	12.592	14.449	15.033	16.812	18.548	22.457
7	8.383	9.037	9.803	12.017	14.067	16.013	16.622	18.475	20.278	24.321
8	9.524	10.219	11.030	13.362	15.507	17.535	18.168	20.090	21.955	26.124
9	10.656	11.389	12.242	14.684	16.919	19.023	19.679	21.666	23.589	27.877
10	11.781	12.549	13.442	15.987	18.307	20.483	21.161	23.209	25.188	29.588
11	12.899	13.701	14.631	17.275	19.675	21.920	22.618	24.725	26.757	31.264
12	14.011	14.845	15.812	18.549	21.026	23.337	24.054	26.217	28.300	32.909
13	15.119	15.984	16.985	19.812	22.362	24.736	25.471	27.688	29.819	34.527
14	16.222	17.117	18.151	21.064	23.685	26.119	26.873	29.141	31.319	36.124
15	17.322	18.245	19.311	22.307	24.996	27.488	28.259	30.578	32.801	37.698
16	18.418	19.369	20.465	23.542	26.296	28.845	29.633	32.000	34.267	39.252
17	19.511	20.489	21.615	24.769	27.587	30.191	30.995	33.409	35.718	40.791
18	20.601	21.605	22.760	25.989	28.869	31.526	32.346	34.805	37.156	42.312
19	21.689	22.718	23.900	27.204	30.144	32.852	33.687	36.191	38.582	43.819
20	22.775	23.828	25.038	28.412	31.410	34.170	35.020	37.566	39.997	45.314
21	23.858	24.935	26.171	29.615	32.671	35.479	36.343	38.932	41.401	46.796
22	24.939	26.039	27.301	30.813	33.924	36.781	37.659	40.289	42.796	48.268
23	26.018	27.141	28.429	32.007	35.172	38.076	38.968	41.638	44.181	49.728
24	27.096	28.241	29.553	33.196	36.415	39.364	40.270	42.980	45.558	51.179
25	28.172	29.339	30.675	34.382	37.652	40.646	41.566	44.314	46.928	52.619
26	29.246	30.435	31.795	35.563	38.885	41.923	42.856	45.642	48.290	54.051
27	30.319	31.528	32.912	36.741	40.113	43.195	44.140	46.963	49.645	55.475
28	31.391	32.620	34.027	37.916	41.337	44.461	45.419	48.278	50.994	56.892
29	32.461	33.711	35.139	39.087	42.557	45.722	46.693	49.588	52.335	58.301
30	33.530	34.800	36.250	40.256	43.773	46.979	47.962	50.892	53.672	59.702
40	44.165	45.616	47.269	51.805	55.758	59.342	60.436	63.691	66.766	73.403
50	54.723	56.334	58.164	63.167	67.505	71.420	72.613	76.154	79.490	86.660
60	65.226	66.981	68.972	74.397	79.082	83.298	84.58	88.379	91.952	99.608

Table Critical Values of the *F*-Distribution

$$f_{0.05}(v_1, v_2)$$

v_2	\multicolumn{9}{c}{v_1}
	1	**2**	**3**	**4**	**5**	**6**	**7**	**8**	**9**
1	161.45	199.50	215.71	224.58	230.16	233.99	236.77	238.88	240.54
2	18.51	19.00	19.16	19.25	19.30	19.33	19.35	19.37	19.38
3	10.13	9.55	9.28	9.12	9.01	8.94	8.89	8.85	8.81
4	7.71	6.94	6.59	6.39	6.26	6.16	6.09	6.04	6.00
5	6.61	5.79	5.41	5.19	5.05	4.95	4.88	4.82	4.77
6	5.99	5.14	4.76	4.53	4.39	4.28	4.21	4.15	4.10
7	5.59	4.74	4.35	4.12	3.97	3.87	3.79	3.73	3.68
8	5.32	4.46	4.07	3.84	3.69	3.58	3.50	3.44	3.39
9	5.12	4.26	3.86	3.63	3.48	3.37	3.29	3.23	3.18
10	4.96	4.10	3.71	3.48	3.33	3.22	3.14	3.07	3.02
11	4.84	3.98	3.59	3.36	3.20	3.09	3.01	2.95	2.90
12	4.75	3.89	3.49	3.26	3.11	3.00	2.91	2.85	2.80
13	4.67	3.81	3.41	3.18	3.03	2.92	2.83	2.77	2.71
14	4.60	3.74	3.34	3.11	2.96	2.85	2.76	2.70	2.65
15	4.54	3.68	3.29	3.06	2.90	2.79	2.71	2.64	2.59
16	4.49	3.63	3.24	3.01	2.85	2.74	2.66	2.59	2.54
17	4.45	3.59	3.20	2.96	2.81	2.70	2.61	2.55	2.49
18	4.41	3.55	3.16	2.93	2.77	2.66	2.58	2.51	2.46
19	4.38	3.52	3.13	2.90	2.74	2.63	2.54	2.48	2.42
20	4.35	3.49	3.10	2.87	2.71	2.60	2.51	2.45	2.39
21	4.32	3.47	3.07	2.84	2.68	2.57	2.49	2.42	2.37
22	4.30	3.44	3.05	2.82	2.66	2.55	2.46	2.40	2.34
23	4.28	3.42	3.03	2.80	2.64	2.53	2.44	2.37	2.32
24	4.26	3.40	3.01	2.78	2.62	2.51	2.42	2.36	2.30
25	4.24	3.39	2.99	2.76	2.60	2.49	2.40	2.34	2.28
26	4.23	3.37	2.98	2.74	2.59	2.47	2.39	2.32	2.27
27	4.21	3.35	2.96	2.73	2.57	2.46	2.37	2.31	2.25
28	4.20	3.34	2.95	2.71	2.56	2.45	2.36	2.29	2.24
29	4.18	3.33	2.93	2.70	2.55	2.43	2.35	2.28	2.22
30	4.17	3.32	2.92	2.69	2.53	2.42	2.33	2.27	2.21
40	4.08	3.23	2.84	2.61	2.45	2.34	2.25	2.18	2.12
60	4.00	3.15	2.76	2.53	2.37	2.25	2.17	2.10	2.04
120	3.92	3.07	2.68	2.45	2.29	2.18	2.09	2.02	1.96
∞	3.84	3.00	2.60	2.37	2.21	2.10	2.01	1.94	1.88

Table (continued) Critical Values of the *F*-Distribution

	$f_{0.05}(v_1, v_2)$									
	v_1									
v_2	10	12	15	20	24	30	40	60	120	∞
1	241.88	243.91	245.95	248.01	249.05	250.10	251.14	252.20	253.25	254.31
2	19.40	19.41	19.43	19.45	19.45	19.46	19.47	19.48	19.49	19.50
3	8.79	8.74	8.70	8.66	8.64	8.62	8.59	8.57	8.55	8.53
4	5.96	5.91	5.86	5.80	5.77	5.75	5.72	5.69	5.66	5.63
5	4.74	4.68	4.62	4.56	4.53	4.50	4.46	4.43	4.40	4.36
6	4.06	4.00	3.94	3.87	3.84	3.81	3.77	3.74	3.70	3.67
7	3.64	3.57	3.51	3.44	3.41	3.38	3.34	3.30	3.27	3.23
8	3.35	3.28	3.22	3.15	3.12	3.08	3.04	3.01	2.97	2.93
9	3.14	3.07	3.01	2.94	2.90	2.86	2.83	2.79	2.75	2.71
10	2.98	2.91	2.85	2.77	2.74	2.70	2.66	2.62	2.58	2.54
11	2.85	2.79	2.72	2.65	2.61	2.57	2.53	2.49	2.45	2.40
12	2.75	2.69	2.62	2.54	2.51	2.47	2.43	2.38	2.34	2.30
13	2.67	2.60	2.53	2.46	2.42	2.38	2.34	2.30	2.25	2.21
14	2.60	2.53	2.46	2.39	2.35	2.31	2.27	2.22	2.18	2.13
15	2.54	2.48	2.40	2.33	2.29	2.25	2.20	2.16	2.11	2.07
16	2.49	2.42	2.35	2.28	2.24	2.19	2.15	2.11	2.06	2.01
17	2.45	2.38	2.31	2.23	2.19	2.15	2.10	2.06	2.01	1.96
18	2.41	2.34	2.27	2.19	2.15	2.11	2.06	2.02	1.97	1.92
19	2.38	2.31	2.23	2.16	2.11	2.07	2.03	1.98	1.93	1.88
20	2.35	2.28	2.20	2.12	2.08	2.04	1.99	1.95	1.90	1.84
21	2.32	2.25	2.18	2.10	2.05	2.01	1.96	1.92	1.87	1.81
22	2.30	2.23	2.15	2.07	2.03	1.98	1.94	1.89	1.84	1.78
23	2.27	2.20	2.13	2.05	2.01	1.96	1.91	1.86	1.81	1.76
24	2.25	2.18	2.11	2.03	1.98	1.94	1.89	1.84	1.79	1.73
25	2.24	2.16	2.09	2.01	1.96	1.92	1.87	1.82	1.77	1.71
26	2.22	2.15	2.07	1.99	1.95	1.90	1.85	1.80	1.75	1.69
27	2.20	2.13	2.06	1.97	1.93	1.88	1.84	1.79	1.73	1.67
28	2.19	2.12	2.04	1.96	1.91	1.87	1.82	1.77	1.71	1.65
29	2.18	2.10	2.03	1.94	1.90	1.85	1.81	1.75	1.70	1.64
30	2.16	2.09	2.01	1.93	1.89	1.84	1.79	1.74	1.68	1.62
40	2.08	2.00	1.92	1.84	1.79	1.74	1.69	1.64	1.58	1.51
60	1.99	1.92	1.84	1.75	1.70	1.65	1.59	1.53	1.47	1.39
120	1.91	1.83	1.75	1.66	1.61	1.55	1.50	1.43	1.35	1.25
∞	1.83	1.75	1.67	1.57	1.52	1.46	1.39	1.32	1.22	1.00

Table (continued) Critical Values of the *F*-Distribution

	$f_{0.01}(v_1, v_2)$								
	v_1								
v_2	1	2	3	4	5	6	7	8	9
1	4052.18	4999.50	5403.35	5624.58	5763.65	5858.99	5928.36	5981.07	6022.47
2	98.50	99.00	99.17	99.25	99.30	99.33	99.36	99.37	99.39
3	34.12	30.82	29.46	28.71	28.24	27.91	27.67	27.49	27.35
4	21.20	18.00	16.69	15.98	15.52	15.21	14.98	14.80	14.66
5	16.26	13.27	12.06	11.39	10.97	10.67	10.46	10.29	10.16
6	13.75	10.92	9.78	9.15	8.75	8.47	8.26	8.10	7.98
7	12.25	9.55	8.45	7.85	7.46	7.19	6.99	6.84	6.72
8	11.26	8.65	7.59	7.01	6.63	6.37	6.18	6.03	5.91
9	10.56	8.02	6.99	6.42	6.06	5.80	5.61	5.47	5.35
10	10.04	7.56	6.55	5.99	5.64	5.39	5.20	5.06	4.94
11	9.65	7.21	6.22	5.67	5.32	5.07	4.89	4.74	4.63
12	9.33	6.93	5.95	5.41	5.06	4.82	4.64	4.50	4.39
13	9.07	6.70	5.74	5.21	4.86	4.62	4.44	4.30	4.19
14	8.86	6.51	5.56	5.04	4.69	4.46	4.28	4.14	4.03
15	8.68	6.36	5.42	4.89	4.56	4.32	4.14	4.00	3.89
16	8.53	6.23	5.29	4.77	4.44	4.20	4.03	3.89	3.78
17	8.40	6.11	5.18	4.67	4.34	4.10	3.93	3.79	3.68
18	8.29	6.01	5.09	4.58	4.25	4.01	3.84	3.71	3.60
19	8.18	5.93	5.01	4.50	4.17	3.94	3.77	3.63	3.52
20	8.10	5.85	4.94	4.43	4.10	3.87	3.70	3.56	3.46
21	8.02	5.78	4.87	4.37	4.04	3.81	3.64	3.51	3.40
22	7.95	5.72	4.82	4.31	3.99	3.76	3.59	3.45	3.35
23	7.88	5.66	4.76	4.26	3.94	3.71	3.54	3.41	3.30
24	7.82	5.61	4.72	4.22	3.90	3.67	3.50	3.36	3.26
25	7.77	5.57	4.68	4.18	3.85	3.63	3.46	3.32	3.22
26	7.72	5.53	4.64	4.14	3.82	3.59	3.42	3.29	3.18
27	7.68	5.49	4.60	4.11	3.78	3.56	3.39	3.26	3.15
28	7.64	5.45	4.57	4.07	3.75	3.53	3.36	3.23	3.12
29	7.60	5.42	4.54	4.04	3.73	3.50	3.33	3.20	3.09
30	7.56	5.39	4.51	4.02	3.70	3.47	3.30	3.17	3.07
40	7.31	5.18	4.31	3.83	3.51	3.29	3.12	2.99	2.89
60	7.08	4.98	4.13	3.65	3.34	3.12	2.95	2.82	2.72
120	6.85	4.79	3.95	3.48	3.17	2.96	2.79	2.66	2.56
∞	6.63	4.61	3.78	3.32	3.02	2.80	2.64	2.51	2.41

Table (continued) Critical Values of the *F*-Distribution

$$f_{0.01}(v_1, v_2)$$

v_2	\multicolumn{10}{c}{v_1}
	10	12	15	20	24	30	40	60	120	∞
1	6055.85	6106.32	6157.28	6208.73	6234.63	6260.65	6286.78	6313.03	6339.39	6365.86
2	99.40	99.42	99.43	99.45	99.46	99.47	99.47	99.48	99.49	99.50
3	27.23	27.05	26.87	26.69	26.60	26.50	26.41	26.32	26.22	26.13
4	14.55	14.37	14.20	14.02	13.93	13.84	13.75	13.65	13.56	13.46
5	10.05	9.89	9.72	9.55	9.47	9.38	9.29	9.20	9.11	9.02
6	7.87	7.72	7.56	7.40	7.31	7.23	7.14	7.06	6.97	6.88
7	6.62	6.47	6.31	6.16	6.07	5.99	5.91	5.82	5.74	5.65
8	5.81	5.67	5.52	5.36	5.28	5.20	5.12	5.03	4.95	4.86
9	5.26	5.11	4.96	4.81	4.73	4.65	4.57	4.48	4.40	4.31
10	4.85	4.71	4.56	4.41	4.33	4.25	4.17	4.08	4.00	3.91
11	4.54	4.40	4.25	4.10	4.02	3.94	3.86	3.78	3.69	3.60
12	4.30	4.16	4.01	3.86	3.78	3.70	3.62	3.54	3.45	3.36
13	4.10	3.96	3.82	3.66	3.59	3.51	3.43	3.34	3.25	3.17
14	3.94	3.80	3.66	3.51	3.43	3.35	3.27	3.18	3.09	3.00
15	3.80	3.67	3.52	3.37	3.29	3.21	3.13	3.05	2.96	2.87
16	3.69	3.55	3.41	3.26	3.18	3.10	3.02	2.93	2.84	2.75
17	3.59	3.46	3.31	3.16	3.08	3.00	2.92	2.83	2.75	2.65
18	3.51	3.37	3.23	3.08	3.00	2.92	2.84	2.75	2.66	2.57
19	3.43	3.30	3.15	3.00	2.92	2.84	2.76	2.67	2.58	2.49
20	3.37	3.23	3.09	2.94	2.86	2.78	2.69	2.61	2.52	2.42
21	3.31	3.17	3.03	2.88	2.80	2.72	2.64	2.55	2.46	2.36
22	3.26	3.12	2.98	2.83	2.75	2.67	2.58	2.50	2.40	2.31
23	3.21	3.07	2.93	2.78	2.70	2.62	2.54	2.45	2.35	2.26
24	3.17	3.03	2.89	2.74	2.66	2.58	2.49	2.40	2.31	2.21
25	3.13	2.99	2.85	2.70	2.62	2.54	2.45	2.36	2.27	2.17
26	3.09	2.96	2.81	2.66	2.58	2.50	2.42	2.33	2.23	2.13
27	3.06	2.93	2.78	2.63	2.55	2.47	2.38	2.29	2.20	2.10
28	3.03	2.90	2.75	2.60	2.52	2.44	2.35	2.26	2.17	2.06
29	3.00	2.87	2.73	2.57	2.49	2.41	2.33	2.23	2.14	2.03
30	2.98	2.84	2.70	2.55	2.47	2.39	2.30	2.21	2.11	2.01
40	2.80	2.66	2.52	2.37	2.29	2.20	2.11	2.02	1.92	1.80
60	2.63	2.50	2.35	2.20	2.12	2.03	1.94	1.84	1.73	1.60
120	2.47	2.34	2.19	2.03	1.95	1.86	1.76	1.66	1.53	1.38
∞	2.32	2.18	2.04	1.88	1.79	1.70	1.59	1.47	1.32	1.00

Table Tolerance Factors for Normal Distributions

	Two-Sided Intervals						One-Sided Intervals					
	$\gamma = 0.05$			$\gamma = 0.01$			$\gamma = 0.05$			$\gamma = 0.01$		
	$1-\alpha$			$1-\alpha$			$1-\alpha$			$1-\alpha$		
n	0.90	0.95	0.99	0.90	0.95	0.99	0.90	0.95	0.99	0.90	0.95	0.99
2	32.019	37.674	48.430	160.193	188.491	242.300	20.581	26.260	37.094	103.029	131.426	185.617
3	8.380	9.916	12.861	18.930	22.401	29.055	6.156	7.656	10.553	13.995	17.170	23.896
4	5.369	6.370	8.299	9.398	11.150	14.527	4.162	5.144	7.042	7.380	9.083	12.387
5	4.275	5.079	6.634	6.612	7.855	10.260	3.407	4.203	5.741	5.362	6.578	8.939
6	3.712	4.414	5.775	5.337	6.345	8.301	3.006	3.708	5.062	4.411	5.406	7.335
7	3.369	4.007	5.248	4.613	5.488	7.187	2.756	3.400	4.642	3.859	4.728	6.412
8	3.136	3.732	4.891	4.147	4.936	6.468	2.582	3.187	4.354	3.497	4.285	5.812
9	2.967	3.532	4.631	3.822	4.550	5.966	2.454	3.031	4.143	3.241	3.972	5.389
10	2.839	3.379	4.433	3.582	4.265	5.594	2.355	2.911	3.981	3.048	3.738	5.074
11	2.737	3.259	4.277	3.397	4.045	5.308	2.275	2.815	3.852	2.898	3.556	4.829
12	2.655	3.162	4.150	3.250	3.870	5.079	2.210	2.736	3.747	2.777	3.410	4.633
13	2.587	3.081	4.044	3.130	3.727	4.893	2.155	2.671	3.659	2.677	3.290	4.472
14	2.529	3.012	3.955	3.029	3.608	4.737	2.109	2.615	3.585	2.593	3.189	4.337
15	2.480	2.954	3.878	2.945	3.507	4.605	2.068	2.566	3.520	2.522	3.102	4.222
16	2.437	2.903	3.812	2.872	3.421	4.492	2.033	2.524	3.464	2.460	3.028	4.123
17	2.400	2.858	3.754	2.808	3.345	4.393	2.002	2.486	3.414	2.405	2.963	4.037
18	2.366	2.819	3.702	2.753	3.279	4.307	1.974	2.453	3.370	2.357	2.905	3.960
19	2.337	2.784	3.656	2.703	3.221	4.230	1.949	2.423	3.331	2.314	2.854	3.892
20	2.310	2.752	3.615	2.659	3.168	4.161	1.926	2.396	3.295	2.276	2.808	3.832
25	2.208	2.631	3.457	2.494	2.972	3.904	1.838	2.292	3.158	2.129	2.633	3.601
30	2.140	2.549	3.350	2.385	2.841	3.733	1.777	2.220	3.064	2.030	2.516	3.447
35	2.090	2.490	3.272	2.306	2.748	3.611	1.732	2.167	2.995	1.957	2.430	3.334
40	2.052	2.445	3.213	2.247	2.677	3.518	1.697	2.126	2.941	1.902	2.364	3.249
45	2.021	2.408	3.165	2.200	2.621	3.444	1.669	2.092	2.898	1.857	2.312	3.180
50	1.996	2.379	3.126	2.162	2.576	3.385	1.646	2.065	2.863	1.821	2.269	3.125
60	1.958	2.333	3.066	2.103	2.506	3.293	1.609	2.022	2.807	1.764	2.202	3.038
70	1.929	2.299	3.021	2.060	2.454	3.225	1.581	1.990	2.765	1.722	2.153	2.974
80	1.907	2.272	2.986	2.026	2.414	3.173	1.559	1.965	2.733	1.688	2.114	2.924
90	1.889	2.251	2.958	1.999	2.382	3.130	1.542	1.944	2.706	1.661	2.082	2.883
100	1.874	2.233	2.934	1.977	2.355	3.096	1.527	1.927	2.684	1.639	2.056	2.850
150	1.825	2.175	2.859	1.905	2.270	2.983	1.478	1.870	2.611	1.566	1.971	2.741
200	1.798	2.143	2.816	1.865	2.222	2.921	1.450	1.837	2.570	1.524	1.923	2.679
250	1.780	2.121	2.788	1.839	2.191	2.880	1.431	1.815	2.542	1.496	1.891	2.638
300	1.767	2.106	2.767	1.820	2.169	2.850	1.417	1.800	2.522	1.476	1.868	2.608
∞	1.645	1.960	2.576	1.645	1.960	2.576	1.282	1.645	2.326	1.282	1.645	2.326

Adapted from C. Eisenhart, M. W. Hastay, and W. A. Wallis, *Techniques of Statistical Analysis*, Chapter 2, McGraw-Hill Book Company, New York, 1947. Used with permission of McGraw-Hill Book Company.

Table Sample Size for the *t*-Test of the Mean

Level of *t*-Test

$\Delta = \|\delta\|/\sigma$	$\alpha=0.005$ (Single) / $\alpha=0.01$ (Double)					$\alpha=0.01$ / $\alpha=0.02$					$\alpha=0.025$ / $\alpha=0.05$					$\alpha=0.05$ / $\alpha=0.1$				
$\beta = 0.1$	.01	.05	.1	.2	.5	.01	.05	.1	.2	.5	.01	.05	.1	.2	.5	.01	.05	.1	.2	.5
0.05																				
0.10																				
0.15																				122
0.20										139					99					70
0.25					110					90				128	64			139	101	45
0.30				134	78				115	63			119	90	45		122	97	71	32
0.35			125	99	58			109	85	47		109	88	67	34		90	72	52	24
0.40		115	97	77	45		101	85	66	37	117	84	68	51	26	101	70	55	40	19
0.45		92	77	62	37	110	81	68	53	30	93	67	54	41	21	80	55	44	33	15
0.50	100	75	63	51	30	90	66	55	43	25	76	54	44	34	18	65	45	36	27	13
0.55	83	63	53	42	26	75	55	46	36	21	63	45	37	28	15	54	38	30	22	11
0.60	71	53	45	36	22	63	47	39	31	18	53	38	32	24	13	46	32	26	19	9
0.65	61	46	39	31	20	55	41	34	27	16	46	33	27	21	12	39	28	22	17	8
0.70	53	40	34	28	17	47	35	30	24	14	40	29	24	19	10	34	24	19	15	8
0.75	47	36	30	25	16	42	31	27	21	13	35	26	21	16	9	30	21	17	13	7
0.80	41	32	27	22	14	37	28	24	19	12	31	22	19	15	9	27	19	15	12	6
0.85	37	29	24	20	13	33	25	21	17	11	28	21	17	13	8	24	17	14	11	6
0.90	34	26	22	18	12	29	23	19	16	10	25	19	16	12	7	21	15	13	10	5
0.95	31	24	20	17	11	27	21	18	14	9	23	17	14	11	7	19	14	11	9	5
1.00	28	22	19	16	10	25	19	16	13	9	21	16	13	10	6	18	13	11	8	5
1.1	24	19	16	14	9	21	16	14	12	8	18	13	11	9	6	15	11	9	7	
1.2	21	16	14	12	8	18	14	12	10	7	15	12	10	8	5	13	10	8	6	
1.3	18	15	13	11	8	16	13	11	9	6	14	10	9	7		11	8	7	6	
1.4	16	13	12	10	7	14	11	10	9	6	12	9	8	7		10	8	7	5	
1.5	15	12	11	9	7	13	10	9	8	6	11	8	7	6		9	7	6		
1.6	13	11	10	8	6	12	10	9	7	5	10	8	7	6		8	6	6		
1.7	12	10	9	8	6	11	9	8	7		9	7	6	5		8	6	5		
1.8	12	10	9	8	6	10	8	7	7		8	7	6			7	6			
1.9	11	9	8	7	6	10	8	7	6		8	6	6			7	5			
2.0	10	8	8	7	5	9	7	7	6		7	6	5			6				
2.1	10	8	7	7		8	7	6	6		7	6				6				
2.2	9	8	7	6		8	7	6	5		7	6				6				
2.3	9	7	7	6		8	6	6			6	5				5				
2.4	8	7	7	6		7	6	6			6									
2.5	8	7	6	6		7	6	6			6									
3.0	7	6	6	5		6	5	5			5									
3.5	6	5	5			5														
4.0	6																			

Value of $\Delta = \|\delta\|/\sigma$

Reproduced with permission from O. L. Davies, ed., *Design and Analysis of Industrial Experiments*, Oliver & Boyd, Edinburgh, 1956.

Table Sample Size for the *t*-Test of the Difference between Two Means

Level of *t*-Test

Single-Sided Test → α = 0.005 · Double-Sided Test → α = 0.01					α = 0.01 / α = 0.02					α = 0.025 / α = 0.05					α = 0.05 / α = 0.1				
.01	.05	.1	.2	.5	.01	.05	.1	.2	.5	.01	.05	.1	.2	.5	.01	.05	.1	.2	.5

Value of $\Delta = |\delta|/\sigma$ (β = 0.1)

Δ	.01	.05	.1	.2	.5	.01	.05	.1	.2	.5	.01	.05	.1	.2	.5	.01	.05	.1	.2	.5
0.05																				
0.10																				
0.15																				
0.20																				137
0.25															124					88
0.30										123					87					61
0.35					110					90					64				102	45
0.40					85					70				100	50			108	78	35
0.45				118	68				101	55			105	79	39		108	86	62	28
0.50				96	55			106	82	45		106	86	64	32		88	70	51	23
0.55			101	79	46		106	88	68	38		87	71	53	27	112	73	58	42	19
0.60		101	85	67	39		90	74	58	32	104	74	60	45	23	89	61	49	36	16
0.65		87	73	57	34	104	77	64	49	27	88	63	51	39	20	76	52	42	30	14
0.70	100	75	63	50	29	90	66	55	43	24	76	55	44	34	17	66	45	36	26	12
0.75	88	66	55	44	26	79	58	48	38	21	67	48	39	29	15	57	40	32	23	11
0.80	77	58	49	39	23	70	51	43	33	19	59	42	34	26	14	50	35	28	21	10
0.85	69	51	43	35	21	62	46	38	30	17	52	37	31	23	12	45	31	25	18	9
0.90	62	46	39	31	19	55	41	34	27	15	47	34	27	21	11	40	28	22	16	8
0.95	55	42	35	28	17	50	37	31	24	14	42	30	25	19	10	36	25	20	15	7
1.00	50	38	32	26	15	45	33	28	22	13	38	27	23	17	9	33	23	18	14	7
1.1	42	32	27	22	13	38	28	23	19	11	32	23	19	14	8	27	19	15	12	6
1.2	36	27	23	18	11	32	24	20	16	9	27	20	16	12	7	23	16	13	10	5
1.3	31	23	20	16	10	28	21	17	14	8	23	17	14	11	6	20	14	11	9	5
1.4	27	20	17	14	9	24	18	15	12	8	20	15	12	10	6	17	12	10	8	4
1.5	24	18	15	13	8	21	16	14	11	7	18	13	11	9	5	15	11	9	7	4
1.6	21	16	14	11	7	19	14	12	10	6	16	12	10	8	5	14	10	8	6	4
1.7	19	15	13	10	7	17	13	11	9	6	14	11	9	7	4	12	9	7	6	3
1.8	17	13	71	10	6	15	12	10	8	5	13	10	8	6	4	11	8	7	5	
1.9	16	12	11	9	6	14	11	9	8	5	12	9	7	6	4	10	7	6	5	
2.0	14	11	10	8	6	13	10	9	7	5	11	8	7	6	4	9	7	6	4	
2.1	13	10	9	8	5	12	9	8	7	5	10	8	6	5	3	8	6	5	4	
2.2	12	10	8	7	5	11	9	7	6	4	9	7	6	5		8	6	5	4	
2.3	11	9	8	7	5	10	8	7	6	4	9	7	6	5		7	5	5	4	
2.4	11	9	8	6	5	10	8	7	6	4	8	6	5	4		7	5	4	4	
2.5	10	8	7	6	4	9	7	6	5	4	8	6	5	4		6	5	4	3	
3.0	8	6	6	5	4	7	6	5	4	3	6	5	4	4		5	4	3		
3.5	6	5	5	4	3	6	5	4	4		5	4	4	3	3	4	3			
4.0	6	5	4	4		5	4	4	3		4	4	3			4				

Reproduced with permission from O. L. Davies, ed., *Design and Analysis of Industrial Experiments*, Oliver & Boyd, Edinburgh, 1956.

Table Critical Values for Bartlett's Test

	$b_k(0.01; n)$								
	Number of Populations, k								
n	2	3	4	5	6	7	8	9	10
3	0.1411	0.1672							
4	0.2843	0.3165	0.3475	0.3729	0.3937	0.4110			
5	0.3984	0.4304	0.4607	0.4850	0.5046	0.5207	0.5343	0.5458	0.5558
6	0.4850	0.5149	0.5430	0.5653	0.5832	O.5978	0.6100	0.6204	0.6293
7	0.5512	0.5787	0.6045	0.6248	0.6410	0.6542	0.6652	0.6744	0.6824
8	0.6031	0.6282	0.6518	0.6704	0.6851	0.6970	0.7069	0.7153	0.7225
9	0.6445	0.6676	0.6892	0.7062	0.7197	0.7305	0.7395	0.7471	0.7536
10	0.6783	0.6996	0.7195	0.7352	0.7475	0.7575	0.7657	0.7726	0.7786
11	0.7063	0.7260	0.7445	0.7590	0.7703	0.7795	0.7871	0.7935	0.7990
12	0.7299	0.7483	0.7654	0.7789	0.7894	0.7980	0.8050	0.8109	0.8160
13	0.7501	0.7672	0.7832	0.7958	0.8056	0.8135	0.8201	0.8256	0.8303
14	0.7674	0.7835	0.7985	0.8103	0.8195	0.8269	0.8330	0.8382	0.8426
15	0.7825	0.7977	0.8118	0.8229	0.8315	0.8385	0.8443	0.8491	0.8532
16	0.7958	0.8101	0.8235	0.8339	0.8421	0.8486	0.8541	0.8586	0.8625
17	0.8076	0.8211	0.8338	0.8436	0.8514	0.8576	0.8627	0.8670	0.8707
18	0.8181	0.8309	0.8429	0.8523	0.8596	0.8655	0.8704	0.8745	0.8780
19	0.8275	0.8397	0.8512	0.8601	0.8670	0.8727	0.8773	0.8811	0.8845
20	0.8360	0.8476	0.8586	0.8671	0.8737	0.8791	0.8835	0.8871	0.8903
21	0.8437	0.8548	0.8653	0.8734	0.8797	0.8848	0.8890	0.8926	0.8956
22	0.8507	0.8614	0.8714	0.8791	0.8852	0.8901	0.8941	0.8975	0.9004
23	0.8571	0.8673	0.8769	0.8844	0.8902	0.8949	0.8988	0.9020	0.9047
24	0.8630	0.8728	0.8820	0.8892	0.8948	0.8993	0.9030	0.9061	0.9087
25	0.8684	0.8779	0.8867	0.8936	0.8990	0.9034	0.9069	0.9099	0.9124
26	0.8734	0.8825	0.8911	0.8977	0.9029	0.9071	0.9105	0.9134	0.9158
27	0.8781	0.8869	0.8951	0.9015	0.9065	0.9105	0.9138	0.9166	0.9190
28	0.8824	0.8909	0.8988	0.9050	0.9099	0.9138	0.9169	0.9196	0.9219
29	0.8864	0.8946	0.9023	0.9083	0.9130	0.9167	0.9198	0.9224	0.9246
30	0.8902	0.8981	0.9056	0.9114	0.9159	0.9195	0.9225	0.9250	0.9271
40	0.9175	0.9235	0.9291	0.9335	0.9370	0.9397	0.9420	0.9439	0.9455
50	0.9339	0.9387	0.9433	0.9468	0.9496	0.9518	0.9536	0.9551	0.9564
60	0.9449	0.9489	0.9527	0.9557	0.9580	0.9599	0.9614	0.9626	0.9637
80	0.9586	0.9617	0.9646	0.9668	0.9685	0.9699	0.9711	0.9720	0.9728
100	0.9669	0.9693	0.9716	0.9734	0.9748	0.9759	0.9769	0.9776	0.9783

Reproduced from D. D. Dyer and J. P. Keating, "On the Determination of Critical Values for Bartlett's Test," *J. Am. Stat. Assoc.*, **75**, 1980, by permission of the Board of Directors.

Table (continued) Critical Values for Bartlett's Test

$b_k(0.05; n)$

n	\multicolumn{9}{c}{Number of Populations, k}
	2	3	4	5	6	7	8	9	10
3	0.3123	0.3058	0.3173	0.3299					
4	0.4780	0.4699	0.4803	0.4921	0.5028	0.5122	0.5204	0.5277	0.5341
5	0.5845	0.5762	0.5850	0.5952	0.6045	0.6126	0.6197	0.6260	0.6315
6	0.6563	0.6483	0.6559	0.6646	0.6727	0.6798	0.6860	0.6914	0.6961
7	0.7075	0.7000	0.7065	0.7142	0.7213	0.7275	0.7329	0.7376	0.7418
8	0.7456	0.7387	0.7444	0.7512	0.7574	0.7629	0.7677	0.7719	0.7757
9	0.7751	0.7686	0.7737	0.7798	0.7854	0.7903	0.7946	0.7984	0.8017
10	0.7984	0.7924	0.7970	0.8025	0.8076	0.8121	0.8160	0.8194	0.8224
11	0.8175	0.8118	0.8160	0.8210	0.8257	0.8298	0.8333	0.8365	0.8392
12	0.8332	0.8280	0.8317	0.8364	0.8407	0.8444	0.8477	0.8506	0.8531
13	0.8465	0.8415	0.8450	0.8493	0.8533	0.8568	0.8598	0.8625	0.8648
14	0.8578	0.8532	0.8564	0.8604	0.8641	0.8673	0.8701	0.8726	0.8748
15	0.8676	0.8632	0.8662	0.8699	0.8734	0.8764	0.8790	0.8814	0.8834
16	0.8761	0.8719	0.8747	0.8782	0.8815	0.8843	0.8868	0.8890	0.8909
17	0.8836	0.8796	0.8823	0.8856	0.8886	0.8913	0.8936	0.8957	0.8975
18	0.8902	0.8865	0.8890	0.8921	0.8949	0.8975	0.8997	0.9016	0.9033
19	0.8961	0.8926	0.8949	0.8979	0.9006	0.9030	0.9051	0.9069	0.9086
20	0.9015	0.8980	0.9003	0.9031	0.9057	0.9080	0.9100	0.9117	0.9132
21	0.9063	0.9030	0.9051	0.9078	0.9103	0.9124	0.9143	0.9160	0.9175
22	0.9106	0.9075	0.9095	0.9120	0.9144	0.9165	0.9183	0.9199	0.9213
23	0.9146	0.9116	0.9135	0.9159	0.9182	0.9202	0.9219	0.9235	0.9248
24	0.9182	0.9153	0.9172	0.9195	0.9217	0.9236	0.9253	0.9267	0.9280
25	0.9216	0.9187	0.9205	0.9228	0.9249	0.9267	0.9283	0.9297	0.9309
26	0.9246	0.9219	0.9236	0.9258	0.9278	0.9296	0.9311	0.9325	0.9336
27	0.9275	0.9249	0.9265	0.9286	0.9305	0.9322	0.9337	0.9350	0.9361
28	0.9301	0.9276	0.9292	0.9312	0.9330	0.9347	0.9361	0.9374	0.9385
29	0.9326	0.9301	0.9316	0.9336	0.9354	0.9370	0.9383	0.9396	0.9406
30	0.9348	0.9325	0.9340	0.9358	0.9376	0.9391	0.9404	0.9416	0.9426
40	0.9513	0.9495	0.9506	0.9520	0.9533	0.9545	0.9555	0.9564	0.9572
50	0.9612	0.9597	0.9606	0.9617	0.9628	0.9637	0.9645	0.9652	0.9658
60	0.9677	0.9665	0.9672	0.9681	0.9690	0.9698	0.9705	0.9710	0.9716
80	0.9758	0.9749	0.9754	0.9761	0.9768	0.9774	0.9779	0.9783	0.9787
100	0.9807	0.9799	0.9804	0.9809	0.9815	0.9819	0.9823	0.9827	0.9830

Table Critical Values for Cochran's Test

$$\alpha = 0.01$$

k	\multicolumn{14}{c}{n}
	2	3	4	5	6	7	8	9	10	11	17	37	145	∞
2	0.9999	0.9950	0.9794	0.9586	0.9373	0.9172	0.8988	0.8823	0.8674	0.8539	0.7949	0.7067	0.6062	0.5000
3	0.9933	0.9423	0.8831	0.8335	0.7933	0.7606	0.7335	0.7107	0.6912	0.6743	0.6059	0.5153	0.4230	0.3333
4	0.9676	0.8643	0.7814	0.7212	0.6761	0.6410	0.6129	0.5897	0.5702	0.5536	0.4884	0.4057	0.3251	0.2500
5	0.9279	0.7885	0.6957	0.6329	0.5875	0.5531	0.5259	0.5037	0.4854	0.4697	0.4094	0.3351	0.2644	0.2000
6	0.8828	0.7218	0.6258	0.5635	0.5195	0.4866	0.4608	0.4401	0.4229	0.4084	0.3529	0.2858	0.2229	0.1667
7	0.8376	0.6644	0.5685	0.5080	0.4659	0.4347	0.4105	0.3911	0.3751	0.3616	0.3105	0.2494	0.1929	0.1429
8	0.7945	0.6152	0.5209	0.4627	0.4226	0.3932	0.3704	0.3522	0.3373	0.3248	0.2779	0.2214	0.1700	0.1250
9	0.7544	0.5727	0.4810	0.4251	0.3870	0.3592	0.3378	0.3207	0.3067	0.2950	0.2514	0.1992	0.1521	0.1111
10	0.7175	0.5358	0.4469	0.3934	0.3572	0.3308	0.3106	0.2945	0.2813	0.2704	0.2297	0.1811	0.1376	0.1000
12	0.6528	0.4751	0.3919	0.3428	0.3099	0.2861	0.2680	0.2535	0.2419	0.2320	0.1961	0.1535	0.1157	0.0833
15	0.5747	0.4069	0.3317	0.2882	0.2593	0.2386	0.2228	0.2104	0.2002	0.1918	0.1612	0.1251	0.0934	0.0667
20	0.4799	0.3297	0.2654	0.2288	0.2048	0.1877	0.1748	0.1646	0.1567	0.1501	0.1248	0.0960	0.0709	0.0500
24	0.4247	0.2871	0.2295	0.1970	0.1759	0.1608	0.1495	0.1406	0.1338	0.1283	0.1060	0.0810	0.0595	0.0417
30	0.3632	0.2412	0.1913	0.1635	0.1454	0.1327	0.1232	0.1157	0.1100	0.1054	0.0867	0.0658	0.0480	0.0333
40	0.2940	0.1915	0.1508	0.1281	0.1135	0.1033	0.0957	0.0898	0.0853	0.0816	0.0668	0.0503	0.0363	0.0250
60	0.2151	0.1371	0.1069	0.0902	0.0796	0.0722	0.0668	0.0625	0.0594	0.0567	0.0461	0.0344	0.0245	0.0167
120	0.1225	0.0759	0.0585	0.0489	0.0429	0.0387	0.0357	0.0334	0.0316	0.0302	0.0242	0.0178	0.0125	0.0083
∞	0	0	0	0	0	0	0	0	0	0	0	0	0	0

Reproduced from C. Eisenhart, M. W. Hastay, and W. A. Wallis, *Techniques of Statistical Analysis*, Chapter 15, McGraw-Hill Book Company, New, York, 1947. Used with permission of McGraw-Hill Book Company.

Table (continued) Critical Values for Cochran's Test

$\alpha = 0.05$

k	n=2	3	4	5	6	7	8	9	10	11	17	37	145	∞
2	0.9985	0.9750	0.9392	0.9057	0.8772	0.8534	0.8332	0.8159	0.8010	0.7880	0.7341	0.6602	0.5813	0.5000
3	0.9669	0.8709	0.7977	0.7457	0.7071	0.6771	0.6530	0.6333	0.6167	0.6025	0.5466	0.4748	0.4031	0.3333
4	0.9065	0.7679	0.6841	0.6287	0.5895	0.5598	0.5365	0.5175	0.5017	0.4884	0.4366	0.3720	0.3093	0.2500
5	0.8412	0.6838	0.5981	0.5441	0.5065	0.4783	0.4564	0.4387	0.4241	0.4118	0.3645	0.3066	0.2513	0.2000
6	0.7808	0.6161	0.5321	0.4803	0.4447	0.4184	0.3980	0.3817	0.3682	0.3568	0.3135	0.2612	0.2119	0.1667
7	0.7271	0.5612	0.4800	0.4307	0.3974	0.3726	0.3535	0.3384	0.3259	0.3154	0.2756	0.2278	0.1833	0.1429
8	0.6798	0.5157	0.4377	0.3910	0.3595	0.3362	0.3185	0.3043	0.2926	0.2829	0.2462	0.2022	0.1616	0.1250
9	0.6385	0.4775	0.4027	0.3584	0.3286	0.3067	0.2901	0.2768	0.2659	0.2568	0.2226	0.1820	0.1446	0.1111
10	6.6020	0.4450	0.3733	0.3311	0.3029	0.2823	0.2666	0.2541	0.2439	0.2353	0.2032	0.1655	0.1308	0.1000
12	0.5410	0.3924	0.3264	0.2880	0.2624	0.2439	0.2299	0.2187	0.2098	0.2020	0.1737	0.1403	0.1100	0.0833
15	0.4709	0.3346	0.2758	0.2419	0.2195	0.2034	0.1911	0.1815	0.1736	0.1671	0.1429	0.1144	0.0889	0.0667
20	0.3894	0.2705	0.2205	0.1921	0.1735	0.1602	0.1501	0.1422	0.1357	0.1303	0.1108	0.0879	0.0675	0.0500
24	0.3434	0.2354	0.1907	0.1656	0.1493	0.1374	0.1286	0.1216	0.1160	0.1113	0.0942	0.0743	0.0567	0.0417
30	0.2929	0.1980	0.1593	0.1377	0.1237	0.1137	0.1061	0.1002	0.0958	0.0921	0.0771	0.0604	0.0457	0.0333
40	0.2370	0.1576	0.1259	0.1082	0.0968	0.0887	0.0827	0.0780	0.0745	0.0713	0.0595	0.0462	0.0347	0.0250
60	0.1737	0.1131	0.0895	0.0765	0.0682	0.0623	0.0583	0.0552	0.0520	0.0497	0.0411	0.0316	0.0234	0.0167
120	0.0998	0.0632	0.0495	0.0419	0.0371	0.0337	0.0312	0.0292	0.0279	0.0266	0.0218	0.0165	0.0120	0.0083
∞	0	0	0	0	0	0	0	0	0	0	0	0	0	0

Table Upper Percentage Points of the Studentized Range Distribution: Values of $q(0.05; k, v)$

Degrees of Freedom, v	Number of Treatments k								
	2	3	4	5	6	7	8	9	10
1	18.0	27.0	32.8	37.2	40.5	43.1	15.1	47.1	49.1
2	6.09	5.33	9.80	10.89	11.73	12.43	13.03	13.54	13.99
3	4.50	5.91	6.83	7.51	8.04	8.47	8.85	9.18	9.46
4	3.93	5.04	5.76	6.29	6.71	7.06	7.35	7.60	7.83
5	3.64	4.60	5.22	5.67	6.03	6.33	6.58	6.80	6.99
6	3.46	4.34	4.90	5.31	5.63	5.89	6.12	6.32	6.49
7	3.34	4.16	4.68	5.06	5.35	5.59	5.80	5.99	6.15
8	3.26	4.04	4.53	4.89	5.17	5.40	5.60	5.77	5.92
9	3.20	3.95	4.42	4.76	5.02	5.24	5.43	5.60	5.74
10	3.15	3.88	4.33	4.66	4.91	5.12	5.30	5.46	5.60
11	3.11	3.82	4.26	4.58	4.82	5.03	5.20	5.35	5.49
12	3.08	3.77	4.20	4.51	4.75	4.95	5.12	5.27	5.40
13	3.06	3.73	4.15	4.46	4.69	4.88	5.05	5.19	5.32
14	3.03	3.70	4.11	4.41	4.65	4.83	4.99	5.13	5.25
15	3.01	3.67	4.08	4.37	4.59	4.78	4.94	5.08	5.20
16	3.00	3.65	4.05	4.34	4.56	4.74	4.90	5.03	5.05
17	2.98	3.62	4.02	4.31	4.52	4.70	4.86	4.99	5.11
18	2.97	3.61	4.00	4.28	4.49	4.67	4.83	4.96	5.07
19	2.96	3.59	3.98	4.26	4.47	4.64	4.79	4.92	5.04
20	2.95	3.58	3.96	4.24	4.45	4.62	4.77	4.90	5.01
24	2.92	3.53	3.90	4.17	4.37	4.54	4.68	4.81	4.92
30	2.89	3.48	3.84	4.11	4.30	4.46	4.60	4.72	4.83
40	2.86	3.44	3.79	4.04	4.23	4.39	4.52	4.63	4.74
60	2.83	3.40	3.74	3.98	4.16	4.31	4.44	4.55	4.65
120	2.80	3.36	3.69	3.92	4.10	4.24	4.36	4.47	4.56
∞	2.77	3.32	3.63	3.86	4.03	4.17	4.29	4.39	4.47

Table Least Significant Studentized Ranges $r_p(0.05; p, v)$

$\alpha = 0.05$

v	p								
	2	**3**	**4**	**5**	**6**	**7**	**8**	**9**	**10**
1	17.97	17.97	17.97	17.97	17.97	17.97	17.97	17.97	17.97
2	6.085	6.085	6.085	6.085	6.085	6.085	6.085	6.085	6.085
3	4.501	4.516	4.516	4.516	4.516	4.516	4.516	4.516	4.516
4	3.927	4.013	4.033	4.033	4.033	4.033	4.033	4.033	4.033
5	3.635	3.749	3.797	3.814	3.814	3.814	3.814	3.814	3.814
6	3.461	3.587	3.649	3.68	3.694	3.697	3.697	3.697	3.697
7	3.344	3.477	3.548	3.588	3.611	3.622	3.626	3.626	3.626
8	3.261	3.399	3.475	3.521	3.549	3.566	3.575	3.579	3.579
9	3.199	3.339	3.420	3.470	3.502	3.523	3.536	3.544	3.547
10	3.151	3.293	3.376	3.430	3.465	3.489	3.505	3.516	3.522
11	3.113	3.256	3.342	3.397	3.435	3.462	3.48	3.493	3.501
12	3.082	3.225	3.313	3.370	3.410	3.439	3.459	3.474	3.484
13	3.055	3.200	3.289	3.348	3.389	3.419	3.442	3.458	3.470
14	3.033	3.178	3.268	3.329	3.372	3.403	3.426	3.444	3.457
15	3.014	3.160	3.25	3.312	3.356	3.389	3.413	3.432	3.446
16	2.998	3.144	3.235	3.298	3.343	3.376	3.402	3.422	3.437
17	2.984	3.130	3.222	3.285	3.331	3.366	3.392	3.412	3.429
18	2.971	3.118	3.210	3.274	3.321	3.356	3.383	3.405	3.421
19	2.960	3.107	3.199	3.264	3.311	3.347	3.375	3.397	3.415
20	2.950	3.097	3.190	3.255	3.303	3.339	3.368	3.391	3.409
24	2.919	3.066	3.160	3.226	3.276	3.315	3.345	3.370	3.390
30	2.888	3.035	3.131	3.199	3.250	3.290	3.322	3.349	3.371
40	2.858	3.006	3.102	3.171	3.224	3.266	3.300	3.328	3.352
60	2.829	2.976	3.073	3.143	3.198	3.241	3.277	3.307	3.333
120	2.800	2.947	3.045	3.116	3.172	3.217	3.254	3.287	3.314
∞	2.772	2.918	3.017	3.089	3.146	3.193	3.232	3.265	3.294

Abridged from H. L. Harter, "Critical Values for Duncan's New Multiple Range Test," *Biometrics*, **16**, No. 4, 1960, by permission of the author and the editor.

Table (continued) Least Significant Studentized Ranges $r_p(0.01; p, v)$

					$\alpha = 0.01$				
					p				
v	2	3	4	5	6	7	8	9	10
1	90.03	90.03	90.03	90.03	90.03	90.03	90.03	90.03	90.03
2	14.04	14.04	14.04	14.04	14.04	14.04	14.04	14.04	14.04
3	8.261	8.321	8.321	8.321	8.321	8.321	8.321	8.321	8.321
4	6.512	6.677	6.740	6.756	6.756	6.756	6.756	6.756	6.756
5	5.702	5.893	5.989	6.040	6.065	6.074	6.074	6.074	6.074
6	5.243	5.439	5.549	5.614	5.655	5.680	5.694	5.701	5.703
7	4.949	5.145	5.260	5.334	5.383	5.416	5.439	5.454	5.464
8	4.746	4.939	5.057	5.135	5.189	5.227	5.256	5.276	5.291
9	4.596	4.787	4.906	4.986	5.043	5.086	5.118	5.142	5.160
10	4.482	4.671	4.790	4.871	4.931	4.975	5.010	5.037	5.058
11	4.392	4.579	4.697	4.780	4.841	4.887	4.924	4.952	4.975
12	4.320	4.504	4.622	4.706	4.767	4.815	4.852	4.883	4.907
13	4.260	4.442	4.560	4.644	4.706	4.755	4.793	4.824	4.850
14	4.210	4.391	4.508	4.591	4.654	4.704	4.743	4.775	4.802
15	4.168	4.347	4.463	4.547	4.610	4.660	4.700	4.733	4.760
16	4.131	4.309	4.425	4.509	4.572	4.622	4.663	4.696	4.724
17	4.099	4.275	4.391	4.475	4.539	4.589	4.630	4.664	4.693
18	4.071	4.246	4.362	4.445	4.509	4.560	4.601	4.635	4.664
19	4.046	4.220	4.335	4.419	4.483	4.534	4.575	4.610	4.639
20	4.024	4.197	4.312	4.395	4.459	4.510	4.552	4.587	4.617
24	3.956	4.126	4.239	4.322	4.386	4.437	4.480	4.516	4.546
30	3.889	4.056	4.168	4.250	4.314	4.366	4.409	4.445	4.477
40	3.825	3.988	4.098	4.180	4.244	4.296	4.339	4.376	4.408
60	3.762	3.922	4.031	4.111	4.174	4.226	4.270	4.307	4.340
120	3.702	3.858	3.965	4.044	4.107	4.158	4.202	4.239	4.272
∞	3.643	3.796	3.900	3.978	4.040	4.091	4.135	4.172	4.205

Table Values of $d_{\alpha/2}(k, v)$ for Two-Sided Comparisons between k Treatments and a Control

	$\alpha = 0.05$								
	k = Number of Treatment Means (excluding control)								
v	1	2	3	4	5	6	7	8	9
5	2.57	3.03	3.29	3.48	3.62	3.73	3.82	3.90	3.97
6	2.45	2.86	3.10	3.26	3.39	3.49	3.57	3.64	3.71
7	2.36	2.75	2.97	3.12	3.24	3.33	3.41	3.47	3.53
8	2.31	2.67	2.88	3.02	3.13	3.22	3.29	3.35	3.41
9	2.26	2.61	2.81	2.95	3.05	3.14	3.20	3.26	3.32
10	2.23	2.57	2.76	2.89	2.99	3.07	3.14	3.19	3.24
11	2.20	2.53	2.72	2.84	2.94	3.02	3.08	3.14	3.19
12	2.18	2.50	2.68	2.81	2.90	2.98	3.04	3.09	3.14
13	2.16	2.48	2.65	2.78	2.87	2.94	3.00	3.06	3.10
14	2.14	2.46	2.63	2.75	2.84	2.91	2.97	3.02	3.07
15	2.13	2.44	2.61	2.73	2.82	2.89	2.95	3.00	3.04
16	2.12	2.42	2.59	2.71	2.80	2.87	2.92	2.97	3.02
17	2.11	2.41	2.58	2.69	2.78	2.85	2.90	2.95	3.00
18	2.10	2.40	2.56	2.68	2.76	2.83	2.89	2.94	2.98
19	2.09	2.39	2.55	2.66	2.75	2.81	2.87	2.92	2.96
20	2.09	2.38	2.54	2.65	2.73	2.80	2.86	2.90	2.95
24	2.06	2.35	2.51	2.61	2.70	2.76	2.81	2.86	2.90
30	2.04	2.32	2.47	2.58	2.66	2.72	2.77	2.82	2.86
40	2.02	2.29	2.44	2.54	2.62	2.68	2.73	2.77	2.81
60	2.00	2.27	2.41	2.51	2.58	2.64	2.69	2.73	2.77
120	1.98	2.24	2.38	2.47	2.55	2.60	2.65	2.69	2.73
∞	1.96	2.21	2.35	2.44	2.51	2.57	2.61	2.65	2.69

Reproduced from Charles W. Dunnett, "New Tables for Multiple Comparison with a Control," *Biometrics*, **20**, No. 3, 1964, by permission of the author and the editor.

Table (continued) Values of $d_{\alpha/2}(k, v)$ for Two-Sided Comparisons between k Treatments and a Control

	$\alpha = 0.01$								
	k = Number of Treatment Means (excluding control)								
v	1	2	3	4	5	6	7	8	9
5	4.03	4.63	4.98	5.22	5.41	5.56	5.69	5.80	5.89
6	3.71	4.21	4.51	4.71	4.87	5.00	5.10	5.20	5.28
7	3.50	3.95	4.21	4.39	4.53	4.64	4.74	4.82	4.89
8	3.36	3.77	4.00	4.17	4.29	4.40	4.48	4.56	4.62
9	3.25	3.63	3.85	4.01	4.12	4.22	4.30	4.37	4.43
10	3.17	3.53	3.74	3.88	3.99	4.08	4.16	4.22	4.28
11	3.11	3.45	3.65	3.79	3.89	3.98	4.05	4.11	4.16
12	3.05	3.39	3.58	3.71	3.81	3.89	3.96	4.02	4.07
13	3.01	3.33	3.52	3.65	3.74	3.82	3.89	3.94	3.99
14	2.98	3.29	3.47	3.59	3.69	3.76	3.83	3.88	3.93
15	2.95	3.25	3.43	3.55	3.64	3.71	3.78	3.83	3.88
16	2.92	3.22	3.39	3.51	3.60	3.67	3.73	3.78	3.83
17	2.90	3.19	3.36	3.47	3.56	3.63	3.69	3.74	3.79
18	2.88	3.17	3.33	3.44	3.53	3.60	3.66	3.71	3.75
19	2.86	3.15	3.31	3.42	3.50	3.57	3.63	3.68	3.72
20	2.85	3.13	3.29	3.40	3.48	3.55	3.60	3.65	3.69
24	2.80	3.07	3.22	3.32	3.40	3.47	3.52	3.57	3.61
30	2.75	3.01	3.15	3.25	3.33	3.39	3.44	3.49	3.52
40	2.70	2.95	3.09	3.19	3.26	3.32	3.37	3.41	3.44
60	2.66	2.90	3.03	3.12	3.19	3.25	3.29	3.33	3.37
120	2.62	2.85	2.97	3.06	3.12	3.18	3.22	3.26	3.29
∞	2.58	2.79	2.92	3.00	3.06	3.11	3.15	3.19	3.22

Appendix: Statistical Tables and Proofs

Table Values of $d_\alpha(k,v)$ for One-Sided Comparisons between k Treatments and a Control

$\alpha = 0.05$

k = Number of Treatment Means (excluding control)

v	1	2	3	4	5	6	7	8	9
5	2.02	2.44	2.68	2.85	2.98	3.08	3.16	3.24	3.30
6	1.94	2.34	2.56	2.71	2.83	2.92	3.00	3.07	3.12
7	1.89	2.27	2.48	2.62	2.73	2.82	2.89	2.95	3.01
8	1.86	2.22	2.42	2.55	2.66	2.74	2.81	2.87	2.92
9	1.83	2.18	2.37	2.50	2.60	2.68	2.75	2.81	2.86
10	1.81	2.15	2.34	2.47	2.56	2.64	2.70	2.76	2.81
11	1.80	2.13	2.31	2.44	2.53	2.60	2.67	2.72	2.77
12	1.78	2.11	2.29	2.41	2.50	2.58	2.64	2.69	2.74
13	1.77	2.09	2.27	2.39	2.48	2.55	2.61	2.66	2.71
14	1.76	2.08	2.25	2.37	2.46	2.53	2.59	2.64	2.69
15	1.75	2.07	2.24	2.36	2.44	2.51	2.57	2.62	2.67
16	1.75	2.06	2.23	2.34	2.43	2.50	2.56	2.61	2.65
17	1.74	2.05	2.22	2.33	2.42	2.49	2.54	2.59	2.64
18	1.73	2.04	2.21	2.32	2.41	2.48	2.53	2.58	2.62
19	1.73	2.03	2.20	2.31	2.40	2.47	2.52	2.57	2.61
20	1.72	2.03	2.19	2.30	2.39	2.46	2.51	2.56	2.60
24	1.71	2.01	2.17	2.28	2.36	2.43	2.48	2.53	2.57
30	1.70	1.99	2.15	2.25	2.33	2.40	2.45	2.50	2.54
40	1.68	1.97	2.13	2.23	2.31	2.37	2.42	2.47	2.51
60	1.67	1.95	2.10	2.21	2.28	2.35	2.39	2.44	2.48
120	1.66	1.93	2.08	2.18	2.26	2.32	2.37	2.41	2.45
∞	1.64	1.92	2.06	2.16	2.23	2.29	2.34	2.38	2.42

Reproduced from Charles W. Dunnett, "A Multiple Comparison Procedure for Comparing Several Treatments with a Control," *J. Am. Stat. Assoc.*, **50**, 1955, 1096–1121, by permission of the author and the editor.

Table (continued) Values of $d_\alpha(k, v)$ for One-Sided Comparisons between k Treatments and a Control

	$\alpha = 0.01$								
	$k =$ **Number of Treatment Means (excluding control)**								
v	**1**	**2**	**3**	**4**	**5**	**6**	**7**	**8**	**9**
5	3.37	3.90	4.21	4.43	4.60	4.73	4.85	4.94	5.03
6	3.14	3.61	3.88	4.07	4.21	4.33	4.43	4.51	4.59
7	3.00	3.42	3.66	3.83	3.96	4.07	4.15	4.23	4.30
8	2.90	3.29	3.51	3.67	3.79	3.88	3.96	4.03	4.09
9	2.82	3.19	3.40	3.55	3.66	3.75	3.82	3.89	3.94
10	2.76	3.11	3.31	3.45	3.56	3.64	3.71	3.78	3.83
11	2.72	3.06	3.25	3.38	3.48	3.56	3.63	3.69	3.74
12	2.68	3.01	3.19	3.32	3.42	3.50	3.56	3.62	3.67
13	2.65	2.97	3.15	3.27	3.37	3.44	3.51	3.56	3.61
14	2.62	2.94	3.11	3.23	3.32	3.40	3.46	3.51	3.56
15	2.60	2.91	3.08	3.20	3.29	3.36	3.42	3.47	3.52
16	2.58	2.88	3.05	3.17	3.26	3.33	3.39	3.44	3.48
17	2.57	2.86	3.03	3.14	3.23	3.30	3.36	3.41	3.45
18	2.55	2.84	3.01	3.12	3.21	3.27	3.33	3.38	3.42
19	2.54	2.83	2.99	3.10	3.18	3.25	3.31	3.36	3.40
20	2.53	2.81	2.97	3.08	3.17	3.23	3.29	3.34	3.38
24	2.49	2.77	2.92	3.03	3.11	3.17	3.22	3.27	3.31
30	2.46	2.72	2.87	2.97	3.05	3.11	3.16	3.21	3.24
40	2.42	2.68	2.82	2.92	2.99	3.05	3.10	3.14	3.18
60	2.39	2.64	2.78	2.87	2.94	3.00	3.04	3.08	3.12
120	2.36	2.60	2.73	2.82	2.89	2.94	2.99	3.03	3.06
∞	2.33	2.56	2.68	2.77	2.84	2.89	2.93	2.97	3.00

Table Critical Values for the Signed-Rank Test

n	One-Sided $\alpha = 0.01$ Two-Sided $\alpha = 0.02$	One-Sided $\alpha = 0.025$ Two-Sided $\alpha = 0.05$	One-Sided $\alpha = 0.05$ Two-Sided $\alpha = 0.1$
5			1
6		1	2
7	0	2	4
8	2	4	6
9	3	6	8
10	5	8	11
11	7	11	14
12	10	14	17
13	13	17	21
14	16	21	26
15	20	25	30
16	24	30	36
17	28	35	41
18	33	40	47
19	38	46	54
20	43	52	60
21	49	59	68
22	56	66	75
23	62	73	83
24	69	81	92
25	77	90	101
26	85	98	110
27	93	107	120
28	102	117	130
29	111	127	141
30	120	137	152

Reproduced from F. Wilcoxon and R. A. Wilcox, *Some Rapid Approximate Statistical Procedures, American Cyanamid Company*, Pearl River, N.Y., 1964, by permission of the American Cyanamid Company.

Table Critical Values for the Wilcoxon Rank-Sum Test

One-Tailed Test at $\alpha = 0.001$ or Two-Tailed Test at $\alpha = 0.002$

n_1	\multicolumn{15}{c}{n_2}														
	6	7	8	9	10	11	12	13	14	15	16	17	18	19	20
1															
2															
3												0	0	0	0
4					0	0	0	1	1	1	2	2	3	3	3
5		0	0	1	1	2	2	3	3	4	5	5	6	7	7
6	0	1	2	2	3	4	4	5	6	7	8	9	10	11	12
7		2	3	3	5	6	7	8	9	10	11	13	14	15	16
8			5	5	6	8	9	11	12	14	15	17	18	20	21
9				7	8	10	12	14	15	17	19	21	23	25	26
10					10	12	14	17	19	21	23	25	27	29	32
11						15	17	20	22	24	27	29	32	34	37
12							20	23	25	28	31	34	37	40	42
13								26	29	32	35	38	42	45	48
14									32	36	39	43	46	50	54
15										40	43	47	51	55	59
16											48	52	56	60	65
17												57	61	66	70
18													66	71	76
19														77	82
20															88

One-Tailed Test at $\alpha = 0.01$ or Two-Tailed Test at $\alpha = 0.02$

n_1	\multicolumn{16}{c}{n_2}															
	5	6	7	8	9	10	11	12	13	14	15	16	17	18	19	20
1																
2									0	0	0	0	0	0	1	1
3			0	0	1	1	1	2	2	2	3	3	4	4	4	5
4	0	1	1	2	3	3	4	5	5	6	7	7	8	9	9	10
5	1	2	3	4	5	6	7	8	9	10	11	12	13	14	15	16
6		3	4	6	7	8	9	11	12	13	15	16	18	19	20	22
7			6	8	9	11	12	14	16	17	19	21	23	24	26	28
8				10	11	13	15	17	20	22	24	26	28	30	32	34
9					14	16	18	21	23	26	28	31	33	36	38	40
10						19	22	24	27	30	33	36	38	41	44	47
11							25	28	31	34	37	41	44	47	50	53
12								31	35	38	42	46	49	53	56	60
13									39	43	47	51	55	59	63	67
14										47	51	56	60	65	69	73
15											56	61	66	70	75	80
16												66	71	76	82	87
17													77	82	88	93
18														88	94	100
19															101	107
20																114

Based in part on Tables 1, 3, 5, and 7 of D. Auble, "Extended Tables for the Mann-Whitney Statistic," *Bulletin of the Institute of Educational Research at Indiana University*, **1**, No. 2, 1953, by permission of the director.

Table (continued) Critical Values for the Wilcoxon Rank-Sum Test

One-Tailed Test at $\alpha = 0.025$ or Two-Tailed Test at $\alpha = 0.05$

n_1	\multicolumn{17}{c}{n_2}																
	4	5	6	7	8	9	10	11	12	13	14	15	16	17	18	19	20
1																	
2					0	0	0	0	1	1	1	1	1	2	2	2	2
3		0	1	1	2	2	3	3	4	4	5	5	6	6	7	7	8
4	0	1	2	3	4	4	5	6	7	8	9	10	11	11	12	13	13
5		2	3	5	6	7	8	9	11	12	13	14	15	17	18	19	20
6			5	6	8	10	11	13	14	16	17	19	21	22	24	25	27
7				8	10	12	14	16	18	20	22	24	26	28	30	32	34
8					13	15	17	19	22	24	26	29	31	34	36	38	41
9						17	20	23	26	28	31	34	37	39	42	45	48
10							23	26	29	33	36	39	42	45	48	52	55
11								30	33	37	40	44	47	51	55	58	62
12									37	41	45	49	53	57	61	65	69
13										45	50	54	59	63	67	72	76
14											55	59	64	67	74	78	83
15												64	70	75	80	85	90
16													75	81	86	92	98
17														87	93	99	105
18															99	106	112
19																113	119
20																	127

One-Tailed Test at $\alpha = 0.05$ or Two-Tailed Test at $\alpha = 0.1$

n_1	\multicolumn{18}{c}{n_2}																	
	3	4	5	6	7	8	9	10	11	12	13	14	15	16	17	18	19	20
1																	0	0
2			0	0	0	1	1	1	1	2	2	3	3	3	3	4	4	4
3	0	0	1	2	2	3	4	4	5	5	6	7	7	8	9	9	10	11
4		1	2	3	4	5	6	7	8	9	10	11	12	14	15	16	17	18
5			4	5	6	8	9	11	12	13	15	16	18	19	20	22	23	25
6				7	8	10	12	14	16	17	19	21	23	25	26	28	30	32
7					11	13	15	17	19	21	24	26	28	30	33	35	37	39
8						15	18	20	23	26	28	31	33	36	39	41	44	47
9							21	24	27	30	33	36	39	42	45	48	51	54
10								27	31	34	37	41	44	48	51	55	58	62
11									34	38	42	46	50	54	57	61	65	69
12										42	47	51	55	60	64	68	72	77
13											51	56	61	65	70	75	80	84
14												61	66	71	77	82	87	92
15													72	77	83	88	94	100
16														83	89	95	101	107
17															96	102	109	115
18																109	116	123
19																	123	130
20																		138

Table $P(V \leq v^*$ when H_0 is true) in the Runs Test

	v^*								
(n_1, n_2)	**2**	**3**	**4**	**5**	**6**	**7**	**8**	**9**	**10**
(2, 3)	0.200	0.500	0.900	1.000					
(2, 4)	0.133	0.400	0.800	1.000					
(2, 5)	0.095	0.333	0.714	1.000					
(2, 6)	0.071	0.286	0.643	1.000					
(2, 7)	0.056	0.250	0.583	1.000					
(2, 8)	0.044	0.222	0.533	1.000					
(2, 9)	0.036	0.200	0.491	1.000					
(2, 10)	0.030	0.182	0.455	1.000					
(3, 3)	0.100	0.300	0.700	0.900	1.000				
(3, 4)	0.057	0.200	0.543	0.800	0.971	1.000			
(3, 5)	0.036	0.143	0.429	0.714	0.929	1.000			
(3, 6)	0.024	0.107	0.345	0.643	0.881	1.000			
(3, 7)	0.017	0.083	0.283	0.583	0.833	1.000			
(3, 8)	0.012	0.067	0.236	0.533	0.788	1.000			
(3, 9)	0.009	0.055	0.200	0.491	0.745	1.000			
(3, 10)	0.007	0.045	0.171	0.455	0.706	1.000			
(4, 4)	0.029	0.114	0.371	0.629	0.886	0.971	1.000		
(4, 5)	0.016	0.071	0.262	0.500	0.786	0.929	0.992	1.000	
(4, 6)	0.010	0.048	0.190	0.405	0.690	0.881	0.976	1.000	
(4, 7)	0.006	0.033	0.142	0.333	0.606	0.833	0.954	1.000	
(4, 8)	0.004	0.024	0.109	0.279	0.533	0.788	0.929	1.000	
(4, 9)	0.003	0.018	0.085	0.236	0.471	0.745	0.902	1.000	
(4, 10)	0.002	0.014	0.068	0.203	0.419	0.706	0.874	1.000	
(5, 5)	0.008	0.040	0.167	0.357	0.643	0.833	0.960	0.992	1.000
(5, 6)	0.004	0.024	0.110	0.262	0.522	0.738	0.911	0.976	0.998
(5, 7)	0.003	0.015	0.076	0.197	0.424	0.652	0.854	0.955	0.992
(5, 8)	0.002	0.010	0.054	0.152	0.347	0.576	0.793	0.929	0.984
(5, 9)	0.001	0.007	0.039	0.119	0.287	0.510	0.734	0.902	0.972
(5, 10)	0.001	0.005	0.029	0.095	0.239	0.455	0.678	0.874	0.958
(6, 6)	0.002	0.013	0.067	0.175	0.392	0.608	0.825	0.933	0.987
(6, 7)	0.001	0.008	0.043	0.121	0.296	0.500	0.733	0.879	0.966
(6, 8)	0.001	0.005	0.028	0.086	0.226	0.413	0.646	0.821	0.937
(6, 9)	0.000	0.003	0.019	0.063	0.175	0.343	0.566	0.762	0.902
(6, 10)	0.000	0.002	0.013	0.047	0.137	0.288	0.497	0.706	0.864
(7, 7)	0.001	0.004	0.025	0.078	0.209	0.383	0.617	0.791	0.922
(7, 8)	0.000	0.002	0.015	0.051	0.149	0.296	0.514	0.704	0.867
(7, 9)	0.000	0.001	0.010	0.035	0.108	0.231	0.427	0.622	0.806
(7, 10)	0.000	0.001	0.006	0.024	0.080	0.182	0.355	0.549	0.743
(8, 8)	0.000	0.001	0.009	0.032	0.100	0.214	0.405	0.595	0.786
(8, 9)	0.000	0.001	0.005	0.020	0.069	0.157	0.319	0.500	0.702
(8, 10)	0.000	0.000	0.003	0.013	0.048	0.117	0.251	0.419	0.621
(9, 9)	0.000	0.000	0.003	0.012	0.044	0.109	0.238	0.399	0.601
(9, 10)	0.000	0.000	0.002	0.008	0.029	0.077	0.179	0.319	0.510
(10, 10)	0.000	0.000	0.001	0.004	0.019	0.051	0.128	0.242	0.414

Reproduced from C. Eisenhart and R. Swed, "Tables for Testing Randomness of Grouping in a Sequence of Alternatives," *Ann. Math. Stat.*, **14**, 1943, by permission of the editor.

Table (continued) $P(V \leq v^*$ when H_0 is true) in the Runs Test

	v^*									
(n_1, n_2)	11	12	13	14	15	16	17	18	19	20
$(2, 3)$										
$(2, 4)$										
$(2, 5)$										
$(2, 6)$										
$(2, 7)$										
$(2, 8)$										
$(2, 9)$										
$(2, 10)$										
$(3, 3)$										
$(3, 4)$										
$(3, 5)$										
$(3, 6)$										
$(3, 7)$										
$(3, 8)$										
$(3, 9)$										
$(3, 10)$										
$(4, 4)$										
$(4, 5)$										
$(4, 6)$										
$(4, 7)$										
$(4, 8)$										
$(4, 9)$										
$(4, 10)$										
$(5, 5)$										
$(5, 6)$	1.000									
$(5, 7)$	1.000									
$(5, 8)$	1.000									
$(5, 9)$	1.000									
$(5, 10)$	1.000									
$(6, 6)$	0.998	1.000								
$(6, 7)$	0.992	0.999	1.000							
$(6, 8)$	0.984	0.998	1.000							
$(6, 9)$	0.972	0.994	1.000							
$(6, 10)$	0.958	0.990	1.000							
$(7, 7)$	0.975	0.996	0.999	1.000						
$(7, 8)$	0.949	0.988	0.998	1.000	1.000					
$(7, 9)$	0.916	0.975	0.994	0.999	1.000					
$(7, 10)$	0.879	0.957	0.990	0.998	1.000					
$(8, 8)$	0.900	0.968	0.991	0.999	1.000	1.000				
$(8, 9)$	0.843	0.939	0.980	0.996	0.999	1.000	1.000			
$(8, 10)$	0.782	0.903	0.964	0.990	0.998	1.000	1.000			
$(9, 9)$	0.762	0.891	0.956	0.988	0.997	1.000	1.000	1.000		
$(9, 10)$	0.681	0.834	0.923	0.974	0.992	0.999	1.000	1.000	1.000	
$(10, 10)$	0.586	0.758	0.872	0.949	0.981	0.996	0.999	1.000	1.000	1.000

Table Sample Size for Two-Sided Nonparametric Tolerance Limits

1 − α	1 − γ					
	0.50	0.70	0.90	0.95	0.99	0.995
0.995	336	488	777	947	1325	1483
0.99	168	244	388	473	662	740
0.95	34	49	77	93	130	146
0.90	17	24	38	46	64	72
0.85	11	16	25	30	42	47
0.80	9	12	18	22	31	34
0.75	7	10	15	18	24	27
0.70	6	8	12	14	20	22
0.60	4	6	9	10	14	16
0.50	3	5	7	8	11	12

Table A–25d of Wilfrid J. Dixon and Frank J. Massey, Jr., *Introduction to Statistical Analysis*, 3rd ed. McGraw-Hill, 1969. Reprinted with permission by The McGraw-Hill Companies, Inc.

Table Sample Size for One-Sided Nonparametric Tolerance Limits

1 − α	1 − γ				
	0.50	0.70	0.95	0.99	0.995
0.995	139	241	598	919	1379
0.99	69	120	299	459	688
0.95	14	24	59	90	135
0.90	7	12	29	44	66
0.85	5	8	19	29	43
0.80	4	6	14	21	31
0.75	3	5	11	7	25
0.70	2	4	9	13	20
0.60	2	3	6	10	14
0.50	1	2	5	7	10

Table A–25e of Wilfrid J. Dixon and Frank J. Massey, Jr., *Introduction to Statistical Analysis*, 3rd ed. McGraw-Hill, 1969. Reprinted with permission by The McGraw-Hill Companies, Inc.

Table Critical Values for Spearman's Rank Correlation Coefficients

n	$\alpha = 0.05$	$\alpha = 0.025$	$\alpha = 0.01$	$\alpha = 0.005$
5	0.900			
6	0.829	0.886	0.943	
7	0.714	0.786	0.893	
8	0.643	0.738	0.833	0.881
9	0.600	0.683	0.783	0.833
10	0.564	0.648	0.745	0.794
11	0.523	0.623	0.736	0.818
12	0.497	0.591	0.703	0.780
13	0.475	0.566	0.673	0.745
14	0.457	0.545	0.646	0.716
15	0.441	0.525	0.623	0.689
16	0.425	0.507	0.601	0.666
17	0.412	0.490	0.582	0.645
18	0.399	0.476	0.564	0.625
19	0.388	0.462	0.549	0.608
20	0.377	0.450	0.534	0.591
21	0.368	0.438	0.521	0.576
22	0.359	0.428	0.508	0.562
23	0.351	0.418	0.496	0.549
24	0.343	0.409	0.485	0.537
25	0.336	0.400	0.475	0.526
26	0.329	0.392	0.465	0.515
27	0.323	0.385	0.456	0.505
28	0.317	0.377	0.448	0.496
29	0.311	0.370	0.440	0.487
30	0.305	0.364	0.432	0.478

Reproduced from E. G. Olds, "Distribution of Sums of Squares of Rank Differences for Small Samples," *Ann. Math. Stat.*, **9**, 1938, by permission of the editor.

Table Factors for Constructing Control Charts

Obs. in Sample	Chart for Averages		Chart for Standard Deviations						Chart for Ranges				
	Factors for Control Limits		Factors for Centerline		Factors for Control Limits				Factors for Centerline		Factors for Control Limits		
n	A_2	A_3	c_4	$1/c_4$	B_3	B_4	B_5	B_6	d_2	$1/d_2$	d_3	D_3	D_4
2	1.880	2.659	0.7979	1.2533	0	3.267	0	2.606	1.128	0.8865	0.853	0	3.267
3	1.023	1.954	0.8862	1.1284	0	2.568	0	2.276	1.693	0.5907	0.888	0	2.574
4	0.729	1.628	0.9213	1.0854	0	2.266	0	2.088	2.059	0.4857	0.880	0	2.282
5	0.577	1.427	0.9400	1.0638	0	2.089	0	1.964	2.326	0.4299	0.864	0	2.114
6	0.483	1.287	0.9515	1.0510	0.030	1.970	0.029	1.874	2.534	0.3946	0.848	0	2.004
7	0.419	1.182	0.9594	1.0423	0.118	1.882	0.113	1.806	2.704	0.3698	0.833	0.076	1.924
8	0.373	1.099	0.9650	1.0363	0.185	1.815	0.179	1.751	2.847	0.3512	0.820	0.136	1.864
9	0.337	1.032	0.9693	1.0317	0.239	1.761	0.232	1.707	2.970	0.3367	0.808	0.184	1.816
10	0.308	0.975	0.9727	1.0281	0.284	1.716	0.276	1.669	3.078	0.3249	0.797	0.223	1.777
11	0.285	0.927	0.9754	1.0252	0.321	1.679	0.313	1.637	3.173	0.3152	0.787	0.256	1.744
12	0.266	0.886	0.9776	1.0229	0.354	1.646	0.346	1.610	3.258	0.3069	0.778	0.283	1.717
13	0.249	0.850	0.9794	1.0210	0.382	1.618	0.374	1.585	3.336	0.2998	0.770	0.307	1.693
14	0.235	0.817	0.9810	1.0194	0.406	1.594	0.399	1.563	3.407	0.2935	0.763	0.328	1.672
15	0.223	0.789	0.9823	1.0180	0.428	1.572	0.421	1.544	3.472	0.2880	0.756	0.347	1.653
16	0.212	0.763	0.9835	1.0168	0.448	1.552	0.440	1.526	3.532	0.2831	0.750	0.363	1.637
17	0.203	0.739	0.9845	1.0157	0.466	1.534	0.458	1.511	3.588	0.2787	0.744	0.378	1.622
18	0.194	0.718	0.9854	1.0148	0.482	1.518	0.475	1.496	3.640	0.2747	0.739	0.391	1.608
19	0.187	0.698	0.9862	1.0140	0.497	1.503	0.490	1.483	3.689	0.2711	0.734	0.403	1.597
20	0.180	0.680	0.9869	1.0133	0.510	1.490	0.504	1.470	3.735	0.2677	0.729	0.415	1.585
21	0.173	0.663	0.9876	1.0126	0.523	1.477	0.516	1.459	3.778	0.2647	0.724	0.425	1.575
22	0.167	0.647	0.9882	1.0119	0.534	1.466	0.528	1.448	3.819	0.2618	0.720	0.434	1.566
23	0.162	0.633	0.9887	1.0114	0.545	1.455	0.539	1.438	3.858	0.2592	0.716	0.443	1.557
24	0.157	0.619	0.9892	1.0109	0.555	1.445	0.549	1.429	3.895	0.2567	0.712	0.451	1.548
25	0.153	0.606	0.9896	1.0105	0.565	1.435	0.559	1.420	3.931	0.2544	0.708	0.459	4.541

Table The Incomplete Gamma Function: $F(x; \alpha) = \int_0^x \frac{1}{\Gamma(\alpha)} y^{\alpha-1} e^{-y} \, dy$

					α					
x	1	2	3	4	5	6	7	8	9	10
1	0.6320	0.2640	0.0800	0.0190	0.0040	0.0010	0.0000	0.0000	0.0000	0.0000
2	0.8650	0.5940	0.3230	0.1430	0.0530	0.0170	0.0050	0.0010	0.0000	0.0000
3	0.9500	0.8010	0.5770	0.3530	0.1850	0.0840	0.0340	0.0120	0.0040	0.0010
4	0.9820	0.9080	0.7620	0.5670	0.3710	0.2150	0.1110	0.0510	0.0210	0.0080
5	0.9930	0.9600	0.8750	0.7350	0.5600	0.3840	0.2380	0.1330	0.0680	0.0320
6	0.9980	0.9830	0.9380	0.8490	0.7150	0.5540	0.3940	0.2560	0.1530	0.0840
7	0.9990	0.9930	0.9700	0.9180	0.8270	0.6990	0.5500	0.4010	0.2710	0.1700
8	1.0000	0.9970	0.9860	0.9580	0.9000	0.8090	0.6870	0.5470	0.4070	0.2830
9		0.9990	0.9940	0.9790	0.9450	0.8840	0.7930	0.6760	0.5440	0.4130
10		1.0000	0.9970	0.9900	0.9710	0.9330	0.8700	0.7800	0.6670	0.5420
11			0.9990	0.9950	0.9850	0.9620	0.9210	0.8570	0.7680	0.6590
12			1.0000	0.9980	0.9920	0.9800	0.9540	0.9110	0.8450	0.7580
13				0.9990	0.9960	0.9890	0.9740	0.9460	0.9000	0.8340
14				1.0000	0.9980	0.9940	0.9860	0.9680	0.9380	0.8910
15					0.9990	0.9970	0.9920	0.9820	0.9630	0.9300

Proof of Mean of the Hypergeometric Distribution

To find the mean of the hypergeometric distribution, we write

$$E(X) = \sum_{x=0}^{n} x \frac{\binom{k}{x}\binom{N-k}{n-x}}{\binom{N}{n}} = k \sum_{x=1}^{n} \frac{(k-1)!}{(x-1)!(k-x)!} \cdot \frac{\binom{N-k}{n-x}}{\binom{N}{n}}$$

$$= k \sum_{x=1}^{n} \frac{\binom{k-1}{x-1}\binom{N-k}{n-x}}{\binom{N}{n}}.$$

Since

$$\binom{N-k}{n-1-y} = \binom{(N-1)-(k-1)}{n-1-y} \quad \text{and} \quad \binom{N}{n} = \frac{N!}{n!(N-n)!} = \frac{N}{n}\binom{N-1}{n-1},$$

letting $y = x - 1$, we obtain

$$E(X) = k \sum_{y=0}^{n-1} \frac{\binom{k-1}{y}\binom{N-k}{n-1-y}}{\binom{N}{n}}$$

$$= \frac{nk}{N} \sum_{y=0}^{n-1} \frac{\binom{k-1}{y}\binom{(N-1)-(k-1)}{n-1-y}}{\binom{N-1}{n-1}} = \frac{nk}{N},$$

since the summation represents the total of all probabilities in a hypergeometric experiment when $N-1$ items are selected at random from $N-1$, of which $k-1$ are labeled success.

Proof of Mean and Variance of the Poisson Distribution

Let $\mu = \lambda t$.

$$E(X) = \sum_{x=0}^{\infty} x \cdot \frac{e^{-\mu}\mu^x}{x!} = \sum_{x=1}^{\infty} x \cdot \frac{e^{-\mu}\mu^x}{x!} = \mu \sum_{x=1}^{\infty} \frac{e^{-\mu}\mu^{x-1}}{(x-1)!}.$$

Since the summation in the last term above is the total probability of a Poisson random variable with mean μ, which can be easily seen by letting $y = x - 1$, it equals 1. Therefore, $E(X) = \mu$. To calculate the variance of X, note that

$$E[X(X-1)] = \sum_{x=0}^{\infty} x(x-1)\frac{e^{-\mu}\mu^x}{x!} = \mu^2 \sum_{x=2}^{\infty} \frac{e^{-\mu}\mu^{x-2}}{(x_2)!}.$$

Again, letting $y = x - 2$, the summation in the last term above is the total probability of a Poisson random variable with mean μ. Hence, we obtain

$$\sigma^2 = E(X^2) - [E(X)]^2 = E[X(X-1)] + E(X) - [E(X)]^2 = \mu^2 + \mu - \mu^2 = \mu = \lambda t.$$

Proof of Mean and Variance of the Gamma Distribution

To find the mean and variance of the gamma distribution, we first calculate

$$E(X^k) = \frac{1}{\beta^\alpha \Gamma(\alpha)} \int_0^\infty x^{\alpha+k-1} e^{-x/\beta} \, dx = \frac{\beta^{k+\alpha}\Gamma(\alpha+k)}{\beta^\alpha \Gamma(\alpha)} \int_0^\infty \frac{x^{\alpha+k-1}e^{-x/\beta}}{\beta^{k+\alpha}\Gamma(\alpha+k)} \, dx,$$

for $k = 0, 1, 2, \dots$. Since the integrand in the last term above is a gamma density function with parameters $\alpha + k$ and β, it equals 1. Therefore,

$$E(X^k) = \beta^k \frac{\Gamma(k+\alpha)}{\Gamma(\alpha)}.$$

Using the recursion formula of the gamma function from page 194, we obtain

$$\mu = \beta \frac{\Gamma(\alpha+1)}{\Gamma(\alpha)} = \alpha\beta \quad \text{and} \quad \sigma^2 = E(X^2) - \mu^2 = \beta^2 \frac{\Gamma(\alpha+2)}{\Gamma(\alpha)} - \mu^2 = \beta^2\alpha(\alpha+1) - (\alpha\beta)^2 = \alpha\beta^2.$$

Index

Page references followed by "f" indicate illustrated figures or photographs; followed by "t" indicates a table.

A

Absolute value
  evaluating, 79, 331
  properties of, 24, 137, 168, 286, 357
Accuracy, 71, 85, 200, 253-254, 286, 347-348
Addition
  Integers, 203
  repeated, 189, 393
Addition property of equations
  defined, 146
Algebra of functions
  product, 105, 134-135, 322
  sum, 133-135, 153
  using, 92-94, 118, 153-154, 210, 321-323
Angle
  right, 22-23
Area
  figures, 190
Arithmetic mean, 115
Average, 5-6, 51, 97, 115-118, 158, 198-199, 238, 285, 354
Axis
  horizontal, 189-191

B

Balance, 12, 275, 354
Banzhaf power index
  applications of, 394
Bar graphs
  reading, 302
Bias
  sample, 239-240, 307
  selection, 239
Binomial, 106, 149-155, 191, 238, 286, 348-350, 430-435
Binomial formula, 390
Bit, 7, 225
Braces, 36, 268
Business
  functions, 145

C

Calculator use
  square roots, 327
  whole numbers, 84-85
Categories, 17, 111, 154, 358
Cells, 49-50, 87, 149, 330, 399
Census Bureau, 393
Central limit theorem, 245-248, 285, 354
Central tendency, 11, 146, 240
Centroid, 12
Chance, 7, 35, 83, 117, 154, 248-249, 356-357
Chebyshev's theorem, 139, 154, 196
Circle
  diameter of, 121
Class, 12, 48-49, 97, 146, 174, 201, 243, 288, 384
Class intervals, 22
Coefficient, 131
Coin-tossing experiment
  probability and, 2, 53
  sample space and, 36, 97
Combinations
  formula for, 138
Commission, 117, 243
Complement, 19, 39, 348
Complementary events, 58
Complex numbers
  dividing, 22
  equality of, 410
  multiplying, 116
Confidence intervals, 301, 369-370

Constants, 16, 132
Continuous variables, 90
Control charts, 470
Control group, 13, 413
Correlation, 129-131, 469
Correlation coefficient, 131
Cost, 30, 61, 122, 173, 244, 335, 408

D

Data (datum)
  collection, 1, 69, 95-96, 145, 225, 361
Data sets
  median of, 13, 222, 267
  standard deviation of, 15, 144-145, 192, 246, 295, 368
Decimal numbers
  repeating, 35, 239, 410
Degrees, 15-16, 216, 256-264, 294-295, 368, 456
Denominator
  common, 17
Descriptive statistics
  box plots, 3, 383
  measures of spread, 15
  median, 11-12, 226, 240-241, 286, 382-383
  percentiles, 27
  quartiles, 27
  variables, 26, 83-84, 116, 149, 239-241, 328, 347
Deviation
  standard, 15-17, 126, 190-193, 241-243, 290-291, 354
Deviations from the mean, 15
Digits
  decimal, 21-22
Discrete variables, 104, 135

E

Empirical probability
  formula, 65, 86-87, 125, 149, 197, 243, 292-293, 390-392, 472
Empty set, 49
English units
  area, 8, 60, 94, 171, 305
  length, 31, 59, 93, 131, 172
  speed, 31, 171
  weight, 51, 93, 122
Equation(s)
  absolute value, 292
Error
  chance, 62, 356-357
  relative, 62, 176, 317
  sampling, 96, 175, 256-258, 285-287, 354
Even numbers, 62
Events
  complementary, 58
Event(s)
  independent, 68, 173-174, 263, 298
Events
  probability of, 52-60, 87, 212
  random, 37, 85-87, 115-117, 211-215, 401
  simple, 42-43, 86, 117, 212-213, 401
Exact number, 122
Exponential functions
  characteristics of, 106
  examples of, 192
  natural, 137, 217

F

Factoring and factorizations
  process of, 36, 266
Fair division
  continuous, 17, 116-117, 169
  discrete, 17, 116-117, 169-171
  elements of, 59
Fibonacci numbers
  in nature, 6, 84
  large, 2, 51, 90, 139, 158, 212, 238-239, 319,

391-392
Formula
  distance, 86, 168
Formula(s)
  recursion, 210, 472
  variation, 95
Frequency
  distribution, 21-24, 79, 105-107, 174-176, 199-201, 266-267, 336-337, 387-389
Frequency distribution, 22, 79, 399
Function
  limit of, 334
Function(s)
  business, 98, 124
  combinations of, 27, 104, 132, 263
  constant, 32-33, 136, 187, 238
  cost, 122
  even, 14, 84, 121, 204, 240
  objective, 266
  odd, 33, 147, 240
  reciprocal, 213
  square root, 15, 124, 161
  step, 89

G

Graphs
  regular, 3
Graphs and graphical data
  histograms, 3, 106, 123, 206, 266
Graphs/graphing
  real numbers, 91

H

Histogram, 22-24, 88-89, 140, 149, 204
Histograms, 3, 106, 123, 206, 266
Horizontal line test
  applying, 141, 403

I

Independent events, 65
Infinite geometric series
  sum of, 142-144
Interest rates
  daily, 222
Is, 2, 36-42, 84, 117-119, 150-151, 193-194, 238-239, 286-288, 349-356, 467

L

Like terms
  collecting, 2
Limit, 23, 221, 245-248, 285, 354
Line(s)
  parallel, 111
  regression, 30, 382
Loans, 298
Logarithmic functions
  graphs of, 211
Logarithmic properties
  involving one, 285
Logarithms
  by, 330

M

Matrix (matrices)
  equal, 330
Measurement
  actual, 254
Measurement numbers
  accuracy of, 292
Measures
  of location, 9, 240
  of spread, 15
  range, 15-16, 241-242
  standard deviation, 15-17, 241-242, 308
Median
  of a data set, 266